Solution Chemistry of Surfactants

Volume 2

Solution Chemistry of Surfactants

Volume 2

Edited by
K. L. Mittal
IBM Corporation
East Fishkill Facility
Hopewell Junction, New York

Plenum Press · New York and London

Library of Congress Cataloging in Publication Data

Colloid and Surface Science Symposium, 52d, University of Tennessee, 1978.
Solution chemistry of surfactants.

"Proceedings of the section on Solution Chemistry of Surfactants, held at fifty-second Colloid and Surface Science Symposium, Knoxville, Tennessee, June 12–14, 1978."

1. Surface active agents—Congresses. 2. Solution (Chemistry)—Congresses. I. Mittal, K. L., 1945- II. Title.

TP994.C64 1978 668'.1 79-15067
ISBN 0-306-40174-6 (v. 1)
ISBN 0-306-40175-4 (v. 2)

Proceedings of the Section on Solution Chemistry of Surfactants, held at the Fifty-second Colloid and Surface Science Symposium, Knoxville, Tennessee, June 12–14, 1978, will be published in two volumes, of which this is volume two

Printed in the United States of America

Preface

The 52nd Colloid and Surface Science Symposium of the Division of Colloid and Surface Chemistry of the American Chemical Society was held in Knoxville, TN, June 12-14, 1978, and one of its Sections was devoted to the topic of Solution Chemistry of Surfactants. Although it was billed as the Section on Solution Chemistry of Surfactants, but it was indeed a veritable international symposium on this topic as 51 papers by about 100 contributors from 12 countries were listed in the program.

The present volume and its companion volume 1 document the proceedings of the above-mentioned Section on Solution Chemistry of Surfactants. In 1976 there was held an international symposium on Micellization, Solubilization and Microemulsions in Albany, the proceedings of which have been chronicled in two volumes.[1] A great deal of material dealing with micelles contributed by a legion of prominent researchers constitutes these volumes but a few subtopics were not adequately covered; so it was deemed appropriate to cover these topics as well as the recent progress in the general area of aggregation of surfactants in this Section. Also as it is the amphiphilicity or amphipathicity* of a surfactant molecule which is responsible for both adsorption at interfaces and aggregation in solution, so it was considered quite apropos to include the topic of adsorption at interfaces in this Section. Concomitantly, the present volumes not only cover the aggregation phenomena but also the adsorption at interfaces.

---

1. K. L. Mittal, Editor, Micellization, Solubilization, and Microemulsions, Vol. 1 and Vol. 2, Plenum Press, New York, June, 1977

*Also described as the molecular schizophrenia (see ref. 1 p. 24) or, humorously, the Dr. Jekyll and Mr. Hyde personality of the surfactant towards the medium.

As the purpose of a Symposium should be to present the current state of the knowledge of the topic under consideration and the best, to my knowledge, way to accomplish such objective is via a number of invited overview papers by leading researchers and these should be complemented and augmented by original research papers. This is exactly what was done for this section. A total of 19 overview papers were invited and all (except two) of these are included in these volumes. It should be added that the topics of electrochemical investigations in micellar media, and applications of surfactants and micelles in analytical chemistry were too important to be excluded from these volumes. So overviews of these topics were specially commissioned after the meeting, and I am pleased to report that such overviews are included in these volumes, and I would like to extend my special thanks to the authors of these overviews for their extra efforts.

Surfactants play a very important role in many human endeavors and the need to understand their adsorption and aggregation behavior is quite manifest. Surfactant aggregation leads to the formation of micelles and the characteristics of micelles which render them so important and intriguing for investigation have been discussed earlier.[2] However, if one scans the literature one will notice that recently there has been an explosive growth of interest in the areas of micellar catalysis, photochemical reactions in micellar media, and surfactant flooding. The study of reactions and interactions in microemulsion media has also gained considerable popularity. Furthermore, there is great deal of interest in the applications of surfactants and micelles in analytical and electro-chemistry. Of course, the energy crisis has given a tremendous boost to the research activity anent surfactant flooding for improved oil recovery. These proceedings volumes bring out clearly the inter- and multidisciplinary aspects of the solution chemistry of surfactants, as researchers with widely varying backgrounds, training, interests and affiliations are actively engaged in the various ramifications of the adsorption and aggregation behavior of surfactants.

These volumes contain a comprehensive coverage of theoretical as well as practical aspects of both the adsorption and aggregation behavior of surfactants. The contents of these volumes are a blend of both invited state-of-the-knowledge overviews covering many subtopics written by world-renowned researchers and original

2. Ref. 1, Vol. 1, pp. 1-21

research papers. A total of 49 papers by 108 contributors from 19 countries grace the pages of these volumes. It should be added that, generally speaking, each paper was reviewed by two qualified reviewers and in some cases the advice of the third reviewer was also sought. As for organization, these have been divided into seven parts. Volume 1 contains Parts I - III and Parts IV - VII constitute Volume 2. The topics covered include: thermodynamics and kinetics of micellization in aqueous media, aggregation in nonaqueous media, effect of solvent on micelle formation, aggregation behavior of biological surfactants, mixed micelles, solubilization, micellar catalysis and inhibition, reactions and interactions in micellar media, use of micellar systems in analytical chemistry, microemulsions, ultralow interfacial tension, tertiary oil recovery, surfactant flooding, microemulsion flooding, liquid crystals, phase stability, surface rheological properties, and adsorption at various interfaces.

I sincerely hope that the present two-volume set along with the set on Micellization, Solubilization and Microemulsions volumes (a total of about 2000 pages) would serve a useful reference source for the seasoned researcher and a guide to the budding scientist who aspires to make a research career in micelles and the wonderful world of the solution chemistry of surfactants in general.

On a more personal side, no doubt a great deal of time and effort went in the editing of these volumes but during this tenure I also made a number of friends whose friendship I would always cherish. One disappointing fact is the absence of Discussion Section(s) in these volumes and it is attributed to the reluctance on the part of the discussants to submit their questions in writing for referral to the respective authors for reply. In spite of the continuous exhortation during the meeting, the number of written questions received did not warrant including a discussion section at the end of each part as was done for Micellization.... Volumes. However, it is gratifying to note that most papers generated a great deal of interest as gauged by the number of questions asked by the attendees and by the brisk corridor conversation that took place. The discussions were mostly lively and enlightening and on occasions may be exothermic.

Acknowledgments. The role of the editor is akin to that of an orchestra leader and many people help in various roles to put together a good performance. Here I would like to take this opportunity to express my thanks to all those who contributed in many and varied ways. First of all I am thankful to the appropriate management of IBM Corporation for permitting me to organize this Section and to edit these volumes. Thanks are due to all those secretaries who helped with the correspondence typing. The help of Dr. A. S. Kertes during the initial stages of the formulation of the program is gratefully acknowledged. I would like to thank Dr. E. L. Fuller, Jr. for his ready and willing help whenever it was needed. My special thanks are due to my wife, Usha, for rendering, without complaint, the home environment conducive to work; to my daughter, Anita, and son, Rajesh, for letting me spend those hours which I would have normally spent with them. The reviewers should be thanked for their time, efforts and many invaluable comments, and thanks are due to all the authors for their cooperation and interest without which these volumes would not have seen the light of day.

K. L. Mittal

IBM Corporation
East Fishkill Facility
Hopewell Junction, New York 12533

Contents of Volume 2

Contents of Volume 1

PART I. GENERAL OVERVIEW PAPERS

PART II. THERMODYNAMICS AND KINETICS OF MICELLIZATION IN AQUEOUS MEDIA

Part IV
Reactions and Interactions in Micellar Media

MICELLAR CATALYSIS AND INHIBITION. SOURCES OF RATE ENHANCEMENTS IN FUNCTIONAL AND NONFUNCTIONAL MICELLES

C. A. Bunton

Department of Chemistry, University of California

Santa Barbara, California 93106

Micellar catalysis and inhibition is generally described in terms of a pseudophase model on the assumption that reaction occurs either in the aqueous or micellar pseudophase, and the variation of the rate constants for the overall reaction with surfactant concentration can be analyzed in terms of the reactant concentrations and rate constants in each pseudophase. There are problems in estimating the concentrations of ionic reactants in the micellar pseudophase and in estimating the volume of the region in the micelles in which the reaction occurs. The analyses show that micellar rate effects upon unimolecular reactions are due wholly to the micelles exerting a favorable or unfavorable medium effect upon reaction, but that for bimolecular reactions the predominant source of rate enhancements is concentration of reactants into a small volume element. This model can also be applied to reactions catalyzed by functional micelles, and it gives a quantitative explanation of observed rate enhancements. A possible failure of the pseudophase model is briefly considered.

INTRODUCTION

Although the ability of aqueous surfactant solutions to influence reaction rates was established many years ago there are still questions as to the source of the observed catalysis and inhibition.[1] The importance of proximity effects was obvious, for example the rates of reactions of a variety of hydrophobic substrates with anions were increased by cationic surfactants, because the micelles could incorporate both the substrate and the reactive anion. These reactions were inhibited by anionic surfactants because the micelles incorporated the substrate and repelled the reactive anion.

Similar behavior was observed with micellized substrates, for example micellization of a long chain monoalkyl sulfate sharply increased its acid hydrolysis, but decreased the rate of reaction with hydroxide ion.[7]

It was obvious that coulombic interactions were of key importance in determining the interactions between ionic micelles and reactive ions, and micellar catalysis and inhibition could be rationalized in terms of the principles which Hartley had applied to micellar effects upon equilibria.[8] These micellar effects upon reaction rates and equilibria in aqueous surfactant systems have been extensively delineated in review articles over the past decade.[2-6,9]

There is no problem in discussing inhibition of bimolecular reactions in terms of proximity effects, because if the micelle, for whatever reason, takes up one reactant and excludes the other, reaction will be inhibited. But bringing reactants together does not guarantee rate enhancement because bimolecular reactions in the micelles may occur more or less readily than in water. Thus in discussing rate enhancements we can conveniently consider the micelles as a reaction medium distinct from bulk solvent.

Micellization and micellar structure have been discussed in terms of various models,[10] but, at least for the kineticist, it is very convenient to use the pseudophase model, i.e., to assume that a micelle can be regarded as a submicroscopic aggregate which behaves as if it were a separate reaction medium with its own properties.[11] We can then regard reaction as occuring either in the aqueous or the micellar pseudophase, with reactants being rapidly equilibrated between the two pseudophases.[12] This model is generally used in discussions of reaction rates and equilibria. I use it in the following discussion accepting its limitations and recognizing that at times it is a convenient cloak for our ignorance.

Although proximity or concentration effects are of evident importance we must also consider reactivity in the micellar pseudophase, not only for catalyzed bimolecular reactions, but also for both catalyzed and inhibited spontaneous, unimolecular, reactions. There are a number of unimolecular reactions whose rates are changed by incorporation in a micelle.[5,6,14] Some examples of these reactions are given in Table I, together with examples of bimolecular reactions. Concentration of substrate into a micelle will not affect the first order rate constant for its reaction, so that micellar rate effects upon unimolecular reactions must arise from the properties of the micelle as a submicroscopic reaction medium.[14]

If micelles exhibit a solvent, or environmental, effect upon unimolecular reactions they may well do so in bimolecular reactions. For example, ion pairing interactions between an ionic head group of a micelle and a counter ionic reagent could decrease the reaction rate, whereas a similar interaction with a transition state could increase it. Another possibility is that incorporation of ionic reagents into the micelle might reduce their hydration and therefore increase their reactivity. The polarity of a micelle should be different from that of water,[2,23,24] and thus there could be a submicroscopic solvent effect upon reaction rates.

It will be convenient first to consider micellar effects upon unimolecular reactions, because these can be related directly to the properties of the micellar surface.

MICELLAR EFFECTS UPON UNIMOLECULAR REACTIONS AND THE NATURE OF THE MICELLAR SURFACE

There is considerable evidence that micellar bound ions and polar molecules are located at the micelle-water interface in the so-called Stern layer,[25] whose thickness is approximately that of the ionic head groups.[26] In addition a large proportion of the counter ions is within this layer, and the extent of charge neutralization of the ionic head groups is considered to be relatively insensitive to the total concentration of counter ions. There is rapid exchange between solutes in the Stern layer and those in water, and we assume that this equilibrium is not perturbed by chemical reaction.

Chemical reactions of polar or ionic reactants generally occur in the Stern layer, so that its properties as a reaction medium are of considerable importance. It is difficult to compare the properties of the Stern layer with those of a bulk solvent, but spectrophotometric measurements suggest that its dielectric constant,[23] or polarity, as measured by Kosower's Z scale is less than that of water.[3,24] These estimates are consistent with micellar effects upon unimolecular reactions (Table I).

The spontaneous hydrolyses of aryl sulfate monoanion[15] and phosphate dianions[16] and the decarboxylations of carboxylate ions[17] are slower in water than in less polar solvents, so that it is understandable that they are faster at the surface of a cationic or nonionic micelle than in water. In addition, decomposition involves movement of negative charge from a sulfate, phosphate, or carboxylate ion into the organic portion of the substrate, so that transition state formation involves charge delocalization.[14] A quaternary ammonium head group should interact readily with such a

Table I. Catalysis and Inhibition by Micelles of Nonfunctional Surfactants.[a]

Unimolecular reactions	Cationic	Anionic	Nonionic	Reference
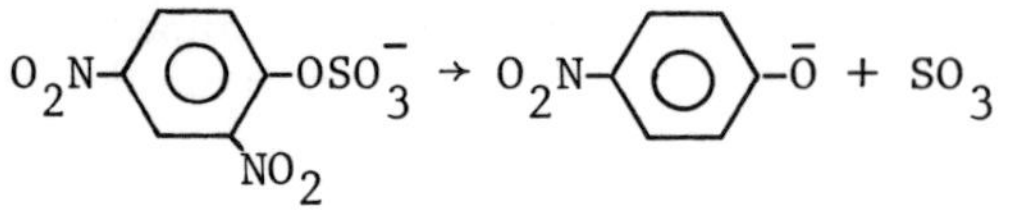	+	0	+	15
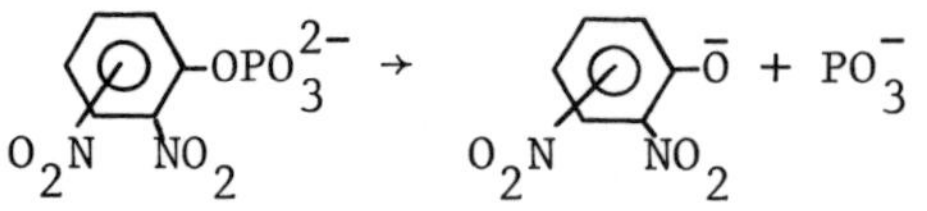	+	0	0	16
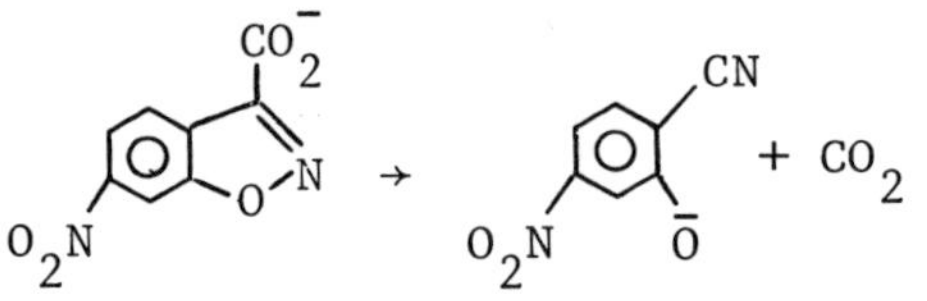	+	0	+	17
$PhCH(CN)CO_2^- \rightarrow Ph\bar{C}HCN + CO_2$	+	-		17
$RX \rightarrow R^+ + X^-$ (S_N1)	-	-		18
Bimolecular reactions				
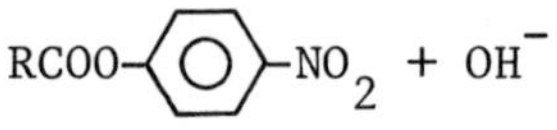	+	-	(-)	19,20
	+	-	-	21
$Ar_3C^+ + OH^-$	+	-		22

[a]Rate enhancement denoted +, inhibition -, no effect 0; parentheses denote small effects.

transition state, e.g., with a carbanion like transition state in decarboxylation, and rate enhancements of up to ca. 700-fold are observed in some of these reactions.[17]

The micellar inhibition of S_N1 reactions[18] can be explained in similar terms because these reactions are much faster in water than in less polar solvents, although the very high ionic content of the Stern layer might be expected to speed the reaction because of the generally observed positive salt effect in these reactions.[27] It may be that water molecules in the Stern layer are so highly organized by its ions that they cannot solvate the polar transition state.

These micellar effects upon unimolecular reactions show that micelles provide media which may favor or inhibit reaction, and this could also be true for bimolecular reactions. However, for bimolecular reactions it is necessary to separate the medium and proximity effects, and to do this we must consider the distribution of two reactants between water and the micelles, but it will be useful to consider the simpler situation first.

The relations between the rate constants of unimolecular reactions and surfactant concentration can be treated very simply by considering the distribution of the substrate between the aqueous and micellar pseudophases (Scheme 1).

Scheme 1

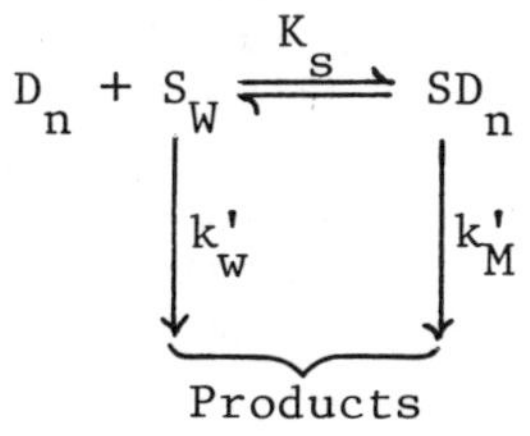

In Scheme 1, k'_w and k'_M are, respectively, the first order rate constant of the substrate S_w in water, and of micelle incorporated substrate, SD_n or S_M. The concentration of micellized surfactant (D_n) is assumed to be that of total surfactant less than that of monomeric surfactant, which is given by the critical micelle concentration, cmc.[28]

Scheme 1 leads to Equation 1, where the first order rate constant is given in terms of the parameters shown in Scheme 1.[20]

$$k_\Psi = \frac{k'_W + k'_M K_s([D]-\text{cmc})}{1 + K_s([D]-\text{cmc})} \quad (1)$$

(This Equation was originally applied to bimolecular micellar inhibited reactions.[20])

The derivation of Equation 1 involves a number of assumptions, which are reasonable provided that the surfactant is in large excess over reactant.[20] Equation 1 is formally similar to the Michaelis-

Menten equation of enzyme kinetics, except that here the substrate is generally in large excess over the enzyme.

Equation 1 fits the rate-surfactant profiles for a number of unimolecular micellar catalyzed reactions where the rate constants increase sigmoidally to constant values when the substrate is fully micellar bound.[15,16]

INHIBITION OF BIMOLECULAR REACTIONS

The treatment of bimolecular micellar inhibited reactions is very simple.[20] If the ionic reagent is excluded from a counterionic micelle by electrostatic repulsions the overall reaction rate will simply depend on the fraction of the substrate which was left in the aqueous pseudophase. The relation between the rate constant and surfactant concentration is identical to that applied to unimolecular reactions, Equation 1. This equation fits micellar inhibition of a number of reactions involving bimolecular attack by nucleophilic anions,[5,6,20,21] and the binding constants, K_s, estimated kinetically, were in reasonable agreement with those determined or estimated independently. The only complication arises from interactions between solutes and the micelles, which may affect such properties as the cmc, and inhibition is often observed at surfactant concentrations below the cmc in water.

CATALYSIS OF BIMOLECULAR REACTIONS

Micellar inhibited and micellar catalyzed unimolecular reactions can be treated quantitatively by considering the distribution of the substrate between the aqueous and micellar pseudophases. But the model which was used successfully in these systems (Scheme 1) fails for bimolecular micellar catalyzed reactions because it considers only the distribution of <u>one</u> reactant between the pseudophases, whereas <u>two</u> reactants are involved in bimolecular reactions.[14,29-32] The failure of the model is illustrated by the rate maxima with increasing surfactant concentration which are typically observed with catalyzed bimolecular reactions; examples of these rate maxima are given in a number of reviews.[2,4-6]

There is extensive evidence for the kinetic significance of the micellar incorporation of relatively hydrophobic substrates,[5,9,30,33,34] and it will be useful to consider qualitative evidence which shows the necessity of also considering the micellar incorporation of reactive counterions.

Micellar catalysis of bimolecular reactions involving ionic attack on a substrate is reduced by added salts. These salt effects depend upon the nature of added counterions, and increase with their increasing hydrophobicity. Ions of like charge to the micelle have only small effects on reaction rate.[35] It is reasonable to assume that these inhibiting salt effects depend largely upon the ability of an inert counterion to compete with a reactive counterion for the micelle. Indeed, it is sometimes possible to displace all the reactive ions from the micelle and thereby completely suppress a micellar catalyzed reaction.

Another piece of evidence is that the rates of micellar catalyzed hydrogen ion reactions, e.g., acetal hydrolysis, depend not on the total concentration (or activity) of hydrogen ions, but on the amount of micellar bound hydrogen ions.[31]

Thus any quantitative treatment of bimolecular micellar catalyzed reactions requires estimation of the extents of micellar incorporation of both reactants. This problem may not be soluble in all cases but two general treatments have been reasonably successful. In one treatment the extents of micellar incorporation of the reactants have been determined directly or indirectly,[34,36] in another, which has been applied only to reactions of hydrophilic ions, an empirical ion exchange model has been used to estimate the amounts of micellar bound reactive ions.[37]

Micellar Incorporation of Reactants

Several methods have been developed for examining micellar incorporation of solutes. The extents of incorporation of relatively hydrophobic solutes have been estimated by gel permeation chromatography,[38,39] solubility,[29,36,40] or ultrafiltration,[34] and, for solutes which contain a convenient chromophoric group, by spectral shifts.[33,36,41] The micellar incorporation of hydrophilic counterions can sometimes be followed electrochemically, for example conductimetrically or by the use of specific ion electrodes.[31,42,43] None of these methods are completely general and they all depend upon assumptions which are sometimes dubious.

It is ncessary in general to estimate independently the extents of incorporation of the two reactants, assuming that neither affect the incorporation of the other. Added solutes can markedly affect micellar properties, for example both electrolytes and hydrophobic solutes decrease the critical micelle concentration (cmc) and they also change the shape and size of micelles which can go from spherical to rodlike in solutions of high salt or surfactant concentration.[17,44] These reactant effects upon micellar structure complicate any quantitative treatment of micellar rate effects, especially in solutions in which the surfactant is not in large excess over the reactants, c.f. Reference 20.

Rate-Surfactant Profiles in Bimolecular Reactions

At low surfactant concentrations the rate-surfactant profiles for catalyzed bimolecular reactions are similar to those found for unimolecular reactions, in that the rate constants increase sigmoidally as the substrate is taken up by the micelles, but instead of reaching a constant value they go through maxima, simply because two opposing effects are at work. The rate constants increase as the concentration of micellar bound reactants increases, but eventually an increase in surfactant concentration dilutes the reactants in the micellar pseudophase, with decrease in the rate constant. Therefore, it should be possible to predict the rate-surfactant profiles by estimating the concentrations of both reactants in the micellar pseudophase, and this approach has been followed by a number of workers.[31,32,24,26,41] In addition, these approaches should, in principle, allow estimation of the true second order rate constants in the micellar pseudophase and therefore allow us to decide whether the catalysis is due merely to an increase of reactant concentration in the micellar pseudophase or to a favorable environmental effect on the reaction. For example, there are many examples of increases in micellar rate enhancements with increasing hydrophobicities of the reactants, which could be due to an increase in the reagent concentrations in the micelles or to the reactants being drawn more deeply into the micelles into a region which favors reaction.[2-6,45]

It is easier to ask this question than to answer it, because any comparison of second order rate constants depends on the units in which the reactant concentrations are measured. Typically solution kineticists measure concentrations in molarity, so that one approach is to estimate the volume of the micellar pseudophase and to use this as the volume element of the reaction.[34,36,41] But this approach has its problems because polar and ionic reactions almost certainly occur in the Stern layer of the micelle rather than in its core,[25] so that perhaps we should estimate second order rate constants in terms of an assumed volume of the Stern layer.[46,47] However, for many ionic micelles the volume of the Stern layer appears to be approximately half that of the micelle,[26,46-48,49] so that our choice of the volume element does not markedly affect the numerical values of the rate constants. Any choice of the volume element of reaction is arbitrary, for example, our ideas about kinetic solvent effects in homogeneous solution might change markedly if we calculated second order rate constants using concentrations measured as mole fractions instead of molarities.[31]

All quantitative kinetic treatments of micellar catalyzed reactions have assumed that the micelles can be treated as if they were a separate phase, and this approach is followed here, although a possible failure of this assumption is discussed later.

The overall observed first order rate constant, k_ψ, is given by Equation 1, and the individual first order rate constants k_W and k_M can be written in terms of the appropriate second order rate constants. Scheme 2 illustrates reaction between a substrate, S, and a nucleophile, N, occuring in the water and in the micelle.

Scheme 2

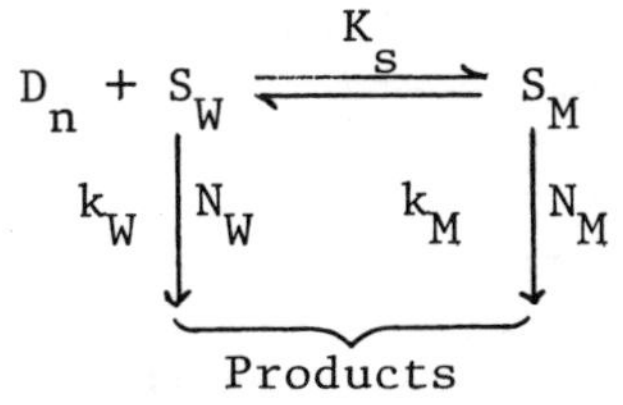

(The subscripts W and M denote the aqueous and micellar pseudo-phases.)

It is convenient to write the second order rate constant in water, k_W, in terms of molarity, and that in the micelles, k_M, in terms of the mole ratio of bound N to micellized surfactant m_S^N, so that:

$$k'_W = k_W[N_W] \text{ and } k'_M = k_M\, m_S^N$$

$$\text{where } m_S^N = [N_M]/([D]-\text{cmc}) \tag{2}$$

The overall first order rate constant, k_ψ, is given by:

$$k_\psi = \frac{k_W[N_W] + k_M\, K_s\, m_S^N([D]-\text{cmc})}{1 + K_s([D]-\text{cmc})} \tag{3}$$

$$= \frac{k_W[N_W] + k_M\, K_s[N_M]}{1 + K_s([D]-\text{cmc})} \tag{3a}$$

Equation 3 can be written in terms of the fraction, f, of micellar bound reagent , N, or in terms of the binding constant, K_N, so that the overall second order rate constant, k_2, is given by:

$$k_2 = \frac{k_W(1-f) + k_M\, K_s f}{1 + K_s([D]-\text{cmc})} \tag{4}$$

$$= \frac{k_W + k_M K_s K_N([D]-cmc)}{\{1 + K_s([D]-cmc)\}\{1 + K_N([D]-cmc)\}} \qquad (4a)$$

It should be noted that by defining the second order rate constant, k_M, in terms of a mole ratio we avoid questions about the volume element of the reaction, although this question has to be faced if we are to compare second order rate constants in micelles with those in bulk solution.

These equations have forms similar to those used by Berezin and his coworkers,[36] and Romsted,[32] and account for the rate maxima observed with bimolecular reactions. The form of Equation 4a is similar to that applied earlier to micellar catalyzed reactions.[29]

The extents of micellar incorporation of nonionic reactants can be determined independently, and provided that there is no mutual interaction or perturbation of micellar structure the rate-surfactant profiles can be fitted using Equations 3 and 4 or equations of similar form.[32,34,36] In some cases independently measured binding constants have been used in fitting the rate data, in other cases they were estimated from the rate surfactant profiles. It should be noted that the fit is often insensitive to the binding constants, especially if they are so large that the substrate is almost wholly micellar bound. In addition, the reactants may promote micellization and it then becomes difficult to decide on the appropriate value of the cmc (Equations 3 and 4).

However, there are problems in treating those reactions in which a hydrophilic ionic reagent is generated by dissociation of a weak acid. For example, many reactions of hydroxide and hydrogen ions are carried out in buffer solutions, but the acid-base equilibria may be perturbed by the micelles.[31]

This micellar effect on acid-base equilibria can also create problems in reactions of hydrophobic nucleophilic anions. For example, micellar effects upon deacylations by anionic alkylimidazoles have been extensively studied and the rate-surfactant profiles have been treated in terms of the extents of micellar incorporation of the ester and the anionic imidazole.[36] However, micellar incorporation of anionic imidazoles cannot be determined directly, because of their instability at high pH, and it was estimated from the micellar effects upon the apparent pKa of the imidazole and the measured binding of the undissociated imidazole. This treatment assumes that acid dissociation in the micellar pseudophase is governed only by the micellar binding of the undissociated imidazole and its conjugate base and pH, as measured in the solution. Scheme 3 illustrates the approach which leads to Equation 5.[36]

Scheme 3

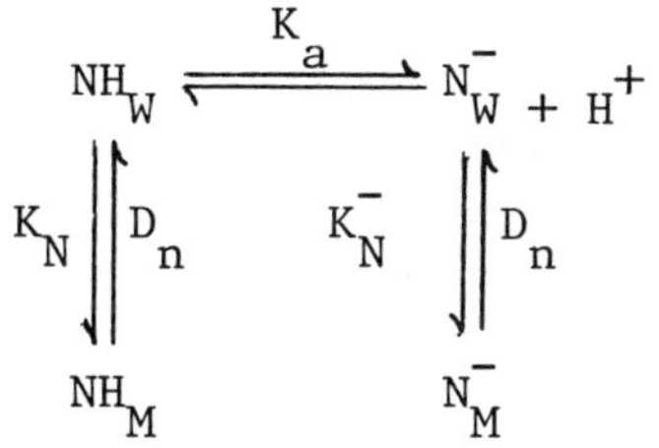

In Scheme 3, K_N and K_N^- are respectively the binding constants to the micelle of the nonionic form of the nucleophile, N, and its reactive anion, N^-, and K_{app} is the overall dissociation constant of NH, so that:

$$K_{app} = K_a \left(\frac{1 + K_N^-[D_n]}{1 + K_N[D_n]} \right) \tag{5}$$

where $[D_n]$ is the concentration of micellized surfactant.

Because ionization increases binding to a cationic micelle the values of K_{app} should increase on addition of surfactant.

This treatment clearly fails in some situations, because although, as predicted, values of the apparent pKa of a number of weak acids initially decrease on addition of cationic surfactants, e.g., CTABr, they often go through minima at relatively high surfactant concentration. These observations have been interpreted as evidence that the extents of micellar incorporation of anionic imidazoles go through maxima with increasing concentration of a cationic surfactant because of competition between bromide ion of the CTABr and the hydrophobic anion.[36] But Br^- should compete poorly with an alkylimidazole anion for the micelle, and it seems more probable that the effects on the apparent pKa are caused by a decreasing extent of micellar incorporation of the buffer anion or hydroxide ion because of its competition with Br^-, the surfactant counter ion.

Romsted has drawn attention to the importance of this competition,[32] for example, in solutions of CTABr we have competition between hydroxide and bromide ion for the micelle:

$$OH_M^- + Br_W^- \rightleftarrows OH_W^- + Br_M^- \tag{6}$$

The concentration of bromide ion in the aqueous pseudophase steadily increases with increasing total surfactant concentration, e.g., of CTABr, with consequent expulsion of hydroxide ion from the micelle.

There is evidence that this explanation is essentially correct. For example, at a given pH the values of the apparent pKa of a number of phenols go through minima with increasing concentration of CTABr, but in this system the extent of micellar binding of the phenoxide ion can be measured directly, and it does not decrease at high surfactant concentration, as predicted by the pKa values.[50]

These problems can be avoided by measuring directly the extent of micellar incorporation of ionic reagents, and it is best to follow this approach whenever possible.

Assuming that the fraction of micellar bound nucleophile or electrophile can be estimated then the concentration in the micellar pseudophase can be calculated in terms of the volume of micelles or of their Stern layers. These estimates involve approximations, and an arbitrary choice of the volume element of reaction.

If it is assumed that reaction occurs only in the Stern layer then estimates of its volume in micelles of CTABr and NaLS lead to the following relation between the second order rate constant,

k_2^m, $M^{-1}s^{-1}$ and k_M, s^{-1}:

$$k_2^m \approx 0.14\ k_M \tag{7}$$

(The conversion factor depends upon the assumed relation of the values of the Stern layer and the micelles, and assumes a micellar density of 1.[46,47])

Although there is considerable uncertainty in this conversion of k_M to k_2^m the approximations do not invalidate conclusions about the source of micellar catalysis. (The value of k_M does not, of course, depend upon the choice of the volume element of reaction in the micelles.)

There are now many examples of bimolecular micellar catalyzed reactions in which the second order rate constants ($M^{-1}\ s^{-1}$) in the micellar pseudophase are not very different from those in water.

For example, Berezin and his coworkers have shown that deacylations and aromatic nucleophilic substitutions by nonionic imidazole derivatives have lower second order rate constants in the micelles than in water,[36] and similar conclusions have been made for the reaction of aniline with 2,4-dinitrofluorobenzene.[34] However, it has been concluded that deacylations by anions of alkyl imidazoles have larger second order rate constants in the micellar pseudophase of CTABr than in water by only one order of magnitude.[36,51]

The true second order rate constants in CTABr micelles for ester deacylation by thiolate ions are very similar to those in water.[41] This system is an especially useful one because the thiols are fully dissociated under the reaction conditions, and the extents of their incorporation into the cationic micelles were measured spectrophotometrically without complications caused by acid dissociation of the thiol.

Some comparisons between second order rate constants in the aqueous and micellar pseudophases (k_W and k_2^m respectively) from the author's group are in Table II. (The rate constants k_2^m are calculated in terms of molarities in the Stern layer. In most of the reactions shown in Table II, the extents of micellar incorporation of the nucleophiles were measured directly. The exceptions were the reactions of Malachite Green (MG^+) with OH^- and BH_4^-, where the extents of nucleophile incorporation were estimated from the kinetics,[47] c.f. References 32 and 37.

For reactions of anionic nucleophiles with nonionic and cationic substrates the second order rate constants in the micelles are similar to those in water, but they are considerably smaller for nonionic nucleophiles, in agreement with other results.[34,36] Hydrogen ion reactions also have smaller rate constants in anionic micelles than in water.[31,46]

Table II. Second Order Rate Constants in the Stern Layers[a]

Substrate	Reagent	Surfactant	k_{rel}	k_2^m, M^{-1} s^{-1}
MG^+	OH^-	CTABr	13	ca. 1 (1.7)
MG^+	BH_4^-	CTABr	274	83 (31)
$2,4(NO_2)_2C_6H_3F$	$PhNH_2$	CTABr	9	0.005 (0.03)
$2,4(NO_2)_2C_6H_3F$	$PhNH_2$	NaLS	4	0.004 (0.03)
$p\text{-}O_2NC_6H_4CH(OEt)_2$	H^+, H_2O	NaLS	ca. 30	0.015 (0.29)
$p\text{-}O_2NC_6H_4OPO(OPh)_2$	PhO^-	CTABr	2000	0.01 (0.03)

[a]Values in parentheses are second order rate constants in water.

It is perhaps unreasonable to compare the rate constants in the aqueous and micellar pseudophases on the basis discussed above, if only because, although the size of some of the reactants is similar to the thickness of the Stern layer, we treat this layer as if it were a uniform liquid phase. Nonetheless the comparison can be justified pragmatically, for example, the negative "solvent" effect of the micelles upon the second order rate constants for reactions of nonionic nucleophiles can be related to known solvent effects.[27] Nonpolar solvents slow reactions between nonionic reagents, and the Stern layer appears to have a lower polarity than water.

The apparent low kinetic acidity of the hydrogen ion (Table II) may be caused by the weakness of micellized alkyl sulfuric acid. The striking enhancement of the acid hydrolysis of monoalkyl sulfates on micellization suggests that it weakens the acid.[7]

APPLICATION OF THE MODEL TO CATALYSIS BY FUNCTIONAL MICELLES

The apparent similarity of the second order rate constants k_W and k_2^m suggests a way of rationalizing catalysis by functional micelles in which the reactive nucleophile or base is covalently bonded to the surfactant. Very large rate enhancements are often observed in reactions, for example deacylations, carried out in the presence of functional micelles, Scheme 4.

Scheme 4

$$\sim\!\sim\overset{+}{N}R_2(CH_2)_n\,XH \rightleftharpoons \sim\!\sim\overset{+}{N}R_2(CH_2)_n X^- + H^+$$

$$\sim\!\sim\overset{+}{N}R_2(CH_2)_n X^- + S \rightarrow \text{products}$$

There are now a number of reactions in the presence of functional micelles whose mechanisms have been well established. In these reactions the reactive group, XH, is often an imidazole,[52-55] hydroxamate or oxime,[56] thiol,[57] or hydroxyl moiety.[58-60] Therefore in analyzing the significance of the rate enhancement over that of the reaction in water we must consider at least three factors: (i) a new reaction involving nucleophilic attack is introduced, (ii) the acid dissociation of the reactive moiety XH in Scheme 4 is increased by micellization,[8,61] and, (iii) there is a proximity, or concentration, effect on incorporation of the substrate into the functional micelle.

The probable importance of (iii) can easily be established using Equation 3, assuming that $k_W \sim k_2^m$ (Table II). In micelles of a functional surfactant, containing a nucleophilic moiety, N, in its headgroup, $m_N^S = 1$, and if all the substrate is incorporated into the micelle:

$$k_\Psi = k_M \sim k_W/0.14 \qquad (7)$$

In other words, the first order rate constant with fully bound substrate should numerically be approximately seven times the second order rate constant in water, measured using a nonmicellized reagent, provided that allowance is made for incomplete acid dissociation of the reactive moiety XH. (The functional headgroups of most functional surfactants are weakly acidic, and are often only partially ionized under the reaction conditions.)

At the present time this hypothesis cannot be tested for such commonly used functional surfactants as oximates and imidazoles because comparable data are not available for micellar and nonmicellar reactions. But a test can be made using available data for reactions in functional micelles of hydroxyethyl surfactants (1).

$$R\overset{+}{N}Me_2CH_2CH_2OH \rightleftarrows R\overset{+}{N}Me_2CH_2CH_2O^- + H^+$$

$$\underline{1} \qquad\qquad\qquad \underline{2}$$

The zwitterionic surfactants (2) are effective nucleophiles, and the apparent pKa of 1 can be estimated kinetically.[58,62-64] The cholinate zwitterion (3) is a reasonable model for the nucleophilic moiety of the surfactant, and the second order rate constants, k_W, for its reactions with a variety of substrates in water are known.[62-65]

$$Me_3\overset{+}{N}CH_2CH_2OH \rightleftarrows Me_3\overset{+}{N}CH_2CH_2O^- + H^+$$

$$\underline{3}$$

The comparisons between k_W for reaction of 3 and the first order rate constants, k'_ψ, corrected for incomplete acid dissociation of 1, R = $C_{16}H_{33}$, are made in Table III, using a kinetically estimated value of 12.4 for the pKa of micellized 1, R = $C_{16}H_{33}$. The simple model predicts that $k'_\psi/k_W \sim 7$, and most of the values fit the prediction within a factor of three, which is not unreasonable in view of the simplications made in the treatment.[66] (Data for reactions of 1, R = $C_{12}H_{25}$ are in agreement with the results in Table III.) The only major failure of the treatment is for reactions of p-nitrophenyldiphenyl phosphate. This substrate is very hydrophobic,[21] and it may be located sufficiently deeply into the micelle that the reactive hydroxyl groups of the surfactant (1) may not be near to the phosphoryl group of the substrate. The other substrates are less hydrophobic and should be located in the Stern layer at the micelle-water surface.

The results given in Table III therefore suggest that proximity, or concentration, effects are of great importance in rate enhancements by functional as well as nonfunctional micelles.

Table III. Comparison of Rate Constants in Water with Those of Reactions in Micelles of a hydroxyethyl Surfactant

Substrate	k_W, M^{-1} s^{-1}	k'_Ψ, s^{-1}	k'_Ψ/k_W	Reference
MG^+	20	70	3.5	65
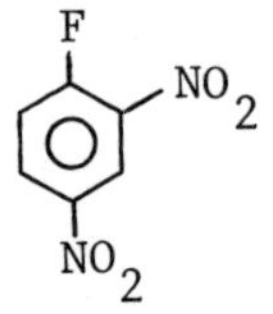	3.2	22	6.9	63
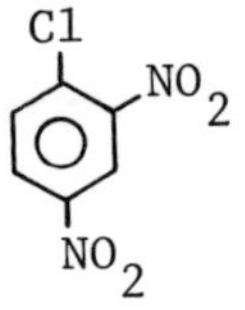	0.0027	0.063	23	63
$p\text{-}O_2NC_6H_4OPO(OPh)_2$	17	3.7	0.22	62
$p\text{-}O_2NC_6H_4COOPO_3^{2-}$	0.019	0.049	2.6	64

VALIDITY OF THE PSEUDOPHASE MODEL OF MICELLAR RATE EFFECTS

This discussion has been based on the assumption that the pseudophase model of a micelle in aqueous solution can be used in treating the kinetics, and this model has been generally used in kinetic treatments. However, micellar structure can also be described in terms of a mass action model,[10] which is probably more satisfying conceptually, but which is not so readily applicable to kinetic systems. The pseudophase model in its simplest form, assumes that reactants do not perturb the micellar structure, and it undoubtedly fails in some conditions. For example in very dilute surfactant solutions close to the cmc the reactants may induce micellization, or may form submicellar aggregates with the surfactant. Such submicellar aggregates may be more or less catalytically effective than normal micelles. It seems probable, from the limited data available,[47,60,67] that small surfactant aggregates may be very good catalysts when both reactants are hydrophobic, but not when one of them is hydrophilic. Such a difference could be rationalized in terms of the inability of hydrophilic ions to interact strongly with small ionic clusters in water, whereas less polar solutes could interact hydrophobically, c.f. Reference 69.

These problems of perturbation of micelles by reactants should be relatively unimportant when the surfactant concentrations are much larger than that of the reactants, and it has been generally recognized that the quantitative treatments are valid only under those conditions.[20] However, there is other evidence which brings into question the assumption that micellar kinetics can be treated in terms of reactions occuring only in the aqueous and micellar pseudophases, i.e., that reaction does not occur at the boundary between water and the micelles.

The rate maxima which are typical of bimolecular reactions can be rationalized in terms of Equations 3 and 4 or their equivalents. Thus if one uses a surfactant in which the only counter ion is the reactive ion the first order rate constant should increase sigmoidally to a plateau value as the substrate becomes fully incorporated in the micelle. Some examples of such reactions are shown in Scheme 4.

Scheme 4

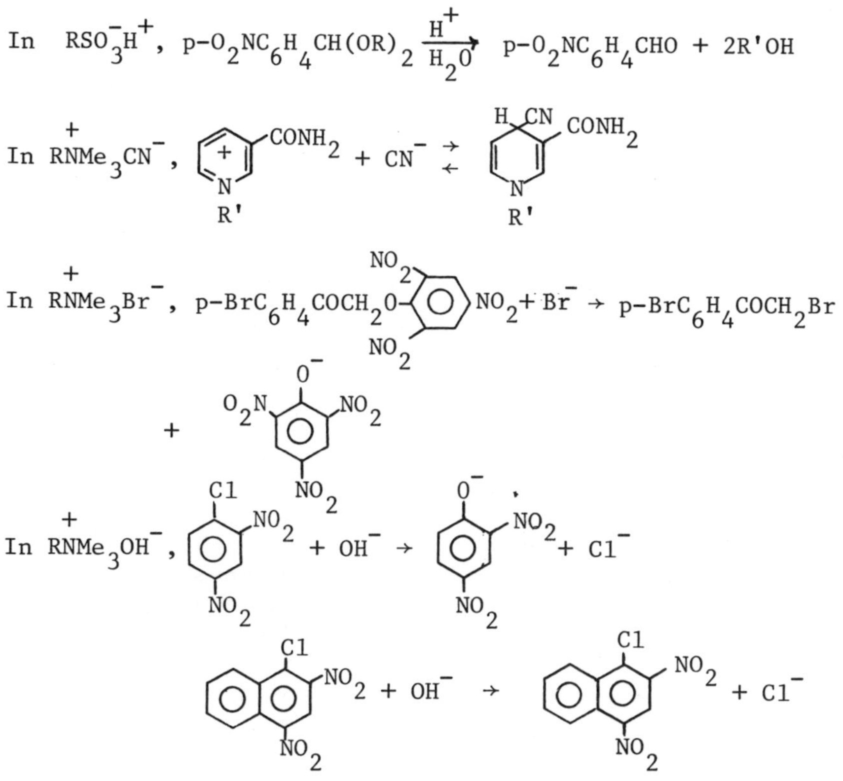

All these reactions, except those involving OH^-, show the predicted behavior with k_ψ increasing to a constant value with increasing surfactant concentration. This rate-surfactant profile is to be expected if, as seems to be the case, the extent of charge neutralization of the head groups by counter ions remains constant over a range of surfactant concentrations.[32,70]

However, for the hydroxide ion reactions k_ψ steadily increases with increasing surfactant concentration, even when all the substrate is apparently bound to the micelle, and under these conditions added hydroxide ion increases k_ψ, contrary to predictions. It might seem that these hydroxide ion reactions are a special case, but we find somewhat similar behavior with the other reactions in that under conditions in which the substrates are fully micellar bound added CN^- or Br^- also increases k_ψ. The relative rate increases are less than found with hydroxide ion, but they are too large to be accounted for by any possible increase in the concentrations of reactive ion in the Stern layer of the micelle.

It is difficult to explain these results in terms of the evidence presented heretofore, but a possible explanation is shown in Scheme 5 for reaction of a substrate, S, with a nucleophilic anion, N^-, in which the broken line represents reaction, with rate constant k_{MW}, occuring at the micelle-water boundary between an ion, *e.g.*, OH^- in water and substrate in the micelle.

Scheme 5

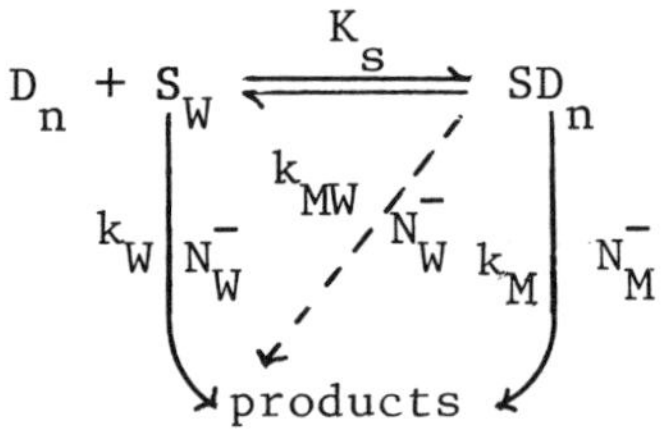

(The subscripts W and M denote incorporation in the aqueous or micellar pseudophases.)

The importance of this cross-term kinetic path should vary from one system to another, and may be relatively unimportant for reactions run under the usual conditions, *i.e.*, with a chemically inert surfactant, such as CTABr or NaLS, with added ionic reagent, *e.g.*, OH^-, H^+, OPh^-, SPh^-, simply because in these systems the surfactant, and therefore its unreactive counterion, is often in appreciable excess over the reactive ion.

We should remember that this question of reaction at a phase or pseudophase boundary is a general problem in nonmicellar systems.

For example, Menger has provided evidence for reaction at a water-hydrocarbon interface,[72] and there is also the question of whether phase-transfer catalysis can involve reaction at an interface, or whether reaction occurs only in the two solvents.[73]

ACKNOWLEDGEMENTS

I am grateful to G. Cerichelli, C. Cowell, L. S. Romsted, G. Savelli, L. Sepulveda, H. J. Smith and C. Thamavit for the unpublished results quoted in this manuscript. Much of the work was supported by the National Science Foundation.

REFERENCES

1. Various aspects of micellar catalysis and inhibition are discussed in References 2-6. In particular, Reference 6 includes a comprehensive compilation of kinetic and equilibrium data up to 1974.
2. E. H. Cordes and C. Gitler, Progr. Bioorg. Chem., 2, 1 (1973).
3. H. Morawetz, Adv. in Catalysis, 20, 341 (1969).
4. W. P. Jencks, "Advances in Enzymology", A. Meister, Editor, p. 219, Wiley, New York, 1975.
5. C. A. Bunton, Prog. Solid State Chem., 8, 239 (1973).
6. J. H. Fendler and E. J. Fendler, "Catalysis in Micellar and Macromolecular Systems", Academic Press, New York, 1975.
7. J. L. Kurz, J. Phys. Chem., 66, 2239 (1962); V.A. Motsavage and H.B. Kostenbauder, J. Colloid Sci., 18, 603 (1963); H. Nogami and Y. Kunakubo, Chem. Pharm. Bull. Tokyo, 11, 943 (1963).
8. G. S. Hartley, Trans Faraday Soc., 30, 444 (1934); Quart. Rev. (London) 2, 152 (1948).
9. I. V. Berezin, K. Martinek and A. K. Yatsimirski, Russ. Chem. Rev., 42, 787 (1973).
10. L. R. Fisher and D. G. Oakenfull, Quart. Rev. Chem. Soc., 6, 25 (1977).
11. K. Shinoda, T. Nakagawa, B-I. Tamamushi and T. Isemura, "Colloidal Surfactants", Academic Press, New York, 1963; "Nonionic Surfactants", M. J. Schick, Editor, Marcel Dekker, New York, 1967.
12. The rates of micelle formation and evidence on incorporation of solutes are discussed in Reference 13.
13. N. Muller in "Reaction Kinetics in Micelles", E. H. Cordes, Editor, p.1, Plenum Press, New York, 1973; J. Phys. Chem., 76, 3017 (1972); 78, 1024 (1974); p. J. Sams, E. Wyn-Jones, and J. Rassing, Chem. Phys. Lett., 13, 323 (1972).
14. C. A. Bunton, Pure App. Chem., 49, 969 (1977).
15. E. J. Fendler, J. H. Fendler, and R.R. Liechti, J. Org. Chem., 35, 1658 (1970).

16. C. A. Bunton, E. J. Fendler, L. Sepulveda and K-U Yang, J. Am. Chem. Soc., 90, 5512 (1968); G. J. Buist, C.A. Bunton, L. Robinson, L. Sepulveda and M. Stam, ibid., 92, 4072 (1970).
17. C. A. Bunton, M. J. Minch, L. Sepulveda and J. Hidalgo, J. Am. Chem. Soc., 95, 3262 (1973); C. A. Bunton, A. Kamego and M. J. Minch, J. Org. Chem., 36, 1388 (1972).
18. C. A. Lapinte and P. Viout, Tetrahedron Lett., 1113 (1973); C. A. Bunton, A. A. Kamego and P. Ng, J. Org. Chem., 39, 3469 (1974).
19. M. T. A. Behme, J. G. Fullington, R. Noel and E. H. Cordes, J. Am. Chem. Soc., 87, 266 (1965); L. S. Romsted and E. H. Cordes, ibid., 90, 4404 (1968).
20. F. M. Menger and C. E. Portnoy, J. Am. Chem. Soc., 89, 4968 (1967).
21. C. A. Bunton and L. Robinson, J. Org. Chem., 34, 773 (1969); C. A. Bunton, L. Robinson and L. Sepulveda, J. Am. Chem. Soc., 91, 4813 (1969).
22. E. F. J. Duynstee and E. Grunwald, J. Am. Chem. Soc., 81, 4540, 4542 (1959); J. Albrizzio, A. Archila, T. Rodulfo, and E. H. Cordes, J. Org. Chem., 37, 871 (1972).
23. P. Mukerjee and A. Ray, J. Phys. Chem., 40, 2144 (1966).
24. E. M. Kosower, J. Am. Chem. Soc., 80, 3253 (1958).
25. J. D. Eriksson and G. Gillberg, Acta Chem. Scand., 20, 2019 (1966); O. H. Griffith and A. S. Waggoner, Accounts Chem. Res., 2, 17 (1969); N. Muller and R. H. Birkhahn, J. Phys. Chem., 71, 957 (1967); A. T. Florence and R. T. Parfitt, ibid., 75 3554 (1971).
26. D. Stigter, J. Phys. Chem, 68, 3603 (1964); ibid., 79, 1008, 1015 (1975) and references cited.
27. C. K. Ingold, "Structure and Mechanism in Organic Chemistry", Chap. 7, Cornell University Press, Ithaca, New York, 1953.
28. A very valuable compilation of critical micelle concentrations is given in "Critical Micelle Concentrations of Aqueous Surfactant Systems", P. Mukerjee and K. J. Mysels, Nat. Bur. Stand. Ref. Data Ser., Washington, D.C., 1971.
29. C. A. Bunton and L. Robinson, J. Am. Chem. Soc., 90, 5872 (1968).
30. A. K. Yatsimirski, K. Martinek and I. V. Berezin, Tetrahedron 27, 2855 (1971).
31. C. A. Bunton and B. Wolfe, J. Am. Chem. Soc., 95, 3742 (1973); C. A. Bunton, L. S. Romsted and H. J. Smith, J. Org. Chem., 43, 4299 (1978).
32. L. S. Romsted in "Micellization, Solubilization and Microemulsions", K. L. Mittal, Editor, Vol. 2, p. 509, Plenum Press, New York, 1977.
33. L. Sepulveda, J. Colloid Interface Sci., 46, 372 (1974)
34. S. J. Dougherty and J. C. Berg, J. Colloid Interface Sci., 48, 110 (1974); 49, 135 (1975).
35. C. A. Bunton in "Reaction Kinetics in Micelles", E. H. Cordes, Editor, p. 76, Plenum Press, New York, 1973.

36. K. Martinek, A. K. Yatsimirski, A. V. Levashov, and I. V. Berezin in "Micellization, Solubilization and Microemulsions", K. L. Mittal, Editor, Vol. 2, p. 489, Plenum Press, New York, 1977.
37. L. S. Romsted, Ph.D. thesis, Indiana University, 1975.
38. D. G. Herries, W. Bishop and F. M. Richards, J. Phys. Chem., 68, 1842 (1964).
39. R. B. Dunlap and E. H. Cordes, J. Am. Chem. Soc., 90, 4395 (1968).
40. L. Sepulveda and R. Soto, Makromol. Chem., 179, 765 (1978).
41. I. M. Cuccovia, E. M. Schroter, P. M. Monteiro and H. Chaimovich, J. Org. Chem., 43, 000 (1978).
42. J. W. Larsen and L. Magid, J. Am. Chem. Soc., 96, 5774 (1974).
43. C. A. Bunton, K. Ohmenzetter and L. Sepulveda, J. Phys. Chem., 81, 2000 (1977).
44. F. Reiss-Husson and V. Luzzatti, J. Phys. Chem., 68, 3504 (1964); J. Colloid Interface Sci., 21, 534 (1966); H. Schott, J. Pharm. Sci., 60, 1594 (1971).
45. J. Baumrucker, M. Calzadilla, M. Centeno, G. Lehmann, M. Urdaneta, P. Lindquist, D. Dunham P. Price, B. Sears, and E. H. Cordes, J. Am. Chem. Soc., 94, 8164 (1972).
46. C. A. Bunton, F. Ramirez and L. Sepulveda, J. Org. Chem., 43, 1166 (1978).
47. C. A. Bunton, N. Carrasco, S. K. Huang, C. Paik and L. S. Ronsted, J. Am. Chem. Soc., 100, 5420 (1978).
48. H. V. Tartar, J. Phys. Chem., 49, 1195 (1955).
49. For discussions of micellar shape and size see C. Tanford, J. Phys. Chem., 76, 3020 (1972); 78, 2469 (1974); Science, 200, 1012 (1978).
50. L. Sepulveda, (1978) unpublished results.
51. It should be noted that these conclusions depend on the estimation of the extent of micellar binding of the anionic nucleophile from values of the apparent pKa.
52. T. C. Bruice, J. Katzhendler and L. R. Fedor, J. Am. Chem. Soc., 90, 1333 (1968); R. G. Shorenstein, C. S. Pratt, C-J. Hsu and T. E. Wagner, ibid., 90, 6199 (1968); K. Martinek, A. P. Osipov, A. K. Yatsimirski, V. A. Dadal and I. V. Berezin, Tetrahedron Lett., 1279 (1975).
53. C. Gitler and A. Ochoa-Solano, J. Am. Chem. Soc., 90, 5004 (1968).
54. U. Tonellato, J. Chem. Soc. Perkin, II, 822 (1977).
55. R. A. Moss, R. C. Nahas and S. Ramaswami, J. Am. Chem. Soc., 94, 627 (1977).
56. T. Kunitake, S. Shinkai and T. Okahata, Bull. Chem. Soc. Jap., 49, 540 (1976); I. Tabushi, Y. Kuroda and S. Kita, Tetrahedron Lett., 643 (1974); R. Ueoka, M. Kato and K. Ohkubo, ibid., 2163 (1977).

57. P. Heitmann, European J. Biochem., 5, 305 (1968); W. Tagaki, T. Amada, Y. Yamashita and Y. Yano, J. Chem. Soc., Chem. Commun., 1131 (1972); R. A. Moss, T. J. Lukas, and R. C. Nahas, Tetrahedron Lett., 507 (1978).
58. C. A. Bunton, L. Robinson and M. Stam, J. Am. Chem. Soc., 92, 7393 (1970).
59. G. Meyer and P. Viout, Tetrahedron, 33, 1959 (1977).
60. R. Schiffman, M. Chevion, J. Katzhendler, Ch. Rav-Acha and S. Sarel, J. Org. Chem., 42, 856 (1977); R. Schiffman, Ch. Rav-Acha, M. Chevion, J. Katzhendler and S. Sarel, ibid., 42, 3279 (1977); K. Martinek, A. V. Levashov and I. V. Berezin, Tetrahedron Lett., 1273 (1975).
61. M. T. A. Behme and E. H. Cordes, J. Am. Chem. Soc., 87, 260 (1965); C. A. Bunton and M. J. Minch, J. Phys. Chem., 78, 1490 (1974).
62. C. A. Bunton and L. G. Ionescu, J. Am. Chem. Soc., 95, 2912 (1973).
63. C. A. Bunton and S. Diaz, J. Am. Chem. Soc., 98, 5663 (1976).
64. C. A. Bunton and M. McAneny, J. Org. Chem., 42, 475 (1977).
65. C. A. Bunton and C. H. Paik, J. Org. Chem., 41, 40 (1976).
66. There are problems in using the concept of an acid dissociation constant K_a, for a micellized functional surfactant because the charges on the head groups change on acid dissociation, which therefore changes the nature of the micelle from cationic towards zwitterionic.
67. Evidence on this point comes in particular from analysis of the micellar catalysis of the benzidine rearrangement whose kinetics had been examined earlier.[31,68]
68. C. A. Bunton and R. J. Rubin, J. Am. Chem. Soc., 98, 4236 (1976).
69. Y. Okahata, R. Ando and T. Kunitake, J. Am. Chem. Soc., 99, 3067 (1977).
70. The values of β, the number of counterions per head group, seem to be in the range 0.6-0.8 for a variety of ionic micelles, and although they depend upon the method of measurement they are apparently insensitive to total counterion concentration.[26,32,71] In other words, the Stern layer is largely saturated with respect to counterions; c.f., C. A. Bunton, L. S. Romsted and G. Savelli, J. Am. Chem. Soc., 101, 000 (1979).
71. A review of experimental β values is given in Reference 37.
72. F. M. Menger, J. Am. Chem. Soc., 92, 5965 (1971).
73. J. Dockx, Synthesis, 441 (1973); c.f. F. M. Menger, J. V. Rhee and H. K. Rhee, J. Org. Chem., 40,3803 (1975).

FUNCTIONAL MICELLAR CATALYSIS

U. Tonellato

Centro Meccanismi di Reazioni Organiche del CNR,
Istituto di Chimica Organica, Università di Padova,
via Marzolo 1, 35100 Padova (Italy)

Functional micelles, aggregates containing nucleophilic or basic moieties incorporated into the head groups of surfactants, are being increasingly investigated as catalysts of organic reactions. Enzyme modelling and catalytic efficacy stimulate the intense interest devoted to the area of functional micellar catalysis. The structures of functional reagents reported in the literature are here illustrated and the basic factors and some mechanistic aspects of functional micellar catalysis of ester hydrolysis are briefly analzed. Data concerning the catalytic efficiency of some micellar reagents are reported. Other interesting features such as the detection of covalent intermediates, the intramicellar acyl transfer from one function to another in the case of bifunctional micelles and the stereochemical aspects so far explored are also reviewed. This contribution is restricted to reactions in aqueous solutions.

INTRODUCTION

Catalysis by micelles depends to some degree on factors (increased effective reagent concentration, favourable entropy and medium effects) that are similar to those that influence enzymic catalysis[1,2]. Quite clearly, differences are much more substantial than similarities and micelles of common detergents are rather poor models for enzymatic interactions.[3] Continuous interest in refining the analogy between micelles and enzymic catalysts has, however, greatly stimulated the study of functional micelles as advanced catalytic models. Since the early reports[4-7] in this field, a decade ago, remarkable achievements have been recorded:enhanced catalytic effectiveness in ester hydrolysis has been observed[8] using functional micelles and several systems come near to enzyme reactions in giving a high rate enhancement. Previous or parallel studies[9,10] of the catalytic properties of functional polymers and polyelectrolytes have certainly favoured rapid progress in the design of effective functional micellar catalysts. Future advancement will probably require a critical evaluation of available results in terms of structures and rates and more detailed mechanistic analysis of the observed effects.

This paper will be restricted to reactions in aqueous solutions. Catalysis by functional surfactants in nonaqueous solvents has been the subject or recent, authoritative reviews.[2,11]

STRUCTURES OF FUNCTIONAL MICELLAR REAGENTS

Functional micelles contain nucleophilic or other reactive groups covalently bound to the surfactant's molecules and are formed from (one or more types of) functional surfactants. Comicelles made up of chemically inert and chemically reactive surfactants are also referred to as functional micelles although there is no definite boundary between functional comicelles (functional micellar catalyzed reactions) and inert micelles containing solubilized organic reagents (bimolecular micellar reactions). An arbitrary border line is here drawn for solubilized functional surfactants to include reagents containing a paraffinic chain of at least 8 carbon atoms or an equivalent hydrophobic moiety. The main types of functional surfactants so far explored are designed to model[12] hydrolytic proteases, particularly serine or cysteine proteinases, and the functions are those used in the active sites of these enzymes. These are indicated in Figure 1: the hydroxyl group[13-29] (also in the active form of oxime[30] or hydroxamic acid derivatives[8,30-32]), the imidazole ring,[5-7,33-40], amino[4,40-42] and sulphydryl groups[43-49]. Other more complex functional systems such as those in flavin[50] or porphyrin[51] derivatives have also been investigated as micellar catalysts. The most common surfactant structures are also schematically indicated in Figure 1: the functions are either bound to a paraffinic chain or to the head of a quater-

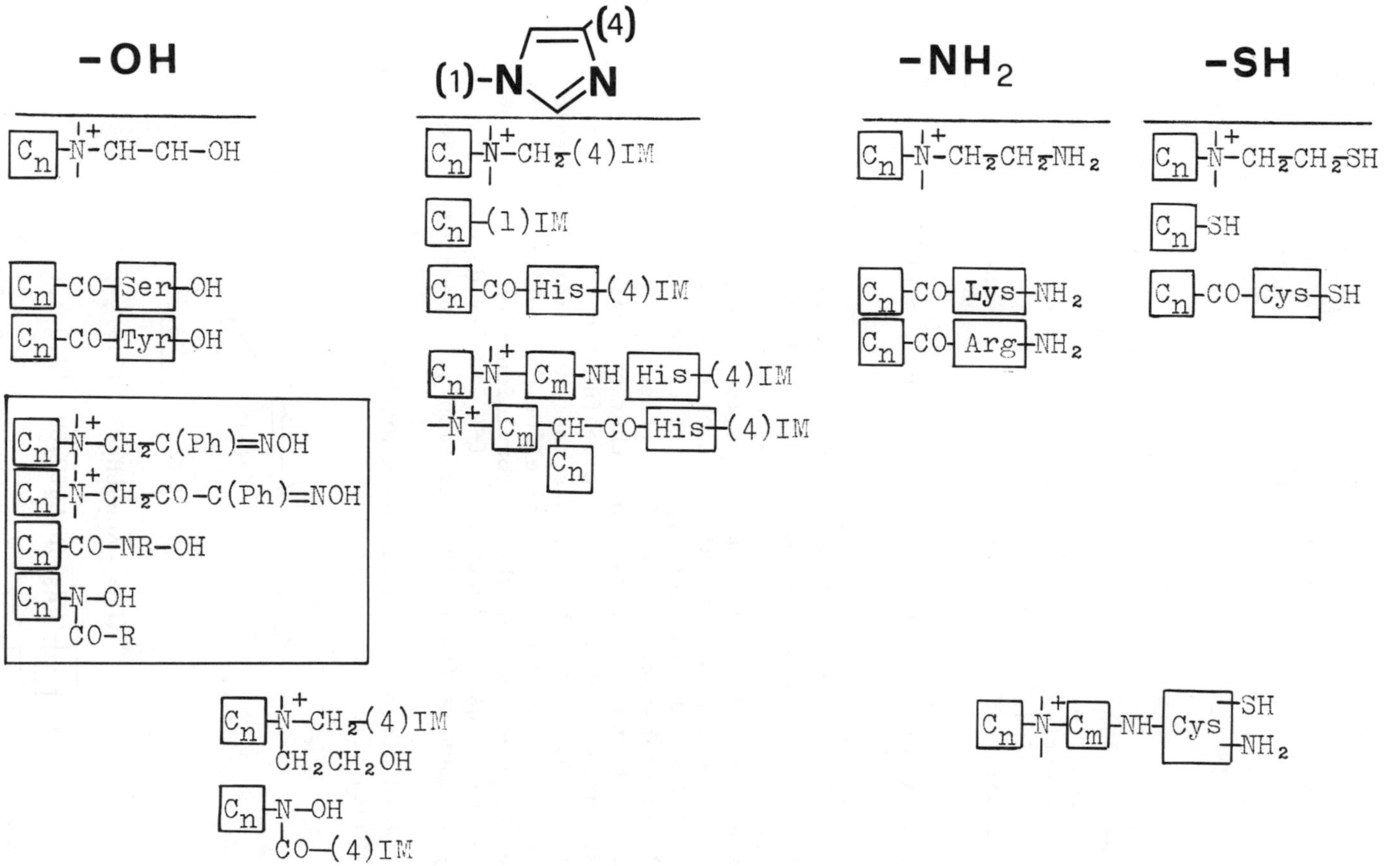

Figure 1. Structures of Functional Surfactants. Abbreviations for paraffinic sequences used here and in the following Figures and Tables: C_n = n-C_nH_{2n+1}; C_m = n-C_mH_{2m}. Counter-ions of quaternary ammonium salts (usually Cl^- or Br^-) are not shown.

nary ammonium salt or are part of an amino acid residue that is attached to a cationic surfactant structure or is N^{α}-acylated. Quaternary ammonium salts are usually fairly soluble in water; most of the other functional reagents are very little or not soluble and studies of their catalytic properties have been performed with comicellar aqueous solutions using inert surfactants such as CTABr as solubilizing agents.

The catalytic properties of functional micellar reagents as enzyme models have been mainly reported for the hydrolysis of activated carboxylic esters or phosphate esters. The use of functional micelles as catalysts in their own right in synthetic organic chemistry has great potential and is still a rather unexplored area which only recently has received attention. Base-catalyzed reactions such as elimination[52] and condensation[53] reactions have been found to be very effectively promoted by functional micelles.

GENERAL FEATURES OF FUNCTIONAL MICELLAR CATALYSIS

Basically, the observed rate changes due to functional micelles are dominated by hydrophobic factors and electrostatic and medium effects which are common to all micellar systems.[1,2] A neutral substrate in aqueous solution containing functional micelles undergoes a phase transfer from bulk solvent to the functionalized micellar pseudophase to an extent which depends on the hydrophobic character of the substrate, on the size of the micelles, and other factors.[1,2] Electrostatic and medium effects are of particular importance for functional micelles since they strongly influence the acid dissociation[54-56] of the reactive functions. The problem is illustrated in Table 1 which shows, as an example, available data due to Bunton and McAneny[24] for micelles of choline-type surfactants: the apparent pK_a of the hydroxyl function, when at the head of cationic micelles, is lowered by 1-1.5 units depending also on a variety of factors (salt concentration[8], temperature). This

Table 1. Acid Dissociation of the Hydroxyl Function of Choline-type Surfactants (from reference 24)

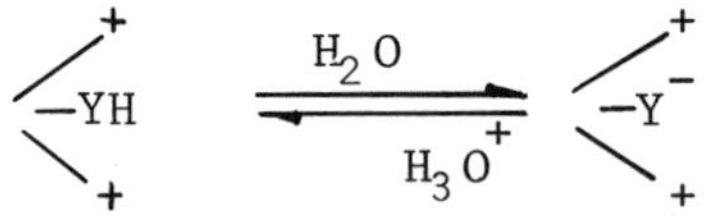

	pK_a
$(CH_3)_3\overset{+}{N}CH_2CH_2OH$	13.9
mic. $\boxed{C_{12}}$–$(CH_3)_2\overset{+}{N}CH_2CH_2OH$	12.9 app.
mic. $\boxed{C_{16}}$–$(CH_3)_2\overset{+}{N}CH_2CH_2OH$	12.4 app.

implies that the relative concentration of unprotonated functions, obviously more effective bases or nucleophiles than their conjugate acids, is much higher at the cationic micellar surface than can be predicted from the pK_a of the monomeric surfactant (or of a non-surfactant analogue)for a given pH of the solution.

The problem of acid dissociation which exists whenever one deals with microscopic pseudophases and complicates the results obtained with micellar reagents as well as with polyelectrolytes or enzymes is also related to that of desolvation, particularly of anionic functions,in the relatively hydrophobic micellar environment. The two related phenomena, changes in acid dissociation of the functions and desolvation of the reaction sites, are of prime importance in the case of functional micellar catalysis: they have been differently evaluated by various authors[8,27,30] and further investigations on this point are needed for a better understanding of the observed catalytic effects.

FUNCTIONAL MICELLAR CATALYSIS OF ESTER HYDROLYSIS: MECHANISTIC CONSIDERATIONS

A general mechanistic scheme for functional micellar catalysis of carboxylate ester hydrolysis is shown in Figure 2. The main

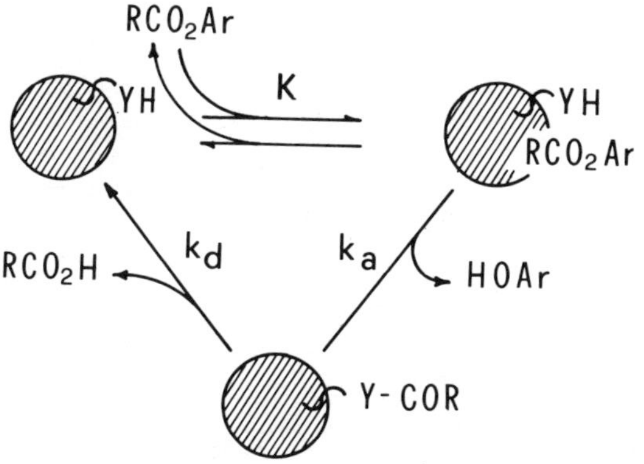

Figure 2. Catalytic Cycle for Functional (Nucleophilic) Micelles and Ester Hydrolysis.

kinetic parameters characterizing the process are the association equilibrium constant, the rate of release of the alcoholic fragment (and acylation of the functions) and the rate of regeneration (deacylation) of the function or the turnover rate of the catalyst. Proper combination of the pre-equilibrium association constant and the first-order rate constant for the release of the alcoholic residue from the micelle-substrate complex gives what is usually referred to as the apparent catalytic second-order rate constant, $\underline{k}_c$.

In the Scheme of Figure 2 it has been assumed that the mode of action of the micellar function is nucleophilic attack at the carbonyl carbon (or phosphoryl phosphorus in the case of phosphate esters). This cannot be taken for granted since other mechanisms may be involved such as general base catalysis, general acid catalysis or activation of hydroxide ions or other external nucleophiles[16,18]. This problem has been particularly debated in the case of choline-type surfactants in mildly alkaline solutions. Independent studies by Bunton's[22,23], Katzhendler's[27] and Berezin's[20] groups have clearly demonstrated, on the basis of the observed kinetic solvent deuterium isotope effect (close or slightly less than unity) and other mechanistic evidence that the catalytic effects in the hydrolysis of carboxylate or phosphate esters are due to the dissociated hydroxyl head group acting as a nucleophile. In the great majority of cases investigated, a nucleophilic mechanism is involved and, in a number of instances, (see Figure 3) the acylated intermediate resulting from esterolysis could be detected and identified.

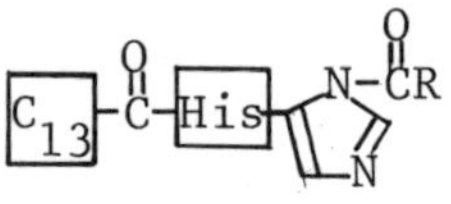

(reference 7)

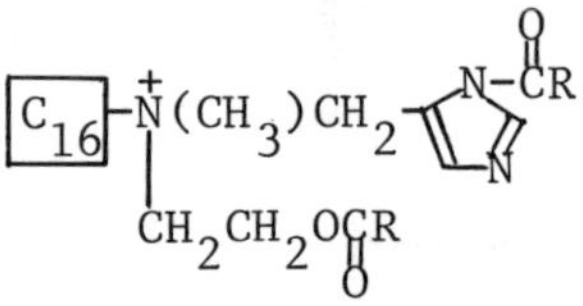

(reference 25)

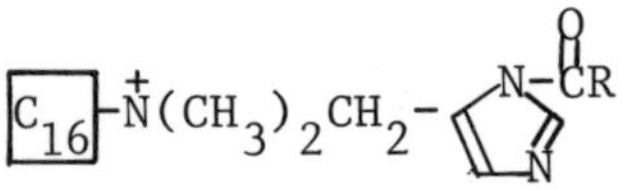

(references 25,33,39)

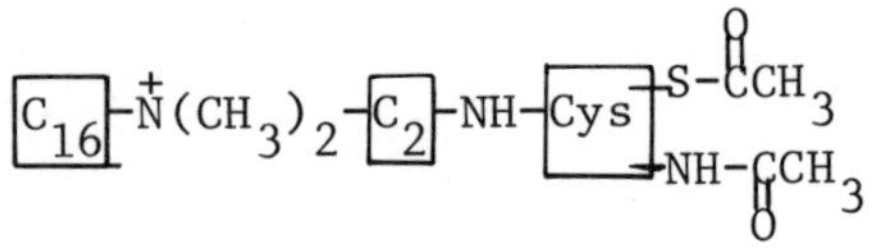

(and mono S-Ac, mono N-Ac; reference 47).

Figure 3. Identified Acylated Intermediates

However, in at least one case, the hydrolysis of diphenyl *p*-nitrophenyl phosphate catalyzed by micelles of the L-histidine containing surfactant shown in Figure 4, investigated by Bunton and coworkers[37], general base catalysis is indicated as the mechanistic pathway by the large kinetic solvent isotope effect: $\underline{k}(H_2O)/\underline{k}(D_2O)\simeq 2.5$.

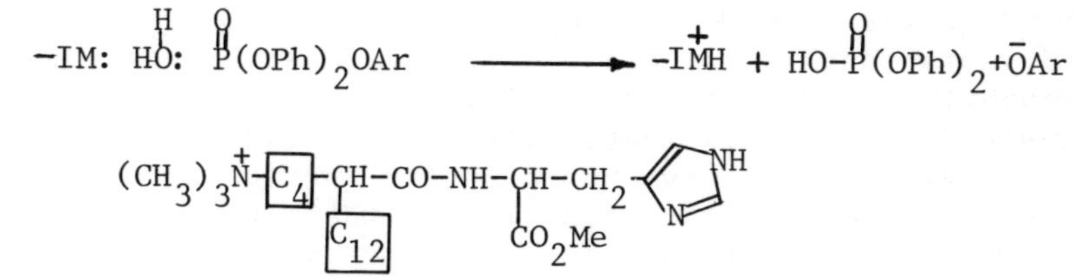

Figure 4. General Base Catalyzed Hydrolysis of Phosphate Esters (from reference 37)

CATALYTIC EFFICIENCY OF FUNCTIONAL MICELLES.

Comparing the catalytic efficiency of the various types of functional micelles from published data is a quite difficult or impossible task due to the different conditions used in the kinetic studies (micelle and solvent composition, pH, buffer, temperature) although, as said above, all new functional micellar reagents have been tested as catalysts of *p*-nitrophenyl ester hydrolysis. Moreover, most of these investigations were conducted under pseudo-first order conditions (low [ester]) so that only the acylation process was followed.

We have recently measured the rates of acylation and deacylation (in the hydrolysis of *p*-nitrophenyl esters) of some of the best micellar reagents so far described under common conditions. Due mainly to solubility problems, kinetic measurement were made for comicelles made up of CTABr and the functional surfactant being tested (in a molar ratio of approximately 6-7:1), in Tris buffers at constant ionic strength (see Table 2). The operational advantages of these conditions, i.e., low cmc values ($3\text{-}5\times10^{-5}$M) and inertness of micelles of CTABr alone toward PNPesters, were first described by Gitler and Ochoa-Solano[7]. Apart from non-entirely rigorous assumptions used in the kinetic treatment of raw kinetic data[7,57], one main limitation in the use of comicelles is that any cooperativity effect due to intermolecular interactions which may be effective in homogeneous functional micelles is here quenched or suppressed as shown by Moss and his coworkers[25] in the case of (imidazole-and hydroxyl-) bifunctional micelles. At any rate, where a comparison[39] is possible as in the case of soluble cationic monofunctional reagents, the apparent catalytic rate constants obtained for comicelles are reasonably close to (generally slightly higher than) those obtained for homogenous micelles under identical conditions.

The catalytic efficiency of some monofunctional surfactants in the hydrolysis of p-nitrophenyl hexanoate (PNPH) at pH 7.95 is indicated by the kinetic data of Table 2. The apparent catalytic rate constants were obtained from measurements carried out under conditions: [ester]≪[functional surfactant] and the turnover constants, when accessible, were derived from steady state data as "burst" kinetics, [ester]≫[funct. surf.]. With the exception of the amino-functionalized surfactant[40] (n.2) and N$^{\alpha}$ myristoylhistidine[7] (n.3) where the nucleophilic form is the neutral free base, the anionic forms of the functions of the reagents listed in Table 2 have been indicated [20,27,30] as the effective nucleophilic species involved in the esterolysis. The degree of ionization of the functions may be roughly estimated from their apparent pK_a values.

Table II. Catalytic Efficiency of Various Functional Micellar Reagents[a,b] in the Hydrolysis[c] of PNPH at pH 7.95,25°.

Catalysts	$k_c\ M^{-1}s^{-1}$	$10^4 k$ turnover s^{-1}
1. [C16]-$\overset{+}{N}(CH_3)_2CH_2CH_2OH$	1.3	-
2. [C16]-$\overset{+}{N}(CH_3)_2CH_2CH_2NH_2$	23	-
3. [C13]-CO-[His]-(4)IM	150	5.1
4. [C16]-$\overset{+}{N}(CH_3)_2CH_2$-(4)IM	250	>50.
5. [C13]-CO-$N(CH_3)OH$	2600	2.6
6. [C16]-$\overset{+}{N}(CH_3)_2CH_2C(Ph)$=NOH	2590	4.
7. [C16]-$\overset{+}{N}(CH_3)_2CH_2COC(Ph)$=NOH	23000[d]	2.

[a]See Figure 1 for abbreviations of structures. [b]Apparent (approximate) pK_a = 1: 12.4 (ref. 24); 2:6.0 (ref 40); 3:(1st ionization) 6.2 (ref.7); 4:(2nd ion.) 11 (ref. 39); 5: 9.6 (ref.30); 6 :9.3; 7 : 8.0 (ref. 32) [c]Conditions:[CTABr]:[catalyst]≃6-7:1; Tris buffer, μ=0.1M(KCl), 1%(v/v) CH_3CN. [d]Approximate value.

Table 2 reveals very large differences in the nucleophilic abilities of the various micellar reagents, a factor greater than 10^4 being involved between the choline-type surfactant (n.1) and the α-oximino-ketone-functionalized term (n.7). On the other hand, the turnover rate for the monofunctional reagents is, not unexpectedly, rather modest (with one notable exception, that of the imidazole functionalized reagent n.4) and this seriously limits their over-all catalytic efficiency.

More data are shown in Table 3 for the hydrolysis of PNPA, pH 7.95 ,relative to some of the most effective mono-and bi-functional reagents. It also includes kinetic data obtained under comparable conditions by Moss and coworkers for the cysteine functionalized reagent[46,47] (n.6) and the thiocholine-type reagent[48] (n.7) and by Kunitake and coworkers[8] for the imidazole containing hydroxamic acid (n.8). The catalytic parameters of α-chymotrypsin are also included for comparison purposes.

Clearly, some of the micellar systems shown in Table 3 are not only powerful nucleophilic reagents but are also very effective

Table III. Catalytic Efficiency of Mono-and Bi-functional Micellar Reagents in the Hydrolysis[a] of PNPA at pH 7.95, 25°C

Catalysts [b]	k_c $M^{-1}s^{-1}$	$10^4 k$ turnover s^{-1}
1. $\boxed{C_{16}}-\overset{+}{N}(CH_3)_2CH_2-(4)IM$	6.8	> 60.
2. $\boxed{C_{16}}-\overset{+}{N}(CH_3)(CH_2CH_2-OH)CH_2-(4)IM$	6.1	> 60.
3. $\boxed{C_{13}}-CO-N(CH_3)OH$	300.	3.6
4. $\boxed{C_{16}}-\overset{+}{N}(CH_3)_2CH_2C(Ph){=}NOH$	300.	4.
5. $\boxed{C_{16}}-\overset{+}{N}(CH_3)_2CH_2COC(Ph){=}NOH$	2500.	2.
6. $\boxed{C_{16}}-\overset{+}{N}(CH_3)_2CH_2CH_2NH-\boxed{Cys}\genfrac{}{}{0pt}{}{-SH}{-NH_2}$ [c]	26.	
7. $\boxed{C_{16}}-\overset{+}{N}(CH_3)_2CH_2CH_2SH$	580. (485)[d]	2.
8. $\boxed{C_{12}}-N(OH)CO-(4)IM$[e]	930.	380.
α-chymotrypsin[f]	560.	150.

[a] See note c of Table 2 for conditions (unless otherwise indicated).
[b] See note a of Table 2. [c] pH 8.0, 0.02M phosphate, μ=0.05, 25° (ref. 46 and 47). [d] pH 7.96, 0.01M phosphate, μ=0.05, 23°, pK_a app. 7.3 (ref. 48). [e] pH 8.0, 0.01M Borate, μ=0.01, CTABr = 1×10^{-3} M, 3% (v/v) EtOH, 30° (ref. 8). [f] pH 7.94, 0.1 M phosphate, 10% (v/v) CH_3CN, 25.1° (ref. 58)

catalysts comparable to or, as in the case of the reagent n.8, even surpassing the hydrolytic enzyme toward a non-specific substrate such as PNPA.

This is quite a remarkable achievement in the field of micellar catalysis. Yet, there are limitations of these systems that must be carefully evaluated before drawing unwarranted generalizations from the present results or conclusions concerning the use of functional micelles as enzymatic models.

The catalytic efficiency illustrated by data of Tables 2 and 3 is about the cleavage of p-nitrophenyl esters, standard substrates with a good leaving group ($pK_a \simeq 7$). We found a dramatic change in the nucleophilic abilities on going from the hydrolysis of PNPH (or PNPA) to that of N-n-butyl 2,4-dinitrotrifluoroacetanilide (and also of N-acylimidazoles[28]). Some of the available data are shown in Table 4. The change is particularly striking in the case of the choline-type surfactant, (n.1) and the imidazole functionalized reagent (n.3); the micellar bifunctional reagent (n.2) is a good catalyst in each case due to the complementarity of the two functions used in the acylation stage. As for the reasons of the observed changes in nucleophilic abilities, we indicated[28] a shift in the slow step of the acylation process. Assuming a nucleophilic mechanism (equation 1) in both hydrolytic processes, it is reasonable to assume that the slow step may change from k_1 to k_2, from formation to decomposition of the tetrahedral intermediate on going from PNPH with a good leaving group to the anilide whose leaving group (N-n-butyl 2,4-dinitroaniline) is a much weaker acid[59] than any micellar function (see Table 2).

$$-Y^- + R\text{-}C(=O)\text{-}L \underset{k_{-1}}{\overset{k_1}{\rightleftharpoons}} Y\text{-}C(O^-)(R)\text{-}L \xrightarrow{k_2} -Y\text{-}C(=O)\text{-}R + L^- \quad (1)$$

Table IV. Apparent Catalytic Rate Constants[a], k_c ($M^{-1}s^{-1}$), pH 7.95,25°.

Catalyst	PNPH	$CF_3\text{-}C(=O)\text{-}N(n\text{-}Bu)\text{-}C_6H_3(NO_2)_2$
1. $[C_{16}]\text{-}\overset{+}{N}(CH_3)_2CH_2CH_2OH$	1.3	53
2. $[C_{16}]\text{-}\overset{+}{N}(CH_3)(CH_2CH_2OH)CH_2\text{-}(4)IM$	190	49
3. $[C_{16}]\text{-}\overset{+}{N}(CH_3)_2CH_2\text{-}(4)IM$	250	≤1
4. $[C_{16}]\text{-}\overset{+}{N}(CH_3)_2CH_2COC(Ph)=NOH$	23000[b]	41

[a] See Table 2 for conditions and abbreviations. [b] Approximate value.

COOPERATIVITY AND ACYL TRANSFER PROCESSES IN BIFUNCTIONAL MICELLES

Bifunctional micelles have been more recently investigated and very interesting results have been reported. Mechanistic exploration of these systems is crucial to the design of useful catalytic models and micellar enzyme analogues.

So far in the case of ester hydrolysis catalyzed by bifunctional micelles, no clear-cut evidence of synergism between different functions in the acylation stage has been reported[8,25,26]. The most interesting feature observed in the cleavage of p-nitrophenyl esters is the facile inter-or intramolecular trans-acylation process occurring from one function to another. Such a process has been first reported to occur in the case of imidazole-and hydroxyl-functionalized micelles independently by Moss and coworkers[25] and by ourselves[26] (using the bifunctional surfactant shown in Figure 5 or mixed micelles of hydroxyl and imidazole monofunctional surfactants) and by Tagaki and coworkers[60] (using mixed micelles of the hydroxyl monofunctional surfactant and of the histidine containing reagent shown in Figure 5). The main catalytic cycle involves acylation of the imidazole ring, acyl transfer to the hydroxyl function, and eventually regeneration. Trans-acylation has been shown by Moss and coworkers[25] to involve an essentially intermolecular process (also in the case of micelles of the bifunctional surfactants) which is faster than deacylation to water. Moreover, it has been shown[25,26] that a supplementary cycle involving the monofunctional O-acylated micelles is effective particularly in the presence of excess substrate. This is schematically shown in Figure 5.

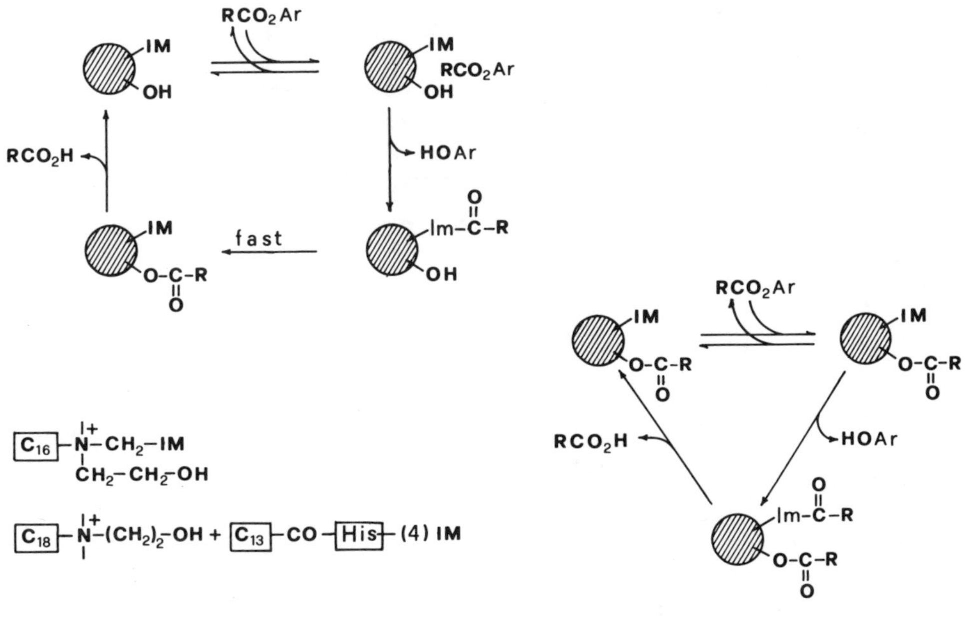

Figure 5. Schematic Representation of the Catalytic Cycles of Bifunctional (Imidazole- and Hydroxyl-) Micelles. The Cleavage of p-nitrophenyl Esters.

Before examining other facile trans-acylation processes in bifunctional micellar catalysis let me briefly summarize and comment on some of the evidence concerning the case of micelles of the imidazole-and hydroxyl-functionalized surfactant shown in Figure 5. In the case of phenolic substrates, the imidazole ring is the nucleophilic site and the acyl residue is rapidly transferred to the hydroxyl function; in the case of carbonyl substrates possessing a worse leaving group (such as the anilide of Table 4), the (dissociated) hydroxyl function is the effective nucleophile. There is a striking (perhaps conicidental) similarity between the above evidence and the hypothesis by Hubbard and Kirsch[61] concerning the mode of action of α-chymotrypsin, illustrated in Figure 6. In the active site of the enzyme, following these authors, the serine hydroxyl function acts as a nucleophide except in the cleavage of nonspecific phenolic (or other active) esters. With these substrates acylation of the enzyme entails nucleophilic attack by the histidine imidazole ring followed by fast acyl transfer to the serine hydroxyl group.

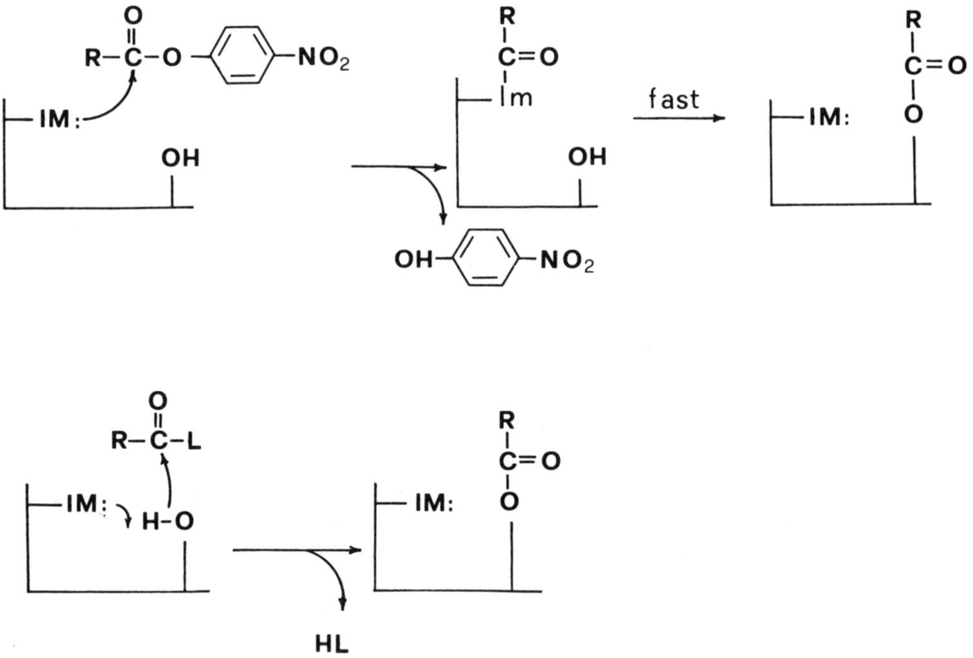

Figure 6. The Acylation of Chymotrypsin by Activated Esters (upper) and by Non-activated Esters (lower) following Hubbard and Kirsch's Hypothesis (reference 61).

Moss and coworkers[46,47] have recently investigated the complex behaviour of the cysteine containing cationic surfactant shown in Figure 7. In this case the catalytic cycle involves rapid S→N acyl transfer, a process which is likely to be intramolecular in character. The single steps have been investigated and their rates, ($\underline{k}_1$-$\underline{k}_4$) individually measured.

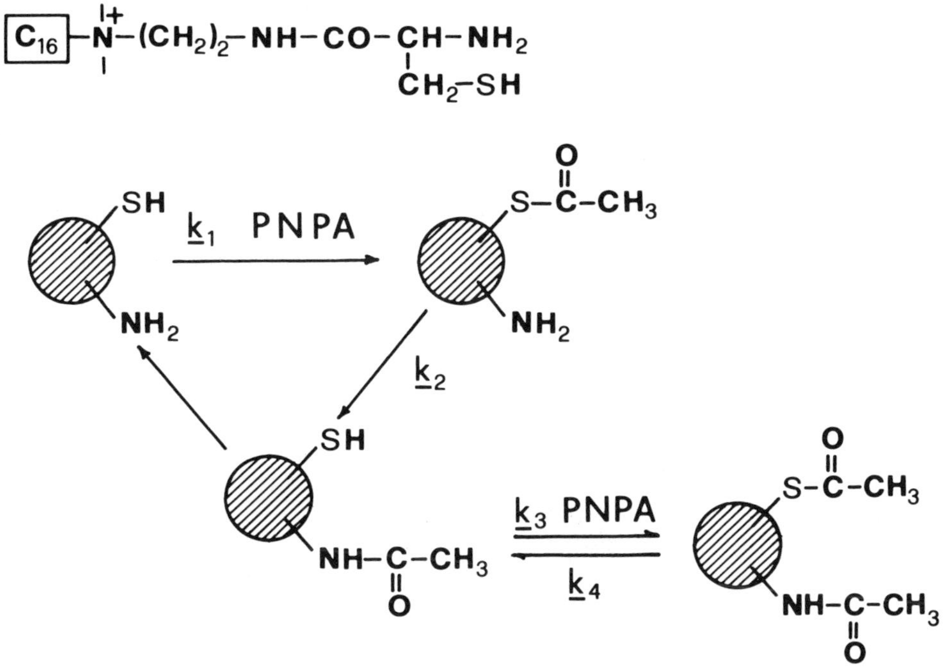

Figure 7. The Catalytic Cycle of a Cysteine containing Cationic Surfactant: from references 46 and 47.

The most effective micellar catalytic system so far reported is that of comicelles made up of the imidazole containing hydroxamic acid shown in Figure 8 (see also Table 3) investigated by Kunitake and coworkers[8]. The most interesting feature of this system is the very large turnover rate measured in the hydrolysis of PNPA. The catalytic cycle, following the authors is that schematically shown in Figure 8: acylation occurs at the oxygen atom of the hydroxamate group, the more reactive function,and its deacylation is very effectively enhanced by the imidazole ring. The mode of intramolecular action of the imidazole in the deacylation stage has been left undefined. The occurence of an effective complementary cycle such as the one shown in Figure 5, involving the activated imidazole (pK_a, 2nd ion. = 10.4; see also the $\underline{k}$ turnover values of Table 3) cannot be entirely excluded on the basis of the reported data. Although one must agree with the authors that a major result is obtained, it would be of the greatest interest for the design of efficient models to elucidate the detailed mechanism of the deacylation stage in this system.

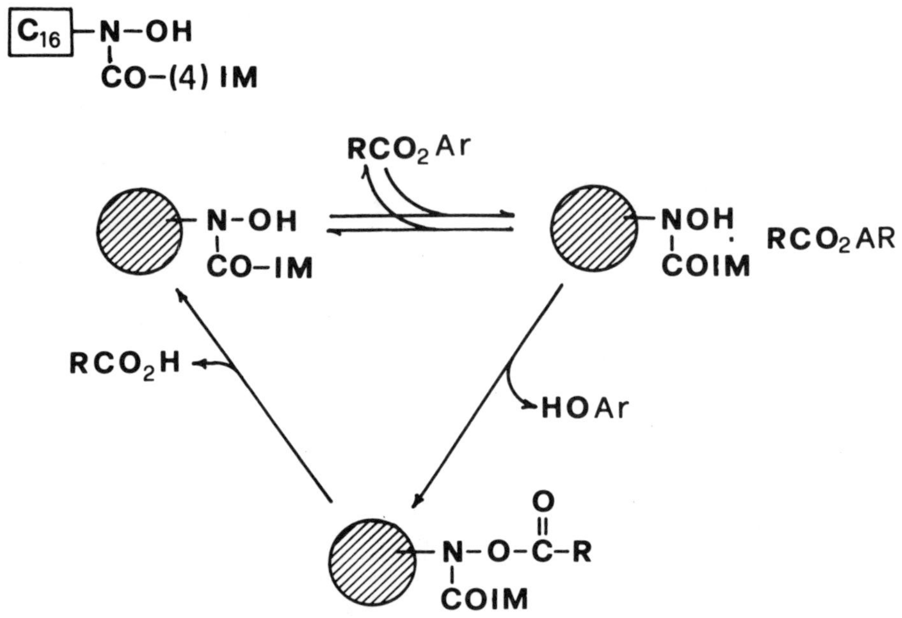

Figure 8. Main Catalytic Cycle of an Imidazole Containing Hydroxamic Acid: from reference 8.

STEREOCHEMISTRY

Chirality is a topical question in micellar catalysis in view of the frequently claimed analogy between micelles and enzymes. The demonstration of micellar control of stereochemistry in deamination reactions by Moss and coworkers[62,64] and the work by Brown and Bunton[37] commented on below are the only significant results of the investigations reported[17,40,65] in the literature.

The enantioselectivity due to functional micelles of the L-histidine containing surfactant shown in Figure 9 in the cleavage of the two enantiomeric N-acetylphenylalanine p-nitrophenyl esters is a well known example[37]. Chiral recognition is in this case larger than revealed by the enantioselectivity factor of 3 since the phenylalanine ester is very reactive[40] and possibly a poor substrate for demonstration of the phenomenon. Strong intermolecular

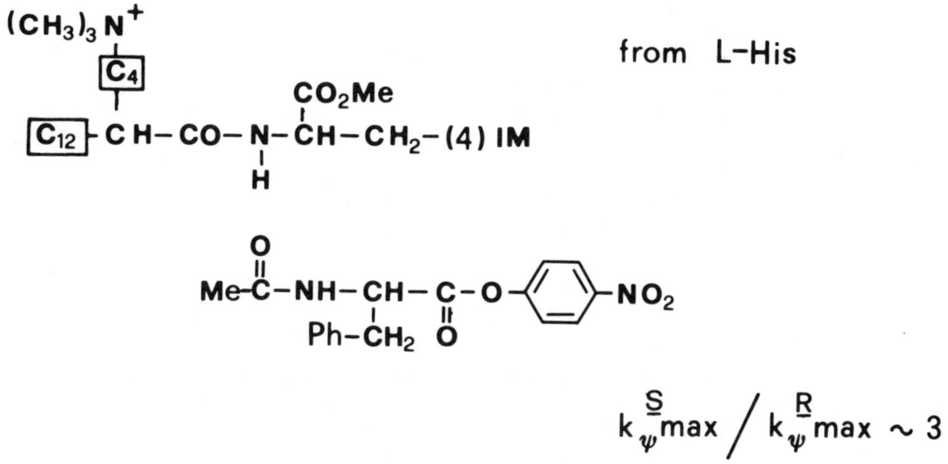

Figure 9. Enantioselective Functional Micellar System; from reference 37.

hydrogen bonds between reagents and substrate seems to be a requirement for enhanced stereoselectivity but the relation between substrate and surfactant structures is probably very complex. Considerable efforts will probably be needed to solve this problem.

CONCLUDING REMARKS

Progress toward very effective catalytic micellar systems and interesting enzyme analogues by the exploitation of functional surfactants has been rapid and significant. Advancement in this area is likely to come from study of micelles made of well designed bi- or polyfunctional reagents, of functional micelles capable of associating metal ions, and from study of reactions other than ester cleavages in aqueous or nonaqueous solutions. Advancement will however require more detailed mechanistic investigations aimed also at better defining the identity of functional micellar catalysis with regard to catalysis by functionalized polymeric and macrocyclic systems.

ACKNOWLEDGMENTS

I thank Professor G. Modena for advice and discussions and Drs. R. Fornasier, L. Anoardi, F. de Buzzaccarini, D. Sostero and Mr. E. Castiglione for their participation in the work done in this laboratory. I am grateful to Professor R.A. Moss, Rutgers University of New Jersey for valuable suggestions and for making available the results obtained in his laboratory prior to publication and to Professor C.A. Bunton, University of California, Santa Barbara, for exchange of correspondence and discussions.

REFERENCES

1. C.A. Bunton in "Applications of Biochemical Systems in Organic Chemistry", J. Bryan Jones, Editor, Part II, Chap. IV, Wiley and Sons, New York, N.Y., 1976.
2. J.H. Fendler and E.J. Fendler, "Catalysis in Micellar and Macromolecular Systems", Academic Press, New York, N.Y., 1975.
3. E. Zeffren and R.E. Watson, Intra-Sci. Chem. Rep. 6, 51(1972).
4. T.C. Bruice, J. Katzhendler, and L.R. Fedor, J. Amer. Chem. Soc., 90, 1333 (1968).
5. A. Ochoa-Solano, G. Romero, and C. Gitler, Science, 156, 1243 (1967).
6. T.E. Wagner, C. Hsu, and C.S. Pratt, J. Amer. Chem. Soc. 89, 6366 (1967)
7. C. Gitler and A. Ochoa-Solano, J. Amer. Chem. Soc. 90, 5004 (1968).
8. T. Kunitake, Y. Okahata, and T. Sakamoto, J. Amer. Chem. Soc., 98, 7799 (1976)
9. T. Kunitake and Y. Okahata, Advances in Polymer Science, 20, 160 (1976).
10. T. Kunitake and Y. Okahata, J. Amer. Chem. Soc., 98, 7793 (1976)
11. J.H. Fendler, Accounts Chem. Res., 9, 153 (1976).
12. T.H. Fife, Adv. Phys. Org. Chem., 11, 1 (1975).
13. C.A. Bunton, L. Robinson, and M. Stam, J. Amer. Chem. Soc., 92, 7393 (1970).
14. C.A. Bunton and L.G. Ionescu, J. Amer. Chem. Soc. 95, 2912 (1973)
15. M. Chevion, J. Katzhendler and S. Sarel, Isr. J. Chem. 10, 975 (1972)
16. V. Gani, C. Lapinte, and P. Viout, Tetrahedron Lett. 4435 (1973)
17. C.A. Bunton, I. Robinson and M. Stam Tetrahedron Lett., 121 (1971)
18. G. Meyer, Tetrahedron Lett., 4581 (1972).

19. G. Meyer, C.R. Acad. Sci, Ser.C, 276, 1599 (1973).
20. K. Martinek, A.A. Levashov and I.V. Berezin, Tetrahedron Lett., 1275 (1975).
21. R.A. Moss, R.C. Nahas, S. Ramaswani, and W.J. Sanders, Tetrahedron Lett., 3379 (1975).
22. C.A. Bunton and S. Diaz, J. Org. Chem., 41, 36 (1976).
23. C.A. Bunton and M. Mc Aneny, J. Org. Chem. 41, 36 (1976).
24. C.A. Bunton and M. Mc Aneny, J. Org. Chem., 42, 475 (1977).
25. R.A. Moss, R.C. Nahas, and S. Ramaswami, J. Amer. Chem. Soc., 99, 627 (1977).
26. U. Tonellato, J. Chem. Soc. Perkin Trans. 2, 821 (1977).
27. R. Shiffman, M. Chevion, J. Katzhender, C. Rav-Acha, and S. Sarel, J. Org. Chem., 42, 856 (1977).
28. L. Anoardi and U. Tonellato, J. Chem. Soc., Chem. Comm., 401 (1977).
29. V. Gani, Tetrahedron Lett., 2277 (1970)
30. T. Kunitake, S. Shinkai, and O. Okahata, Bull. Chem. Soc. Jpn., 49, 540 (1976).
31. L. Anoardi, F. de Buzzaccarini, R. Fornasier, and U. Tonellato, Tetrahedron Lett., submitted for publication.
32. I. Tabushi, Y. Kuroda, and S. Kita, Tetrahedron Lett., 643, 3613 (1974).
33. W. Tagaki, M. Chigira, T. Amada, and Y. Yano, J. Chem. Soc., Chem. Comm. 219 (1972).
34. P. Heitmann, R. Husung-Bublitz, and H.J. Zunft, Tetrahedron, 30, 4137 (1974).
35. D.G. Oakenfull and D.E. Fenwick, Aust. J. Chem., 27, 2149 (1974)
36. J.M. Brown and C.A. Bunton, J. Chem. Soc, Chem. Comm., 969 (1974).
37. J.M. Brown, C.A. Bunton, and S. Diaz., J. Chem. Soc., Chem. Comm., 971 (1974).
38. J.P. Guthrie and Y. Ueda, J. Chem. Soc, Chem. Comm., 898 (1973)
39. U. Tonellato, J. Chem. Soc., Perkin Trans. 2, 771 (1976).
40. R.A. Moss, T.J. Lukas, and R.C. Nahas, Tetrahedron Lett., 3851 (1977).
41. K. Nomura, T. Inoue and H. Kimizuka, Mem. Fac. Sci., Univ. Kyushu, Ser. C., 10, 71 (1976).
42. T. Inoue, K. Nomura, and H. Kimizuka, Bull. Chem. Soc. Jpn., 49, 719 (1976).
43. P. Heitmann, Eur.J. Biochem., 5, 305 (1968)
44. W. Tagaki, T. Amada, Y. Yamashita, and Y. Yano, J. Chem. Soc., Chem. Comm., 1131 (1972).
45. S. Shinkai and T. Kunitake, Bull. Chem. Soc. Jpn., 49, 3219 (1976).
46. R.A. Moss, R.C. Nahas, and T.J. Lukas, Tetrahedron Lett., 507 (1978).
47. R.A. Moss, T.J. Lukas, and R.C. Nahas, J. Amer. Chem. Soc., in press.
48. R.A. Moss, G.O. Bizzigotti, T.J. Lukas, and W.J. Sanders, Tetrahedron Lett., submitted for publication.

49. L. Anoardi, R. Fornasier, D. Sostero, and U. Tonellato, Gazz. Chim. Ital. submitted for publication.
50. S. Shinkai, R. Ando, and F. Yoneda, Chem. Lett., 147 (1977).
51. T. Yamamura, Chem. Lett., 773 (1977).
52. V. Gani, C. Lapinte, and P. Viout, Tetrahedron Lett., 4435 (1973).
53. S. Shinkai and T. Kunitake, J. Chem. Soc., Perkin Trans.2, 980 (1976).
54. P. Mukerjee and K. Banerjee, J. Phys. Chem. 68, 3567 (1964).
55. C.A. Bunton and B. Wolfe, J. Amer. Chem. Soc., 95, 3742 (1973).
56. M.S. Fernandez and P. Fromherz, J. Phys. Chem. 81, 1755 (1977).
57. T. Maugh III and T.C. Bruice, J. Amer. Chem. Soc., 93, 6584 (1971).
58. M.L. Bender and N. Nakamura, J. Amer. Chem. Soc., 84, 2577 (1962).
59. D. Dolman and R. Stewart, Can. J. Chem. 45, 911 (1967).
60. W. Tagaki, S. Kobayashi, and D. Fukushima, J. Chem. Soc., Chem. Comm., 29 (1977).
61. C.D. Hubbard and J.F. Kirsch, Biochemistry, 11, 2483 (1972).
62. R.A. Moss and D.W. Reger, J. Amer. Chem. Soc., 91, 7539 (1969).
63. R.A. Moss and C.J. Talkowski, J. Amer. Chem. Soc., 94, 4767 (1972).
64. R.A. Moss, C.J. Talkowski, D.W. Reger, and W.L. Sunshine, J. Amer. Chem. Soc., 95, 5215 (1973).
65. R.A. Moss and W. Sunshine, J. Org. Chem., 39 1083 (1974).

PROMOTION OF PHOTOCHEMICAL REACTIONS BY MICELLAR SYSTEMS

J.K. Thomas and M. Almgren[1]
Radiation Laboratory
University of Notre Dame
Notre Dame, IN 46556

The effect of micelles on photochemically induced reactions is discussed in terms of conventional theories of micellar catalysis of reactions. In particular, photo-induced electron transfer and photo-ionization are discussed where micelles both increase the yield of these processes and also in the case of photo-ionization lower the ionization threshold. The influence of reactant solubilization site on the processes is also discussed.

INTRODUCTION

It is now well documented that micelles often have a profound influence on the course and rate of chemical reactions.[2,3,4] Indeed it is stated that micelles are reminiscent of enzymes, by the catalytic effects that they produce.[2] The last few years have seen an increasing interest in the possible influence that micelles may have on radiation induced processes, i.e. photochemical or radiolytic processes.[4,5,6] This overview will concern itself mainly with the effects of micellar systems on photochemical reactions, drawing attention to the possibility of storage of light energy in these systems. This latter aspect has become quite an important feature of the solar energy programme.

A possible framework for discussing the effects of micellar systems on photochemical reactions is provided by considering the structure of a simple micelle in an aqueous system. The top part of Fig. 1 shows a representative micelle in water. The structure, which is a cluster of monomeric surfactant units e.g. sodium lauryl sulfate NaLS, or cetyl trimethyl ammonium bromide CTAB, is roughly spherical or oval in shape and contains 50 to 100 monomer units. Some of the surfactant molecules are ionized leading to net charges of 20-30 on the micelle and to counter ions e.g. Na^+ or Br^- in the solution and in the vicinity of the micelle surface. This effect gives rise to high electric fields (>10^5 volts/cm) at the micelle surface. The surface of the micelle contains the hydrophillic moiety of the molecule i.e. SO_4^- or $(\overset{+}{N}(CH_3)_3)$, while the interior consists of alkane chains and is sometimes referred to as an oil drop. The degree of order in the micellar core is a subject of some debate and will not concern us here.

The lower portion of Fig. I depicts four types of processes that are directed by or occur as a direct consequence of micelles. The micelles are represented as spherical objects with the reactants A, B, or C in different locations with respect to the micelle. The nature of the site for A, B, or C will be discussed subsequently. The main object to be learnt from this diagram is that at least one of the reactants has to reside for a major portion of its time with the micelle.

In case I both reactants A and B reside primarily in the micelle and not in the aqueous phase, due to their hydrophobic like character. Excitation by light of one of the reactants leads to reaction when the excited species meets with the other reactant. Such a reaction is strongly promoted over that in homogeneous solution due to the close proximity of the reactants. Several examples of this proximity effect will be discussed subsequently.

In process II one of the reactants A, which is hydrophobic, is with the micelle while the other which is hydrophillic is in the water phase. Excitation of A leads to the excited state A* and for reaction to occur C must penetrate the micelle to A*. It will be shown that usually A* does not exit the micelle in order to react with C. Unlike Type I no catalysis of reaction is observed but frequently a retardation is experienced and the excited molecule is actually protected from damage by impurities such as C in the aqueous phase. This is particularly true if C and the micelle has like charge, when electrostatic repulsions keeps C away from the micelle containing A*.

Systems of Type III are a derivation of the systems in Type I. Both A and B are with the micelle with the stipulation that one reactant say B, is only weakly solubilized by the micelle. Excitation by light may lead to electron transfer from A to B, forming A^- and B^+, or B to A depending on the system. This is the proximity effect of Type I. However if the surface charge of the micelle is positive or the same as that of B^+ then repulsion of B^+ from the micelle occurs. This leads to efficient separation of A^- and B^+ (or A^+ and B^- if the micelle is anionic) and prevents the ion neutralization $A^- + B^+ \rightarrow A + B$. Thus light energy is efficiently stored as chemical energy of the ions.

Type IV is a variation of Type III where the light induced electron transfer process involves transfer of e^- to the aqueous phase to give the hydrated electron e^-_{aq}. Again an anionic micelle prevents the back neutralization of A^+ and e^-_{aq}. Another unique

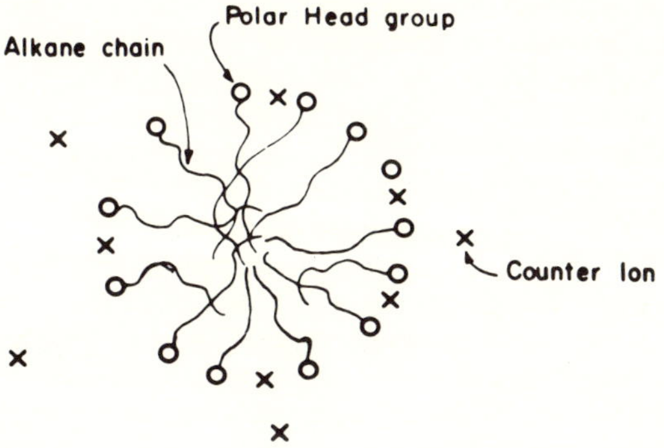

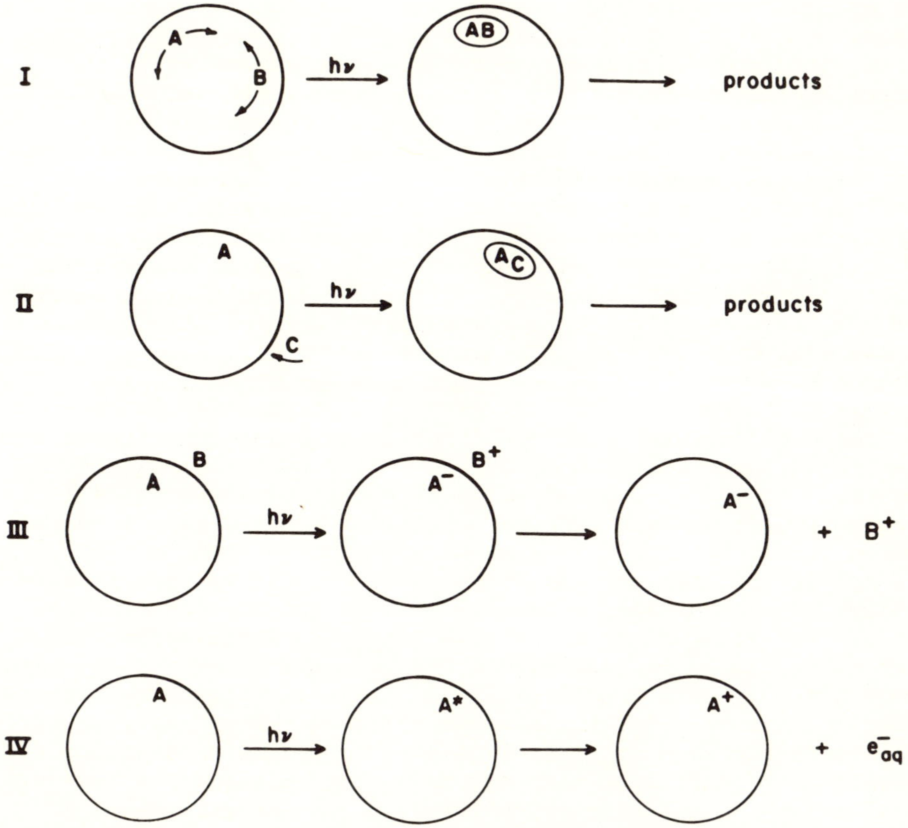

Figure 1. Representation of the four possible situations where micelles may influence the photo-induced reaction of A and B.

feature of this system is the lowering of the energy required to promote the ionization process compared to that in the gas phase. Both systems III and IV are of importance in solar energy research.

Site of Solubilization of Molecules

An important parameter in the foregoing discussion is the site of solubilization of the reactant. Two basic positions are considered for the probe in this discussion: a) On the micelle surface and b) In the micelle interior. NMR studies[7,8] and thermodynamic considerations[8] indicate that benzene and naphthalene are located in the micelle surface of CTAB. Similar studies[10] with pyrene indicate that this molecule is more towards the interior of the micelle although still in contact with the surface. Molecules with polar substituents e.g. $-NH_2$, -OH, -CHO tend to locate at the surface of the micelle. The molecule pyrene carboxyaldehyde has been used to measure the environment of the surface and its fluorescence properties follow changes induced at the micellar surface by addition of salt and/or alcohols.[11]

The environment of molecules such as pyrene can be ascertained from their fluorescence fine structure. It is found that the environment of pyrene in NaLS and CTAB is similar to that of alcohols and quite different from the alkane like environment of the micelle center. This is interpreted as a partial interaction of pyrene with the polar water like region of the micelle surface. Quenching molecules that interact with the micelle surface as counter ions e.g., Tl^+ on NaLS or Br^- on CTAB strongly quench pyrene fluorescence indicating the proximity of the two reactants.[12,13,14]

The data indicate that hydrophobic molecules are solubilized close to the micelle surface the precise location being uncertain however. The molecule could sit at the surface towards the aqueous phase as with molecules containing hydrophillic groups, or towards the interior but in contact with the surface as with pyrene. It is stressed that these systems are dynamic in nature and that the solubilized molecules move in the micelle and also out into the aqueous phase. When a site of solubilization is referred to, it is the site where the molecule spends most of its time. A molecule in the micelle will certainly reach the surface on exiting the micelle, the time it spends in this environment compared to the micelle interior will depend on the nature of the molecule. Another important feature is the relatively large size of the molecules (∿7 Å) used compared to micelle radius (∿15 Å) which tends to obscure precise locations of the molecule in the micelle.

It is sufficient for our subsequent discussion to describe the molecules as being <u>inside</u> the micelle surface or <u>on</u> the surface, and to also state some properties of the solubilization site, i.e. polarity etc. which are available from spectroscopic measurements.

Photoionization

One of the most interesting features of micellar effects on photochemical reactions is the pronounced photoionization promoted in certain micellar systems. This was first noted for pyrene in NaLS micelles,[15] where two photon excitation of pyrene led to the absorption spectra of the cation of pyrene P^+, (λ_{max}=453 nm), and the hydrated electron e^-_{aq} (absorption spectrum increasing in the red to λ_{max}=720 nm). Figure 2 shows the short lived spectra of P^+ and e^-_{aq} produced at the end of a 20 nsec pulse of 347.1 nm light, also shown are the spectra of the excited singlet P_s and triplet P_T of pyrene produced in the photolysis of pyrene in C_6H_{12}.[16] Photoionization is not observed optically in C_6H_{12} in marked contrast to pyrene in NaLS micelles. Photoionization of pyrene in C_6H_{12} is observed by sensitive conductivity methods[17] and also in methanol,[16] but the yields of photoionization at the end of a 20 nsec pulse are much smaller in these systems. This is due to a rapid ($<10^{-10}$sec) initial recombination of the ions following photoionization,[18] in C_6H_{12} and alcohol. This is prevented in micelles where P^+ remains with the negatively charged NaLS which separates and shields the cation from e^-_{aq} in the aqueous phase. The electron is ejected into the Gouy-Chapman layer at some 10 - 15 Å from the micelle surface;[19] and subsequently diffuses into the aqueous bulk.

Several other molecules also exhibit strong photoionization in the micellar solution, e.g. phenothiazine,[20] tetramethyl-benzidine,[21] and amino-pyrene.[22] Unlike the pyrene/NaLS system, photoionization occurs with one photon of 347.1 nm light in these systems. This means that the ionization potentials of these molecules are <3.6 ev in NaLS compared to >6.3 ev in the gas phase. This has been explained in terms of a tunnelling mechanism for the electron from the lipid region of the micelle into the aqueous phase.[20] Another way of looking at this process is via the short time solvation energies that the ions pick up from the micellar and aqueous phase. In the process $P \rightarrow P^+ + e$, the ionization potential in solution I_s, is related to that in the gas plan I_g, by the expression $I_s = I_g + P_+ + V_o$ where P_+ is the polarization energy of the cation and V_o the energy state of e^- in water which is reported as -1.5ev.[23] The polarization P_+ may be calculated from the Born charging expression:

$$P_+ = \frac{e^2}{2r}\left(1 - \frac{1}{\varepsilon}\right)$$

where r is the interaction distance of the ion and the surrounding solvent molecules, e the electronic charge and ε the fast dielectric constant of the medium, which is normally 2. If ε for some systems is much greater than two then P_+ may double in this system compared to simple liquids. P_+ is normally -1.5 to -2.0 ev. So $I_g - I_s \simeq$ 3.0 ev for water or even 4.5 ev if the micelle introduces an $\varepsilon \gg 2$.

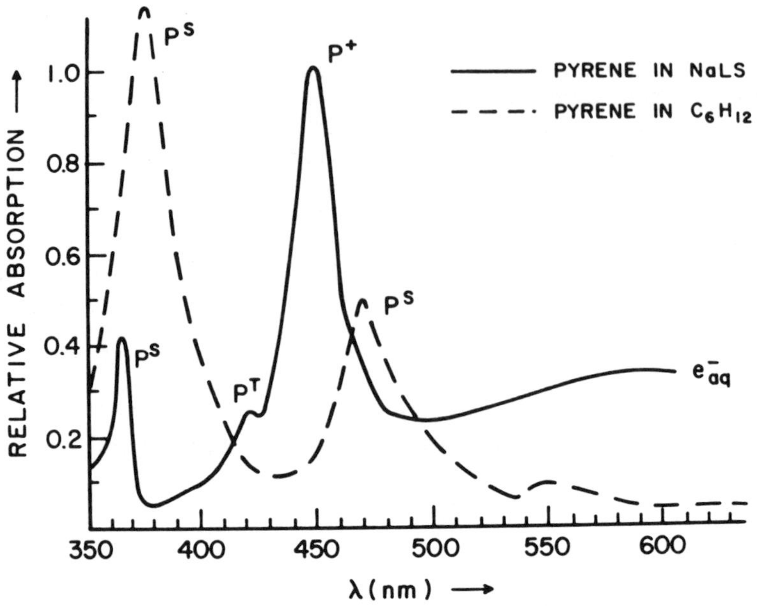

Figure 2. Spectra of short-lived species, i.e., pyrene triplet, pyrene singlet, pyrene cation and hydrated electron in the laser photolysis of pyrene in C_6H_{12}.

With these concepts in mind a system was designed to produce photoionization with long wavelength light. The molecule chosen was amino-perylene where the $-NH_2$ group locates the molecule in the sulfate groups of the surface of NaLS micelles.[24] The one photon photoionization of amino-perylene was achieved in NaLS micelles with light $\lambda = 530.0$ nm. It is concluded that micelles in particular anionic sulfate micelles provide ideal vehicles for promotion of photoionization and subsequent protection of the ionic products.

Electron Transfer

Electron transfer in micellar systems is often facilitated by the proximity effect and subsequently stabilized by the micellar charge. It was noted quite early on by the Berlin groups[20,21] that excitation of phenothiazine and duroquinone in NaLS leads to rapid formation of phenothiazine cations and duroquinone anions.[21] Triplet phenothiazine which is also formed transfer e^- to duroquinone more slowly. The yield of photoionization giving e^-_{aq} is decreased in these systems as the electron is now captured by the duroquinone. It was also found that reduction of metal ions e.g. Cu^{++} or Eu^{3+}, occurred efficiently on micellar NaLS via electron transfer from excited phenothiazine or tetramethylbenzidine to these cations.

The micellar environment can also control the nature of decomposition of photolysis products. Excitation of pyrene in the presence of dimethyl aniline D, leads in alkanes to the excited complex or exciplex (PD)* and to triplet pyrene P^T, or in polar solvents to electron transfer and the ions P^- and D^+. The photoproduced ions subsequently react rapidly in homogeneous solution. However micelles promote the electron transfer reaction leading to P^- and D^+ [25,26] as shown in Figure 3 where the spectra of the products following the 20 nsec laser photolysis of pyrene/dimethyl aniline in various media is shown. In C_6H_{12} non-ionic chemistry predominates and the triplet state of pyrene is observed; in methanol both triplet pyrene and ionic states are observed; in micellar NaLS the ionic chemistry is strong, while in micellar CTAB ionic chemistry predominates. The inserts in Figure 3 show the time dependence of P^- in NaLS and CTAB. In NaLS D^+ does not escape the micelle due to its negative charge and rapid recombination of D^+ and P^- ensure. In CATB however D^+ is repelled from the positively charged micelle and long lived ($>10^{-2}$ sec) ions are observed. Such systems serve as models for solar energy storage systems.

Quenching of Excited States

The micelle may promote or retard the reaction of an excited arene A* molecule with a quencher Q.[5] For example singlet excited pyrene P* is quenched by iodide ion with a rate constant k_q of $>10^9 M^{-1} sec^{-1}$ in homogeneous solution. However, the quenching is much slower ($k_q \sim 10^6 M^{-1} sec^{-1}$) in NaLS due to a repulsion of I^- away from P* by the negatively charged micellar surface. Similar effects are noted with the quenching of P* by thallous Tl^+ ions in CTAB where the rate drops from $k_q = 10^{10} M^{-1} sec^{-1}$ in homogeneous solution to $<10^7$ in CTAB. However if P* is solubilized in NaLS then Tl^+ is bound to the micelle surface in close proximity to P* and the quenching reaction is very efficient. These electrostatic effects do not apply to neutral species where Q is the triethylamine or nitromethane. Some retardation of the quenching reaction is noted due to the more rigid nature of the micelle compared to most homogeneous solvents.[5] However if Q, e.g. iodoheptane is solubilized in the micelle along with P* then quenching again is catalyzed by the proximity effect.

Phosphorescence in Micelles

Phosphorescence or light emission from the triplet excited state of arenes is rarely observed in fluid solution as the radi-

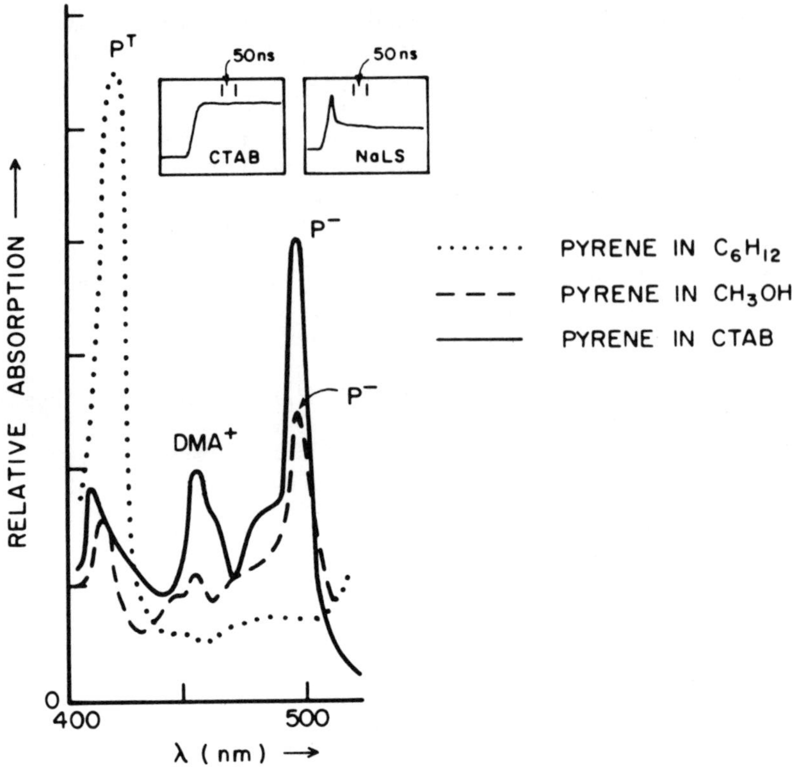

Figure 3. Spectra of short-lived species in the laser photolysis of pyrene and dimethylaniline in C_6H_{12}, CH_3OH and CTAB micelles. Insert: oscilloscope time traces of pyrene anion P^- in CTAB and NaLS micelles. (P^t is the pyrene triplet, P^- the pyrene anion and DMA^+ the dimethylaniline cation.)

ative lifetime is so long (>1sec) that the triplet is removed by impurity quenching or triplet triplet annihilation. Phosphorescence is normally observed in low temperature glasses where reactants are immobilized. However phosphorescence has been observed in fluid micellar solution[14b,c] as the micelles protect the arene triplet from impurity quenching. Indeed, phosphorescence has been used to measure the exit rate of molecules from micelles. Exit times on the order of 50 μsec have been measured for bromonaphthalene. This supports the earlier concept that quenching of excited singlet states which occurs at times shorter than 10^{-7}sec is due to a motion of the quencher into or within the micelle to the excited state rather than to exit of the excited state into the aqueous phase.

Excitation Energy Transfer

The proximity of molecules solubilized by a micelle leads to very favourable conditions for excitation energy transfer. Sometimes dramatic effects are observed as illustrated by Figure 4.[27] Here the naphthalene fluorescence intensities of solutions containing a constant concentration of naphthalene and varying concentrations of the surfactant sodium phenylundecanoate are given vs the reciprocal total absorbance at the excitation wavelength. The surfactant concentration thus increases from right to left in the figure. At low concentration the intensity decreases in proportion to 1/A reflecting the competition between naphthalene and the phenyl groups for the excitation light. At the cmc the fluorescence intensity suddenly increases. Micelles are formed into which naphthalene enters, and light absorbed both by the phenyl groups and naphthalene itself in these micelles gives rise to naphthalene fluorescence. At still higher surfactant concentrations the naphthalene fluorescence intensity decreases again, due to the fact that an increasing fraction of the incident light is absorbed by micelles without naphthalene. In this example the UV-absorbing phenyl groups of the surfactant acts in the micelle as a light harvesting unit, or an antenna pigment system, for the acceptor, naphthalene. In this way the acceptor can be excited at a much higher rate than if it absorbed alone. Photochemical

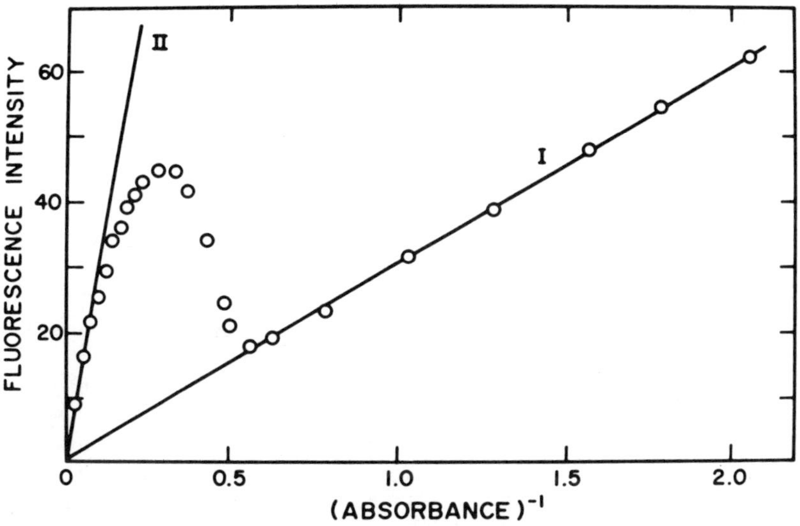

Figure 4. Naphthalene fluorescence intensity vs. reciprocal total absorbance for solutions containing a constant concentration of naphthalene and varying concentrations of the surfactant sodium phenylundecanoate.

reactions that involve participation of more than one photon for the production of the stable end products such as photodecomposition of water into H_2 and O_2, can in this way be facilitated. A light harvesting unit of this type may further have some application in laser systems, where it should be much easier to achieve an inverse population of the acceptor.

Photosynthetic pigments such as chlorophyll a, b and lutein can be solubilized in micelles up to the concentrations of the photosynthetic membranes. Various aspects of energy transfer between these has been studied in micelles, first by Teale in 1958[28] and more recently by others.[29]

Excitation energy transfer from methylene blue to thionine both solubilized by an anionic micelle has been studied by Singhal et al.[30] These systems where both donor and acceptor are attached to the surface seem to be less effective as energy harvesting units. Each acceptor seems to quench at most 5-7 donor molecules.[30,32]

Some other energy-transfer situations have also been studied in micellar systems. Transfer of energy from phenoxy groups of a nonionic surfactant to solubilized pyrene,[33] and transfer from solubilized naphthalene to terbium counter ions of an anionic micelle[34] are examples.

Excimer Emission

The proximity introduced by micelles is well illustrated by efficient formation of excimers or excited dimers of arenes in micellar solution

$$\text{arene} \xrightarrow{h\nu} (\text{arene})^* \xrightarrow{\text{arene}} (\text{arene})_2^*$$

$(\text{arene})^* \searrow$ monomer fluorescence; $(\text{arene})_2^* \searrow$ excimer fluorescence

The most striking example of eximer fluorescence is that of pyrene, first investigated by Förster and Kasper[35] in normal solutions, and by Förster and Selinger[36] in micelles. It has since then been frequently used and abused to probe micelle properties.[37] The salient features of excimer formation in micelles were clearly revealed in Förster and Selingers[36] study of pyrene and 2-methylnaphthalene in micelles of CDBA (cetyl dimethyl benzyl ammonium chloride). These two probes are very different with respect to the ease of excimer formation as measured by the "half-value concentration," i.e. the concentration at which the monomer fluorescence has been 50% quenched, and at which the excimer emission has risen to one half of its maximum value obtained in very concentrated solutions. The half-value concentrations are 1.2×10^{-3}M for pyrene and 1.35 M for 2-methylnaphthalene in hexadecane (cetane). In a 0.04 M CDBA solution the half-value concentrations are reduced to 17 mM for 2-methylnaphthalene and

0.3 mM for pyrene, clearly showing the proximity effect of the micelles. Converting these macroconcentrations to concentrations in the micellar phase, Förster and Selinger found a half-value microconcentration of 1.46 M for 2-methylnaphthalene and 26 mM for pyrene. Thus for 2-methylnaphthalene cetan and the micelles seem to be about equivalent with respect to the ease of excimer formation and emission, whereas for pyrene a much higher concentration is needed in the micelles to obtain the same effect as in cetan. The latter effect with pyrene is due to the statistical distribution of the solubilized molecules among the micelles. The half-value concentrations for pyrene in cetan corresponds to only about 0.06 molecules of pyrene per micelle. Since it takes two molecules to make an excimer a much higher mean occupancy number is of course needed. The half-value concentration calculated in micelles corresponds to 1.3 molecules per micelle which is of the right order of magnitude.

The strong dependence of the ratio pyrene monomer/excimer fluorescence on the distribution of pyrene molecules among the micelles offers possibilities for studying and acertaining the type of statistics which operates in these systems. On the other hand, if the distribution is known then the micellar size can be calculated from the monomer/excimer ratio.[37a] The statistical distribution of solubilized molecules among micelles are of importance for many types of reactions. Poisson statistics has been assumed by most authors[30,37f,g,h] which is the distribution that applies if the solubilized molecules are distributed at random among the micelles. It is less well known that these statistics follows if the solubilization has the characteristics of a partitioning between two phases, i.e. is characterized by a constant ratio P_m/P_{aq} where P_m and P_{aq} are the concentrations in the micellar and aqueous phase respectively.[38] Conversely, other types of statistics imply a dependence of this ratio on the mean occupancy number $\bar{n}$. Dorrance and Hunter[37c,d,e] have used a different distribution function in their studies of pyrene excimers in CTAB micelles; their distribution function predicts that the ratio P_m/P_{aq} is proportional to $1 + \bar{n}$.[38] Data for a number of arenes in CTAB and NaLS show no such dependence of P_m/P_{aq} on $\bar{n}$, but are in accord with the expectation for a Poisson distribution.[38]

It is implicit in the early paper by Förster and Selinger, and more explicit in some of the later publications, that pyrene is solubilized in the interior of the micelles. However, excimer formation can readily take place at the surface of micelles as shown by the surface probe pyrene sulfonic acid,[39] and there are strong indications that pyrene is preferentially solubilized close to the surface of CTAB, but probably more evenly distributed in NaLS micelles.[38] It is found that the solubility of pyrene in CTAB micelles is about 6 times higher than in a hydrocarbon solvent, whereas the solubilities are about the same for hydrocarbon and NaLS.[38]

Excited State Acid-Base Equilibira

The fluorescence of many molecules exhibit pH-dependent behavior classic examples being naphthols and naphthlyamines. The unique behavior of these molecules have also been investigated in micellar solutions.[37f,g,40,41]

The acidity of β-naphthol in aqueous solutions is $pK_a = 9.6$ in the ground state but in the singlet excited state decreases to 2.8. Thus at neutral pH, where the ground state is undissociated the naphthol excitation leads to dissociation giving both naphthol and the naphtholate fluorescence. The lifetimes of the excited states are too short for equilibration.

In micelles of 0.1M sodium dodecyl sulfate, Hauser and Klein[40] have shown that the apparent pK_a of the β-naphthol ground state is increased considerably, to 10.8. This change is expected, and is similar to the behavior displayed by acid-base indicators in micellar solutions. However, no dissociation of the excited β-naphtol could be detected in micellar solutions and the β-naphtholate fluorescence only appeared at pH close to or greater than the apparent pK_a of the ground state.

The complete depression of the excited state dissociation in micelles seems unusual at first sight. Both Hauser and Klein[40c] and Selinger et al.[37g,41] speculate that β-naphthol is buried in the micellar interior or else solubilized at a site of high viscosity. However, the explanation may be simpler. Hauser and Klein considered their pK_a change data as being due to the equilibrium

$$(ROH)_{micelle} \rightleftharpoons (ROH)_{aq} \rightleftharpoons RO^-_{aq} + H^+_{aq}$$

and calculated a distribution constant from the above mechanism. Thus these data do not permit the determination of $(pK_a)_m$ for the micellar bound naphthol, i.e. the pK_a for

$$(ROH)_{micelle} \rightleftharpoons RO^-_{micelle} + H^+_{aq}$$

It must be appreciably bigger than 10.6. We may estimate the effect of the anionic micelle on this intrinsic pK_a from measurements of the micelle potential or more directly by a comparison to the effect on a definitely micelle bound indicator studied by Fromherz and Fernandez.[42] They observed a difference in pK_a of 3.4 between water and NaLS for an indicator

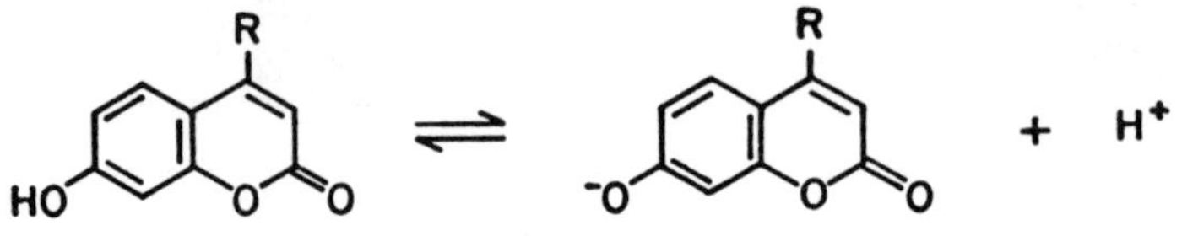

which had been rendered completely micelle bound also in the ionic form by the use of a dodecyl chain for R.

A shift of this magnitude, say 3, is to be expected also for the naphthol. For the excited state this means a pK_a of 5.8. The dissociation rate constant, which has been determined as $7 \times 10^7 s^{-1}$ [43] in aqueous solution, should then be in the order of $10^5 s^{-1}$ in the micelle and since the lifetime of the excited state should remain somewhat smaller than 10 nsec no observable dissociation should take place.

Thus, there is no need to invoke anything other than normal solubilization at the micelle-water interface for the naphthols. In fact, the distribution constant determined by Hauser and Klein, given as 880 for NaLS/water as compared to 2 for dodekane/water, is a strong indication of surface solubilization.

CONCLUSIONS

Micelles offer the photochemist unique opportunities to organize their systems on a molecular scale. By careful control of the micellar-solute conditions it is possible to strongly promote certain features of the photo-induced reaction e.g. electron transfer and also to direct the course of subsequent secondary reactions. Several systems are of interest for studying storage of light energy as chemical energy.

REFERENCES

1. This report was written with support from the Office of Basic Energy Sciences of the Department of Energy. This is Document No. NDRL-1900 from the Notre Dame Radiation Laboratory.
2. E. H. Cordes, "Reaction Kinetics in Micelles" Plenum Press, New York, 1973.
3. C. A. Bunton, Prog. Solid State Chem., 8, 239 (1973).
4. J. H. Fendler and E. J. Fendler, "Catalysis in Micellar and Macromolecule Systems" Academic Press, New York, 1975.
5. M. Grätzel and J. K. Thomas, in "Modern Fluorescence Spec. troscopy," Vol. 2, E. Wehry, Editor, Plenum, New York, 1976.
6. J. K. Thomas, Accounts Chem. Res., 10, 133 (1977).
7. M. Grätzel, K. Kalyanasundaram and J. K. Thomas, J. Am. Chem. Soc., 96, 7869 (1974).
8. J. G. Eriksson and G. Gillberg, Acta Chem. Scand., 20, 2019 (1966).
9. P. Mukerjee, J. R. Cardinal and N. R. Desai, in "Micellization, Solubilization and Microemulsions," K. Mittal, Editor, Vol. 2 p. 241, Plenum Press, New York, 1977.
10. K. Kalyanasundaram and J. K. Thomas, J. Am. Chem. Soc., 99, 2039 (1977).

11. K. Kalyanasundaram and J. K. Thomas, J. Phys. Chem., 81, 2126 (1977).
12. M. Grätzel and J. K. Thomas, J. Am. Chem. Soc., 95, 6885 (1973).
13. L. K. Patterson and E. Vieil, J. Phys. Chem., 77, 1191 (1973).
14. a. M. Chen, M. Grätzel and J. K. Thomas, J. Am. Chem. Soc., 97, 2052 (1975); b. K. Kalyanasundaraum, F. Grieser, and J. K. Thomas, Chem. Phys. Lett. 51, 501 (1977); c. N. J. Turro, K. C. Lin, M.F. Chow, and P. Lee, Photochem. Photobiol. 27, 523 (1978).
15. S. C. Wallace, M. Grätzel and J. K. Thomas, Chem. Phys. Lett. 23, 359 (1973).
16. J. T. Richards, G. West and J. K. Thomas, Chem. Phys., 74, 4137 (1970).
17. G. Beck and J. K. Thomas, J. Chem Phys., 57, 3649 (1972).
18. P. Picuilo and J. K. Thomas, J. Chem Phys., in press.
19. M. Grätzel and J. K. Thomas, J. Phys. Chem., 78, 2248 (1974)
20. S.A. Alkaitis, G. Beck and M. Grätzel, J. Am. Chem. Soc., 97, 5723 (1975); S.A. Alkaitis, M. Grätzel and A. Henglein, Ber. Bun., 79, 541 (1975).
21. S.A. Alkaitis and M. Grätzel, J. Am. Chem. Soc., 98, 3549 (1976).
22. P. Picuilo, Ph.D. Dissertation, University of Notre Dame, 1977.
23. G.C. Barker, G. Bottura, G. Cloke, A.W. Gardner and M.J. Williams, Electronanal, Chem. Interfacial Electrochem., 50, 323 (1974).
24. P. Picuilo and J.K. Thomas, J. Am. Chem. Soc., 100, 3239 (1978).
25. B. Razem, M. Wong and J.K. Thomas, J. Am. Chem. Soc., 100, 1679 (1978).
26. H. Masuhara, K. Kaji and N. Mataga, Bull. Chem. Soc. Japan, 50, 2084 (1977).
27. a) M. Almgren, Photochem. Photobiol., 15, 297 (1972); b) M. Almgren, A.Ch. Svensson, Chemica Scripta, 9, 145 (1976).
28. F.W.J. Teale, Nature, 181, 415 (1958).
29. a) E.I. Zenkevich, A.P. Losev, G.P. Guirnovich, Mol. Biol., 6, 824 (1972); b) E. Lehoczki, K. Csatorday, Biochim. Biophys. Acta, 39b, 86 (1975); c) J. Szabad, E. Lehoczki, L. Szalay, K. Csatorday, Biophys. Struct. Mech., 1, 65 (1973); d) K. Csatorday, E. Lehoczki, L. Szalay, Biochim. Biophys. Acta, 37b, 268 (1975).
30. G.S. Singhal, E. Rabinovitch, J. Hevesi, V. Srinavasan, Photochem. Photobiol., 11, 531 (1970).
31. a) J. Hevesi, Z.S. Rozsa, Acta Phys. Chem., 20, 231 (1975); b) E. Bor, J. Hevesi, Acta Phys. Chem., 20, 357 (1974).
32. A.K. Ghosh, Indian J. Chem., 11, 1014 (1973).
33. K. Kalyanasundaram and J.K. Thomas, in "Micellization, Solubilization, and Microemulsions," K. Mittal, Editor, p. 569 Plenum Press, New York, 1977.
34. J.R. Escabi-Perez, F. Nonie and J.H. Fendler, J. Am. Chem. Soc., 99, 7749 (1977).
35. Th. Förster and K. Kasper, Z. Electrochem., 59, 977 (1955).

36. Th. Förster and B. Selinger, Z. Naturforsch., 19a, 38 (1964).
37. a) M. Hauser and U. Klein, Z. Physik. Chem. NF, 78, 32 (1972); b) M. Hauser and U. Klein, Acta Phys. Chem. NF, 19, 363 (1973); c) R.C. Dorrance and T.F. Hunter, J. Chem. Soc. Faraday I, 68, 1312 (1972); d) R.C. Dorrance and T.F. Hunter, J. Chem. Soc. Faraday I, 70, 1572 (1974); e) R.C. Dorrance and T.F. Hunter, J. Chem. Soc. Faraday I, 73, 1891 (1977); f) U. Khuanga, B.K. Selinger and R. McDonald, Aust. J. Chem., 29, 1 (1976); g) U. Khuanga, R. McDonald and B.K. Selinger, Z. Phys. Chem. NF, 101, 209 (1976); h) K. Kalyanasundaram, M. Grätzel and J.K. Thomas, J. Am. Chem. Soc., 97, 3915 (1975); i) H.J. Pownall and L.S. Smith, J. Am. Chem. Soc., 95, 3136 (1973).
38. M. Almgren, F. Grieser and J.K. Thomas, J.Am.Chem. Soc. (in press).
39. K. Kalyanasundaram, M. Grätzel and J.K. Thomas, J. Am. Chem. Soc., 97, 3915 (1975).
40. a) U. Klein and M. Hauser, Z. Physik Chem. NF, 90, 215 (1974); b) U. Klein and M. Hauser, Ber. Bunsen. Phys. Chem., 78, 1272 (1974); c) U. Klein and M. Hauser, Z. Phys. Chem. NF, 96, 139 (1975).
41. B.K. Selinger and A. Weller, Aust. J. Chem., 30, 2377 (1977).
42. M.S. Fernández and P. Fromherz, J. Phys. Chem., 81, 1755 (1977).
43. a) A. Weller, Z. Physik. Chem. NF, 17, 224 (1958); b) M. Almgren, Chem. Scripta, 6, 193 (1974); 6, 171 (1974).

INTERACTIONS AND CATALYSIS IN THE PRESENCE OF STEROIDAL SURFACTANTS IN DIPOLAR APROTIC SOLVENTS

Eleanor J. Fendler, David J. Koranek and
Steven N. Rosenthal
Department of Chemistry
Texas A&M University
College Station, Texas 77843

Reactions and interactions of a variety of chemically diverse substrates (such as phosphoric, sulfuric, and phosphonic acid esters, benzamides, and benzisoxazole carboxylates) have been investigated in the presence of bile salts in dipolar aprotic solvents. The displacement of p-nitrophenoxide ion from bis-p-nitrophenyl phenylphosphonate has been investigated as a function of varying stoichiometric sodium cholate and water concentrations in dipolar aprotic dimethyl sulfoxide in order to elucidate both the reaction mechanism and the dependence on water concentration. The observed rate constant as a function of increasing sodium cholate concentration exhibits sigmoidal dependence followed by a plateau. At constant sodium cholate concentration the rate of the reaction has been found to decrease curvilinearly as a function of increasing water concentration. N-tert-butyl-2,4,6-trinitrobenzamide in the presence of bile salts and other carboxylates in dimethyl sulfoxide-water solution undergoes facile nucleophilic aromatic substitution at C-1, forming a highly stable σ, or Meisenheimer complex. Formation of the 1,1-hydroxy complex has been found to be kinetically controlled while formation of the 1,3-hydroxy complex, which could be formed either directly or from the 1,1-hydroxy complex, is thermodynamically favored. Decomposition of the complexes results in the formation of nitrite ion and aromatic compounds via a process which is light catalyzed. The formation of these products probably occurs via a 2,2- or a 4,4-hydroxynitro cyclohexadienylide species. A mechanistic scheme is proposed and the role of water is discussed. The above results are compared to and contrasted with those for a variety of reactions occurring in bile salt-DMSO solution and for other micellar systems.

INTRODUCTION

The effects of surfactants on the rates of chemical reactions, or micellar catalysis, is an active area of research as evidenced by the mushrooming number of research papers in this area as well as by the numerous publications which survey this field.[1-10] Rate enhancement or retardation in these systems can be the consequence of one of two types of catalysis or a combination of both: (1) true chemical catalysis in which the surfactant reacts with the substrate and is subsequently regenerated and (2) physical catalysis in which reactants are brought into closer proximity via electrostatic and/or hydrophobic interactions with the catalytic micellar aggregate. Some of the more important factors responsible for micellar catalysis of organic reactions (i.e., rate acceleration and inhibition) are: differences in the reaction rates in the micellar pseudo-phase and in the bulk phase due to electrostatic and hydrophobic interactions, structural reorganization of the solvent in the solvation spheres of the reactants, and partitioning of the reactants between the pseudo-phases. Although kinetic and thermodynamic parameters have been determined, analyzed, and discussed for a variety of "normal" and inverted micellar systems,[1-10] two areas remained unexplored - these being (1) catalysis in dipolar aprotic solvents, which are of intermediate polarity, and (2) catalysis by relatively rigid aggregates such as those formed from monomers without a long and mobile hydrocarbon chain. Consequently, we have investigated both the aggregate structure[11] and the kinetic effects of steroidal surfactants (bile salts) on the reactions of structurally diverse solubilized substrates in dipolar aprotic dimethyl sulfoxide (DMSO).

Bile acids or salts are naturally occurring steroidal surfactants which are synthesized in the liver from cholesterol. The compounds, which constitute one of the major components of biliary fluid, play a primary role in the digestion and absorption of fats and the fat-soluble vitamins A, D, E, and K. They are also responsible for the emulsification of a variety of water insoluble compounds, e.g., long chain triglycerides, and for stimulating the hydrolytic activity of pancreatic lipase. The bile acids are 24-carbon tetracyclic monocarboxylic acids comprised of a saturated cyclopentanophenanthrene or steroid nucleus with a 5-carbon branched-aliphatic chain carboxylic acid moiety bonded to carbon-17 (Figure 1).

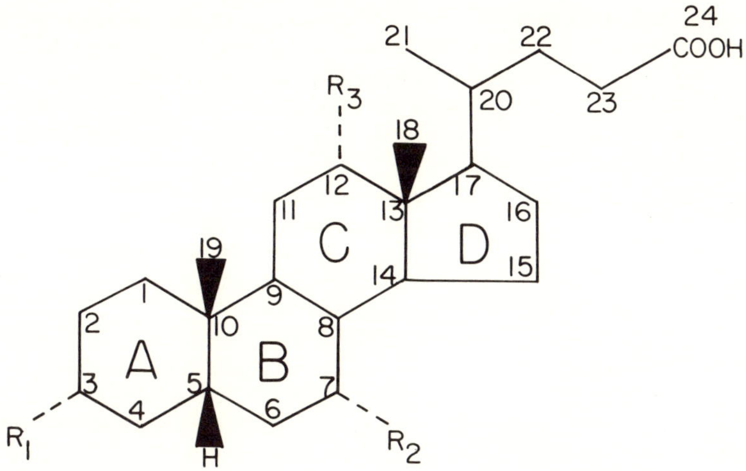

Figure 1. Conventional chemical representation of cholanic acid and hydroxyl derivatives:

$R_1=R_2=R_3=H$ Cholanic acid

$R_1=R_2=R_3=OH$ Cholic acid (3α,7α,12α-trihydroxycholanic acid)

$R_1=R_2=OH$, $R_3=H$ Chenodeoxycholic acid (3α,7α-dihydroxycholanic acid)

$R_1=R_3=OH$, $R_2=H$ Deoxycholic acid (3α,12α-dihydroxycholanic acid)

$R_1=OH$, $R_2=R_3=H$ Lithocholic acid (3α-hydroxycholanic acid)

In man, and most higher vertebrates, the bile salts are mainly comprised of the sodium and potassium salts of the glycine and taurine conjugates of cholic, chenodeoxycholic and deoxycholic acids, but also contain small amounts of the monohydroxy compound, salts of lithocholic acid. Unlike most other amphiphilic molecules, bile salts have a rigid carbon backbone with a cis A/B ring juncture (5β-hydrogen) which is responsible for the characteristic crescent shape of the molecule (see Figure 3 of reference 11). Bile acids, where all the hydroxyl and acid moieties lie on one side of the plane of the steroid nucleus and the angular methyl groups on the other, have hydrophobic and hydrophilic faces (i.e., they possess planar polarity to a striking degree). Consequently, bile salts, like long hydrocarbon chain ionic surfactants, form small aggregates or micelles above a critical micelle concentration (CMC) when dissolved in water.[12-14] THe shape of the bile salt micelles in aqueous solution has been postulated to be a cylinder containing from 4 to 10 or 15 monomeric units, with the hydrophobic face of the steroid nucleus in the interior and the hydroxyl and acid groups oriented toward the bulk solvent.[12] In relatively less polar media (ternary, or three component, systems composed of bile salt, water, and n-decanol), two different types of micellar structures have been demonstrated.[20-22] In the phase region of low decanol content, normal micelles exist with the hydrophobic face oriented toward the interior and the polar groups toward the bulk solvent. However, the micellar structure is the converse, and reversed or inverted micelles[14] are formed when the concentration of n-decanol exceeds 50 mole-percent. In nonpolar solvents, i.e., carbon tetrachloride, cyclohexane, benzene, etc., a variety of surfactants differing in both charge type and structure form reversed or inverted micelles which, in general, are structurally the inverse of the so-called "normal" micelles. In this case the polar moieties surround an interior "cavity" or core of high polarity in which water, counterions, and other solubilizates may be localized.[1] Since bile salts form reversed micelles in polar ternary systems, it would be expected that they would also form polar reversed type micelles in relatively nonpolar solvents, but the bile salts themselves are only sparingly soluble in nonpolar solvents. Conversely, most bile salts are quite soluble in dipolar aprotic solvents, and bile acid derivatives such as esters and amides are soluble in both nonpolar and dipolar aprotic solvents. Hence, we are currently investigating the nature and type of aggregation as well as the micellar structure in these systems.[11,15]

Dipolar aprotic solvents have been shown to enhance the rate of bimolecular substitution reactions by factors of ca. 10^5, in some cases, relative to the rate in protic solvents.[23,24] Addition of even small amounts of dimethyl sulfoxide (DMSO) to protic or nonpolar aprotic solvents leads to an enhanced reactivity of nucleophiles in these reactions, and rate increases by factors of 10^6 are not uncommon upon transferring the reactants from a protic solvent, such as water, to DMSO. Nucleophilic substitution at alkyl, aryl, and acyl carbon atoms; addition reactions of multiple bond systems; as well as anionic and radical polymerization proceed more rapidly, under milder conditions, and with higher yields in DMSO than in protic solvents. These observations are generally interpreted in terms of the selective solvation effects of DMSO.

Although a large number of kinetic and thermodynamic investigations have been reported for normal and reversed micellar systems of synthetic surfactants,[1-10] very few mechanistic studies have employed bile salts as the catalytic agent and none of these have been carried out in nonaqueous solvent systems. Rates of hydrolysis of p-nitrophenyl esters of long chain carboxylic acids have been examined in the presence of bile salt micelles in aqueous solution and the results have been interpreted in terms of micellar structure and binding properties.[25] The base catalyzed hydrolysis of benzocaine (ethyl p-aminobenzoate) has also been investigated in the presence of aqueous micellar bile salts.[26] Not unexpectedly, this reaction is slightly inhibited by anionic micellar cholic acid and deoxycholic acid.[1]

In order to elucidate the primary factors responsible for catalysis by bile salts in dipolar aprotic media, reactions differing in charge type and structure of the reactants, molecularity, and stereochemistry were chosen for investigation. One of these is bis-p-nitrophenyl phenylphosphonate. Its hydrolysis in aqueous solution is catalyzed by hydroxide ion and proceeds with halflives at 25.0°C ranging from greater than 2 hours at pH 8.0 to less than 10 seconds at pH 11.0 where hydrolysis of the monoester becomes apparent, i.e. $k_2 >> k_2'$ (Equation 1).[27] In the presence of synthetic surfactants in aqueous solution, micellar effects on the first reaction, i.e., on the second order rate constant, k_2, follow the usual trend[1] for anion-molecule reactions: cationic micellar hexadecyltrimethylammonium bromide (CTAB) enhances the rate by 260-fold whereas anionic sodium dodecyl sulfate (NaLS) and nonionic polyoxyethylene (20) nonylphenol (Igepal CO-850) retard it by factors of <u>ca</u>. 100 and 5, respectively - the rate enhancement in CTAB arising from a marked decrease in the activation entropy.[1,27] Not unexpectedly, both aqueous micellar trihydroxy bile salts, sodium cholate (NaC) and taurocholate (NaTC), and mixed micellar bile salt - fatty acid systems have been found

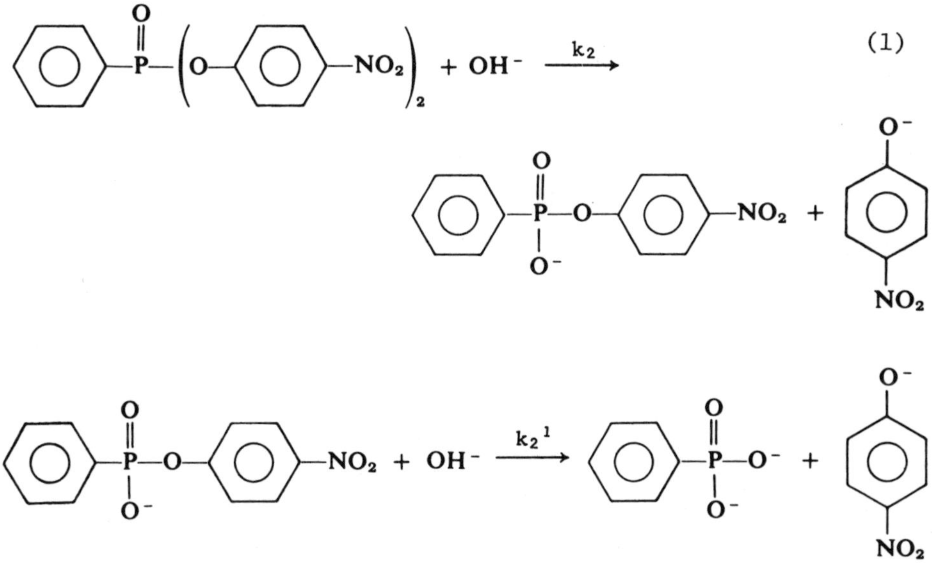

(1)

to retard this reaction - the effect being 10-fold less for the latter systems (NaC and NaTC plus dodecanoic acid, 1:1).[28]

Micellar effects on nucleophilic aromatic substitution reactions have also been investigated by ourselves and others[1,29] in the presence of both normal and reversed micelles. However, neither dipolar aprotic solvents, such as DMSO, nor any naturally occurring surfactants, such as bile acids or salts, have been utilized in these studies. Bile acid (salt)/DMSO systems can be considered to be a relevant model for related physiological reactions occurring in or near membranes and other similar biological structures as well as for some phases of digestive processes. Consequently, the nucleophilic aromatic substitution of a benzamide was chosen for investigation in dipolar aprotic bile salt systems. In water or methanol, the interaction of hydroxide or methoxide ion with N-tert-butyl-2,4,6-trinitrobenzamide results in the equilibrium formation of the hydroxy adduct and the methoxy adduct, respectively, followed by nitrite ion elimination.[30] The rate constants for the attainment of the equilibria (Equation 2) as well as for the subsequent formation of nitrite ions have been determined at different lyate ion concentrations, and the structures of the complexes have been unequivocally established from ^1H nuclear magnetic resonance spectra.[30]

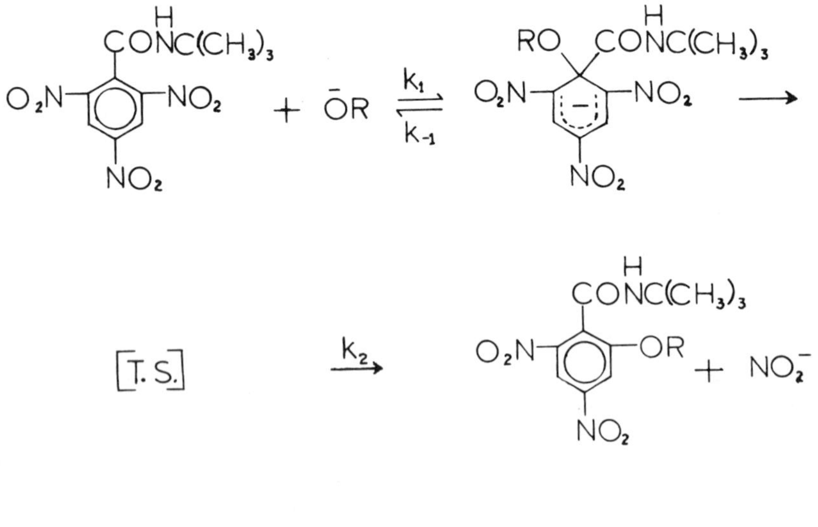

(2)

EXPERIMENTAL

Bis-p-nitrophenyl phenylphosphonate was prepared using a modified procedure of Tolkmith for bis-p-nitrophenyl methylphosphonate.[31] p-Nitrophenol (8.20 g, 0.059 mole) and dry pyridine (5.62 ml, 0.0695 mole) dissolved in 70 ml of anhydrous ether was added slowly to a solution of 5.60 g (0.0287 mole) of phenylphosphonic dichloride in 50 ml of anhydrous ether. The reaction mixture was then refluxed for 3.5 hours, vacuum filtered and washed with anhydrous ether. The filtrate was rotary evaporated to dryness and dried in vacuo over phosphorus pentoxide yielding a crude solid (mp 65-68°C). The crude product was purified by dissolution in dry acetonitrile, addition of neutral alumina (Woelm), rapid filtration under nitrogen and rotary evaporation of the filtrate to dryness. This process was then repeated. The resulting product which had a melting point of 94-97°C was established to be at least 98% pure using UV-visible and infrared spectrophotometry and ^{1}H nmr spectroscopy.

The preparation of N-tert-butyl-2,4,6-trinitrobenzamide has been previously reported.[30] Other substrates, bile salts, and solvents were reagent grade materials obtained from commercial sources and were analyzed for purity prior to use. Water content was monitored on a Photovolt Aquatest II (for details, see Addendum).

The kinetic experiments were carried out on a Durrum-Gibson Model D-110 stopped-flow spectrophotometer, a Cary 118-C, and Beckman DU, DU-2 and DK spectrophotometers. The reactions were run under pseudo-first order conditions and the temperatures were maintained within ±0.1°C.

RESULTS AND DISCUSSION

Kinetic Studies of Bis-p-nitrophenyl Phenylphosphonate in Bile Salt/DMSO Systems

The observed rate constants for the formation of the p-nitrophenoxide ion from bis-p-nitrophenyl phenylphosphonate, bis-PNPP (Equation 1) in the presence of sodium cholate (NaC) in dipolar aprotic DMSO have been determined at three water concentrations by monitoring the change in absorbance of p-nitrophenoxide ion. A typical sigmoidal type dependence of the observed rate constant, k_ψ, on surfactant concentration is evident in each case (Figure 2). At high surfactant concentrations the curves tend to flatten out (Figure 2), which is characteristic of Michaelis-Menten saturation-type kinetic behavior found in numerous ionic micellar systems in both aqueous and non-aqueous solvents. The effect of increasing the water content in the plateau region is a curvilinear decrease in the observed rate constant for solvolysis (Figure 3).

At 0.147 M NaC in DMSO the rate constant for the solvolysis of bis-PNPP is 1.89 x 10^5-fold greater than that in water at pH 7 (k_2 = 83.5 ℓ $mole^{-1}$ sec^{-1} at 25.0°C). No product formation could be detected in more than 3 months in solutions containing 6.0 x 10^{-5} M bis-PNPP in DMSO ([H_2O] = 1.1 x 10^{-2} M) in the absence of surfactant. Therefore, the rate constant for solvolysis in the bulk dipolar aprotic solvent must be very much less than 10^{-7} sec^{-1} This very slow rate of reaction is in accord with the low concentration of water and the pseudo-first order rate constant for hydrolysis in pure water at pH 7.0. Additionally, there is no kinetic solvent deuterium isotope effect over the range of water concentration employed (Table 1). Therefore, in terms of the reaction mechanism, water is neither acting as a nucleophile nor is it covalently bonded in the transition state for the rate-limiting step. It is probable, however, that water is hydrogen bonded strongly to the carboxylate ion of sodium cholate and to a lesser extent to the phosphonyl oxygen atom and the solvent DMSO.

Table I. Solvent Deuterium Isotope Effects on the Solvolysis of Bis-p-nitrophenyl Phenylphosphonate in Sodium Cholate/DMSO Systems at 25.0°C.[a]

[Water], M[b]	$\frac{k_{H_2O}}{k_{D_2O}}$
0.055	1.00
0.110	0.989
0.165	0.993
0.220	1.00
0.275	1.00

[a] [Bis-PNPP] = 6.0 x 10^{-5} M.

[b] Concentration of H_2O or D_2O added to DMSO solutions containing 0.055 M H_2O.

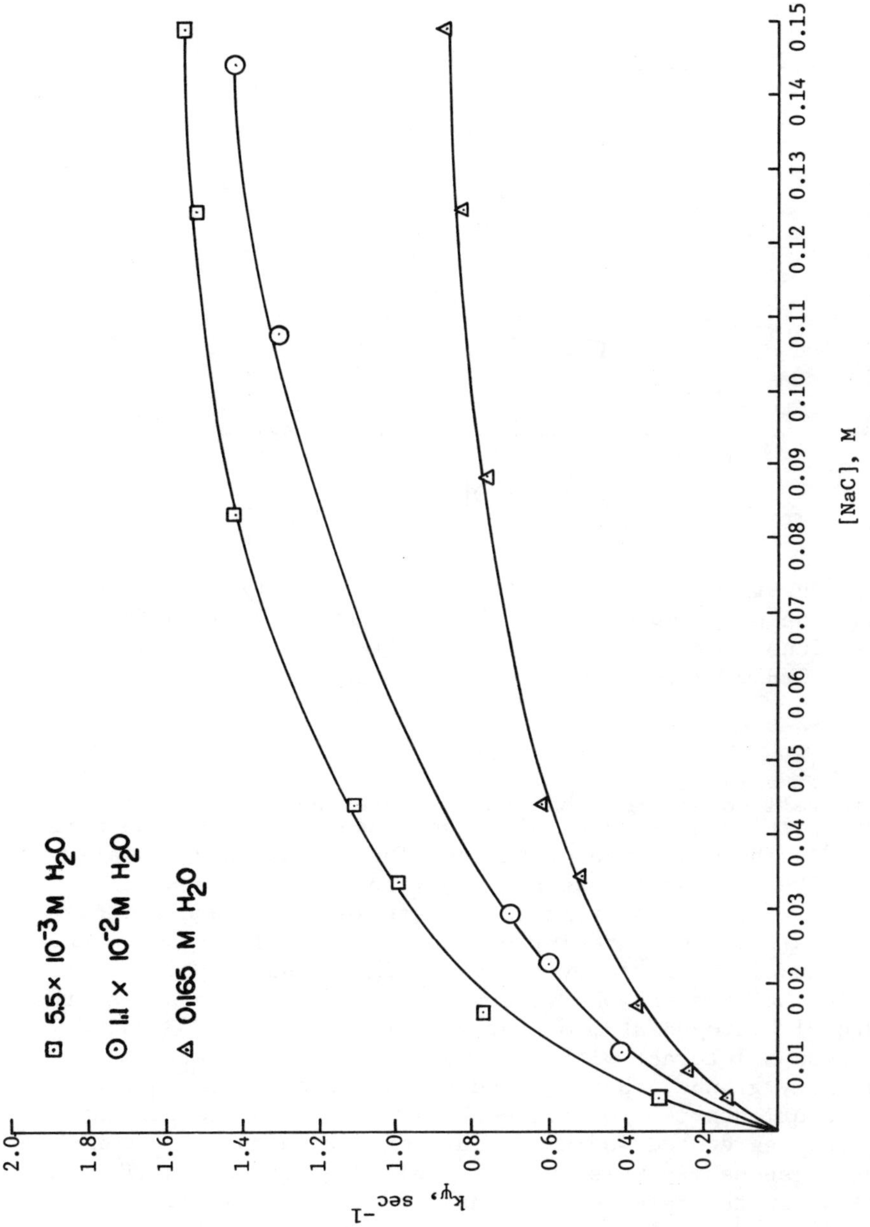

Figure 2. Observed rate constants, k_ψ, for solvolysis of bis-p-nitrophenyl phenylphosphonate as a function of sodium cholate (NaC) concentration in DMSO at 25.0°C.

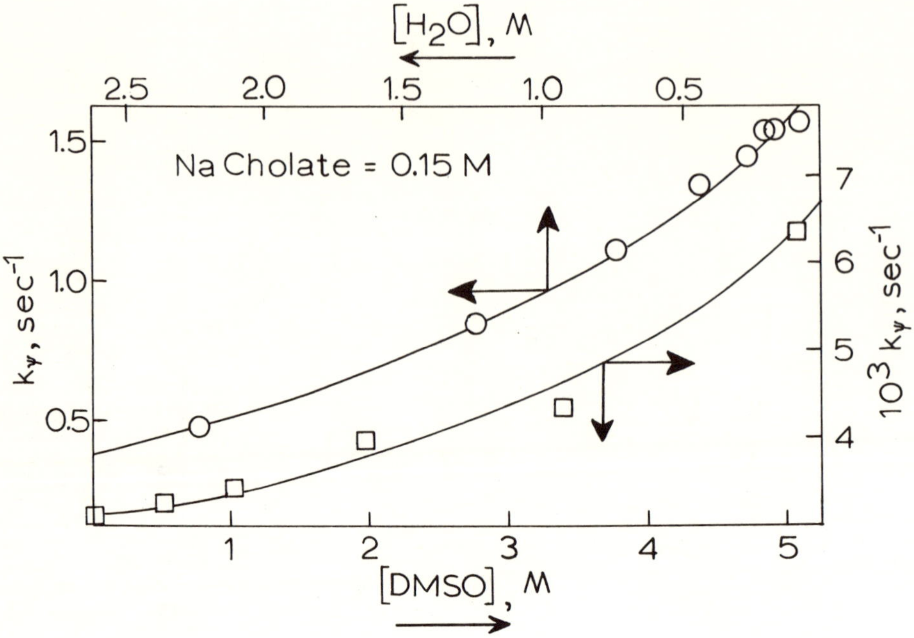

Figure 3. Observed rate constants, k_{ψ}, for solvolysis of bis-p-nitrophenyl phenylphosphonate in the presence of 0.147 M sodium cholate as functions of the molar concentration of DMSO and of water in DMSO/H_2O systems at 25.0°C.

It is well documented that carboxylate anions can facilitate the intermolecular hydrolyses of organophosphate and phosphonate esters.[32-34] The magnitude of the catalysis, the role of water, and the activation parameters are consistent with a catalytic mechanism in which the aggregated cholate ion binds and orients the phosphonate in the interior of the aggregate in such a manner that it is in close proximity to the insipient nucleophile. It is probable that the phosphonyl oxygen atom hydrogen bonds to the C-12 hydroxyl hydrogen atom of the cholate while the C-3 and C-7 hydroxyl groups interact with at least one of the substrate p-nitrophenoxy groups, thereby binding the phosphonate in the appropriate orientation for nucleophilic attack by the carboxylate anion of the aggregated sodium cholate on phosphorus with concerted or subsequent expulsion of a p-nitrophenoxide ion (Figure 4). The decrease in the rate constant as a function of increasing water concentration and the lack of a solvent deuterium isotope effect are explicable in terms of this proposed mechanism. Addition of water would result in preferential solvation of the most polar and highest charge density entity, the carboxylate ion of the bile salt catalyst, and secondly the phosphonyl group of the sub-

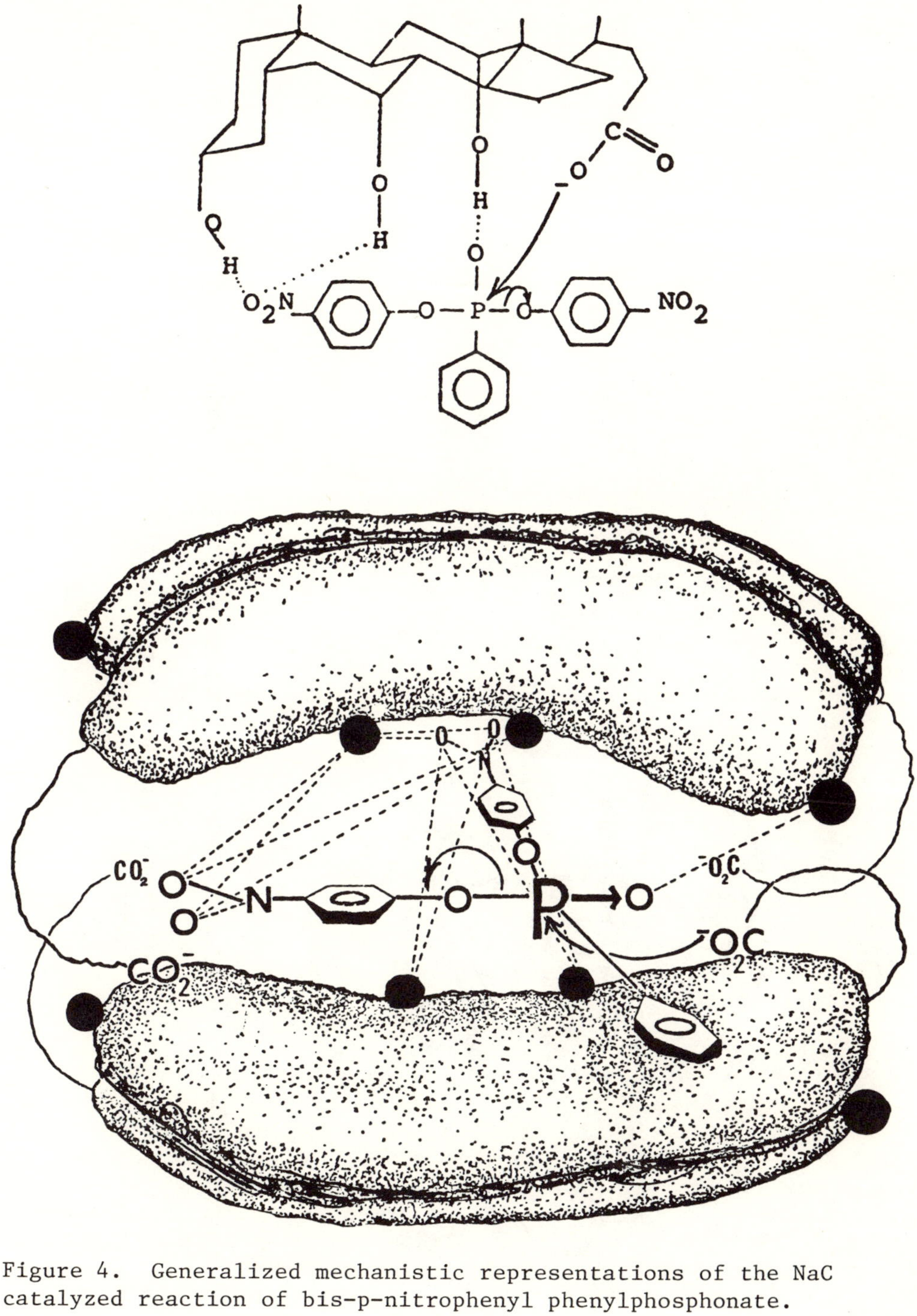

Figure 4. Generalized mechanistic representations of the NaC catalyzed reaction of bis-p-nitrophenyl phenylphosphonate.

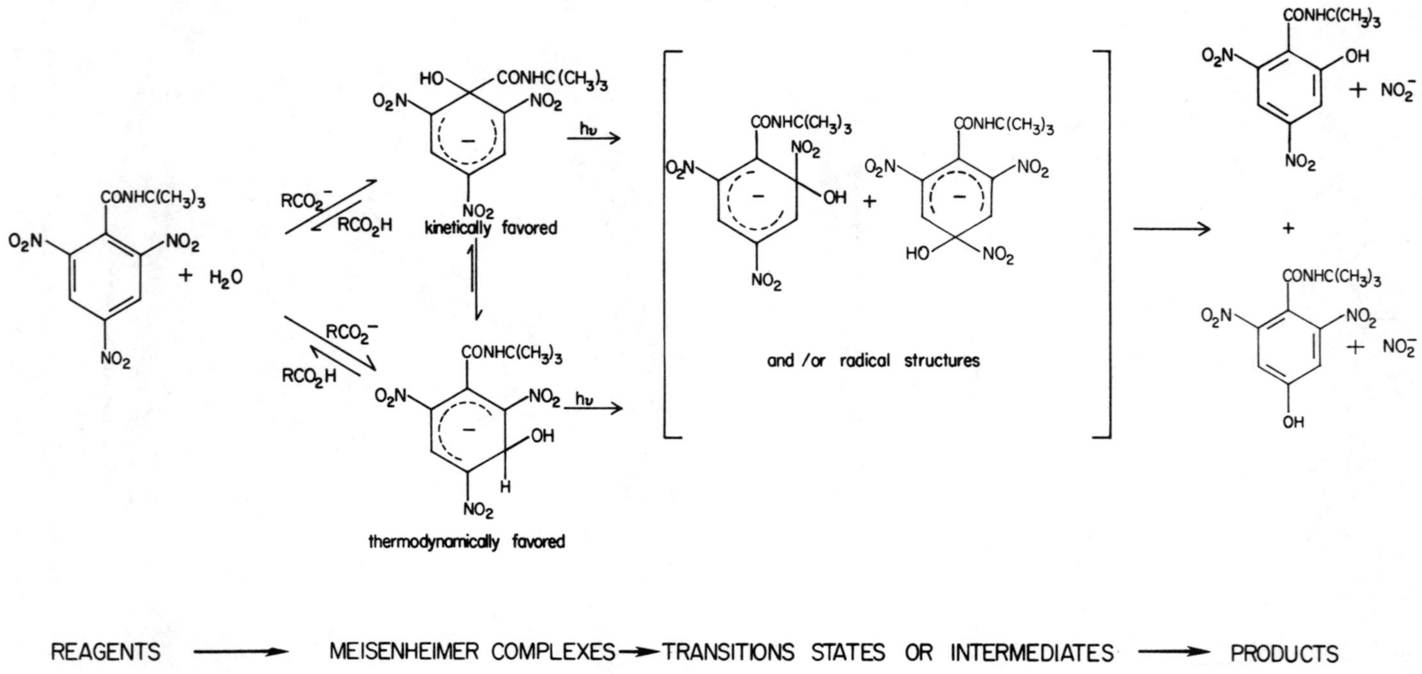

Figure 5. General reaction scheme for the interaction of N-tert-butyl-2,4,6-trinitrobenzamide in bile salt/DMSO/water systems.

strate. In both cases, formation of hydration spheres would result in a decrease in the reaction rate.

In order to further substantiate this postulated mechanism, the solvolysis of bis-PNPP was investigated in the presence of 0.20 M methyl cholate in dry DMSO ($[H_2O] = 5.5 \times 10^{-4}$ M). If the carboxylate ion of the aggregated or micellar sodium cholate acted as the nucleophile, then the observed rate constant would predictably be quite small in the presence of this methyl ester whereas the binding or association behavior would not be altered appreciably. Not surprisingly, no reaction could be detected spectrophotometrically in this system after more than one month ($k_\psi << 10^{-7}$ sec^{-1}).

Effects of Bile Salts on the Reactions of N-tert-Butyl-2,4,6-Trinitrobenzamide in Dimethyl Sulfoxide-Water Solutions

The rate of σ (or Meisenheimer) complex formation of N-tert-butyl-2,4,6-trinitrobenzamide (NtBB) in sodium cholate/water/DMSO and sodium deoxycholate/water/DMSO systems have been determined spectrophotometrically and a generalized reaction scheme for the overall process is given in Figure 5. The observed rate constants for complex formation increase curvilinearly as a function of increasing bile salt concentration at constant water concentration (Figures 6 and 7), but it is apparent that the dependence is neither sigmoidal nor is a plateau reached at the solubility limit of the bile salt amphiphiles. The effects of water on the observed rate constants for complex formation at constant bile salt concentration are illustrated in Figure 8. In general, the rate constants increase with the addition of water until the range of 2 to 3 M is reached whereupon the rate constants begin to gradually decrease with increasing water concentration. Consequently, water is either a source of the nucleophile or is acting to increase the effective concentration or reactivity of the nucleophile. The decrease in the rate constants at water concentrations in excess of 2 M is not attributable to the change in solvent structure that occurs as the solvent composition varies from one that is predominantly dipolar aprotic DMSO to one that is primarily aqueous in nature. The structural reorganization of the DMSO-water solvent system occurs at about 32% water by volume, or <u>ca</u>. 18 M water in DMSO, whereas the maximum rate constants were found at about 5% water by volume.

The rate accelerations by water and bile salt in these systems indicate that both of these species play an important role in the mechanism for Meisenheimer complex formation. The dependence of the second-order rate constant for the forward reaction, $k_2^f = \frac{k_\psi}{[H_2O]}$, on the concentration of both bile salt

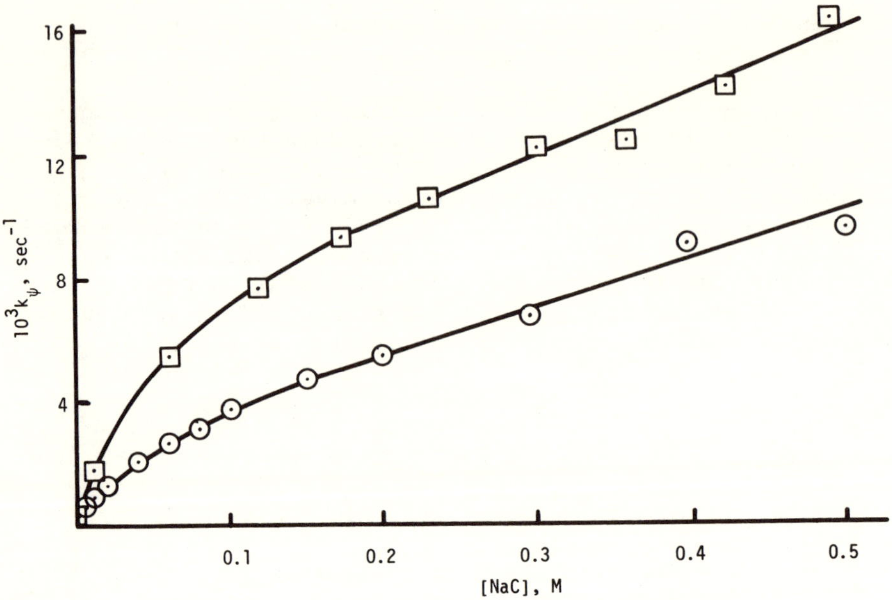

Figure 6. Observed rate constants, k_ψ, for complex formation as a function of sodium cholate (NaC) concentration in DMSO at 25.0°C: ⊙, $[H_2O] = 0.11 \pm 0.02$ M, [NtBB] = 6.4×10^{-5} M; ⊡, $[H_2O] = 1.47 \pm 0.04$ M, [NtBB] = 4.4×10^{-5} M.

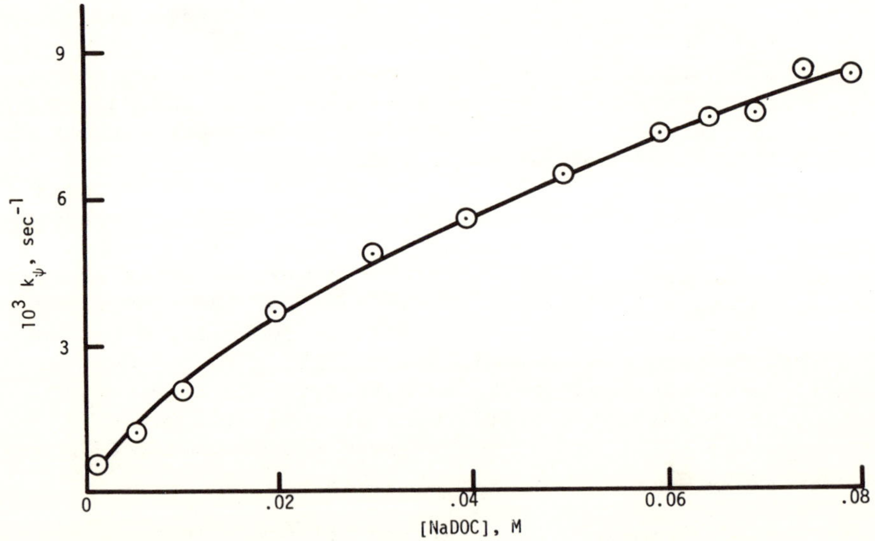

Figure 7. Observed rate constants, k_ψ, for complex formation as a function of sodium deoxycholate (NaDOC) concentration in DMSO at 25.0°C; $[H_2O] = 2.7 \pm 0.4$ M, [NtBB] - 4.4×10^{-5} M.

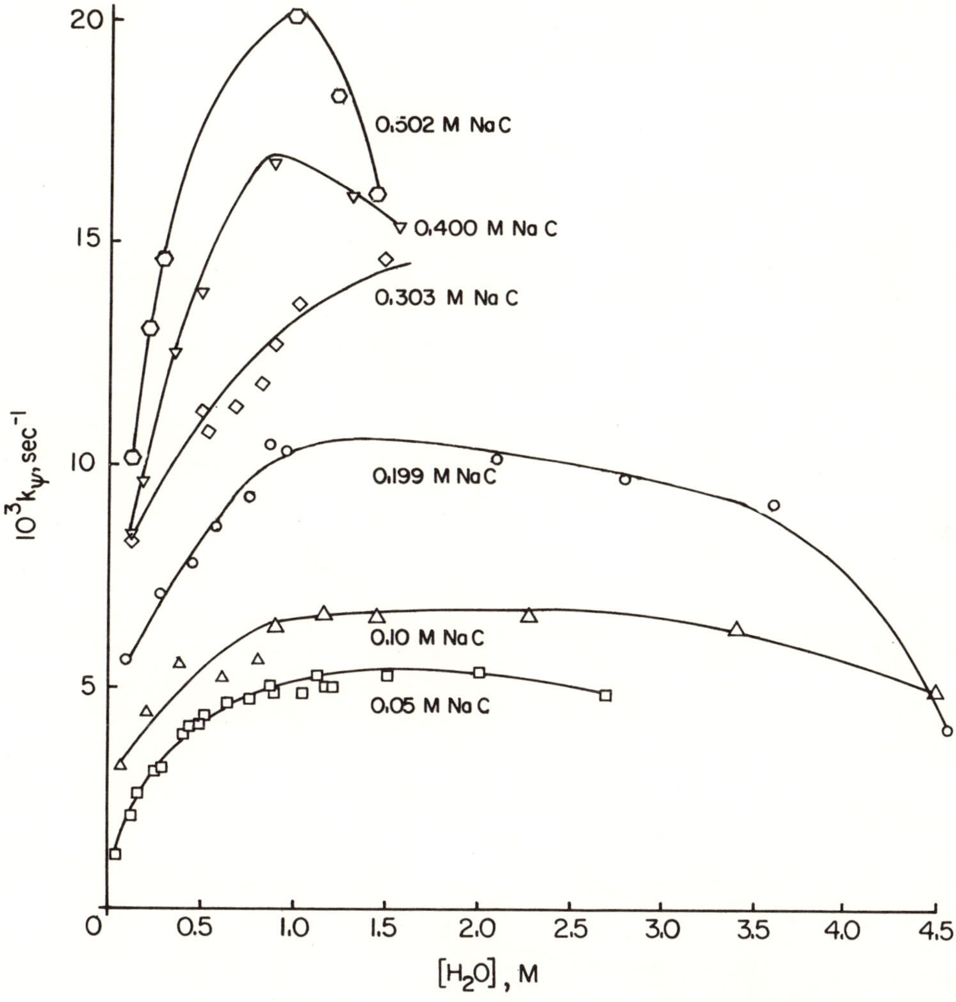

Figure 8. Observed rate constants, k_ψ, for complex formation as a function of water concentration in the presence of sodium cholate (NaC) at 25.0°C.

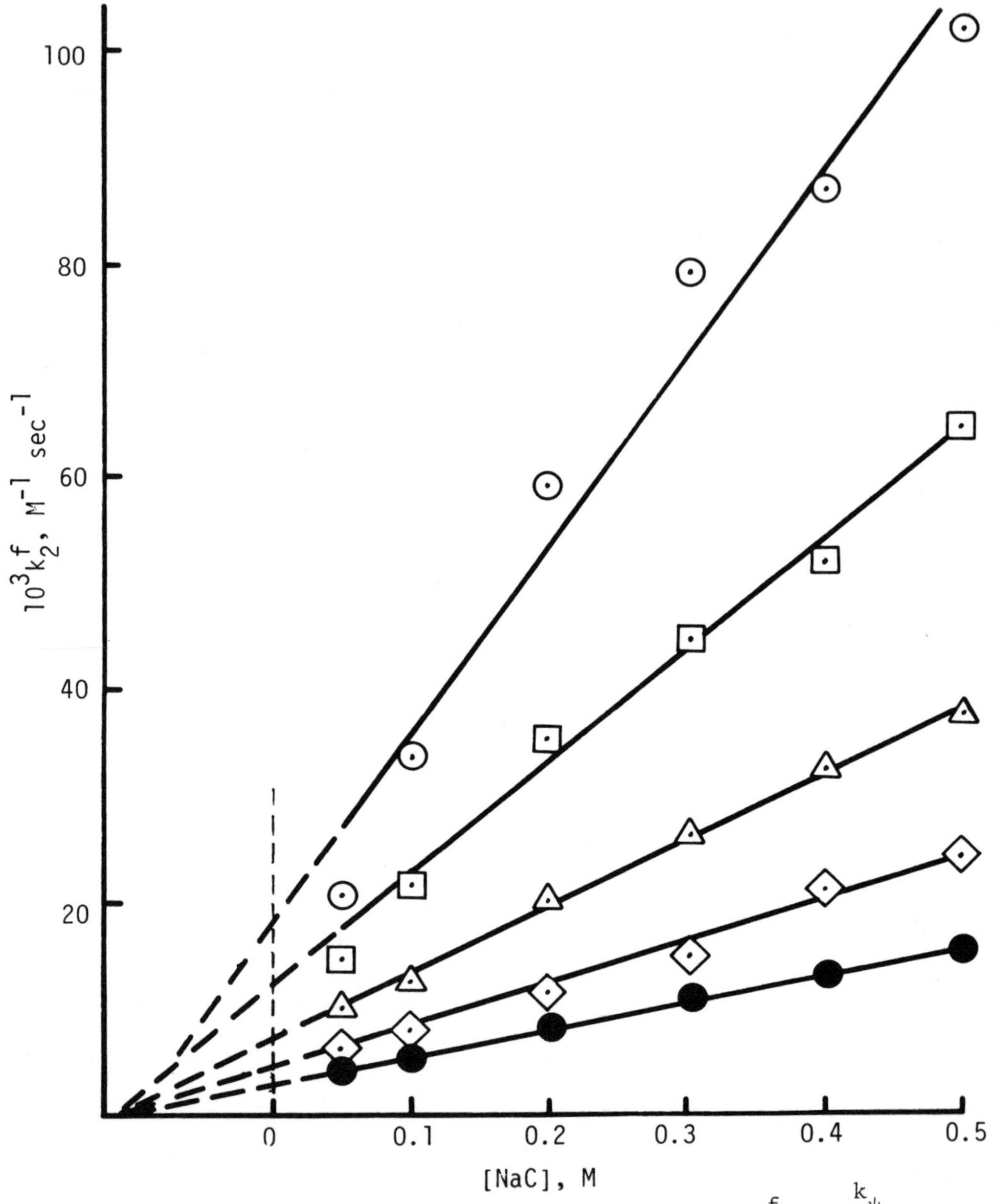

Figure 9. Second order rate constants for complex $k^f_2 = \frac{k_\psi}{[H_2O]}$) as a function of sodium cholate concentration at 25.0°C; $[H_2O]$, M = 0.10 (⊙), 0.20 (⊡), 0.40 (△), 0.80 (◇), 1.20 (●).

and water is illustrated in Figure 9. Inspection of these plots reveals that k_2^f decreases as the water concentration is increased at a constant sodium cholate concentration indicating that increases in the observed rate constant for the same system is not a direct consequence of increasing water concentration. Conversely, as the sodium cholate concentration is increased at a constant water concentration, k_2^f increases as does the observed rate constant. The rate acceleration, then, must be due to enhancement of the nucleophilicity of water by the carboxylate anion. A plausible mechanism for the carboxylate anion activation of the water molecule for nucleophilic aromatic substitution of N-tert-butyl-2,4,6-trinitrobenzamide involves a concerted process in which an insipient hydroxide ion is generated via proton transfer to the bile salt carboxylate ion:

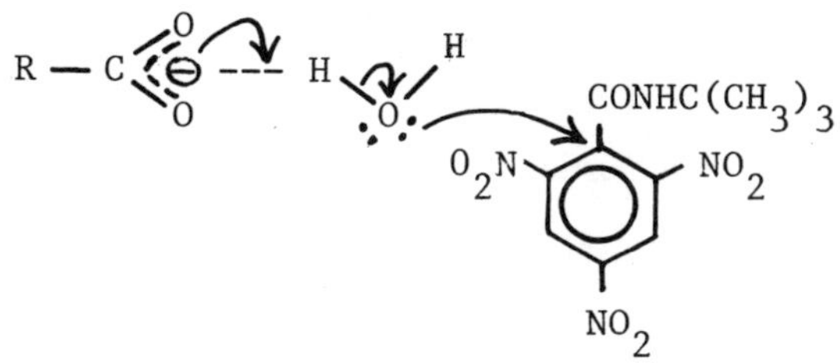

By weakening a hydrogen-oxygen bond of the water molecule the carboxylate anion increases the nucleophilicity of water sufficiently to promote attack at C-1 of the aromatic substrate. Formation of the 1,1-hydroxy-σ-complex rather than some other species is substantiated by the excellent agreement between both the uv-visible and nmr spectra of the _in situ_ generated complex and those of the isolated 1,1-hydroxy compound in the same solvent (Table II). In the _in situ_ nmr experiments, no species other than the 1,1-hydroxy complex could be detected on either a short (2 min) or a long (_ca_. 1 month) timescale.

The observed enhancement of the rate of complex formation by both aggregated carboxylate salts and water is consistent with the postulated mechanism. By increasing the concentration of the bile salt, the reactivity of water is increased as a consequence of the greater availability of the proton-abstracting carboxylate group. Likewise, at higher concentrations of water more of the carboxylate salt-water association complex is present to effect complex formation. After sufficient water is present in the system to form a tight solvation shell around the carboxylate anion, a reduction in rate should be observed. The experimental data show that the observed rate does increase as a function of increasing water concentration and that at higher concentrations of water the rate decreases.

Table II. ^{1}H Nmr Spectral Parameters for N-tert-Butyl-2,4,6-trinitrobenzamide (NtBB) and Its σ-Complexes in $DMSO-d_6$.

	NtBB[a]	1,1-Hydroxy Complex[a]	"NaC Complex"[b]
$\delta_{C(CH_3)_3}$, ppm	1.35	1.29	1.35
δ_{NH}, ppm	8.72	7.18	7.17
δ_{H-3}, ppm	9.07	8.45	8.42

[a]Data taken from reference 30.

[b]Complex generated *in situ* by dropwise addition of *ca*. 0.5 M NaC to a 15 wt. % solution of NtBB in $DMSO-d_6$ at 32.5°C.

Table III. Deuterium Isotope Effects for Complex Formation in Sodium Cholate at 25.0 C.[a]

[NaC], M[b]	[Water], M[b]	10^3k_H, sec^{-1} [c]	10^3k_D, sec^{-1} [c]	k_H/k_D [c]
0.11	5.7	0.718	0.382	1.9
0.30	0.89	8.08	3.97	2.0
0.30	1.35	10.2	6.32	1.6
0.30	1.62	11.7	9.13	1.3
0.48	2.0	17.7	13.4	1.3
0.48	2.4	16.8	10.8	1.6

[a][NtBB] = $(4-6) \times 10^{-5}$ M.

[b]NaC/H_2O for k_H and $NaC-d_3/D_2O$ for k_D.

[c]k_H and k_D = observed pseudo-first order rate constants for complex formation.

The solvent deuterium isotope effect, k_H/k_D, where k_H and k_D are the observed rate constants for formation of the complex in NaC/H_2O/DMSO and NaC-d_3/D_2O/DMSO, respectively, was found to range from 1.3 to 2.0 for a variety of sodium cholate and water concentrations (Table III). This behavior is expected for a proton transfer of this type.[35,36] The relative case of proton abstraction from H_2O compared to abstraction of the less acidic deuteron of D_2O results in a more rapid rate of reaction in the presence of H_2O as compared to D_2O.

The first step in the decomposition process is possibly an interconversion of the initially formed 1,1-σ complex to a more thermodynamically stable 1,3-σ complex. Nucleophilic attack at C-1 results in the kinetically determined 1,1-σ complex as a consequence of C-1 having the lowest electron density due to electron withdrawal by both the ortho and para nitro groups and the carbonyl group. Since C-3 is less electropositive than C-1, nucleophilic attack at this position involves a higher energy barrier. The greater thermodynamic stability of the 1,3-σ complex as compared to the 1,1-complex[37] is primarily due to less steric hindrance at C-3, where the nucleophile is orthogonal to a proton, than at C-1 where the nucleophile is bonded to the sp^3 carbon bearing the bulky t-butylamido group. The mechanism for formation of these complexes probably involves multiple equilibria, some of which lie far to one side and/or contribute to a negligible extent depending upon the reaction conditions (e.g., concentration, solvent composition, and temperature). The observed spectral changes in light-protected solutions are consistent with this reaction scheme (Figure 5). No new absorptions appear as those near 440 nm and 520 nm decrease in intensity, indicating, not unexpectedly, that the absorptivity coefficients of 1,3-σ complex(es) are smaller than those for the 1,1-σ complex(es).

The appearance of additional absorption bands in the uv-visible spectra of these solutions upon exposure to light immediately suggests formation of free radicals; however, the species responsible for these absorptions could also be due to ionic or neutral molecules generated in a light-catalyzed process via an excited species. A radical anion mode of substitution at aromatic carbon has been proposed by J. F. Bunnett.[38] Based mainly on esr and nmr evidence which indicated the presence of radical anions generated from nitroaromatics and nucleophiles, particularly in dipolar aprotic solvents, it has been proposed that σ-complex formation may proceed through prior radical anion formation rather than by direct nucleophilic substitution.[29] However, there is no compelling evidence that these radicals are located on the reaction coordinate of the substitution reaction other than as competing side reactions. Most investigations of free radical formation have employed a strong base as a source of electrons,[39,40] but photolysis in liquid ammonia was found to be a particularly effective means of promoting acetone enolate substitution of arenes containing leaving groups.[41] Additionally, irradiation of ethanol solutions containing nitrobenzene and methoxide ion and of chloroform solutions of 1,3,5-trinitrobenzene and cyanide ion gives rise to free radical species.[39] In this perspective, the observation that low intensity light affects the stability of the Meisenheimer complex in bile salt/H_2O/DMSO solutions is not surprising. The observed uv-visible spectral changes are explicable in terms of an additional radical intermediate and/or σ-complex.

Elimination of nitrite ion from the σ-complex probably occurs through a 2,2- or a 4,4-hydroxy nitro cyclohexadienylide species, or a radical entity. Analogous species have been postulated as transition states for the elimination of nitrite ion from 1,3,5-trinitrobenzene in the presence of base in protic solvents[42] and from N-t-butyl-2,4,6-trinitrobenzamide in the presence of hydroxide ion in water and methoxide ion in methanol.[30] Since these species could not be detected using spectrophotometric or nmr techniques, they were postulated to be transition states rather than intermediates. However, analogous 2,2-alkoxynitrocyclohexadienylides have been found to be the thermodynamically stable intermediates in the nucleophilic aromatic substitution of 1-methoxy and 1-ethoxy-2,4-dinitrobenzene by alkoxide ions.[43] The rate of nitrite ion formation is roughly proportional to the rate of Meisenheimer complex decomposition both in the absence and presence of light which is consistent with elimination of nitrite from the Meisenheimer complex via an ionic mechanism. However, the rate of appearance of nitrite ion in irradiated solutions is faster than in light-protected ones, which indicates that elimination of nitrite is enhanced either through a radical mechanism or an excited state species.

SUMMARY

Kinetic and mechanistic studies of the solvolysis of bis-PNPP and the nucleophilic aromatic substitution of NtBB in bile salt/DMSO systems are reported. In the phosphonate studies it was proposed that the carboxylate anion of aggregated sodium cholate and not the water was the species responsible for the nucleophilic attack on the P atom with the concerted displacement of the p-nitrophenoxide ion. Confirmation of this postulate was obtained as follows: no observable solvent deuterium isotope effects were observed and no reaction could be detected in the presence of methyl cholate. The inhibitory effect of water on the rate of reaction is primarily due to the formation and/or increase in the hydration sphere surrounding both the carboxylate ion of the bile salt and the phosphonyl group of the substrate. In the case of NtBB, the situation is just the reverse of bis-PNPP, and water plays a major role in this reaction. Here, water is the nucleophile and the bile salt anion acts as a catalyst assisting in the attack at the C-1 position of the polynitroaromatic by enhancing the nucleophilicity of the water. Formation of this relatively very stable Meisenheimer or σ-1,1-hydroxy complex is kinetically controlled, while formation of the 1,3-hydroxy complex, which could be formed either directly or via the 1,1-complex, is a thermodynamically favored process. Decomposition of the complexes, either in the presence or absence of light, yields aromatic compounds and nitrite ions. The formation of these products probably occurs via 2,2- or a 4,4-hydroxy nitro cyclohexadienylide species or a radical process.

In addition to continuing our research on the self-association behavior of bile acid esters in both aqueous and non-aqueous media, we are concurrently investigating the following problems: the preparation of amides of bile acid conjugates, and studies of their self-association, reactions and interactions (including mixed associations with fats, drugs, etc.); the interactions and solubilization by bile salts, their derivatives and mixed bile salt/lipid systems with cholesterol and drugs; interaction and reaction of 6-nitrobezisoxazole-3-carboxylate and other anions, p-nitrophenyl phosphate, p-nitrophenyl sulfate, and ATP in the presence and absence of bile salts; and the mutagenic, carcinogenic, and cocarcinogenic properties of bile salt metabolites formed _in vitro_ via anaerobic gut bacteria.

ACKNOWLEDGMENTS

This work was supported, in part, by Grant No. GM-23877 from the National Institutes of Health.

REFERENCES

1. J. H. Fendler and E. J. Fendler, "Catalysis in Micellar and Macromolecular Systems," Academic Press, New York, 1975; and references cited therein.
2. W. P. Jencks, Adv. Enzymology, 43, 219 (1975).
3. E. H. Cordes, Editor, "Reaction Kinetics in Micelles," Plenum Press, New York, 1973.
4. C. A. Bunton, Prog. Solid State Chem., 8, 239 (1973).
5. E. H. Cordes and C. Gitler, Prog. Bioorg. Chem., 2, 1 (1973).
6. I. V. Berezin, K. Martinek and A. K. Yatsimirskii, Russ. Chem. Rev., 42, 787 (1973).
7. E. J. Fendler and J. H. Fendler, Advan. Phys. Org. Chem., 8, 271 (1970).
8. H. Morawetz, Accounts Chem. Res., 3, 354 (1970).
9. E. H. Cordes and R. B. Dunlap, Accounts Chem. Res., 2, 329 (1969).
10. H. Morawetz, Advan. Catal., 20, 341 (1969).

11. E. J. Fendler and S. N. Rosenthal, in "Solution Chemistry of Surfactants," K. L. Mittal, Editor, Vol. 1 , pp. 455-472, Plenum Press, New York, 1979.
12. M. C. Carey and D. M. Small, Arch. Intern. Med., 130, 506 (1972).
13. D. M. Small, in "Molecular Association in Biological and Related Systems," Adv. Chem. Ser., No. 84, pp. 31-52, American Chemical Society, Washington, D. C., 1968.
14. Note: Micellization or aggregation of bile salts in water proceeds by a sequential indefinite type of self-association.[15-17] Hence, the existence of a critical micelle concentration or concentrations is a matter of semantics,[18] dependent upon the definition of the CMC.[19] Using the generally accepted definition that the CMC is the concentration at which micelles would not exist if the concentration of monomers was lowered,[1,19] a measurable CMC does exist for tri- and dihydroxy bile salts in aqueous solution,[15-17] but the value for the system is meaningless in physical terms unless defined.[11]
15. E. T. Adams, Jr. and E. J. Fendler, Unpublished results, 1978.
16. R. Zana, J. Lang, S. H. Yiv, A. Djavanbakht and C. Abad, in "Micellization, Solubilization, and Microemulsions, K. Mittal, Editor, Vol. 1, pp. 291-304, Plenum Press, New York, 1977.
17. A. Djavanbakht, K. Kale, and R. Zana, J. Colloid. Interface Sci., 59, 139 (1977).
18. D. G. Oakenfull and L. R. Fisher, J. Phys. Chem., 82, 2443 (1978).
19. P. Mukerjee and K. J. Mysels, "Critical Micelle Concentrations of Aqueous Surfactant Systems, "NSRDS-NBS 36, U.S. Govt. Printing Office, Washington, D. C.
20. K. Fontell, Chim. Phys.-Appl. Prat. Ag. Surface, C. R. Congr. Int. Deterg. 5th, 9-13 Sept., 1968 (Publ. 1969), 2 (Pt. 2), 1033 (1968).
21. K. Fontell, Koll.-Z. Z. Polym., 250, 333 (1972).
22. K. Fontell, Koll.-Z. Z. Polym., 250, 825 (1972).
23. J. Miller and A. J. Parker, J. Amer. Chem. Soc., 83, 117 (1961).
24. A. J. Parker, Chem. Rev., 69, 1 (1969).
25. F. M. Menger and M. J. McCreery, J. Amer. Chem. Soc., 96, 121 (1974).
26. J. L. Lach and W. A. Pauli, Drug. Stand., 27, 104 (1959).
27. E. P. Mazzola, Ph.D. Dissertation, University of Pittsburgh, Pittsburgh, Pa., 1971.
28. E. J. Fendler and D. J. Koranek, Unpublished results, 1978; C. J. Chow, Ph.D. Dissertation, Texas A&M University, College Station, Texas, 1976.
29. C. F. Bernasconi, MTP Int. Rev. Sci.: Org. Chem., Ser. One, 3, 33 (1973); and references cited therein.
30. E. J. Fendler, D. M. Camaioni, and J. H. Fendler, J. Org. Chem., 36, 1544 (1971).
31. H. Tolkmith, U. S. Patent No. 2668845 (to Dow Chemical Co.), 1954 (Chem. Abs., 49, 5519i).
32. J. C. Cox and O. B. Ramsay, Chem. Rev., 64, 317 (1964); and references cited therein.

33. M. Gordon, V. A. Notaro, and C. E. Griffin, J. Amer. Chem. Soc., 86, 1898 (1964).
34. G. M. Blackburn and M. J. Brown, J. Amer. Chem. Soc., 91, 525 (1968).
35. F. H. Westheimer, Chem. Rev., 61, 265 (1961); and references cited therein.
36. M. A. Paul, Baskerville Chem. J. of the City College of New York, 12, 3 (1963); and references cited therein.
37. D. J. Koranek, Masters Thesis, Texas A&M University, College Station, Texas 1977.
38. J. K. Kim and J. F. Bunnett, J. Amer. Chem. Soc., 92, 7463, 7464 (1970).
39. E. Buncel, A. R. Norris and K. E. Russell, Quart. Rev. (London), 22, 123 (1968).
40. J. A. Zoltewicz, Topics Curr. Chem., 59, 33 (1975).
41. R. Rossi and J. Bunnett, J. Org. Chem., 38, 1407 (1973).
42. V. Gold and C. Rochester, J. Chem. Soc., 1710 (1964).
43. E. J. Fendler, J. Org. Chem., in press, 1979.

ADDENDUM

The Photovolt Aquatest II (Photovolt Corp., 1115 Broadway, New York, N. Y. 10010) is a coulometer, designed specifically for Kark Fisher titrations of water. Classically, titration indicates the addition of volumes of reagent; however in the Aquatest II, the reagent is added by an electrical current. It requires no standardization, since Faraday's Law pertains (1 equivalent = 96,500 coulombs), and the instrument digitally reads out in micrograms of water present in the sample. Its accuracy, sensitivity, and reproducibility is 10 micrograms of water and its useful range is 10 micrograms to 10 milligrams of water.

ELECTROCHEMICAL INVESTIGATIONS IN MICELLAR MEDIA

N. Shinozuka and S. Hayano
Institute of Industrial Science, University of Tokyo, Roppongi, Minato-ku, Tokyo 106
JAPAN

The effects of surfactants and micelles on the electrode reactions are outlined. The adsorption layers of surfactants influence the electrode reaction rate in micellar media. The maximum suppressive action of surfactants was noted.

Electrochemical behaviour of the water-insoluble electroactive substances solubilized in micellar solution was studied. These substances are able to transfer electrons with the electrode which is covered with surfactant molecules. Polarographic reduction currents of solubilized anthraquinone dyes were diffusion-controlled, and the diffusion co-efficients of the micelle with dye were calculated; the values thus obtained are in good agreement with those in the literature. The electrode process of the solubilized systems was also investigated. The electrode process of the irreversible reaction was greatly affected by the surfactant micelle, while the reversible reaction remained less influenced.

The electrochemical methods for determining cmc are presented. Tensammetry and ion selective electrode methods were used as rapid and convenient methods for the evaluation of cmc of surfactant solution. The polarographic method for determining diffusion co-efficients of micellar solutions is discussed.

INTRODUCTION

One of the most important properties of a surfactant solution is its ability to form micelles. Each surfactant has its own specific micelle formation concentration which is characterized as critical micelle concentration (cmc). Below the cmc, thermodynamic properties of surfactant solutions are not very different from those of other water soluble organic molecules. Above the cmc, the solution shows marked non-ideality and the activity does not change appreciably.[1]

From an electrochemical standpoint, a surfactant, whether it is ionic or not, in the solution is considered as an indifferent electrolyte or substance. Ionic surfactants, such as tetrapentylammonium chloride, have at times been used as supporting electrolytes in electrochemical systems. The formation of the oriented adsorption layer of the surfactant at the interface between the solution and the electrode is very important, the effects of which will be discussed later. The cmc of the surfactant solution generally decreases by the addition of an electrolyte[2]. In an electrochemical measurement a fairly high concentration of supporting electrolyte is necessary, which favours the surfactant micelle formation.

The addition of an electroactive substance to a surfactant solution, where the surfactant concentration is much higher than depolarizer concentration, results in one of two cases depending on whether the electroactive substance is water soluble or not. The water soluble substance which does not interact with micelles in bulk solution will diffuse to and react on the electrode. The adsorption layer of the surfactant often disturbs the electron transfer to the depolarizers. Sometimes a complex is formed between the depolarizer and the surfactant. The polarographic maximum suppressive action of the surfactant is noticeable. A water insoluble substance will be solubilized by the micelle in the bulk solution and the substance thus solubilized will react on the electrode. The solubilized substance does not seem to be a complex with the surfactant micelle in the case where the reduction potential is independent of the concentration of surfactant micelle. Such solubilized depolarizer appears to behave as if it is in a non-micellar solution. Further work is required to provide a detailed elucidation of the mechanism of this phenomenon.

As invited by Dr. Mittal, we will summarize the electrochemical investigations in micellar media including our studies in the past ten years.

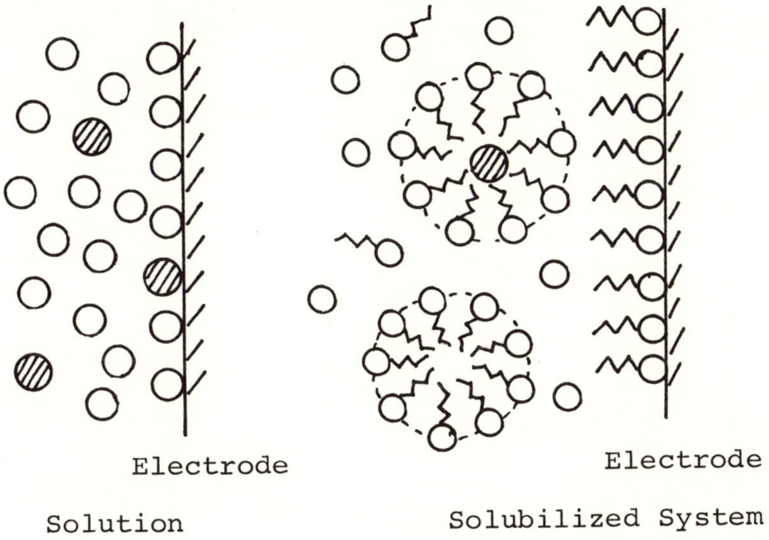

Figure 1. Schematic model of reaction of a solubilized substance on an electrode. o → electrolyte; ● → solubilizate; o~ → surfactant.

ELECTROCHEMICAL EFFECTS OF SURFACTANTS

In the following we briefly present an outline of the electrochemical effects of surfactants, which must be kept in mind when surfactant solutions are used in electrochemical investigations.

Adsorption on Electrodes

Surfactant molecules when adsorbed at the solution-electrode interface change the interfacial tension and the structure of the double layer, and measurements of the interfacial tension and the differential capacity of the double layer have been the general methods for studying adsorption of substances.[3,4] The interfacial tension plotted against the applied potential of the electrode is called the electrocapillary curve. As the interfacial tension of the liquid electrode interface can be easily measured, electrocapillary curves with mercury electrodes have been utilized to evaluate the adsorption of organic substances. The typical effects of surfactant adsorption on electrocapillary curve are shown in Figure 2.[5] With solid electrodes, interfacial tension measurement technique has limited usefulness; but radiotracer method and photo-

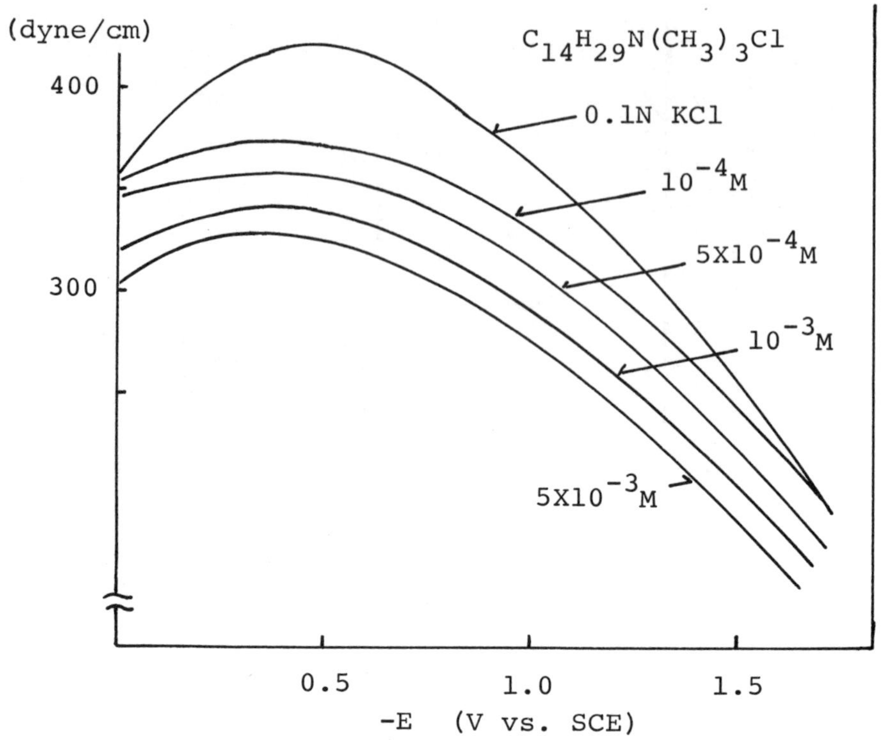

Figure 2. Electrocapillary curves in the presence of surfactants.

metric methods (reflection, transmittance) can be applied to investigate the adsorption on solid electrodes.[6]

The differential capacity of the double layer can be obtained from the electrocapillary curves by the use of Lippman's equation. It can also be measured directly by means of AC bridges or phase sensitive AC polarography. Differential capacity is so sensitive to the adsorption of surface active substances that it should provide more information than electrocapillary curves. A number of reports [7-11] concerning differential capacity measurements of surface active substances have shown that the structures of the adsorbed layers of surfactants from micellar solution on the electrode are complicated. The orientation of adsorbed layers depends on the potential of the electrode. Differential capacity peaks may appear corresponding to the adsorption-desorption of surfactant monomers, small aggregates, and micelles and also to the reorientation of adsorbed molecules.

The differential capacity curves of a cationic surfactant are shown in Figure 3.[9] The inner peaks are ascribed to the reorienta-

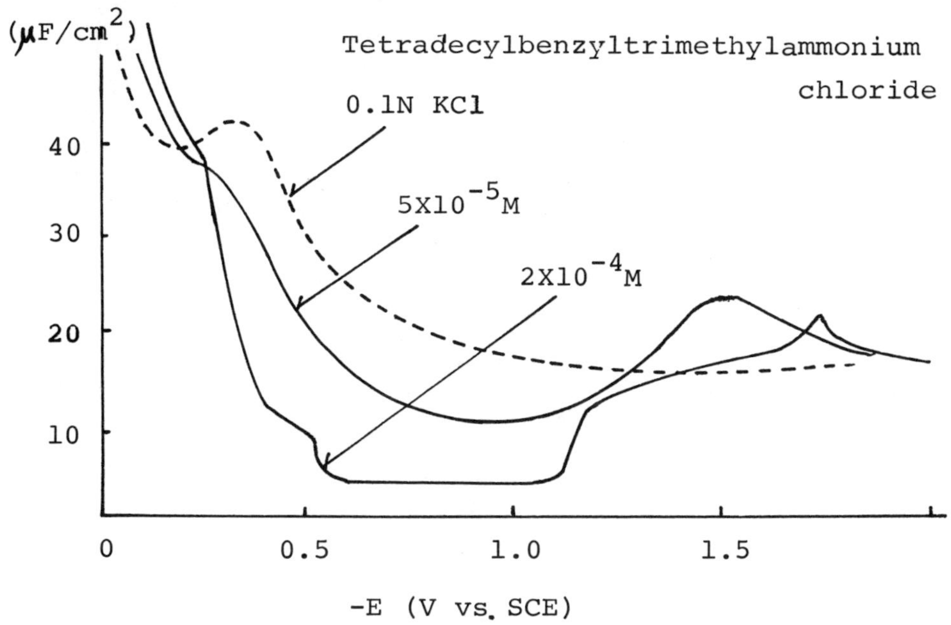

Figure 3. Differential capacity curves in the presence of surfactants.

tion process of the adsorbed surfactant. Similar curves were obtained with anionic surfactants such as sodium n-alkyl sulphates. Three capacity peaks appear in the potential range from 0V to -2.0V (vs. SCE) with sodium dodecyl sulphate solution above the cmc. The first peak in the 0 ~ -0.5V region was thought to be due to the reorientation of the adsorption layer. The inner peak in the cathodic region (-0.8 ~ -1.4V) was attributed to the desorption process of the micelles, and the outer one to the monomer surfactant. The differential capacity curves of non-ionic polyoxyethylene ether type surfactants showed a reorientation peak near -1.0V (vs. SCE) and three peaks in the more cathodic region, which were attributed to the desorption process of (from less negative potential) monomers, hemimicelles, and micelles respectively.[11]

The rate of formation of the adsorbed layer at the dropping mercury electrode has been studied by instantaneous current-time curves or the AC method using different frequencies.[12] The rate is limited both by the rate of adsorption and of diffusion of the surfactant from the bulk of the solution toward the electrode surface. If the rate of adsorption is very fast and the process is diffusion-limited, the following Koryta's equation can be applied to the system.[13]

$$\tau = 1.85 \times 10^6 \frac{\Gamma^2 m}{C_A{}^2 D_A}$$

Where τ represents the time in seconds when coverage of the electrode surface is complete, Γm is the maximum number of moles adsorbed per cm^2, C_A is the bulk concentration in moles/dm^3, D_A is the diffusion coefficient in cm^2/sec. When the coverage is not complete, the degree of coverage θ at time t is given by

$$\theta = \frac{\Gamma}{\Gamma_m} = \left(\frac{t}{\tau}\right)^{1/2}$$

In the other case, where the rate of adsorption is very small and the adsorption process is limited by the adsorption itself, the basic equation for the rate of coverage has also been deduced.[14]

As far as the mercury electrode is concerned, the electrode surface is thought to be covered with surfactant in various orientations in almost throughout the applied potential range.

Effects on Electrode Reaction

Electroinactive surfactants adsorbed on the electrode affect the rate of electrode processes. They have two main effects,[15] namely a blocking effect and an electrostatic effect. The adsorbed surfactants may block the electrode surface, impede charge transfer and thus slow down the electrode reactions. Usually surfactants have long carbon chains or long polyoxyethylene chain and occasionally play an essential role as inhibitors of the electrode reaction. The electrostatic effect is due to the electrostatic interactions between the reacting species and the adsorbed surfactant.[16] Sometimes the electrode process takes place at an increased rate. This acceleration effect may be caused by the change in the ψ - potential, ψ being the mean electrostatic potential at the distance of an ionic radius from the surface of the electrode.

Concerning the effect of the adsorbed layer on the rate of the electrode process, a simple assumption has been made. The rate constant of charge transfer at the electrode covered with uncharged surfactant, k_θ, is a linear function of the electrode coverage.[17,18] The equation is given as:

$$k_\theta = k_{\theta=o}(1-\theta) + k_{\theta=1}\theta \qquad (1)$$

where θ is the coverage of the electrode, $k_{\theta=o}$ and $k_{\theta=1}$ being the rate constants at the free and covered surface of the electrode, respectively. In the particular case, where $k_{\theta=1}\theta \ll k_{\theta=o}(1-\theta)$, the following approximate relation exists:

$$k_\theta = k_{\theta=0}\ (1 - \theta) \tag{2}$$

After accumulation of experimental data, deviations from the linear relation expressed in Equations (1) and (2) have frequently been found. Theoretical approaches have been presented in the literature,[19,20] so only a few recent works will be described here.

Issa and co-workers[21] studied the effects of charged and uncharged surfactants on the polarographic waves of uranium (VI) in phosphoric acid solutions. They found that the nonionic surfactants caused retardation of reactions in all media, whereas the effects of a charged surfactant depended on the acid concentration. The results were discussed in terms of the complexing action of the supporting electrolyte, the effect of the adsorbed surfactant layer on the charge distribution of the double layer, and the specific adsorption of phosphate anions. They also examined the polarographic behaviour of Mn(III) sulphate and phosphate complexes in the presence of charged and uncharged surfactants.[22] Simao and von Stackelberg[23] investigated the electrochemical reduction of In(III) ions on a dropping mercury electrode in the presence of sodium dodecyl sulphate (SDS), tetrabutylammonium perchlorate, and Triton X-305. The influence of ionic surfactants was explained on the basis of their effect on the ψ-potential, but that of Triton X-305 seemed to be related to the structure of the adsorbed layer of the surfactant. Shakunthala and Narayan[24] concluded that the split of oxygen reduction wave in the presence of SDS micelles could be interpreted by an assumption that SDS was adsorbed at the electrode in two different orientations: monomer and micelle. Jacobsen and Lindseth[25] examined the effect of surfactants on differential pulse polarography (DPP) and found that differential pulse polaragraphic waves of reducible substances (Cd^{2+}, Cu^{2+}, Pb^{2+}, etc.) were much more sensitive to the presence of nonionic surfactants than the conventional direct current waves. The presence of surfactant affects the polarograms of organic depolarizers; in most cases the peak current decreases, but in the presence of ionic surfactants the current may increase. These results indicate that surfactants may be of great value in analytical DPP. Shams El Din and co-workers[26] reported that the surfactants influenced the reduction waves of iodate in two distinct ways: they acted as inhibitors or catalyzers.

Guidelli and Foresti[27] studied systematically the inhibitory effects of neutral organic surfactants on simple electrode reactions such as $V^{2+} \rightleftarrows V^{3+}$, $Eu^{2+} \rightleftarrows Eu^{3+}$, $Cr^{2+} \rightleftarrows Cr^{3+}$ and $Cd^{2+} \rightarrow Cd(Hg)$, $Pb^{2+} \rightarrow Pb(Hg)$ etc. at a fully covered dropping mercury electrode by the polarographic technique. The decrease in the charge transfer rate constant caused by the surfactant apparently did not depend on the surfactant adsorptivity in the case of simple electron transfer reaction; whereas, in the case of metal-amalgam formation, the high adsorptivity of the surfactant caused greater decrease. This behaviour was interpreted on the basis of a simple model of charge transfer at a fully covered electrode. Loshkaryov and Loshkaryov[28] discussed the main trends in the action of various classes of surfactants and their effects on the kinetics of electroreduction of metal ions.

Most reported cases, including those cited above, deal with the effects of surfactants on electrode processes involving inorganic depolarizers. Less work has been done on organic depolarizers. Kastening and co-workers[29] studied the effect of surfactants on the reduction of aromatic nitro-compounds and the effects were treated theoretically. The effects of surfactant adsorption processes are being studied at present and the quantitative theory of general validity should be established in the near future. In polarographic practice using surfactants, the possibility of the effects such as those shown above should be taken into account.

Maximum Suppression

It is well known that a peak or a hump which is called "polarographic maximum", is often observed in the polarographic waves. Two or three kinds of maxima, to which surfactants are effective as maximum suppressors, are distinguished.[30] The maximum suppressive action of surfactants can be explained by their being adsorbed on the electrode, lowering the surface tension, thus producing a tendency for the surface to counteract the streaming motion. The theory developed to describe hindrance by adsorbed substances of the motion of the mercury-solution interface can be applied to explain the maximum suppression.[31] As nonionic surfactants are adsorbed over a wider range of potential than ionic surfactants, the former are more effective in suppressing maxima. Ionic surfactants may react with many inorganic and organic ions to form complexes, and this is another disadvantage of ionic maximum suppressors. At present Triton X-100 is the most popular maximum suppressor.

Sodium alkylsulphates ($C_8 \sim C_{18}$) were examined[32] as maximum suppressors, and it is concluded that as a maximum suppressor, sodium dodecyl sulphate is the most efficient in most cases. Higher members lose effectiveness through micellization or insolubility. Lower members have smaller intrinsic surface activity. The maximum suppression points were found to occur at much lower concentrations than the cmc.

In the polarographic maxima region, where mass transfer takes place under convective processes, Koryta's equation does not hold. The equation which can be applied to the maximum region was derived by Barradas and Kimmerle[33], and Phillips.[34] The equation was proved to be applicable to the oxygen maximum suppressed with Triton X-305.

Surfactant concentration used as a maximum suppressor is usually very low, e.g. 0.004% Triton X-100, 10^{-4}M SDS; so, care must be excercised in practical work to use the minimum surfactant required to suppress a maximum or to ensure no alteration of the wave by the presence of surfactants.

In addition, the degree of maximum suppression can be utilized to determine the concentration of surfactant. This is inherently nonspecific because most surfactants have qualitatively similar effects on maxima. Hence this method is suitable to determine surfactants in natural water or seawater and to evaluate water pollution by surfactants.[35,36]

ELECTROCHEMISTRY OF SOLUBILIZED SUBSTANCES

Surfactant solutions were utilized for solubilizing water insoluble substances, and solubilized substances thus were reduced polarographically on the dropping mercury electrode. Proske[37] examined the relation between the polarographic wave height and the concentration of solubilized substances or solubilizing agents and showed the usefulness of surfactant solution in polarographic investigations. However, as surfactants have been considered undesirable for polarographic systems, except for the suppression of polarographic maxima, the principle has so far been little exploited.

Hayano and Shinozuka[38] found that the electrode process of the anthraquinone dyes which are reduced reversibly on the dropping mercury electrode were not affected by solubilization with nonionic surfactant. 1,4-diamino- and 1,4,5,8-tetraamino-anthraquinones, (1,4-DAA and 1,4,5,8-TAA), which are insoluble in water, solubilized in nonionic surfactants (Poloxyethylene nonylphenyl ether NP-$\overline{10}$, NP-$\overline{19}$, and polyoxyethlene dodecyl ether LA-$\overline{14}$) were reduced on the dropping mercury electrode. The DC and AC polarograms appeared unaffected by large amounts of surfactants and dye-solubilized micelles. The half-wave potentials of the solubilized-dye did not change with either the concentration or the type of surfactants. The relation between the current and the square root of the mercury head was linear in all cases of nonionic solutions and a 50% alcoholic solution, which indicated that the limiting current was diffusion controlled. Therefore, the Ilkovic equation, presented below, was applicable to the system.

$$i_d = 607\ n\ CD^{1/2}\ m^{2/3}\ t^{1/6}$$

in which
- i_d : limiting current (μA)
- n : number of electron transferred
- m : flow-rate (mg/sec)
- t : drop time (sec)
- D : diffusion coefficient (cm^2/sec)
- C : concentration (m mol/dm^3)

The number of electrons involved in the reduction of the dye was estimated to be 2 from the log-plot of the currents and the analogy of the reduction of anthraquinone derivatives. The diffusion coefficient calculated from the polarographic data is affected by the composition of the solution[39], the ionic strength and the species of the solvent; also, it may have an uncertainty of about ± 10%. However, the polarographic diffusion coefficients calculated were in good agreement with the known values of non-ionic surfactant micelles[40]. By means of Stokes-Einstein's law for diffusion coefficients of spherical particles[41], the apparent mean radii of dye particles at different concentrations of surfactant solutions were obtained and are shown in Table I.

Table I. Apparent Mean Particle Radii of 1,4,5,8-TAA in NP-19 Solutions.

Surfactant concn. (M)	Dye concn. (10^{-4}M)	Diffusion coefficient (10^{-7} cm^2/sec)	Particle radius (Å)
$1x10^{-1}$	1.000	2.26	38
$5x10^{-2}$	1.000	2.41	63
$1x10^{-2}$	0.922	2.45	85
$5x10^{-3}$	0.865	2.57	84
$1x10^{-3}$	0.732	3.04	73
$5x10^{-4}$	0.619	2.83	79
$3x10^{-4}$	0.451	4.41	51
$1x10^{-4}$	0.446	13.6	16
50% Alcoholic solution	0.718	36.5	2.5

As the surfactant/dye ratio is increased, the apparent mean radii become constant at about 80Å in the surfactant concentration range of $5x10^{-4}$M ~ 10^{-2}M. The corresponding diffusion coefficient of about $3x10^{-7}$ cm^2/sec is in good agreement with that of the nonionic surfactant micelles.

The diffusion coefficients of the particles at various dye concentrations are given in Figure 4 for the system 1,4-DAA and 10^{-1}M NP-$\overline{19}$, NP-$\overline{10}$. From this, the radius of the particle increases with the dye concentration. On the other hand, in the case of 1,4,5,8-TAA solubilized in a 10^{-2}M NP-$\overline{19}$ solution, the dye particle size seems to be independent of the dye concentration. The particle size of 1,4,5,8-TAA solubilized into a LA-$\overline{14}$ surfactant solution markedly decreases with the dye concentration. The above results indicate that the diffusing particle from the bulk solution to the electrode is the micelle with the dye and the electrode process of the solubilized dye is similar to that of the dissolved dye.

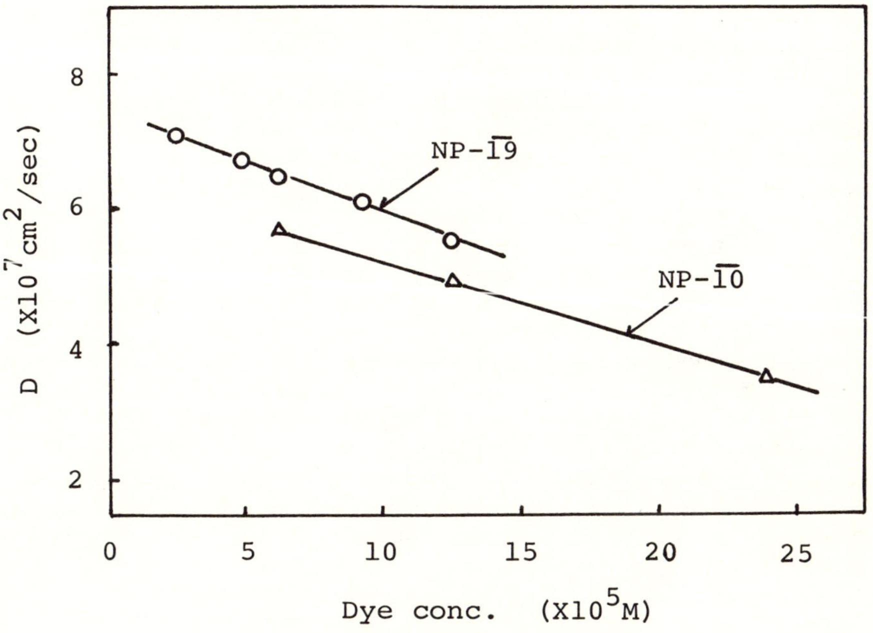

Figure 4. Dependence of diffusion coefficient on dye concentration.

The properties of polarographic limiting current of solubilized dye in nonionic surfactant solutions was further elucidated. 1-amino-2-methoxy-4-hydroxy anthraquinone was solubilized into polyoxyethylene nonylphenyl ether (NP-10, NP-19), polyoxyethylene dodecyl ether (L-9) and Triton X-100 (TX-100) solutions and the limiting currents of these systems showed linear dependence on the dye concentration for surfactant concentration between 10^{-3} and 10^{-1}M. This fact proves that the diffusion coefficient of the surfactant micelle with the dye molecule is not affected by the surfactant concentration or the dye concentration. The linear dependence of the current on the square root of the mercury column height and the results from the instantaneous current-time curves ($i \propto t^{1/6}$), indicate again that the limiting current is diffusion controlled. The log-plots of the current against the potential yielded a straight line with a slope of about 30 mV/log unit showing that the reversibility of the reduction of solubilized dye is not affected by its solubilization with surfactants. It is interesting to note that although the electrode reaction of the solubilized dye occurs at a potential where the surfactant molecule is strongly adsorbed, the current is controlled by the diffusion of micelle with dye and the reversibility of the reduction is not affected.

The other system, involving an irreversibly reducible dye and anionic surfactants, was investigated.[43] Orange OT (1-0-tolyl-azo-β - naphthol) in an acidic 40% ethanolic solution showed a well-defined wave. From the log-plots of the waves, a value of α n=1.22 (α being the transfer coefficient) was obtained. Supposing that the reduction of Orange OT proceeds with a two-electron transfer,[44] the diffusion coefficient of the dye in ethanolic solution at pH = 4.6 was calculated to be 3.8×10^{-6} cm^2/sec. Orange OT solubilized in a sodium dodecylbenzene sulfonate (SDBS) showed a well-defined, irreversible wave, (Figure 5). In the polarograms of the solubilized dye in anionic surfactant solutions, waves due to the adsorption-desorption process of the surfactant molecules on the electrode appear. In Figure 5, wave-A is attributed to the reduction of Orange OT, while waves-B and C indicate adsorption and desorption waves of SDBS molecules respectively. As the limiting current was proved to be diffusion-controlled, diffusion coefficient D, with other parameters $E_{1/2}$, i_d, αn, are summarized in Table II. The same parameters for the system in which Orange OT was solubilized in SDS solution are given in Table III. The apparent diffusion coefficient of the dye decreases markedly with the increase in the surfactant concentration. The value of α n increases with the surfactant concentration. The concentration dependence of D was attributed to the interaction with other micelles, however, the change in α n remains unexplained.

The transfer coefficients of reversible (DAA) and irreversible (Orange OT) cases with various surfactants used as solubilizers are given in Table IV.[45] The values of α correspond to the

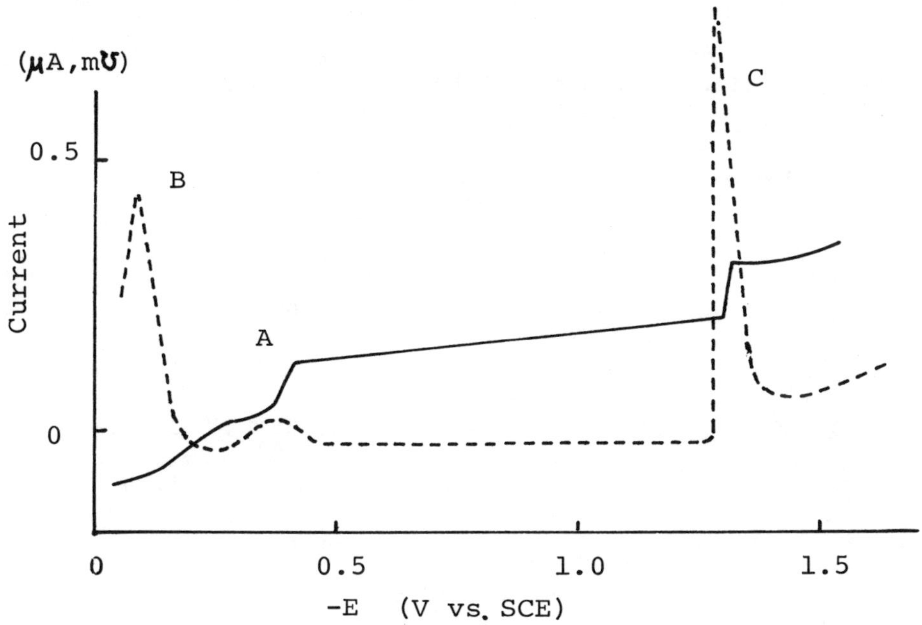

Figure 5. DC and AC polarograms of the solubilized Orange OT in SDBS solution.

Table II. Dependence of Polarographic Parameters on SDBS Concentration.

SDBS concn. (M)	-E (V)	i_d (μA)	D ($\times 10^{-6}$ cm^2/sec)	nα
10^{-2}	0.380	0.182	1.77	0.72
3×10^{-2}	0.375	0.166	1.35	0.71
5×10^{-2}	0.392	0.152	1.14	-
8×10^{-2}	0.410	0.120	0.71	0.80
10^{-1}	0.400	0.104	0.53	0.81

Dye concn. 5.78×10^{-5} M

Table III. Dependence of Polarographic Parameters on SDS Concentration.

SDS concn. (M)	-E (V)	id (μA)	D ($\times 10^{-6}$ cm^2/sec)	nα
2×10^{-2}	0.295	0.170	2.18	1.13
3×10^{-2}	0.303	0.150	1.80	1.14
5×10^{-2}	0.301	0.115	1.06	1.23
7×10^{-2}	0.295	0.108	0.935	1.25
9×10^{-2}	0.303	0.085	0.580	1.25

Dye concn. 5.0×10^{-5} M

Table IV. Transfer Coefficients for Various Solutions.

Solution	Temp. (°C)	Transfer Coefficient (α) DAA	Orange OT
SDBS	45	0.90	0.4
SDS	25	0.92	0.6
HTMAC	25	0.94	0.9
HDMBAC	25	0.88	0.6
50%	25	0.98	0.6
water	45	1.00	0.6

adsorption of surfactant molecules on the electrode, which suggests the condensed adsorption state of surfactant molecules.[46]

The electrode process of Orange OT solubilized in various surfactant solutions was studied in detail.[47] The reduction of Orange-OT depends on the pH of the solution. The relationship between the half-wave potential and the pH value differed with the type of surfactant. The apparent values of α n are plotted against the half-wave potential, (Figure 6). The curve pass through a minimum in the anionic surfactant solutions and a maximum in the cationic surfactant solution.

The $(\alpha\ n)_{app}$ in the nonionic surfactant solution remains constant. The apparent value of α n is markedly different from its true value.[48] The relationship between the observed value and the true value of α n is generally expressed by

$$(\alpha\ n)_{app} = \alpha\ n + (Z - \alpha\ n)\ (\partial\psi/\partial\phi)_E$$

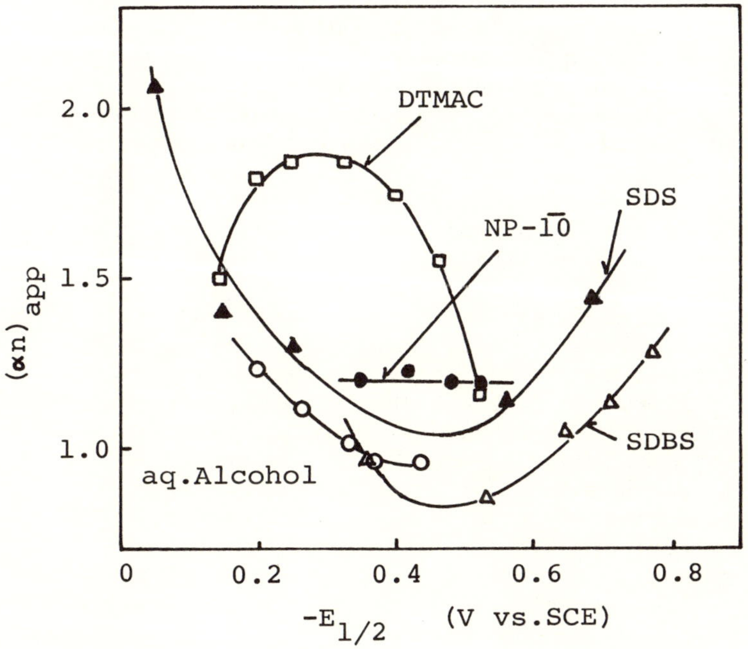

Figure 6. Dependence of $(\alpha\ n)_{app}$ on $E^{1/2}$.

where Z is the electric-charge on the reaction species, ψ_1 is the potential of the outer Helmholtz plane, and ϕ is the potential difference between the electrode potential and the potential of zero charge. The change of α n show that the electric-charge of the surfactant affects the electrode reaction of Orange-OT. Orange OT itself is an uncharged species; however, it seems to behave in the electrode process as if it were ionic when solubilized in ionic micelles. In the cationic surfactant solution, ($Z-\alpha n$) attains a positive value, judging from the fact that the plot of $\alpha n - E_{1/2}$ indicates a maximum. This means that the electric-charge of the cationic surfactant micelle is not less than 2. On the other hand, ($Z- \alpha n$) becomes zero in the nonionic surfactant solution because the value of α n is constant. From this ($Z = \alpha$ n), Orange OT solubilized in the nonionic micelle seems to behave as an ionic species of unit electric-charge.

Azobenzene solubilized in micelles was investigated polarographically by Westmoreland and co-workers.[49] Cationic and anionic surfactants were used as solubilizers. The electrode reaction of azobenzene proceeds as two 1-electron reduction steps in aprotic solvent and as a single 2-electron reduction step in aqueous alcohol solution. Azobenzene solubilized in aqueous micellar systems containing buffers of citric acid-disodium hydrogen phosphate are reduced irreversibly in a single 2-electron step. The polarographic limiting current is diffusion controlled. The half-wave potential of azobenzene reduction shifted more negative with surfactant concentration increment. The chain length, nature of the charged group and nature of the counterion may all influence the apparent half-wave potential of the solubilized dye. The limiting current was strongly affected by the surfactant concentration. In SDS solutions, the limiting current decreased from 0.68 μA to 0.2 μA when the surfactant concentration increased from 0.02 M to 0.5 M. The irreversibility of the reduction was strongly dependent on the surfactant concentration. Large amounts of micelles decreased reversibility.

The surfactant solubilized system can be applied to the field of biological electron transfer processes. Fujihira and co-workers[50] used the oxidant ferricinium ion, which was electrochemically generated from ferrocene solubilized by surfactant (nonionic; Tween 20) in repetitive reversible equilibrium titrations of cytochrome c, cytochrome c oxidase and mixtures. Apparently, the ferrocene-micelles underwent heterogeneous electron transfer with the electrode. The electrochemistry of micelle-solubilized ferrocene was further investigated by Yeh and Kuwana.[51] The ferrocene-micelle served as an excellent mediator - titrant to couple electron transfer between an electrode and the heme proteins of cytochrome c, cytochrome c oxidase and mixtures. Cyclic voltammetric curves indicated a reversible one-electron transfer reaction. The anodic peak current, ip, was dependent on the Tween-20 concentration. The diffusion coefficients calculated from the slopes of the plots of ip vs. $\nu^{1/2}$ (ν being potential scan rate) decreased as the Tween 20 concentration increased. The D value dependence on Tween 20 concentration was assumed to be due to the changing viscosity of the solutions. The micelle size and micellar weight were determined as 43 Å in radius and 127,000, respectively. They increased slightly with the surfactant concentration. The average aggregation number of micelle was calculated to be 77±5. These values resulted in the ferrocene to micelle ratio of about 3 : 1 for the given experiments. Solubilization of mediator-titrant (M-T) by micelles provides a wide variety of M-T's, means of designing experiments to model biological electron transfer mechanisms and an approach to kinetic studies of electron transfer rates with micelle-bound M-T's.

Solubilization in micelles was carried out by Erabi and coworkers[52] for ubiquinone-10(UQ_{10})*which plays an important role in the photosynthetic electron transport system. Both in 80% ethanolic solution and in SDS micellar solution, UQ_{10} showed a pH dependent well-defined wave. The limiting current depended linearly on the UQ_{10} concentration and was proportional to the square root of the mercury-column height. These facts indicated the wave to be diffusion-controlled. The α n-value was 1.0 in 80% ethanolic solution and 0.4 in SDS solution. The α n value and E of UQ_{10} in SDS solution remained almost constant with surfactant concentration change. The diffusion coefficients calculated from the diffusion currents were strongly affected by the surfactant concentration.

The effects of surfactants on electro-oxidation in micellar systems were also investigated.[53] Benzhydrol solubilized in cationic, anionic and nonionic surfactant solutions of 2N sodium hydroxide was electrolyzed anodically. The yield of benzophenone was markedly increased with a cationic surfactant, while anionic and nonionic surfactants had only small effects. From the current-voltage curves of surfactant solutions, it was concluded that in cationic surfactant solution hydrophobic film formed on the surface of the electrode and excluded water from the electrode surface. This film was apparently conductive and the organic compound was oxidized on the surface of the film. The increased yield in the presence of the cationic surfactant then could be attributed in part to the inhibition of the competing oxidation process (oxygen evolution).

*See end of Reference section.

ELECTROCHEMICAL STUDIES OF MICELLAR SOLUTIONS

Determination of Critical Micelle Concentration

There are a number of methods which have been applied to determine the cmc of surfactants. The polarographic technique based on the maximum suppressive action of the surfactant has rarely been used heretofore; because the polarographic method necessitates the presence of a large amount of supporting electrolyte and the maximum suppression point of the surfactant seems to differ from the cmc.

Colichman[54] reported that the cmc values of nonionic and cationic surfactants were identical with the concentration just sufficient to suppress the polarographic maxima of the inorganic ions. Tamamushi and Yamanaka[55] also studied the influence of a few surfactants on the polarographic waves of inorganic ions. Malik and Chand[56] showed that the polarographic method could be applied to determine the cmc of nonionic surfactants. Malik et al.,[57] later reported that the polarographic method gave the cmc only in the presence of electrolyte. The maximum suppression method cannot be recommended for evaluating cmc. Here, tensammetry and ion-selective electrode methods will be presented for the electrochemical determination of cmc values.

Tensammetry (or Electrosorption Analysis). The values of cmc were determined by measurement of adsorption or desorption phenomena of surfactants on the electrode with DC, AC, and oscillographic polarography.

The cmc values of anionic surfactants were determined on the basis of the fact that the desorption waves of anionic surfactants are directly detected by DC polarography and that desorption potential changes with the surfactant concentration.[58,59] The merit of this method is that, as a supporting electrolyte is unnecessary to measure the desorption potential of anionic surfactant, the cmc can be obtained without the influence of supporting electrolyte. DC and AC polarograms of Aerosol OT are shown in Figure 7.

The adsorption wave, which was always smaller than the desorption wave, could not be detected quantitatively below the cmc, therefore only the desorption wave was used. The desorption potential (which was measured for the DC wave, at one-half of the wave height) plotted against the logarithm of Aerosol OT concentration shifted negatively with increase of surfactant concentration, becoming constant above a certain concentration, (Figure 8).

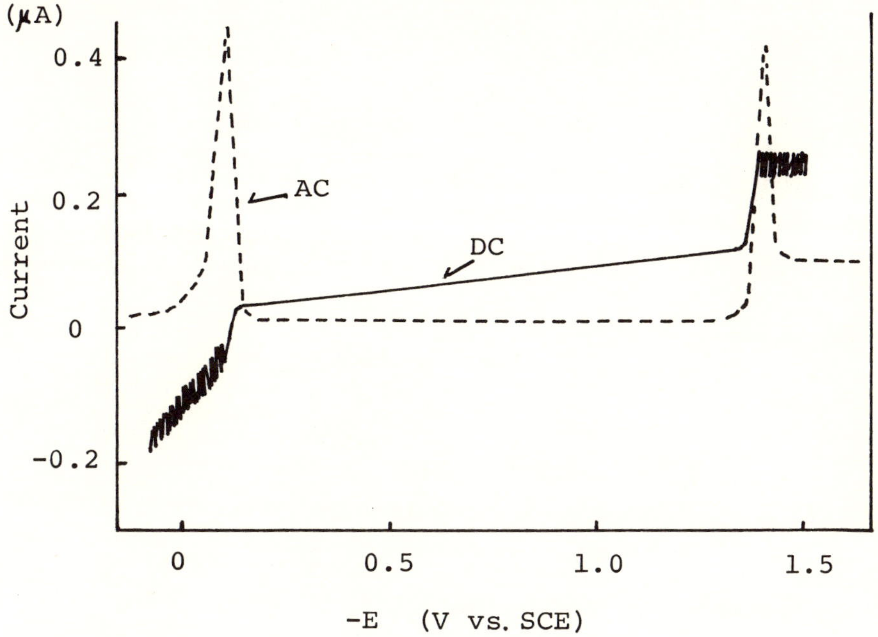

Figure 7. DC and AC polarograms of Aerosol OT.

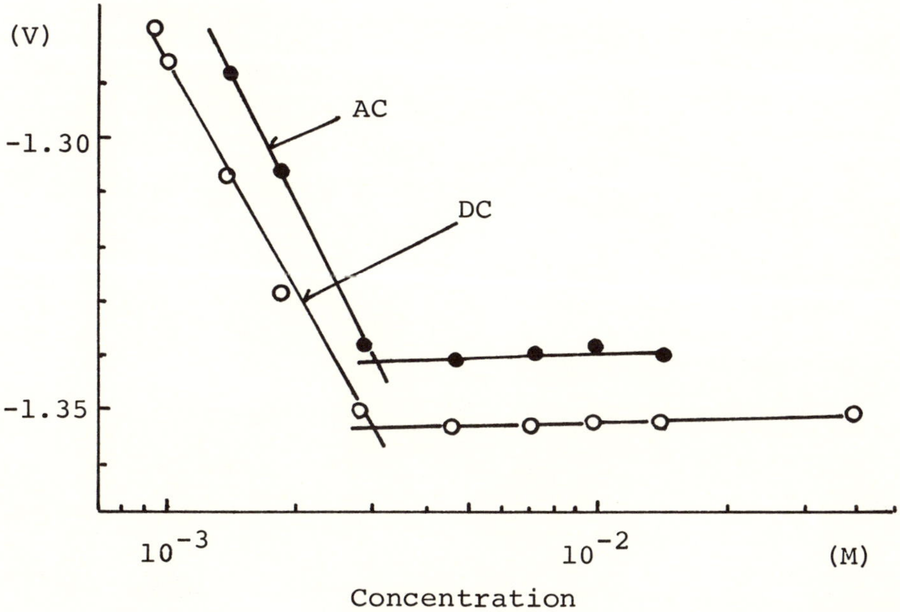

Figure 8. Desorption potential vs. log concentration curve for Aerosol OT.

Similar relations of DC desorption potential against log c were obtained with sodium dodecylbenzene sulfonate, sodium butylnaphtalene sulfonate and sodium dodecyl sulphate.

The values of cmc of non-ionic surfactants were determined by electrocapillary curve measurements.[57,60] The drop times were plotted against surfactant concentration at potentials near desorption and the cmc value was obtained at the intersection of the extrapolations of the steep part of the curve and of the final horizontal portion. Cmc values thus obtained were comparable with those obtained by other methods.

Pályi[61] observed that AC polarograms of 4,4'-bis [(4", 6" - di-phenoxytriazinyl) amino] stilbene-2,2' - disulphonic acid showed irregular oscillations at concentrations higher than or equal to the cmc. The irregular oscillations observed were attributed to the effect of the colloidal micelles on the electrode capacity.

Vollhardt[62] determined directly the cmc of anionic, cationic and nonionic surfactants by AC polarographic method in the presence of a base electrolyte. The method is based on the record of capacitance against the surfactant concentration at different potentials in the region of the desorption peak by diluting the surfactant solution at concentrations higher than cmc with water. The cmc was obtained as the concentration of the solution at the discontinuous point of the curve. The cmc values obtained from the above method were in good agreement with those from desorption peak potential changes and from desorption peak height changes. The cmc values of anionic surfactants in the presence of supporting electrolyte were evaluated on the basis of AC current-potential curves.[63] The discontinuities in the concentration dependence of height and summit potentials of AC polarographic desorption maxima indicated cmc. Sodium-n-alkyl sulphate homologues and N'-alkyl, N,N'-di-alkyl substituted sodium 2-ureidoethane sulfonate were used. This study again showed good agreement between the cmc values obtained from desorption peak height or desorption peak potential change with the values from surface tension measurement.

Ion-Selective Electrode Method. The recent development of ion-selective electrodes permits the measurement of surfactant ion activity. Generally the potential change of the surfactant sensitive electrodes with changes in surfactant ion concentration exhibits near-Nernstian response until the concentration reaches the cmc. After cmc the potential becomes constant, since surfactant ion activity remains unchanged. Thus the surfactant selective electrodes offer a rapid and convenient method for the determination of cmc, though the selectivity of the electrodes reported are still inadequate.

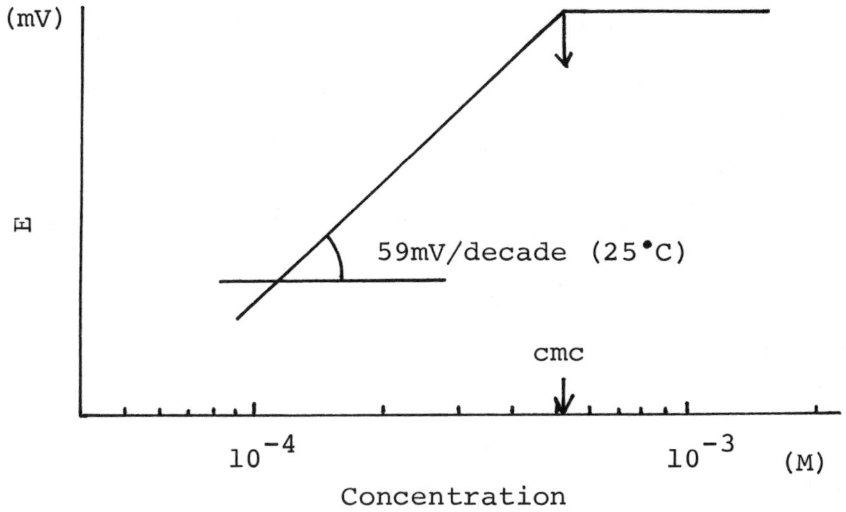

Figure 9. Dependence of potential on the surfactant concentration.

Gavach and Bertrand[64] reported that the liquid membrane electrodes which were specific for the ions of dodecyl sulfate, tetrapropylenebenzene sulfonate and dioctylsulfosuccinate could be used for the determination of cmc. Birch and Clark[65] commented that care must be taken to determine cmc potentiometrically, because some surfactant selective electrodes containing unsuitable solvent led to an incorrect cmc. An improved surfactant selective electrode with liquid ion-exchanger was obtained and showed the cmc value of sodium dodecyl sulphate completely consistent with the accepted value.[66,67] Fujinaga and co-workers[68] stated that the surfactant selective electrode which was composed of quarternary ammonium salt in polyvinyl chloride could be applied to the determination of the cmc of n-dodecylbenzene sulfonate, iso-dodecylbenzene sulfonate and n-dodecyl sulphate. The cmc values were in good agreement with those from the surface tension method. Efforts to obtain a new type of surfactant sensitive electrode for cmc determination were made by Anghel and Ciocan.[69] Ferrous o-phenanthroline dodecyl sulphate was used as an exchanging site. This liquid membrane electrode could be used to precisely determine the cmc of anionic surfactants in the presence and absence of electrolytes.

Determination of Micelle Size and Diffusion Coefficient

It has already been shown that the diffusion coefficient of surfactant micelles can be determined by polarography in solubilization system of electroactive substances. Micelles tagged with an electroactive substance were used to determine the diffusion coefficients of sodium alkyl sulphate micelles.[70] Cadmium ion was used as the tagging cation because the well-defined cadmium polarographic wave is unaffected by the surfactant. The micellar diffusion coefficient was determined using the Ilkovic equation.

$$i_d/C = M = 607\ nD^{1/2}\ m^{2/3}t^{1/6}$$

with the surfactant solution,

$$i_d'/C' = M', \quad M'/M = (D'/D)^{\frac{1}{2}}$$

From the ratio of the slope of $i_d \sim C$ curves, micellar diffusion coefficient D' was calculated. The hypothesis that the cadmium ion associated with the micelle surface was supported by monolayer and electromotive force studies. However, several questions have arisen concerning these studies. The first being that if the slope of $i_d \sim C$ curves is used to calculate the diffusion coefficient, the values for m and t in Ilkovic equation must be the same in the cadmium solution and in the micellar solution; however, usually it is not the case. Secondly, the tagging substance is not necessarily adsorbed on the surface of the micelle. The polarographic method to determine diffusion coefficients of micelles is very convenient but the results must be treated carefully, examining the polarographic process of the system in detail.

The partition of dyes between the aqueous and the micellar phases was examined polarographically.[72] Since the free dye molecules diffuse to the electrode more rapidly than the solubilized dye molecules, the concentration of the free dye molecule becomes lower than that under the partition equilibrium in the diffuse layer. However, if the rate of dissociation of the dye molecule from the micelle is sufficiently slow compared with the rate of diffusion, the diffusion current for such a system is obtained by

$$i = \text{const.}\ Co\ \{(1-x)\ D_f^{\frac{1}{2}} + xD_m^{\frac{1}{2}}\}$$

from a modification of the Ilkovic equation. Where x is the fraction of the dye present in the micellar phase to the total dye molecules; D_f, D_m are diffusion coefficient of free dye and dye in micelle, respectively. Sodium 2-anthraquinone sulfonate in decaoxyethylene nonylphenyl ether solution was studied polarographically in comparison with the results from spectrophotometry. It was concluded that the effect of the dissociation of the solubilized dye from the micelle on the diffusion of the whole dye in the micellar solution could not be neglected.

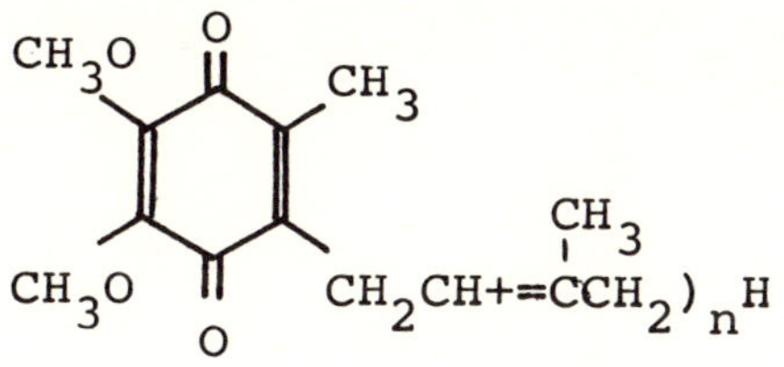

Ubiquinone n

REFERENCES

1. E. Hutchinson and K. Shinoda, in "Solvent Properties of Surfactant Solutions" K. Shinoda Editor, Chapter 1, Marcel Dekkar, New York, 1967.
2. M.L. Corrin and W.D. Harkins, J.Am. Chem. Soc., 69, 638 (1947)
3. B.B. Damaskin, O.A. Petrii, and V.V. Batrakov, "Adsorption of Organic Compounds on Electrodes", Plenum Press, New York, 1971.
4. A.N. Fumkin and B.B. Damaskin, in "Modern Aspects of Electrochemistry" J. O'M Bockris and B.E. Conway, Editors, Vol. 3, Butterworths, London, 1964.
5. N. Shinozuka, (1973) unpublished data.
6. Reference 3 p.181
7. J.B. Hayter and R.J. Hunter, J. Electroanal. chem., 37 71, 81, (1972).
8. K. Eda, J. Chem. Soc. Japan, 80, 343, 437, 461, 465, 708 (1959).
K. Eda and B. Tamamushi, in"Proc. 3rd Intern. Congr.Surface Activity" Vol 2, p. 291, (1960).
9. N. Shinozuka, (1974) unpublished data.
M. Zembra, J. Electroanal. Chem., 66, 45 (1975).
10. H.D. Dorfler and E. Muller, Tenside, 13, 322 (1976).
11. H. Jehring and A. Weiss, Tenside, 6, 251 (1969).
12. H. Jehring, J. Electroanal. Chem. 20, 33 (1969).
13. J. Koryta, Collection Czech. Chem. Communs, 18, 206 (1953).
14. J. Wever and J. Kouteck'y, Collection Czech. Chem. Communs, 25, 2993 (1960).
15. R. Guidelli and M.L. Foresti, Electrochim. Acta, 18, 301, (1973).
16. R.W. Schmid and C.N. Reilley, J. Am. Chem. Soc., 80, 2087 (1958).
17. J. Heyrovsky and J. Kuta, "Principles of Polarography" Academic Press, New York, 1966.
18. R. Guidelli, J. Electroanal. Chem., 53, 205 (1974).
19. J. Lipkowski and Z. Galus, J. Electoanal Chem., 61, 11 (1975).
20. R. Guidelli, J. Electroanal. Chem., 74, 347 (1976).
21. I.M. Issa, M. Tharwat and Y.A. Elewady, Electrochim. Acta, 17, 1075 (1972).

22. I.M. Issa, M.M. Ghoneim, A.A. El-Samahy and M. Tharwat, Electrochim. Acta, 17, 1251 (1972).
23. J. Simão and M. Von Stackelberg, J. Electroanal. Chem., 50, 247 (1974).
24. K. Shakunthala and R. Narayan, Electrochim. Acta, 22, 551 (1977).
25. E. Jacobsen and H. Lindseth, Anal. Chim. Acta, 86, 123 (1976).
26. A.M. Shams El Din, T.M.H. Saber, and H. A. El Shayeb, J. Electroanal. Chem, 57, 241 (1974).
27. R. Guidelli and M.L. Foresti, J. Electroanal. Chem., 77, 73 (1977).
28. M.A. Loshkaryov and Y.M. Loshkaryov, Surf. Technol., 6, 397 (1978).
29. B. Kastening and L. Holleck, Z. Electrochem., 64, 823 (1960).
B. Kastening, Naturwissenschaften, 49, 130 (1962).
B. Kastening, Ber. Bunsenges, Phys. Chem., 68, 979 (1964).
30. H.H. Bauer, in "Electroanalytical Chemistry", A.J. Bard Editor, vol. 8. p.169 Marcel Dekker Inc., New York, 1975.
31. V.G. Levich, "Physicochemical Hydrodynamics", p.561, Prentice-Hall, Englewood Cliffs, N.J., 1962.
T. A. Krynkova and A.N. Frumkin, Zh. Fiz. Khim. 23, 819 (1949).
32. V. Kumar and T.W. Gilbert, J. Electroanal. Chem., 40, 419 (1972).
33. R.G. Barradas and F.M. Kimmerle, J. Electroanal. Chem., 11, 163 (1966).
34. S.L. Phillips, Anal. Chem., 39, 679 (1967).
35. V. Zutic, J. Electroanal. Chem., 78, 113 (1977).
36. T. Fujinaga and S. Okazaki. Bunsekikagaku, 14, 832 (1965).
L. Linhart, Tenside Detergents, 9, 241 (1972).
37. G.E.O. Proske, Anal. Chem., 24, 1834 (1952).
38. S. Hayano and N. Shinozuka, Bull. Chem. Soc. Japan., 42, 1469 (1969).
39. L. Meites, "Polarographic Techniques" 2nd ed. p. 144, John Wiley & Sons, New York, 1965.
40. H. Okuyama and K. Tyuzyo, Bull. Chem. Soc.Japan, 29, 259 (1954).
41. H. Schott, J. Colloid Interface Sci., 24, 193 (1967).
42. S. Hayano and N. Shinozuka, Bull Chem. Soc. Japan, 43, 2083 (1970).
43. S. Hayano and N. Shinozuka, Bull Chem. Soc. Japan, 44, 1503 (1971).
44. I.F. Wladimirzew and I.J. Posstowski, Ber. Akad. Wiss. USSR, 83, 855 (1952).
45. S. Hayano, N. Shinozuka, H. Suzuki and T. Asahara, in "Proc. V1th Int. Congr. on Surface Active Substances", p.899, Carl Hanser Verlag, München, 1973.
46. K. Eda, Nippon Kagaku Zasshi, 80, 349 (1959).

47. H. Suzuki, N. Shinozuka and S. Hayano, Bull. Chem. Soc. Japan, 47, 1093 (1974).
48. R. Parsons, in "Advance in Electrochemistry and Electrochemical Engineering", P. Delahay, Editor, vol. 1., Chap. 1, Interscience, New York, 1971.
49. P.G. Westmoreland, R.A. Day, Jr., and A.L. Underwood, Anal. Chem., 44, 737 (1972).
50. Y. Fujihira, T. Kuwana and C.R. Hartzell, Biochem. Biophy. Res. Commun. 61, 538 (1974).
51. P. Yeh and T. Kuwana, J. Electrochem. Soc., 123, 1334 (176).
52. T. Erabi, H. Hiura and M. Tanaka, Bull, Chem. Soc. Japan, 48, 1354 (1975).
53. T.C. Franklin and L. Sidarous, J. Electrochem, Soc., 124, 65 (1977).
54. E.L. Colichman, J.Am. Chem. Soc., 72, 4036 (1950).
55. R. Tamamushi and T. Yamanaka, Bull, Chem. Soc. Japan, 28, 673 (1955).
56. W.U. Malik and P. Chand, J. Am. Oil Chem. Soc., 43, 446 (1966).
57. W. U. Malik and O.P. Thamb, J.Am. Oil. Chem. Soc., 49, 170 (1972).
58. S. Hayano, N. Shinozuka, M. Fujihira and H. Suzuki, Seisankenkyu, 22, 407 (1970).
59. N. Shinozuka, H. Suzuki and S. Hayano, Kolloid-Z. u.Z. Polym., 248, 959 (1971).
60. W. U. Malik, P. Chand and S.M. Saleem, Talanta, 15,133 (1968).
61. G. Pályi, Kolloid-Z. u. Z. Polym. 249, 1158.
62. D. Vollhardt, Tenside Detergents, 12, 225 (1975).
63. D. Vollhardt, Colloid Polym. Sci., 254, 64 (1976).
64. D. Gavach and C. Bertrand, Anal. Chim. Acta, 55, 385 (1971).
65. B. J. Birch and D. E. Clark, Anal. Chim. Acta, 61, 159 (1972).
66. B.J. Birch and D.E. Clark, Anal. Chim. Acta, 67, 387 (1973).
67. B.J. Birch, D.E. Clark, R.S. Lee and J. Oakes, Anal. Chim. Acta, 70, 417 (1974).
68. T. Fujinaga, S. Okazaki and H. Freiser, Anal. Chem., 46, 1842 (1974).
69. D. Anghel and N. Ciocan, Colloid Polym. Sci., 254, 114 (1976).
70. J. Novodoff, H.L. Rosano and H. W. Hoyer, J. Colloid Interface Sci., 38, 424 (1972).
H. W. Hoyer and J. Novodoff, J. Colloid Interface Sci., 26, 490 (1968).
71. S. Hayano and M. Fujihira in "Proc. International Conference on Colloid and Surface Science," E. Wolfrom, Editor, Vol. 1, pp. 609 - 616, Akademiai Kiado, Budapest, 1975.

Part V
Microemulsions and Reactions in Microemulsion Media

AN APPROACH TO THE DESIGN OF FLUIDS FOR MICROEMULSION FLOODING

K. D. Dreher and S. C. Jones

Marathon Oil Company

P. O. Box 269 Littleton, Colorado 80160

To formulate a microemulsion/mobility buffer fluid system for the successful recovery of tertiary oil, the designer must select components and concentrations from a bewildering array of possible combinations. This overview suggests an approach that should help find workable systems quickly. The key is to formulate a microemulsion that has a balanced affinity for both reservoir crude oil and the aqueous, polymer-thickened drive fluid... in the presence of reservoir rock. Phase behavior studies in glassware provide a starting point. Liquid-liquid interactions and microemulsion component influences, particularly those of cosurfactant and electrolyte, on phase behavior are reviewed briefly from the perspective of how they affect the oil versus water solubility in a microemulsion, and how they affect its viscosity.

Fine tuning compositions in glassware is meaningless, because the dynamics of fluid-rock interactions cannot be properly incorporated. Instead, a series of core flooding experiments is proposed. These floods are designed to identify deficiencies so that microemulsion compositional adjustments can be made. We review fractional flow theory and relate oil production performance in continuous microemulsion injection experiments to microemulsion affinity toward oil versus water.

Finally, surfactant retention and dissipation are discussed. Suggested interpretation of small-slug-size core floods shows which microemulsion/mobility buffer systems exhibit the least retention, and permits selection of the most cost-effective system.

INTRODUCTION

At the conclusion of economic waterflooding, considerable volumes of oil remain in oil-bearing strata, and can amount to 30% to 50% of the pore volume. Several factors are important in the retention of this oil under waterflooding conditions.[1] These same factors influence the mobilization and tertiary recovery of the residual oil. Besides brine and oil composition, pore size, pore size distribution and mineralogy of the reservoir rock are important. The distribution of oil and the factors influencing its retention under moderate pressure gradients are important design considerations in surfactant flooding. In those zones contacted during waterflooding, wettability can range from completely water-wet to completely oil-wet. Best recovery is predicted for the water-wet state.[2] In this case, discontinuous "oil ganglia" are retained by capillary forces, which are proportional to the oil/water interfacial tension.

Elimination, or significant reduction of capillary forces by surfactants allows mobilization of this oil,[2] opposite to the direction of the imposed pressure gradient. Mobilized oil contacts other residual oil, resulting in the formation of a flowing oil bank.[3] Continued displacement depends on mobilities of the flowing oil and water and displacing fluids. Thus, requirements for successful tertiary oil recovery are: 1) ability to eliminate or adequately reduce capillary forces that retain oil under waterflood conditions, 2) proper viscosity of the surfactant-containing fluid to ensure good volumetric sweep efficiency so that much of the residual oil is contacted, 3) proper mobility of a drive fluid to ensure continued displacement of mobilized oil and water, and 4) adequately low interfacial tension between the surfactant-containing fluid and the drive fluid to minimize surfactant retention.

Physical and chemical properties of surfactant formulations are affected by compositional variations. Composition also distinguishes three types of injection formulations: dilute aqueous surfactant solutions,[4,5,6] microemulsions,[3,7,8,9] and "soluble oils."[10] In general, microemulsions useful for oil recovery are comprised of five components: surfactant (usually a mixture of petroleum sulfonates), cosurfactant, water, hydrocarbon, and salt. Soluble oils lack significant water and salt, and aqueous surfactant solutions lack oil, and generally contain lower surfactant concentrations. Each component has an important effect on the physical properties of these formulations and, thus, on their ability to recover oil.

Both concentrated[11,12,13,14] and dilute[15,16] formulations of surfactant have been field tested. Figure 1 shows the recovery for an ongoing project.[17] In this test, a water-external microemulsion was used to displace residual oil toward producing wells. The microemulsion was followed by a dilute aqueous polymer solution for mobility control.

Considerable confusion exists with regard to appropriate definitions of surfactant formulations for oil recovery. Within the petroleum industry, microemulsion and micellar solution have been used to designate equivalent compositions.[18] Shah et al[19] have distinguished micellar solutions and microemulsions based on dimensions of the dispersed phase and amount of oil or water solubilized relative to the concentration of surfactant. However, not all compositions will have a distinct dispersed phase and continuous phase. As observed by Winsor,[20] and Bowcott and Schulman,[21] it is possible for a composition that has the characteristics of being water continuous to exist in equilibrium with excess aqueous phase. Further, compositions of interest can exist in equilibrium with both an aqueous phase and a hydrocarbon phase simultaneously. The structure of these surfactant-rich phases that contain both oil and water is poorly understood. Shah et al[22] have suggested these systems are "cosolubilized" in that the surfactant and cosurfactant form a liquid that can solubilize both oil and water as a molecular solution. Scriven[23] has suggested that these systems are "bicontinuous" in that both water and hydrocarbon form continuous phases.

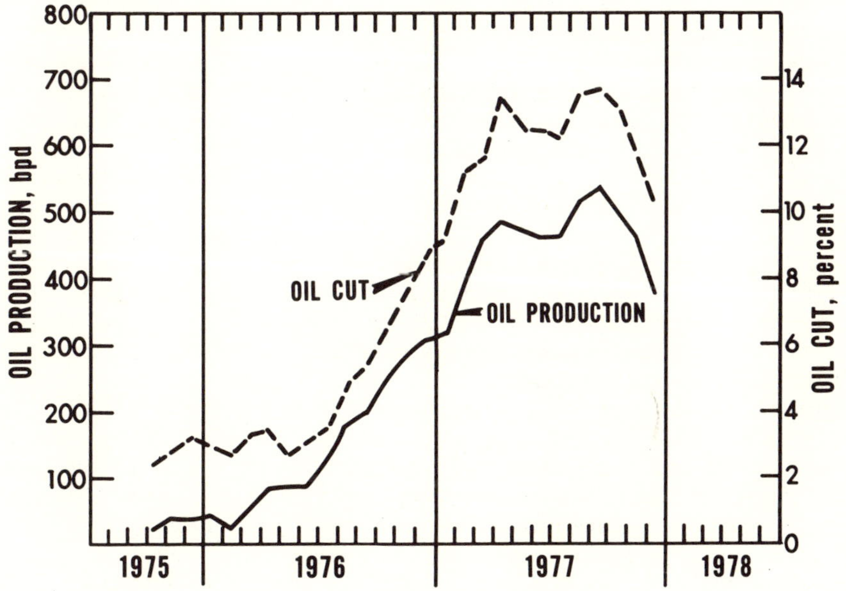

Figure 1. Oil recovery versus time for microemulsion/polymer oil recovery project.[17]

Because of the lack of knowledge regarding the structure of oil recovery fluids, it seems appropriate not to attempt presenting another definition in this review. The term, microemulsion, will be used to describe a surfactant-rich phase that is translucent and phase stable. These systems can be saturated or undersaturated with regard to water, hydrocarbon, or both.

The design of an effective microemulsion/drive fluid (mobility buffer) system to recover tertiary oil from a particular reservoir is a complex procedure. Because a microemulsion may contain five or more components, each of which may be a mixture of many compounds, and because literally hundreds of surfactants are commercially available, the preparation of a microemulsion alone, without consideration of the drive fluid composition, involves an overwhelming number of possible combinations. Ion exchange that occurs among injected fluids, the resident brine, and reservoir rock and clays further complicates the achievement of any sort of optimal design. Ion exchange phenomena are incompletely understood, and at best, reservoir behavior is only approximately simulated in laboratory core flooding experiments.

Thus, the need for a systematic design procedure that incorporates rock effects is evident. This paper suggests such an approach. Briefly, it is the following:

- The first step consists of preparing several microemulsion compositions of a desired viscosity that exhibit a range of affinities toward fresh reservoir crude oil, reservoir brine, and the injected drive fluids at reservoir temperature. Measurements are made in the absence of rock. State-of-the-art microemulsion compositions are very compatible with crude oil or brine (i.e., they produce ultra-low interfacial tensions, and have capacity to solubilize reasonably large amounts of oil or brine); however, oil compatibility is gained only by a corresponding loss in brine compatibility, and vice versa. A delicate balance is required for successful oil recovery. Factors that promote brine or oil affinity and that modify microemulsion viscosity have been well explored, and are reviewed in the first part of this paper.

- In the second step, large slugs of the more promising microemulsions from the previous step are injected into reservoir rock samples in a simulated post-waterflood condition. Ion exchange modifies microemulsion viscosity and oil or water affinity. A section of this paper reviews fractional flow theory and relates oil production performance to *in situ* microemulsion compatibility with oil and brine. Interpretation of differential pressure data and oil production behavior in large-slug-size or continuous-microemulsion-injection core floods allows one to identify shortcomings in the microemulsion composition and to make suitable adjustments in viscosity and oil compatibility

- A series of small slug sizes of each microemulsion surviving, or modified from step two is injected into reservoir core samples. Here, the complication of microemulsion/polymer-thickened drive fluid interaction is introduced. Surfactant retention and dissipation are discussed. The slope of an oil recovery versus slug size curve obtained with small slug sizes is directly related to surfactant retention.

- Finally, intermediate slug sizes, those sizes that might be used in a commercial application, of the remaining best performers are injected to acertain that adequate mobility control is achieved.

PHASE BEHAVIOR

The purpose of this section is to review aspects of phase behavior of microemulsions and to show how compositional changes shift their relative affinities toward oil or water. An understanding of these shifts will serve as background information on how a microemulsion composition might be modified when deficiencies in core flooding behavior (to be discussed later) are observed.

Each component of a microemulsion has an influence on phase behavior. The component that has the greatest impact on a microemulsion's oil or water solubilizing capacity is the surfactant. Petroleum sulfonates have been the surfactants of choice. They are relatively cheap, effective, and can be made with a broad spectrum of solubilities. Unfortunately, little is known about the effect of petroleum sulfonate structure on phase behavior. A few generalizations can be made, however. With sulfonates of similar structure, affinity toward oil increases with increasing equivalent weight. Molecules containing two or more sulfonate groups have a much greater preference for water than similar monosulfonates. Further, two sulfonates of widely different properties, e.g., a high equivalent weight monosulfonate and a low equivalent weight disulfonate (both of which are really mixtures of many molecular species), often can be blended with resulting properties that are linear interpolations between the properties of the individual sulfonates.[24 25 26]

Next to the surfactant, cosurfactant and electrolyte type and concentration probably influence microemulsion behavior most strongly.

Cosurfactants (or cosolvents) that have been used effectively are aliphatic, aromatic, and ethoxylated alcohols with intermediate oil/water solubility. Electrolyte type (monovalent vs divalent) and concentration of reservoir brine have more influence than the reservoir hydrocarbon. In this review, the effect of electrolyte and cosurfactant on phase behavior will be emphasized.

Healy, et al[27 28] have suggested that once a microemulsion has been injected into a porous medium, the resulting liquid is composed of three phases: surfactant, reservoir brine, and crude oil. Thus, one method of representing the phase behavior is with pseudo-ternary diagrams. An example of this type of diagram as it applies to tertiary oil recovery is shown in Figure 2.[27] Dilution at the leading edge of the microemulsion is in the direction of the stabilized flowing oil/brine bank. At the back edge of the microemulsion, dilution is towards drive water or polymer solution. To represent these two conditions, two multiphase envelopes have been superimposed in Figure 2. Miscible and immiscible displacements have been distinguished with these types of diagrams. Within the single-phase region, the displacement is considered miscible. The surfactant-rich phase is undersaturated with respect to oil and water, and 100% of the oil contacted is mobilized. Once sufficient dilution has occurred, the system (surfactant, oil, and water)

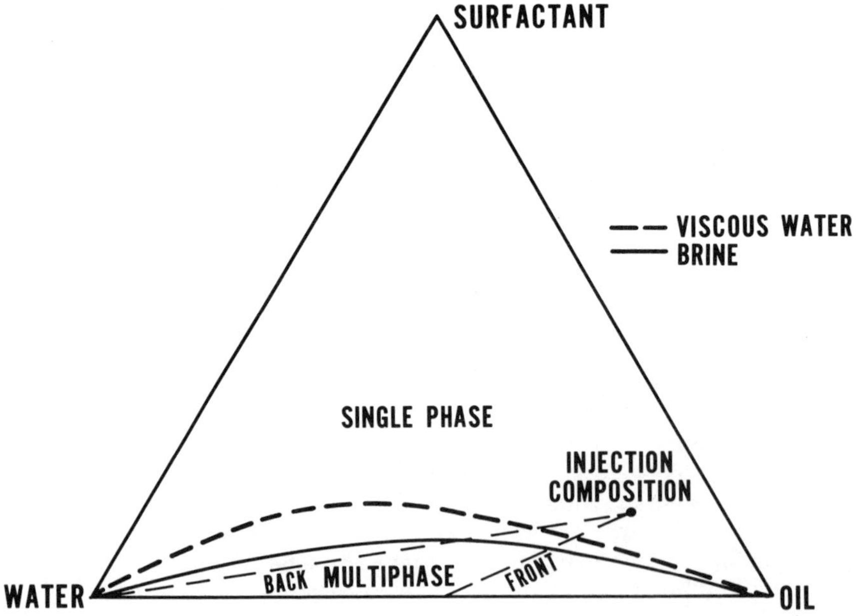

Figure 2. Dilution path for microemulsion flooding.[27]

passes into the multiphase region and immiscible displacement dominates. In this region, oil/brine,[29] microemulsion/brine, and microemulsion/oil[30] interfacial tensions control the efficiency of the displacement.

Ternary representation has proved useful in helping elucidate mechanisms involved in the mobilization of tertiary oil by microemulsions. However, when applying such diagrams it is assumed that the selection of pseduocomponents is adequate. Recent work[31 32] has shown that pseudoquarternary phase diagrams may be more useful (remember that microemulsions contain five components). Regardless of the representation selected, extreme care in the interpretation must be taken because a single pseudocomponent may distribute in the multiphase region in different ways. Multicomponent oils, petroleum sulfonate, and cosurfactant are particularly subject to varying distribution in the multiphase region. Further, fluid flow and the influence of reservoir rock can overshadow phase behavior in oil recovery operations. Therefore, in this review phase behavior, only as it pertains to microemulsion design, is discussed. The two most easily altered components are electrolyte and cosurfactant.

Electrolyte. Salt has a marked effect on the phase behavior of microemulsion prepared with a petroleum sulfonate.[8 27 33] Single-phase and multiphase regions on the pseudoternary representation are significantly changed by altering the electroltye content of the brine phase. Within the single-phase region, physical properties and structure are modified due to changing the preference of the sulfonate for the oil phase or water phase; decreasing salinity favoring the aqueous phase.

Given proper viscosity properties, the most important characteristic in the single-phase region is controlled solubilization of oil and brine. Figure 3 shows the solubilization of brine and crude for a microemulsion composed of petroleum sulfonate, n-hexanol, hydrocarbon, and water. Equal volumes of crude oil and brine were added to 100 ml of microemulsion. These equal added volumes of oil and brine represent the oil bank, with equal oil/brine saturations, adjacent to the microemulsion slug. The dashed lines in Figure 3 indicate the portions of the total fluid that would have separated as oil and brine phases, had none of the added oil or water been solubilized by the microemulsion. Data shown in Figure 3 were obtained with a relatively low-salinity brine. All of the added brine was solubilized; no separate aqueous phase formed. A hydrocarbon top layer appeared at 17 ml oil added (plus 17 ml brine)/100 ml microemulsion. Similar data are shown in Figure 4, except that the added brine contained a higher electrolyte (both Na^+ and Ca^{++}) concentration. A water bottom layer appeared at 2.5 ml/100 ml microemulsion. More crude oil was solubilized than the system represented by Figure 3. It is important

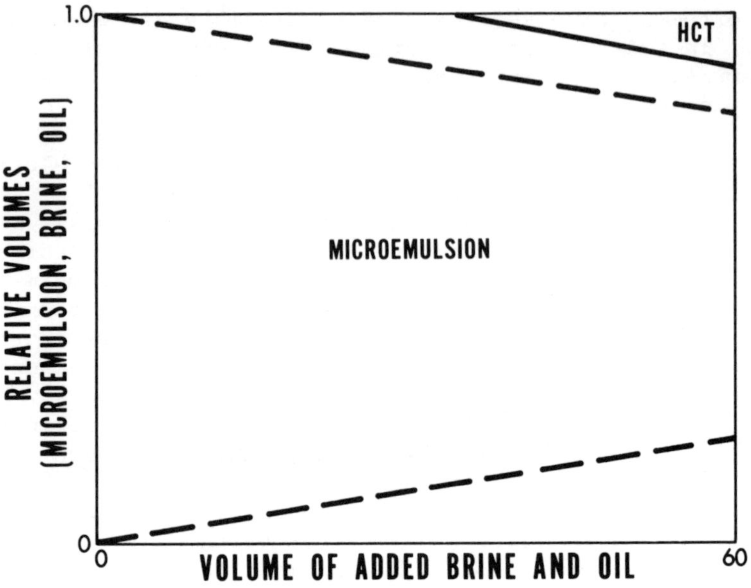

Figure 3. Phase volume fraction versus added brine and oil for microemulsion composed of 10 wt. % petroleum sulfonate, 2.1 vol. % n-hexanol, 75 vol. % water, and 12.9% hydrocarbon. Brine composition: 130 ppm Ca^{++} and 2000 ppm Na^{+}. HCT=Hydrocarbon Top Layer.

to note that the brines in Figures 3 and 4 do not have the same electrolyte composition or concentration as the water contained in the microemulsion. Nor is the added crude the same as the hydrocarbon contained in the microemulsion. These effects are significantly altered with lower equivalent weight sulfonate or lower molecular weight alochol in that brine solubility can be increased and oil solubility decreased.

Healy et al[27 28 30] have examined the effect of salinity in the multiphase region. When salt is added to a lower-phase microemulsion in equilibrium with excess hydrocarbon, a brine-phase and middle-phase microemulsion eventually appear. Continued addition of salt leads to an upper-phase microemulsion in equilibrium with a brine phase. This effect is shown schematically in Figure 5.

Within the multiphase region, the microemulsion is saturated with respect to brine, oil or both, thus, the designation of

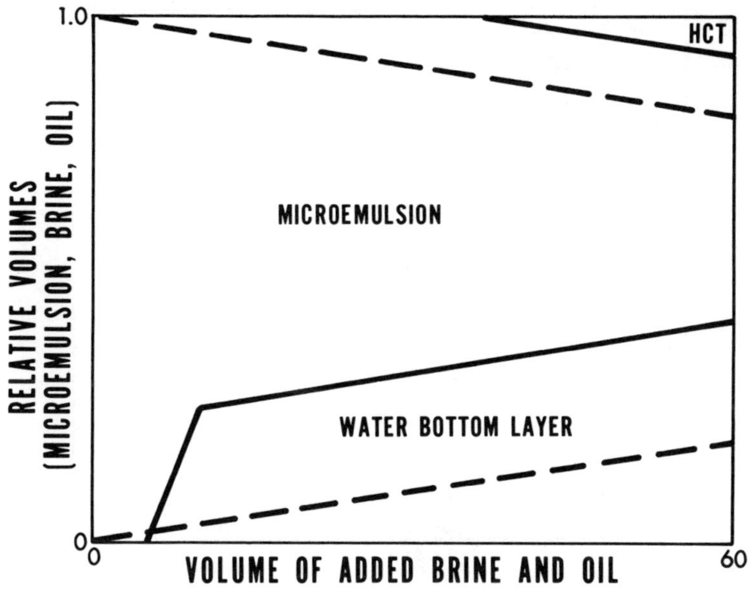

Figure 4. Phase volume fraction versus added brine and oil for microemulsion composed of 10 wt. % petroleum sulfonate, 2.1 vol. % n-hexanol, 75 vol. % water, and 12.9% hydrocarbon. Brine composition: 260 ppm Ca^+ and 8500 ppm Na^+.

immiscible displacement. Interfacial tensions between these phases are a function of added salt. In the case of the system studied by Healy et al,[33] the microemulsion/oil interfacial tension decreased, while microemulsion/water interfacial tension increased with increasing salinity. These data are shown in Figure 6. A thorough discussion of interfacial tension appears in another review in this volume.

Concurrently, the volume of oil and water solubilized relative to the amount of surfactant increases as the interfacial tension decreases. Healy et al,[33] thus, designate an optimal salinity for interfacial tension and solubilization. Middle-phase microemulsions are optimal in this sense. More recently,[34] an attempt has been made to relate an optimum salinity for a three-phase system to several other parameters, including surfactant structure and alcohol type and concentration. The conclusion was made that high solubilization and low interfacial tension are related phenomena.

Cosurfactant. The effect of cosurfactant on phase behavior

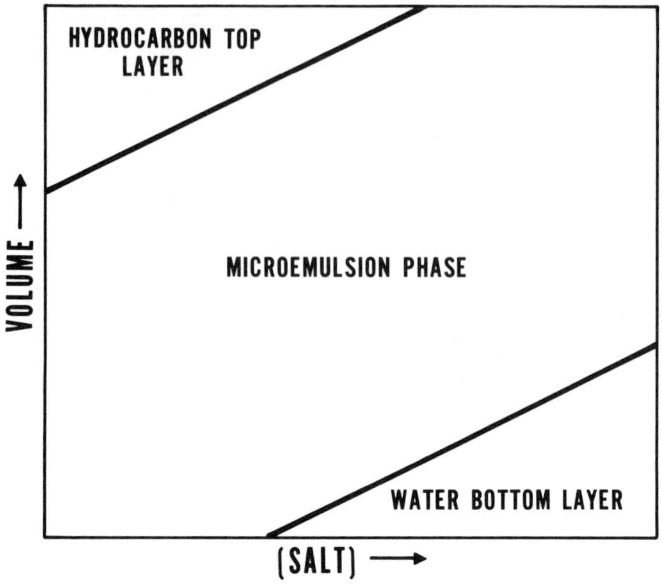

Figure 5. Schematic diagram of the effect of increasing salt concentration on phase volumes of multiphase microemulsion system.

has been given in a number of papers.[8 27 34 35 36 37 38] Short chain alcohols, used as cosurfactants, can be used to modify the phase behavior and viscosity of brine-hydrocarbon-surfactant systems. A system composed of a predominantly oil-soluble sulfonate (470 equivalent weight), 28 weight percent water, and hydrocarbon separates into an upper-phase microemulsion in equilibrium with an excess aqueous phase. As isopropyl alcohol is added, the brine phase is incorporated into the upper-phase microemulsion. Eventually the entire system becomes single phase. Continued addition of IPA results in a two-phase system with a lower-phase microemulsion in equilibrium with excess hydrocarbon phase. Viscosity versus added IPA is shown in Figure 7. Thus, cosurfactant can be used to alter viscosity.

The capacity to solubilize additional brine and hydrocarbon is significantly altered in the single-phase region as IPA is added. Brine and hydrocarbon solubility for this system are shown in Figure 8. Brine and hydrocarbon were added separately in this case. As can be seen, hydrocarbon solubility diminished and brine solubility increased in the microemulsion phase. Thus, IPA, a predominantly water-soluble cosurfactant, makes the microemulsion more compatible with reservoir brines.[8 38]

Preferentially oil-soluble alcohols tend to have the opposite effect in that microemulsions are made more compatible (increased solubility) with hydrocarbons. Figure 9 shows viscosity versus alcohol concentration data for a microemulsion composed of a water-soluble sulfonate (420 equivalent weight), 70 weight percent brine, and hydrocarbon. The curves depict the single-phase region. The zone to the left of each curve is two-phase with excess hydrocarbon in equilibrium with lower-phase microemulsion, whereas, to the right, an excess aqueous phase is in equilibrium with an upper-phase microemulsion. Although viscosities represent a structural change, this system did not invert from water-external to oil-external on addition of the alcohol. It remained water-external. Often, as is shown in Figure 9, high viscosities are obtained with water-insoluble alcohols; the more water-soluble alcohols cause lower microemulsion viscosities.

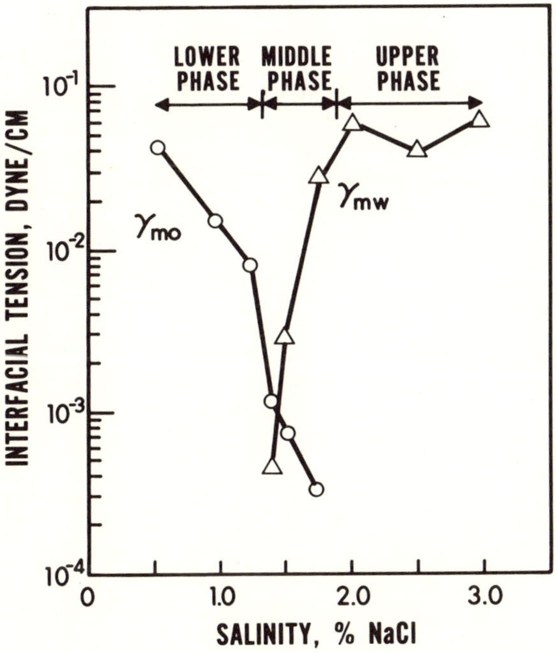

Figure 6. Interfacial tension versus salinity for multiphase microemulsion system.[33]

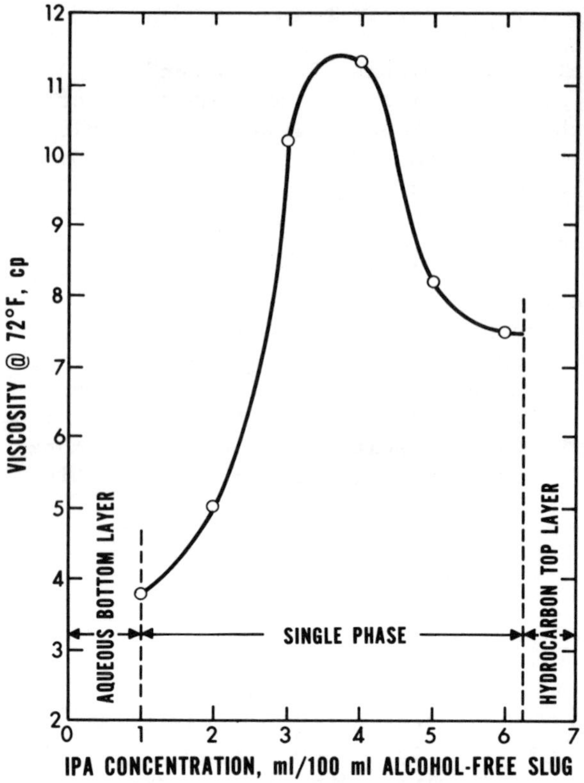

Figure 7. Viscosity of a microemulsion composed of 12 vol. % petroleum sulfonate, 24.9 vol. % water, and 63.1 vol. % hydrocarbon versus added cosurfactant, isopropyl alcohol.[35]

Brine and hydrocarbon solubility are shown in Figure 10 for this system as 1-hexanol was added. Thus, with a water-soluble sulfonate, an oil-soluble cosurfactant increases hydrocarbon solubility and decreases brine solubility.

Addition of brine or hydrocarbon can cause unusual phase behavior. An example is shown in Figure 11. Hydrocarbon solubilization increases linearly with increasing 1-pentanol concentration. Above the line, two phases exist — a lower phase microemulsion and excess hydrocarbon. Brine, however, causes the separation of hydrocarbon — not an aqueous phase as might be expected. Only the dashed curve at the right corresponds to brine solubilization shown in Figures 8 and 10.

Electrolyte modifies the effect of cosurfactant. In general,

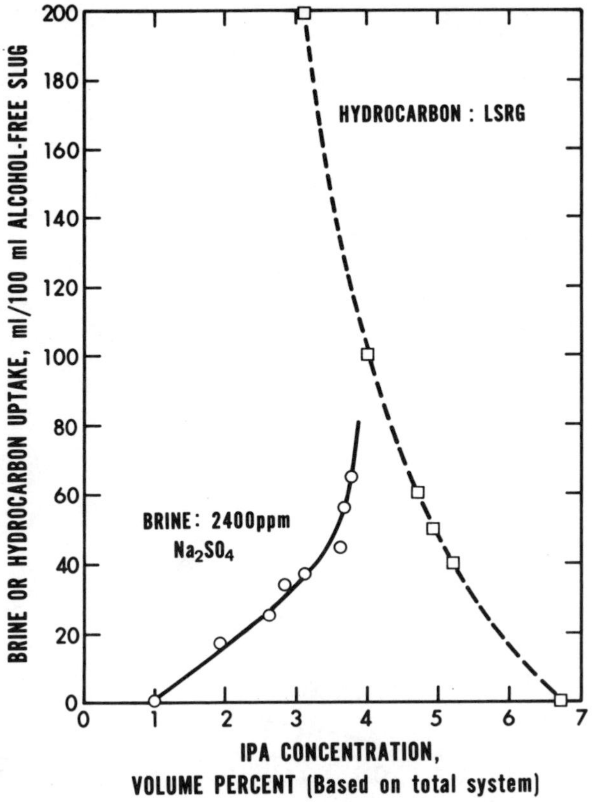

Figure 8. Brine and hydrocarbon solubility in a microemulsion composed of 12 vol. % petroleum sulfonate, 24.9 vol. % water, and 63.1 vol. % hydrocarbon versus added cosurfactant, isopropyl alcohol.[35]

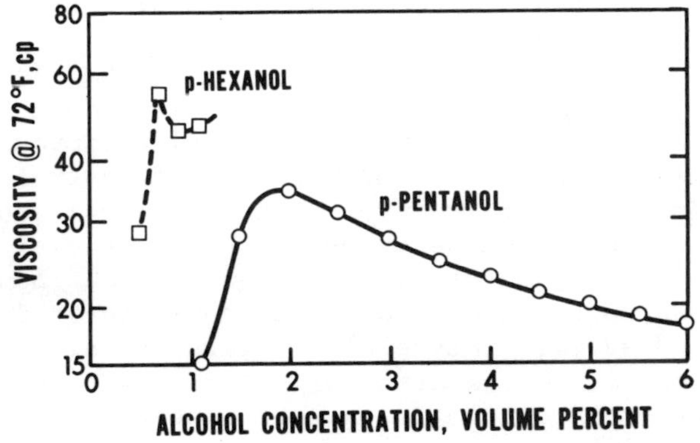

Figure 9. Viscosity and stability limits of a microemulsion composed of 11.7 vol. % petroleum sulfonate, 65.5 vol. % water, and 22.8 vol. % hydrocarbon versus added cosurfactant, p-hexanol or p-pentanol.[35]

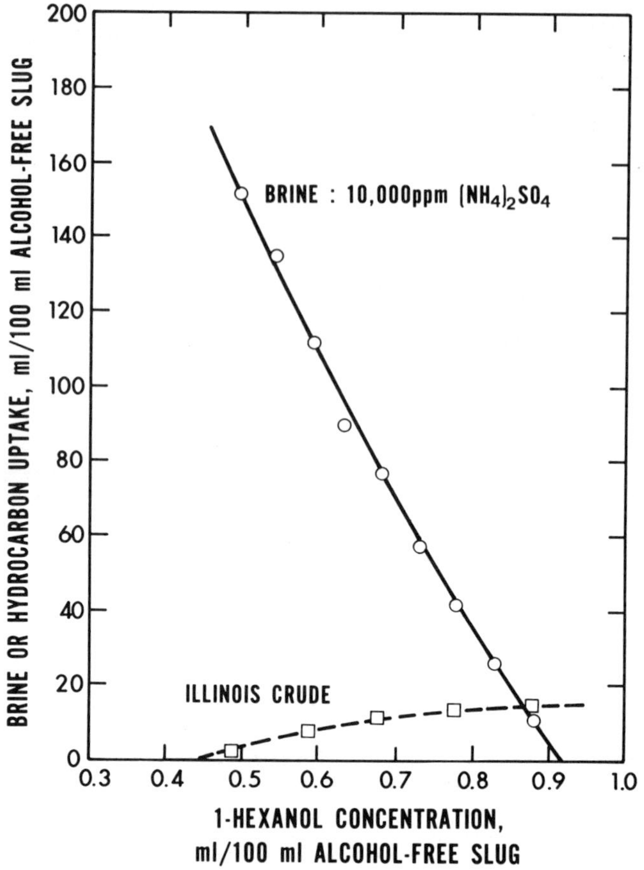

Figure 10. Brine and hydrocarbon solubility in a microemulsion composed of 11.7 vol. % petroleum sulfonate, 65.5 vol. % water, and 22.8 vol. % hydrocarbon versus added cosurfactant, 1-hexanol.[35]

addition of electrolyte increases a particular composition's affinity for hydrocarbon and decreases its affinity for water. Figure 12 shows the interaction between 1-pentanol and electrolyte concentration on the phase behavior for a microemulsion composed of 440 eq. wt. sulfonate, 55 wt. % water, and hydrocarbon. Added electrolyte reduces the amount of 1-pentanol required to solubilize hydrocarbon. Added electrolyte also lowers the alcohol concentration required to cause separation of an aqueous phase. With the proper sulfonate, IPA allows for higher electrolyte concentrations before phase separation occurs.[8]

These results are in agreement with data shown in Figure 13 presented by Salter,[39] which show that there is a linear relation-

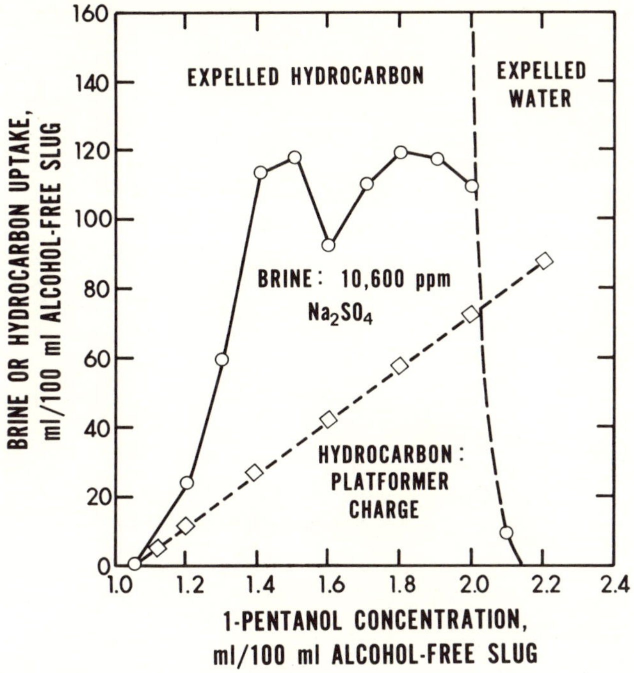

Figure 11. Brine and hydrocarbon solubility in a microemulsion composed of 11.9 vol. % petroleum sulfonate, 35 vol. % water, and 53.1 vol. % hydrocarbon versus added cosurfactant, 1-pentanol.[35]

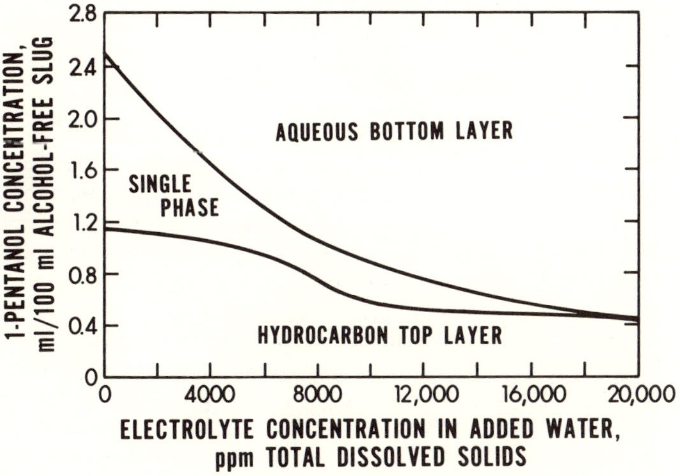

Figure 12. Cosurfactant versus electrolyte concentration for a microemulsion composed of 10 vol. % petroleum sulfonate, 50 vol. % water, and 40 vol. % hydrocarbon.[35]

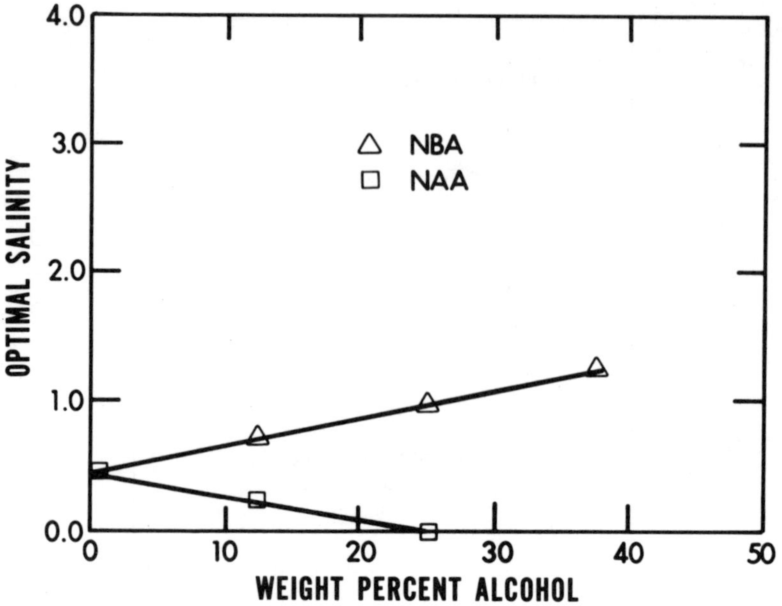

Figure 13. Optimal salinity versus cosurfactant, n-butyl alcohol and n-amyl alcohol.[39]

ship between optimal salinity and alcohol content. The more water soluble alcohol (n-butanol) gives an increase and the more oil soluble alcohol (n-amyl alcohol) gives a decrease in optimal salinity.

FLUID FLOW

Fluid flow in a microemulsion flood, to a good approximation, is comprised of a series of shock fronts. The saturation and fractional flow of any fluid, e.g., oil, changes discontinuously at each front. Saturation and fractional flow between two shock fronts is essentially constant. These regions of constant saturation and fractional flow are called "banks."

The first bank in a tertiary displacement is water flowing in the presence of residual oil. If residual oil saturation has been reached during waterflooding operations, the flowing fluid is entirely water. If the oil saturation is slightly above residual, then the water flow is accompanied by a small fractional flow of oil.

The chemicals contained in an injected microemulsion mobilize and displace part or all of the residual oil. The mobilized oil accumulates and forms a region of increased oil saturation, the "stabilized oil bank." Material balance considerations dictate a definite relationship between the saturation and fractional flow of oil in the stabilized oil bank. If the microemulsion displaces all fluids it contacts, then the fractional flow of oil is numerically equal to oil saturation. The diagonal line in Figure 14 illustrates this relationship. In certain situations, the microemulsion displaces oil incompletely, leaving residual oil in the smaller pores. Here, the fractional flow of oil is always less than oil saturation, as shown by the lower line in Figure 14. Some microemulsions have such a great affinity for oil (they are undersaturated with oil) that they are incapable of displacing water completely. The remaining water saturation, S_{wrc}, causes the fractional flow of oil in the oil bank to be higher than its saturation (upper line in Figure 14).

Thus, the fractional flow of oil can be higher than, equal to, or lower than oil saturation, depending on whether the microemulsion has left residual water, nothing, or residual oil, respectively. However, another relationship is required to fix the particular values of f_{ob} and S_{ob} in an oil bank.

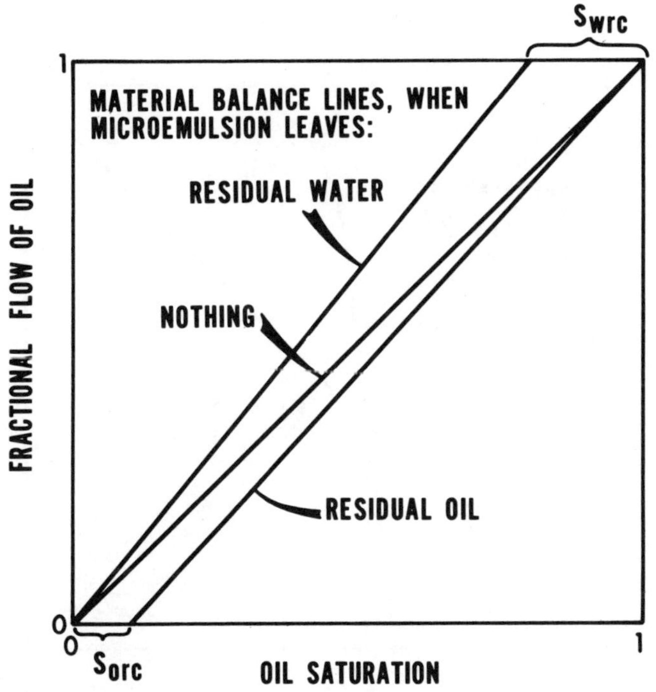

Figure 14. Saturation — fractional flow relationships in stabilized oil bank.

This relationship is a fractional flow curve, which can be calculated from drainage oil/water relative permeability data. The shape of the fractional-flow-versus-saturation curve is determined by the relative mobilities of oil and water during an oil flooding experiment. The saturation and fractional flow in the oil bank must satisfy both the material balance and fractional flow curve relationships. These are satisfied at the point of intersection of the two curves, as illustrated in Figure 15. The material balance line illustrated corresponds to the complete displacement case. If one of the other two material balance lines shown in Figure 14 intersected the fractional flow curve, then the fractional flow would be higher or lower. Because of the steepness of the fractional flow curve, however, saturation would be changed relatively little.

It is possible for all three material balance lines to apply during a single displacement. For example, if a microemulsion is injected that is undersaturated with respect to oil, or that produces an ultra-low interfacial tension with oil, but higher interfacial tension with brine, it could displace all the oil, but leave residual brine. This situation has been observed in laboratory core floods.[3] The upper line of Figure 14 would apply. Later, during injection of aqueous polymer solution, the residual brine would be displaced because the polymer solution is miscible with brine, and

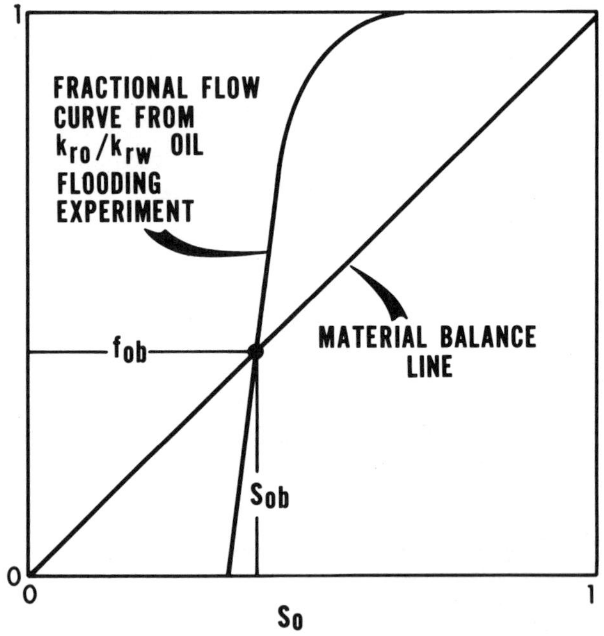

Figure 15. Specific fractional flow and saturation values in oil bank.

the middle material balance line would apply. Still later in the displacement, after deterioration due to dispersion and surfactant loss, the microemulsion would be incapable of mobilizing and displacing all the oil. The saturation remaining, S_{orc}, is generally less than the oil saturation remaining after a waterflood. The applicable material balance would indicate a considerably reduced fractional flow of oil. As the microemulsion slug deteriorates further, S_{orc} gradually becomes higher, approaching the waterflood residual saturation. As that happens, the fractional flow of oil approaches zero. The graphical representation of a gradually deteriorating slug would be a family of material balance lines fanning downward until S_{orc} reaches the foot of the fractional flow curve.

CONTINUOUS MICROEMULSION INJECTION

Analysis of fractional flow behavior in laboratory core floods can provide useful information on the ability of the surfactant-containing fluid to displace oil in a simulated reservoir environment. To illustrate, Figure 16 shows cumulative oil recovery versus pore volume injected for a single displacement. This recovery curve will be compared to three other displacements (Figures 17-19). Microemulsion is injected continuously in each of these

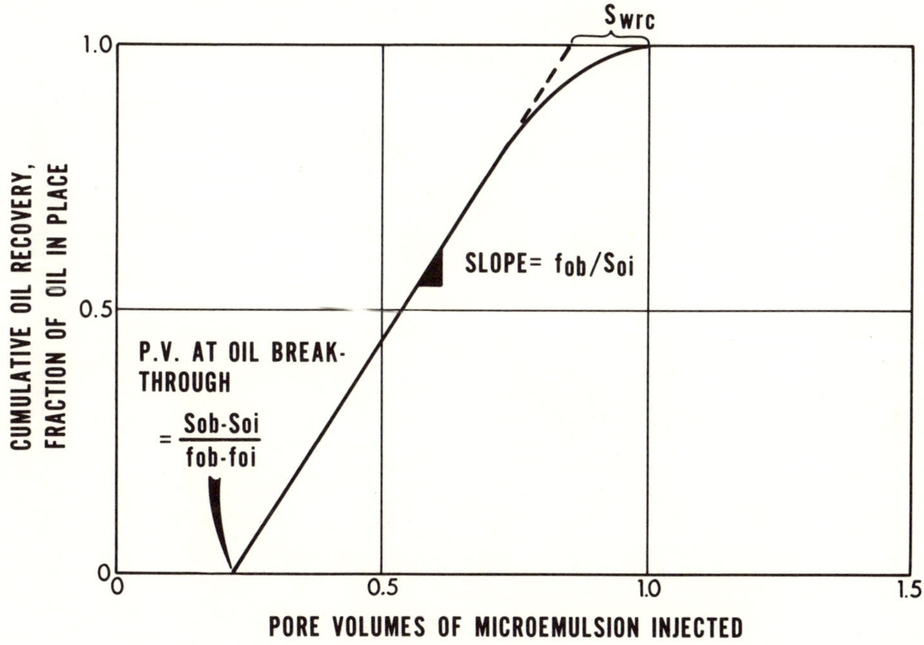

Figure 16. Schematic of oil recovery versus pore volume of microemulsion injected when microemulsion leaves residual water (S_{wrc}).

displacements. The number of pore volumes injected at oil bank breakthrough is given by the ratio of the difference between oil bank saturation and initial oil saturation to the difference between oil bank and initial oil fractional flow. The slope of the early portion of each curve after oil bank breakthrough is equal to the ratio of fractional flow of oil in the oil bank to the initial oil saturation. An extrapolation of the straight line portion of the curve shows that complete oil recovery would occur before one pore volume throughput, indicating that the microemulsion displaces all the oil it contacts, but leaves residual water. A curve from another core flood is shown in Figure 17. Here, the extrapolated oil recovery is complete at one pore volume throughput; the microemulsion displaces all fluids ahead of it.

Figures 18 and 19 illustrate displacements in which microemulsion leaves residual oil. Interpretation of these curves is aided by the dashed line that extends from complete recovery at one pore volume, to a value corresponding to $1 - S_{oi}$. A straight line extrapolation of the early portion of a recovery curve in which residual oil is left (Figure 19) will intersect the dashed line at the point of theoretical microemulsion breakthrough if dispersion is absent. If no further oil is mobilized behind the microemulsion front, recovery will not increase to a value greater than that at the intersection point. The maximum recovery is given by $1 - S_{orc}/S_{oi}$.

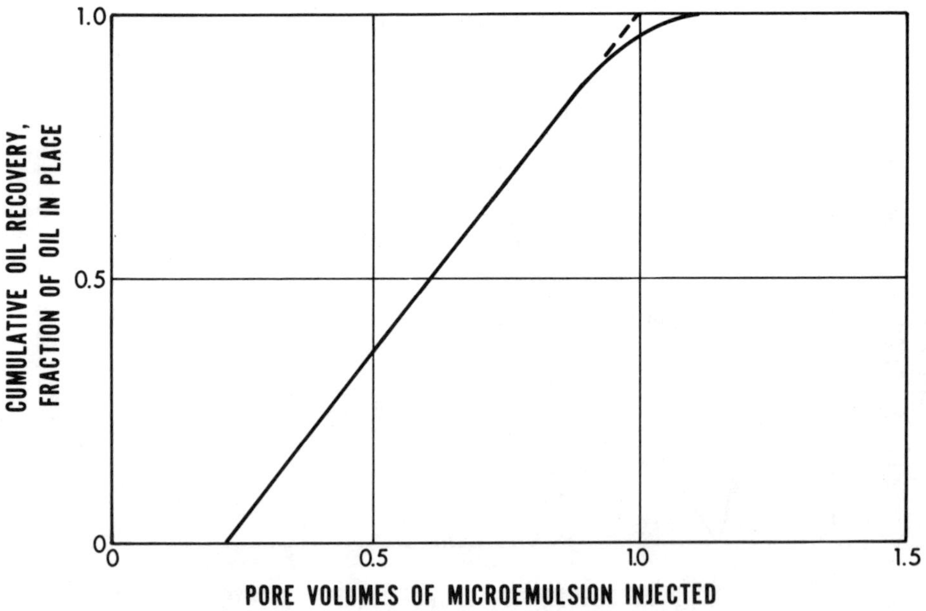

Figure 17. Schematic of oil recovery versus pore volume of microemulsion injected when microemulsion displaces both oil and water completely.

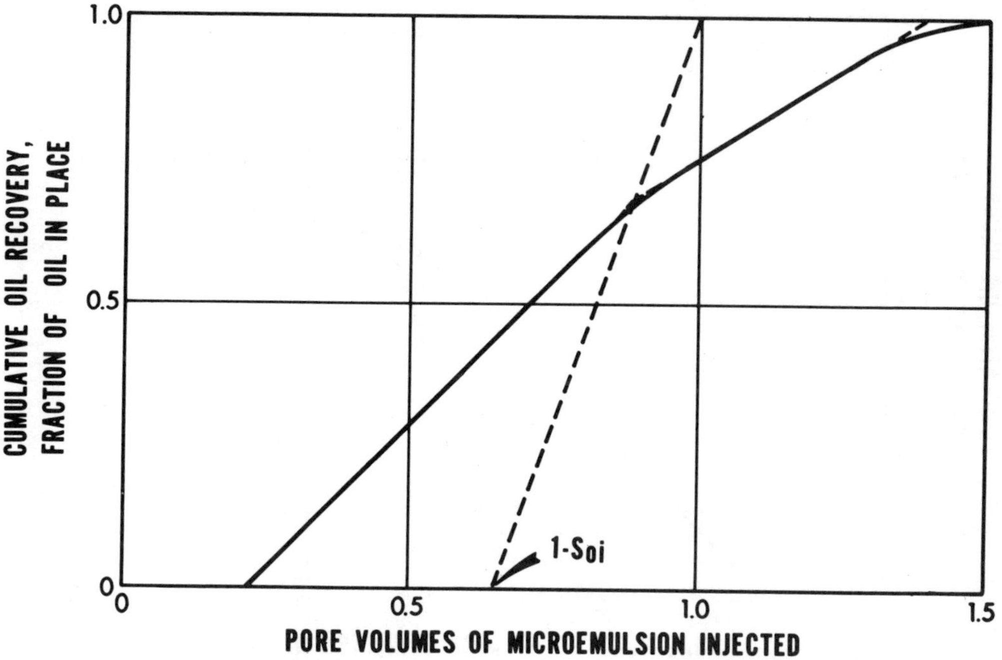

Figure 18. Schematic of oil recovery versus pore volume of microemulsion injected when microemulsion displaces oil inefficiently at the leading edge.

The curve in Figure 18 shows slightly more complicated behavior. Again, this curve (straight line extrapolation) intersects the dashed line at theoretical microemulsion breakthrough. However, recovery continues to increase after the point of intersection. That results from continued oil mobilization some distance behind the leading edge of the microemulsion.

Even though Figure 16 represents a highly efficient displacement in the sense that all the oil is recovered with the least throughput of any of the four curves, the microemulsion composition may not be the one of choice. It is so oleophilic that it has high interfacial tension with resident water and cannot mobilize all of it. Although residual water saturation is not detrimental per se, it does indicate that trouble may lie ahead. When microemulsion and resident water have little affinity for each other due to surfactant and cosurfactant type, the microemulsion and polymer-containing drive fluid are likely to be similarly incompatible. This could lead to a high surfactant loss through retention in a residual microemulsion phase, incapable of being mobilized by the drive fluid. Surfactant loss can be minimized by keeping the polymer solution salt-free as practicable.[40]

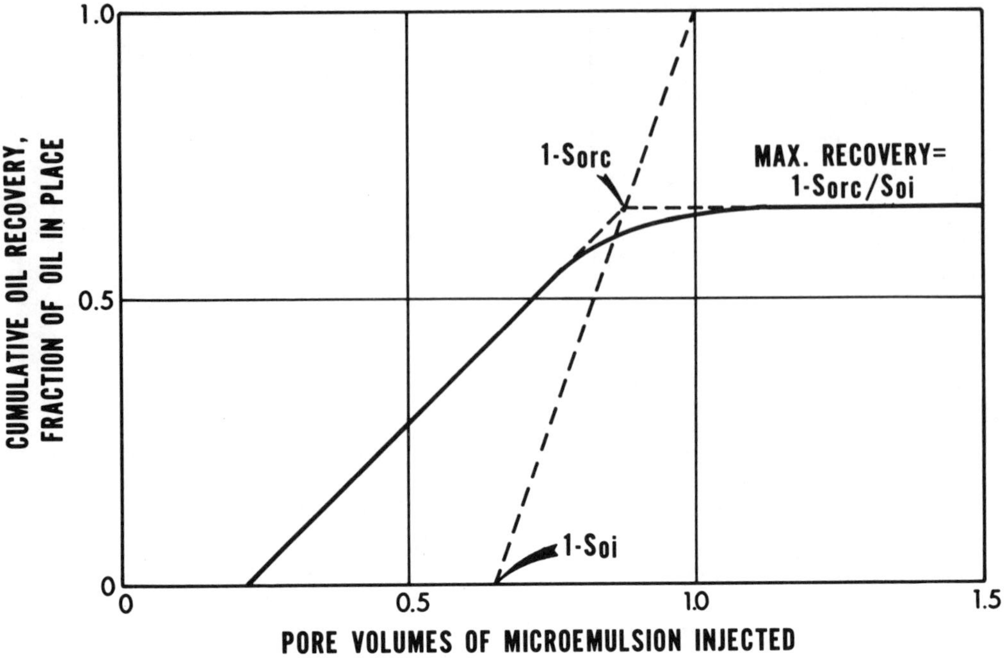

Figure 19. Schematic of oil recovery versus pore volume of microemulsion injected when microemulsion leaves residual oil (S_{orc}).

Because microemulsion compositions that leave residual oil lead to reduced oil recovery regardless of slug size, and because compositions that leave residual water are likely to require excessive slug sizes to compensate for large surfactant losses, the most efficient composition should be the one that leaves neither residual oil nor water. This represents a balanced composition that is capable of displacing all oil it contacts, and yet, one which can be displaced efficiently by an appropriate polymer solution.

When reservoir oil, water, and rock are used at reservoir temperature for the tests illustrated by Figures 16-19, the analysis presented should accurately select the optimum microemulsion composition. Phase behavior tests performed in glassware, which are very important in the initial design stages, simply cannot account for many of the interactions that affect the displacement tests.

Although Figures 16-19 show recovery histories for continuous injection of microemulsion, the injection of large, finite slugs of microemulsion, amounting to 20% of the pore volume or larger, will produce similar injection histories. A straight line extrapolation of the *initial portion* of such a curve to 100% recovery can be interpreted in the same manner as the extrapolation of a curve from a continuous-injection experiment.

The previous discussion has alluded to differences in oil recovery efficiency that are affected by surfactant losses. Because surfactant losses can be influenced by ion exchange, microemulsion composition, and microemulsion/mobility buffer (polymer solution) interaction, another type of evaluation is needed to ensure selection of the most efficient microemulsion and mobility buffer compositions. This evaluation procedure, which will be discussed later, employs a series of small-slug-size displacements. First, however, a discussion of surfactant loss mechanisms is appropriate.

SURFACTANT LOSSES

Once several effective chemical systems have been found through phase studies and continuous injection tests, the ultimate choice of a micellar/polymer system will depend on cost-effectiveness. One way to maximize cost-effectiveness is to minimize surfactant losses. At least four mechanisms contribute to these losses: 1) adsorption; 2) surfactant precipitation; 3) an immobile surfactant-rich phase; and 4) surfactant dissipation.

Adsorption. Adsorption of petroleum sulfonates has been the subject of numerous reports,[15 41 42 43 44 45] while other work has been devoted to the examination of relatively well defined alkyl aryl sulfonates.[46 47] These static adsorption experiments reflect potential loss of surfactant due to physical or chemical attachment to reservoir rock and clay. From these adsorption studies, it has been found that 1) maximum adsorption occurs near the critical micelle concentration, 2) maxima in adsorption isotherms occur with mixtures of petroleum sulfonates, 3) higher equivalent weight sulfonates are more readily adsorbed, 4) electrolyte influences adsorption (a single surfactant formulation may show increased or decreased adsorption with electrolyte present), and 5) cosurfactants tend to decrease sulfonate adsorption.

Physical adsorption may not represent a major portion of total surfactant loss in an oil displacement experiment unless the clay content of the core material is high. Surfactant losses significantly lower than expected adsorption values have been observed in core flooding experiments.[48] Also, petroleum sulfonate losses in core flooding experiments have been reported to be flow rate dependent.[49]

Precipitation. Results of adsorption studies have often been obscured by surfactant precipitation. The immobile precipitate is effectively removed from the flooding system. Reduced solubility of calcium and magnesium sulfonates is of primary importance.[50] Thus, precipitation and phase separation are strongly influenced by dynamics of surfactant/rock ion exchange.

Immobile Surfactant Phase. Provided that clay content and polyvalent cation concentration are not inordinately high, the largest surfactant retention loss is due to the inability of an aqueous polymer solution to mobilize a surfactant-rich phase.[40] Thus, surfactant is deposited throughout the reservoir.

Any change that causes a microemulsion to become more hydrophobic will increase surfactant retention. This is strictly a solvent effect. Because the surfactant must be displaced by an aqueous solution, any change that increases the interfacial tension between water and the surfactant-containing fluid must increase surfactant retention by virtue of reducing the ability of water to mobilize the surfactant-rich fluid. "Adsorbed" or retained surfactant can be flushed from the reservoir rock readily by a suitable semipolar or nonpolar solvent.

If, for some reason, we chose to drive the surfactant-rich fluid with an oleic solution instead of an aqueous solution, (this is obviously not feasible economically), then it follows that the retention relationship would be reversed. That is, any change that caused the surfactant system to become more hydrophobic would result in decreased retention.

Returning now to the aqueous drive system, factors that promote retention are high surfactant equivalent weight, low solubility of cosurfactant in water, high electrolyte concentration (particularly di- or tri-valent cation concentration), and low temperature. The injected surfactant/cosurfactant composition may be altered to reduce retention at the risk of reducing oil-displacing capability. Electrolyte concentration and composition can be modified to a limited extent (in view of ion exchange) by employing a controlled-salinity preslug and by reducing drive fluid salinity. Temperature is fixed by the reservoir. Thus, it would appear that surfactant and cosurfactant selection are the primary controllable variables, and to a limited extent, salinity.

Retention may be affected by partioning. Because the drive fluid is aqueous, surfactant displacement depends on its partitioning into the drive fluid. If surfactant preferentially partitions into an oleic phase which cannot be displaced by the aqueous drive fluid, or onto the reservoir rock, it is lost from the system. Thus, surfactant losses can be minimized by enhancing partitioning into the aqueous phase and by minimizing surfactant fluid/drive fluid interfacial tension.

Surfactant loss minimization at the trailing edge of a microemulsion slug is achieved at the expense of reducing oil-displacing ability at the leading edge. Factors that increase aqueous partitioning and reduce microemulsion/water interfacial tension correspondingly increase interfacial tension with reservoir crude oil and decrease surfactant partitioning into this oil. The optimum system must be a delicate balance of these factors.

Surfactant Dissipation. Surfactant effectiveness is also reduced by dissipation, which includes dispersion, dilution, and viscous fingering. Dispersion and dilution are out of the designer's control. However, a major cause of apparent dispersion is viscous fingering. Viscous fingering occurs when the mobility of the driving fluid is greater than the mobility of the driven fluid. Equivalently stated, viscous fingering occurs when the "effective viscosity" (reciprocal relative mobility) of the drive fluid is less than the effective viscosity of the driven fluid. It can occur at both ends of a microemulsion slug. Microemulsion that has a lower viscosity than the effective viscosity of the oil bank forms viscous fingers in the oil bank and displaces oil only within the confines of these fingers; part of the oil is not even contacted by surfactant. The situation is further aggravated when polymer solution reaches these unswept areas. Because the polymer has low relative permeability in oil-containing zones, it virtually will not penetrate them. However, polymer solution follows easily in the path swept by the surfactant-containing fluid.

Except for very high polymer concentrations, polymer solution usually fingers into the back end of a microemulsion slug. Polymer/microemulsion mixtures often form a high mobility, low viscosity, milky macroemulsion. This high mobility mixing zone penetrates the entire microemulsion slug at roughly twice the velocity expected for piston-like displacement. Visual studies suggest that it moves stably after it reaches the oil bank at the leading edge of the microemulsion slug. Surfactant concentration in the oil bank, which decreases with increasing distance from the microemulsion/oil bank interface, eventually becomes too low to increase significantly the relative permeability of polymer solution in the oil bank. This low relative permeability inhibits polymer solution penetration into the oil bank, thereby stabilizing the viscous fingering tendencies.

Portions of the high mobility polymer solution/microemulsion mixing zone can be bypassed, however, if polymer concentration is decreased too rapidly or if the volume of polymer solution injected is too small.

FINITE MICROEMULSION INJECTION

Because microemulsion components are expensive, it is desirable to maximize oil recovery per unit of chemicals injected. After initial screening is accomplished through phase behavior studies, viscosity measurements, interfacial tension determinations, and continuous microemulsion injection displacements, the following test is needed for selecting the best microemulsion composition from the final candidates. This final testing sequence enables one to select a system that requires minimum surfactant injection. It is recommended because of the additional complications imposed by surfactant/polymer interactions.

Each of the final microemulsion candidates is injected in a series of displacements utilizing reservoir fluids and reservoir rock. Microemulsion slug size is variable, starting with very small sizes and proceeding to larger sizes. The oil recovery obtained from each displacement is plotted versus slug size. Figure 20 illustrates four representative cases. The uppermost curve represents a very efficient system that is capable of displacing all the oil. It is characterized by a straight line throughout all but the highest slug size range (approaching 100 percent recovery). The fact that 100 percent oil recovery is achievable indicates that the microemulsion has adequate affinity for oil. The predominant linearity of the curve suggests that oil recovery is controlled by surfactant retention. That is, a small slug size injection recovers oil efficiently until all the surfactant is immobilized. Injecting larger slug sizes results in proportionately more oil recovery because the surfactant can traverse a correspondingly larger portion of the core before it is consumed.

The next highest curve (Figure 20) also represents an effective oil-displacement agent. However, it suffers from higher surfactant retention, and requires a correspondingly larger slug size to achieve a given oil recovery. The third curve is characteristic of a microemulsion that is capable of displacing all the oil, but suffers from either inadequate mobility control or reservoir rocks having high permeability heterogeneity. Its performance can be improved by increasing the microemulsion slug viscosity and polymer concentration or by increasing the size of the mobility buffer.

The final case illustrated in Figure 20 is one in which the microemulsion/polymer system has inadequate oil-displacing capability, regardless of slug size. This system must be altered to yield a lower oil/microemulsion interfacial tension.

The curves in Figure 20 all pass through the origin; i.e.,

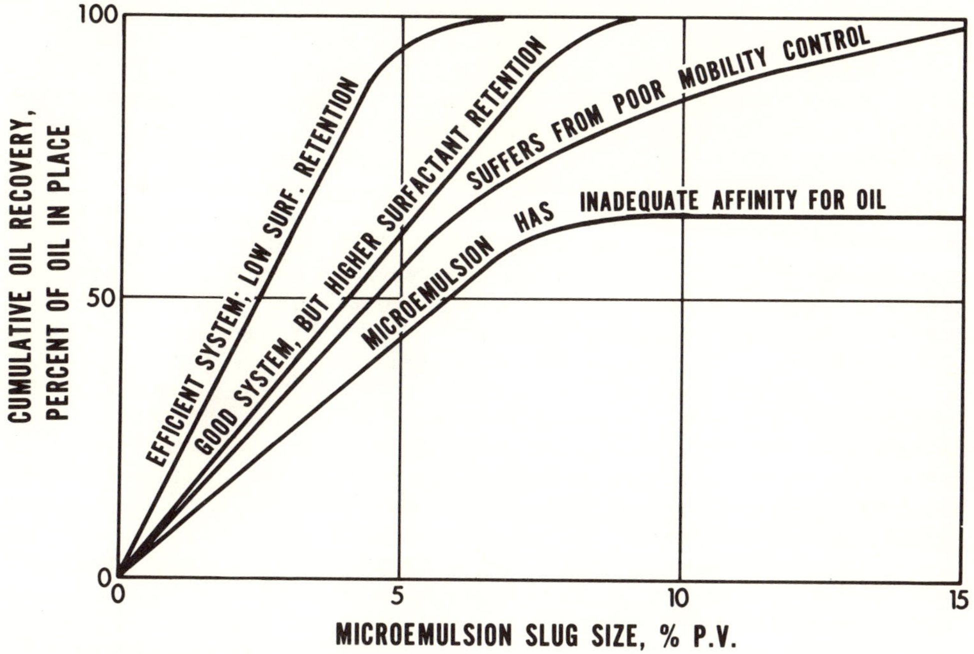

Figure 20. Schematic of oil recovery versus finite microemulsion slug size.

recovery is zero at zero microemulsion slug size. Generally, this is the case *only* when the waterflood is conducted at a much higher rate than the tertiary displacement. Otherwise, small amounts of oil can be recovered from a tertiary polymer flood without any surfactant present.

SALINITY GRADIENT

Experimental evidence suggests that one of the essential keys to successful oil recovery by a micellar/polymer system may be the establishment of a salinity gradient. This provides a driving force for oil recovery and reduces the demands for a perfect oleophilic/hydrophilic balance. The highest salt concentration must reside in the oil bank, near the leading edge of the microemulsion slug. As mentioned previously, microemulsion/oil interfacial tension is reduced with increasing salinity.[30] High salinity also limits the water-holding ability of a microemulsion If a microemulsion containing a high concentration of relatively fresh water encounters water of higher salinity, water is expelled from the surfactant-rich phase. This action suppresses surfactant dilution by water, and can actually increase surfactant concentration.

The polymer solution, which encounters the trailing edge of the microemulsion, must contain a low concentration of salt to minimize the polymer solution/microemulsion interfacial tension. This is necessary to avoid phase trapping of the microemulsion.[40]

This type of salinity gradient can be created by injecting a microemulsion with a lower electrolyte concentration in its aqueous phase than the electrolyte concentration in the reservoir water. The microemulsion is then displaced by polymer solution of even lower electrolyte concentration.

The sequence of phases that appear in produced fluids from a core flood reflect the effects of the salinity gradient.[51] Results of such a core flood are shown in Figure 21. As noted on the diagram, 10% pore volume of chemical slug was displaced by polymer solution. After production of the oil bank, two phases appeared; upper phase microemulsion and brine (Type II(+) by these authors' designation). Following two phase production, three phases appeared; oil, middle phase microemulsion, and brine (Type III). Finally, two phases were produced; lower phase microemulsion and oil

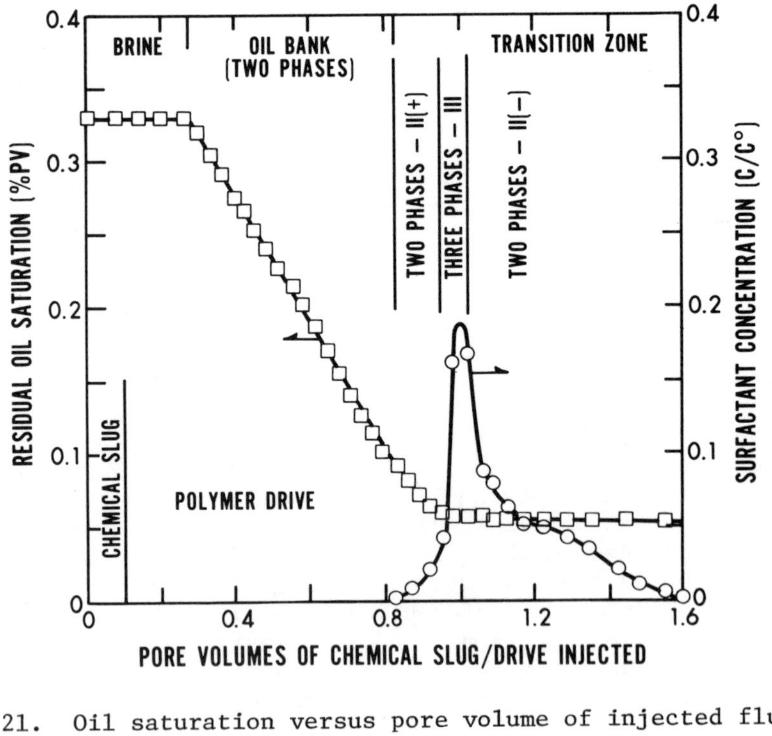

Figure 21. Oil saturation versus pore volume of injected fluids.[51]

(Type II (-)). These results are consistent with moving from right to left on the phase diagram shown in Figure 5.

Passing through such a salinity gradient in a microemulsion flood is advantageous in maintaining movement of the surfactant-rich phase. As a consequence of the forces that tend to dehydrate or to de-oil the microemulsion, it probably makes little difference in which form the surfactant and cosurfactant are injected, provided that adequate mobility control is maintained. That is, for a given surfactant/cosurfactant composition, the initial injected water concentration or oil concentration in a microemulsion probably has little bearing on the *in-situ* oil and water concentration as dictated by the displacement dynamics. A system containing a high initial water concentration will be dehydrated and will pick up oil. Conversely, a low water concentration system that has the same surfactant and cosurfactant composition will lose oil and will pick up water in the presence of the same salinity gradient; the two widely difference systems will end up having similar compositions after a certain distance of travel through the rock.

SUMMARY AND CONCLUSIONS

This paper reviews how the capacity of a microemulsion to solubilize water or oil is affected by its components, particularly electrolyte and cosurfactant. High electrolyte concentration and water-insoluble cosurfactants promote oil solubilization and inhibit water takeup into the surfactant-rich phase. Conversely, low electrolyte concentration and/or water-soluble alcohols favor water solubilization and limit oil solubilization.

Efficient tertiary oil recovery can be achieved only when the oil versus water affinity of a microemulsion is carefully balanced. Cation exchange with reservoir rock and clays can severely tip the balance. Too little oil solubility results in a high residual oil saturation after chemical flooding; too little water solubility causes high surfactant retention, and large slug sizes are required for high oil recovery. Because of the impact that reservoir solids can have, we recommend a series of carefully designed core floods to improve oil recovery performance rather than extensive phase behavior studies and interfacial tension measurements made in the absence of reservoir solids. In this paper, production performance (fractional flow behavior and the completion of oil production) of continuous microemulsion core floods is related to the oil/water affinity of the microemulsions so that systematic adjustments in microemulsion composition for improved performance can be made.

Mechanisms of surfactant losses are reviewed. These include losses in effectiveness due to adsorption, precipitation, deposition of an immobile surfactant-rich phase, and surfactant dissipation, caused by dispersion, dilution, and viscous fingering. Core flood experiments in reservoir rock with small microemulsion slug sizes and intermediate slug sizes when properly interpreted show which microemulsion/polymer systems are most efficient.

Because the role of a microemulsion shifts from an oil-displacing agent at its front edge to a water-displaceable agent at its trailing edge, and because electrolyte concentration plays an important role in controlling this function, the importance of a salinity gradient with high salinity near the leading edge of the microemulsion and low salinity near its trailing edge is discussed.

ACKNOWLEDGEMENTS

Figures 1,2,6,7,8,9,10,11,12,13, and 21 have been reproduced with the permission of the Society of Petroleum Engineers of the American Institute of Mining, Metallurgical, and Mechanical Engineers.

REFERENCES

1. C. L. Stegemeier, in "Improved Oil Recovery by Surfactant and Polymer Flooding," D. O. Shah and R. S. Schechter, Editors, Academic Press, New York, 1977.
2. J. C. Melrose and C. F. Brandner, J. Can. Pet. Tech. 13, 54 (1974).
3. J. A. Davis, and S. C. Jones, Trans AIME 243, 1415 (1968).
4. M. De Groot, "Flooding Process for Recovering Oil from Oil-Bearing Strata," U.S. Patent No. 1,823,439 (1929).
5. M. De Groot, "Flooding Process for Recovering Fixed Oil from Subterranean Oil-Bearing Strata," U.S. Patent No. 1,823,440 (1930).
6. O. C. Holbrook "Surfactant-Water Secondary Recovery Process," U.S. Patent No. 3,006,411 (1958).
7. W. B. Gogarty, and R. W. Olson, "Use of Microemulsions in Miscible Type Oil Recovery Procedure," U.S. Patent No. 3,254,714 (1962).
8. W. B. Gogarty, and W. C. Tosch, Trans. AIME 243, 1407 (1968)
9. R. L. Reed, R. N. Healy, D. G. Stenmark, and W. W. Gale, "Recovery of Oil Using Microemulsions," U.S. Patent No. 3,885,628 (1975).
10. L. W. Holm, and G. G. Bernard, "Secondary Recovery Water-Flood Process," U.S. Patent No. 3,082,822 (1959).
11. R. C. Earlougher, Jr., J. E. O'Neal, and H. Surkalo, SPE Paper No. 5337 presented at the SPE-AIME Rocky Mountain Regional Meeting, Denver, April 1975.
12. W. B. Gogarty, and H. Surkalo, J. Pet. Tech., 24, 1161 (Sept. 1972).

13. R. K. Knight, and J. P. Baer, J. Pet. Tech., 25, 9 (Jan. 1973).
14. H. H. Danielson, W. T. Paynter, and H. W. Milton, J. Pet. Tech., 28, 129 (1976).
15. H. J. Hill, J. Reisberg, and G. L. Stegemeier, J. Pet. Tech., 25, 186 (Feb. 1973).
16. S. A. Pursley, R. N. Healey, and E. I. Sandvik, J. Pet. Tech., 25, 793 (July 1973).
17. J. C. Howell, R. W. McAtee, W. O. Snyder, and K. L. Tonso, SPE Paper No. 7089 presented at the SPE-AIME Improved Oil Symposium, Tulsa, April 1978.
18. R. L. Reed, and R. N. Healy, in "Improved Oil Recovery by Surfactant and Polymer Flooding," D. O. Shah and R. S. Schechter, Editors, Academic Press, New York, 1977.
19. D. O. Shah, V. K. Bansal, K. Chan, and W. C. Hsieh, in "Improved Oil Recovery by Surfactant and Polymer Flooding," D. O. Shah and R. S. Schechter, Editors, Academic Press, New York, 1977.
20. P. A. Winsor, Trans. Faraday Soc. 46, 762 (1950).
21. J. E. Bowcott, and J. H. Schulman, Zeit. f. Elektro Chemie 59 (4), 283 (1955).
22. D. O. Shah, R. D. Walker, Jr., W. C. Hsieh, N. J. Shah, S. Dwivedi, J. Helander, R. Pepinsky, and D. W. Deamer, SPE Paper No. 5815 presented at the SPE-AIME Improved Oil Recovery Symposium, Tulsa, March 1976.
23. L. E. Scriven, Nature, 263, 123 (1976).
24. W. H. Wade, J. C. Morgan, J. K. Jacobson, and R. S. Schechter, Soc. Pet. Eng. J., 17, 122 (1977).
25. E. I. Sandvik, W. W. Gale, and M. O. Denekas, Soc. Pet. Eng. J., 17, 184 (1977).
26. M. C. Puerto and W. W. Gale, Soc. Pet. Eng. J., 17, 192 (1977).
27. R. N. Healy, and R. L. Reed, Soc. Pet. Eng. J., 14, 491 (1974).
28. R. N. Healy, R. L. Reed, and C. W. Carpenter, Soc. Pet. Eng. J., 15, 87 (1975).
29. J. J. Tabor, Soc. Pet. Eng. J., 9, 3 (1969).
30. R. N. Healy, and R. L. Reed, Soc. Pet. Eng. J., 17, 129 (1977).
31. S. J. Salter, SPE preprint No. 7056, presented at the SPE-AIME Fifth Oil Recovery Symposium, Tulsa, April 1978.
32. J. E. Vinatieri, and P. D. Fleming, SPE preprint No. 7057, presented at the SPE-AIME Fifth Oil Recovery Symposium, Tulsa, April 1978.
33. R. N. Healy, R. L. Reed, and D. G. Stenmark, Soc. Pet. Eng. J., 16, 147 (1976).
34. J. L. Salager, E. Vasquez, J. C. Morgan, R. S. Schechter, and W. H. Wade, SPE preprint No. 7054 presented at the Fifth Oil Recovery Symposium, Tulsa, April 1978.
35. S. C. Jones, and K. D. Dreher, Soc. Pet. Eng. J., 16, 161 (1976).
36. W. C. Hsieh, and D. O. Shah, SPE preprint No. 6594 presented at the Symposium on Oilfield and Geothermal Chemistry, La Jolla, June 1977.

37. K. D. Dreher, and R. D. Sydansk, J. Pet. Tech., 23, 1437 (1971).
38. P. B. Lorenz, and A. F. Bayazeed, SPE preprint No. 4751 presented at the Third Improved Oil Recovery Symposium, Tulsa, (1974).
39. S. J. Salter, SPE preprint No. 6843 presented at the 52nd. Annual Fall Meeting, Denver, October 1977.
40. S. P. Trushenski, in "Improved Oil Recovery by Surfactant and Polymer Flooding," D. O. Shah and R. S. Schechter, Editors, Academic Press, Inc., New York, (1977).
41. W. W. Gale, and E. I. Sandvik, Soc. Pet. Eng. J., 13, 191-199 (1973).
42. J. B. Lawson, and R. E. Dilgren, SPE preprint No. 6121 presented at the 51st. SPE-AIME Annual Fall Meeting, New Orleans, October 1976.
43. B. G. Hurd, SPE preprint No. 5818, presented at the SPE-AIME Improved Oil Recovery Symposium, Tulsa, March 1976.
44. J. B. Lawson, SPE preprint No. 7052, presented at the SPE-AIME Improved Oil Recovery Symposium, Tulsa, April 1978.
45. P. Somasundaran, and H. S. Hanna, SPE preprint No. 7059, presented at the SPE-AIME Fifth Improved Oil Recovery Symposium, Tulsa, April 1978.
46. M. Fernandez, F. J. Trogus, M. El. Emery, R. S. Schechter, and W. H. Wade, SPE Preprint No. 7058 presented at the SPE-AIME Fifth Improved Oil Recovery Symposium, Tulsa, April 1978.
47. P. Somasundaran, and H. S. Hanna, in "Improved Oil Recovery by Surfactant and Polymer Flooding," D. O. Shah and R. S. Schechter, Editors, Academic Press, New York, 1977.
48. E. M. Malberg, and L. Smith, in "Improved Oil Recovery by Surfactant and Polymer Flooding," D. O. Shah and R. S. Schechter, Editors, Academic Press, Inc., New York, 1977.
49. J. H. Bae, and C. B. Petrick, So. Pet. Eng. J., 17(5), 353 (1977).
50. H. S. Hanna, and P. Somasundaran, in "Improved Oil Recovery by Surfactant Flooding," D. O. Shah and R. S. Schechter, Editors, Academic Press, Inc., New York, 1977.
51. R. C. Nelson, and G. A. Pope, SPE preprint No. 6733, presented at the SPE-AIME 52nd. Annual Fall Meeting, Denver, October, 1977.

INVERTED MICELLAR SYSTEMS AND THEIR RELATIONS TO MICROEMULSIONS

I. Danielsson, M. R. Hakala and M. Jorpes-Friman

Department of Physical Chemistry, Åbo Akademi,

Porthansgatan 3-5, 20500 Åbo (Turku) 50, Finland

The relations between inverted micellar systems and microemulsions water in oil are briefly discussed. Typical of these are so called L_2-phases with inverted micelles of surfactants containing internal polar regions of water and polar groups.

As a model for these systems the extension of the L_2-region in the quaternary phase diagram of the system water-sodium octanoate-decanol-octane at 25°C is investigated.

The L_2-phase in the tetrahedroid phase diagram is characterized by two different regions. At low ratios of soap-water and a relatively high content of water the system solubilizes appreciable amounts of n-octane, but only above certain well-defined concentrations of the mixed solute soap-water in the decanol solution. At high ratios of soap-water octane is almost mutually soluble in the system. According to calorimetric and volumetric measurements the first region is characterized by inverted micelles with an internal region resembling a concentrated soap solution.

In the second region of the L_2-solutions all the water present is bound as hydrate water, but there is no longer any aquatic internal environment detectable in the aggregates.

The conclusion drawn is that these properties of the model systems characterize microemulsions in general.

INTRODUCTION

Many years ago Schulman introduced the concept 'microemulsion', which he defined as the clear or nearly clear mixtures formed in ternary or quaternary systems containing water, surfactant and oil.[1,2] He extrapolated the linearity between interfacial tension and composition found in such systems to negative values to which he ascribed the formation of microemulsions. It is, however, quite clear that interfacial tension never actually attains negative values. On the other hand, as P. Rehbinder and E. D. Shchukin have shown for binary mixtures of certain organic compounds, near the critical solution temperature there is a region, where the interfacial tension attains very low values and the thermal motion may be able to keep an emulsion stable almost infinitely.[3]

Nowadays the concept microemulsion is used only for definitely thermodynamically homogeneous stable water-oil systems containing surfactants as an active component. These systems are often used in technology, for example, in the extraction of metals. New applications are coming, for instance in tertiary oil recovery. In spite of this the structure of microemulsions has not yet been clarified. There are many indications that microemulsions should be regarded as inverted micellar systems, i.e. analogous to the conventional micelles of surfactants in aqueous solutions.[4] The inverted micelles may be built up from a polar internal part surrounded by an apolar 'shell' and dispersed in the hydrophobic medium, the oil.[5,6] On the other hand, Kertes, for example, has pointed out that the oil phases poor in water used in metal extraction may not contain any higher aggregates at all.[7,8] In order to chart the structure of microemulsions w/o we studied a model system water-sodium octanoate-n-decanol-n-octane at 25°C.

EXPERIMENTAL

Chemicals. Sodium octanoate (NaC_8) was prepared by neutralization of octanoic acid (Fluka Ag, purissimum grade (min. 99%)) with sodium hydroxide (Merck p.a.). The molecular weight of the dried crystalline soap was determined by titration with perchloric acid in glacial acetic acid using crystal violet as an indicator. The molecular weight of the soap differed less than 0.5% from the theoretical value. The water used was passed through anion and cation-exchanging resins and then distilled. The conductivity was less than 10^{-6} ohm^{-1} cm^{-1}. The n-decanol and the n-octane were of the quality Fluka purissimum.

Methods. The phase equilibria in the system water-sodium octanoate-n-decanol-n-octane were studied in preparates heated to about 70°C, vigorously mixed for several hours and finally stored in a thermostat at 25° for at least 24 hours. The occurrence of heterogeneity was checked both by eye and by microscope with different illuminations and between crossed Nicol prisms. The calorimetric measurements were made with the LKB precision calorimetry system 8700 and with the LKB microcalorimetry system 10700. All these measurements were made at 25 °C. The dilatometric measurements were made at 25 ±0.001 °C with an apparatus analogous to that described by Geffcken.[9]

RESULTS AND DISCUSSION

The quaternary system water-sodium octanoate-n-decanol-n-octane may be considered a suitable model as we can start from the well-known phase equilibria in the ternary system water-sodium octanoate-n-decanol described in Figure 1.[10] In spite of the poor solubility of water in decanol and the insolubility of octanoate in decanol the mixed solute soap-water forms by cooperation a homogeneous microemulsion-phase (L_2).

At maximum water content the L_2 solutions are in equilibrium with aqueous octanoate solutions (L_1), but after a break in the left-hand boundary of the L_2 area the equilibrium phase L_1 is exchanged for the lamellar mesophase D. At the lower boundary of the triangular area L_2 the equilibrium phase is a hexagonal mesophase F and at the right-hand boundary the equilibrium phase is hydratized crystalline octanoate.

By adding octane the system becomes quaternary and the description of the phase equilibria requires a tetrahedroid diagram. We shall not try to describe the complete phase equilibria; we wish here only to define the extension of the microemulsion phase (L_2) in the quaternary phase diagram. To visualize this we have cut the tetrahedroid diagram along the axis decanol-octane at different molar ratios of soap-water and projected the sections in the plane of the table as illustrated in Figure 2.

This is carried out for seven constant molar ratios of soap-water in Figure 3. Here the triangle A, farthest to the left, is identical with the earlier described ternary phase diagram (Figure 1), but in Figure 3 we have omitted all other phases except L_2. The triangle B, is the water-decanol-octane side of the quaternary tetrahedroid phase diagram. The narrow region in this phase diagram for the system decanol-octane-water illustrates the low solubility of water in the mutually soluble mixtures of octane and decanol.

The triangle at the bottom of Figure 3 is a section of the tetrahedron at the molar ratio soap-water 0.039, as shown in Figure 2. The microemulsion area L_2 is obviously strongly influenced by the addition of octanoate, as is seen by comparison with triangle B. In the decanol-rich region the microemulsion area is somewhat broadened but above all, there is a minimum for the solubility of octane (2 per cent octane) in the solution containing approx. 90 per cent decanol and 10 per cent mixed solute soap-water. At higher

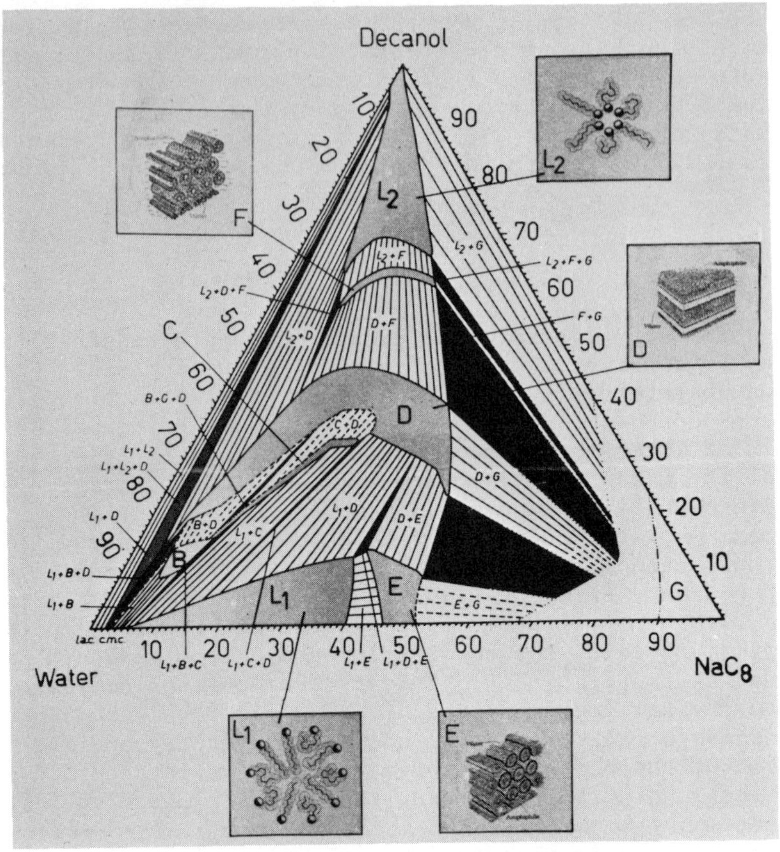

Figure 1. Phase equilibria at 20°C and structure of different aggregates in the system water-sodium-n-octanoate-n-decanol;[10]

- L_1 premicellar and Hartley-micelles in isotropic water-rich solution
- L_2 'inverted' micelles in isotropic oil-rich solution
- D lamellar mesoaggregates
- E hexagonally ordered hydrophilic rods
- F hexagonally ordered hydrophobic rods

concentrations of the mixed solute soap-water the solubility of octane reaches a 'plateau value' of 10 per cent by weight of octane. Finally, the solubility of octane diminishes rapidly to 0 at about 36 per cent of the mixed solute soap-water (i.e. 60% on the $C_{10}OH$-axis in Figure 3). If we compare the solubility area obtained for octane with the solubilization of hydrocarbons in aqueous soap solutions it could be said that there exists some kind of 'critical concentration' for the mixed solute soap-water.

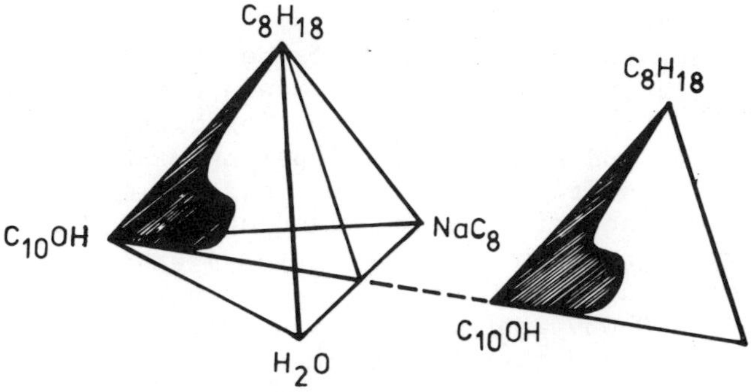

Figure 2. Illustration of a tetrahedroid quaternary phase diagram cut by a plane along one of the edges.

Only above this concentration can the octane be solubilized by the mixed solute soap-water in decanolic solution.

These conditions are still more pronounced in the next three sections, the triangle at the molar ratio 0.047, the triangle at the molar ratio 0.063 and the triangle at 0.076 (bottom right). The position of the solubility minimum of octane, i.e. the concentration of the mixed solute soap-water at this minimum, and the level of the solubility plateau of octane, all increase with increasing molar ratio of soap-water. At the molar ratio 0.076 soap-water the plateau for the solubility of octane reaches a value of 30 per cent by weight. In all the above sections the solubility of octane decreases rapidly to 0 at a concentration of 40 per cent by weight of mixed solute soap-water.

If the molar ratio of soap-water characterizing the sections of the tetrahedron is increased further to a value of 0.092 as in the case of the triangles top left in Figure 3 there is again a pronounced change for the solubility of octane. The L_2 area is still very narrow at the top, but with decreasing decanol content there appears a broad 'belly' extending as far as to the 40 per cent by weight of mixed solute soap-water. There are no longer any minima or maxima in the solubility of octane.

The situation is nearly the same delate for the microemulsion phase in the two final sections of the tetrahedroid phase diagram that were studied, the triangle at 0.142 and the triangle at 0.180 moles of soap per mole of water. It is characteristic of these two last sections that the L_2 region no longer reaches close to the axis of decanol-octane. There appears a narrow heterogeneous region between this axis and the homogeneous microemulsion region. Furthermore, in these two sections as in the 0.063, 0.076 and 0.092 section planes the microemulsion region no longer reaches up the pure octane. This is rather surprising, as decanol and octane are mutually soluble in each other. Obviously we have not been able to detect the extremely narrow homogeneous solution belt, which must exist close to the decanol-octane axis.

With respect to the influence of the primarily active mixed solute soap-water it is possible to obtain three different types of systems L_2 in Figure 3. At molar ratios of soap-water less than 0.039, water and soap are only sparingly soluble in the mutually soluble, nearly ideal solvent mixture of decanol and octane. These characteristics are also found for the other section planes at very high decanol-octane contents except for the planes of the highest relative sodium caprylate concentrations. Between the molar ratios 0.039 and 0.076 at the section-planes in the lower part of Figure 3 there is another type of L_2-solution with

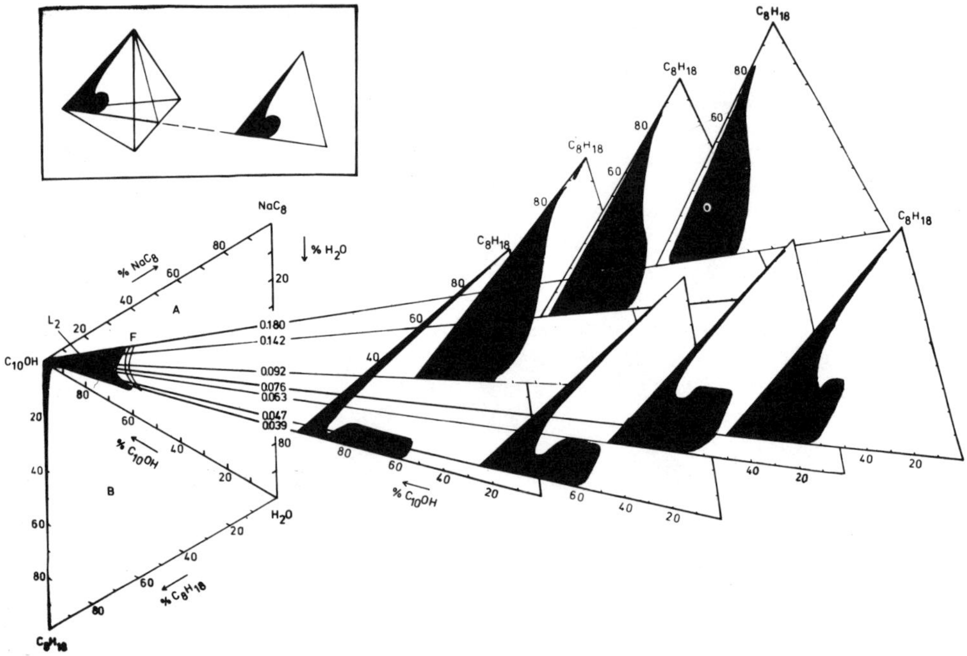

Figure 3. The extension of the microemulsion phase L_2 in the tetrahedroid phase diagram for the system water-sodium octanoate-n-decanol-n-octane at 25°C. Concentrations are expressed in weight per cent.

A. The 'base triangle' water-octanoate-decanol
B. The 'side triangle' water-decanol-octane
0.039 A section of the tetrahedron through the decanol-octane axis at the ratio 0.039 moles of soap per mole of water
0.047 The section at value 0.042 of the molar ratio soap-water
0.063 The section at molar ratio 0.063
0.076 The section at molar ratio 0.076
0.092 The section at molar ratio 0.092
0.142 The section at molar ratio 0.142
0.180 The section at molar ratio 0.180

minima and maxima in the solubility of octane. Here the mixed solute octanoate-water can, if it is present in amounts above some critical value, solubilize appreciable amounts of octane. On the 'plateau' the L_2 solutions are in equilibrium with an aqueous octanoate solution. The critical amount of mixed solute necessary for solubilization of octane increases with the molar ratio soap-water, i.e. addition of water reduces the 'critical concentration' for the solubilization of octane. On the other hand, the solubilization capacity of the mixed solute increases with the ratio soap-water. At the steep decrease in the solubility curve for octane at approx. 60% on the $C_{10}OH$-axis the solutions are in equilibrium with the lamellar mesophase.

The third type of L_2-solutions is that occurring at molar ratios of octanoate-water higher than 0.092. The corresponding sections are described in the upper part of Figure 3. As long as the weight ratio between mixed solute and decanol is less than 1/3, considerable amounts of octane are solubilized at nearly all concentrations of mixed solute. At high content of octane, however, the phase L_2 is no longer stable. Through addition of small amounts of octane to the three-component system, water-octanoate-decanol, the existence region of the phase L_2 extends appreciably in the direction of increasing concentration of the mixed solute, soap-water. These L_2-solutions are in equilibrium with the hexagonal F phase constructed of hydrophobic rods.

In all these systems it must, however, be observed that the octane is not to be considered only as an indifferent solubilized component. The addition of octane also increases the amount of water and octanoate which can be bound to the homogeneous phase L_2.

We have also studied the roles of the different components in the L_2-solutions with aid of their volumetric, thermochemical and spectrometric properties. The left-hand diagram in Figure 4 gives the partial molar volume of water determined along two lines drawn from the decanol-corner in the 'bottom triangle' water-octanoate-decanol as shown in the middle of the Figure. In the part of L_2 richest in water, line A having low ratios of soap-water, the water has a relatively high molar volume. This water is reminiscent of that in a concentrated aqueous electrolyte solution. At low ratios soap-water the water behaves in neighbourhood of pure decanol as free water.

According to the second curve (line B) in the left-hand diagram of Figure 4 the partial volume of water at high ratios of soap-water decreases especially in the environment most rich in decanol. Nearly all water present at the right-hand boundary of the region L_2 must be strongly bound to the ionic groups.

The right-hand diagram in Figure 4 shows the partial molar volumes for octanoate along the lines mentioned earlier. The partial volume of octanoate changes with changes in the composition in the opposite direction compared with the case for water. This is consequence of the fact that the partial volume of decanol is nearly invariable. The decanol thus behaves here like an indifferent component.

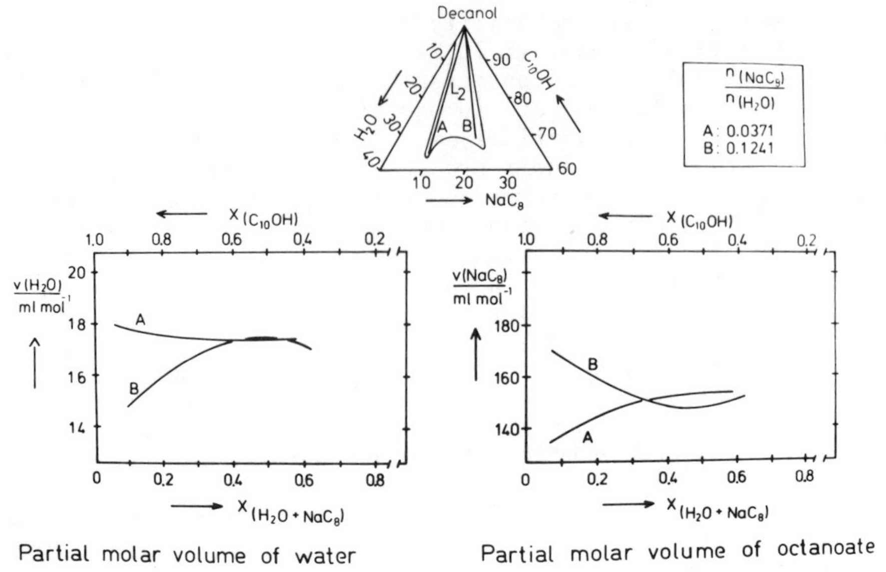

Figure 4. The partial molar volume of water (left-hand diagram) and the partial molar volume of octanoate (right-hand diagram) as functions of mole fractions in L_2-solutions.
Curves A correspond to the ratio 0.037 moles of soap per mole of water.
Curves B correspond to the ratio 0.124 moles of soap per mole of water.

The nature of the L_2 solutions is also reflected in the partial molar enthalpy of water and octanoate.[11] From Figure 5 it can be seen that the water behaves at a high content of water and low ratios of soap-water almost as in a concentrated aqueous electrolyte solution. At high ratios of soap-water nearly all the water present, almost 5 moles water per mole of soap, is bound as 'first hydrate water' as was pointed out by Ekwall many years ago.[12] This is reflected as a slight decrease in the enthalpy of water, the overall properties being the same as for the enthalpy in the water-rich part. The enthalpy of octanoate (right-hand diagram Figure 5) reflects the same structural changes as Figure 4.

It was stated above that the octane seems to participate actively in the formation of microemulsions, especially those rich in water. This is also reflected in the thermochemistry of the system. According to Figure 6 the apparent heat of solution of octane is higher in the typical microemulsion region of the phase L_2 than in the case of pure decanol or decanol saturated with water. Also it is lowered still further as the octane-content is increased.

The molecular interactions governing the formation of micro-

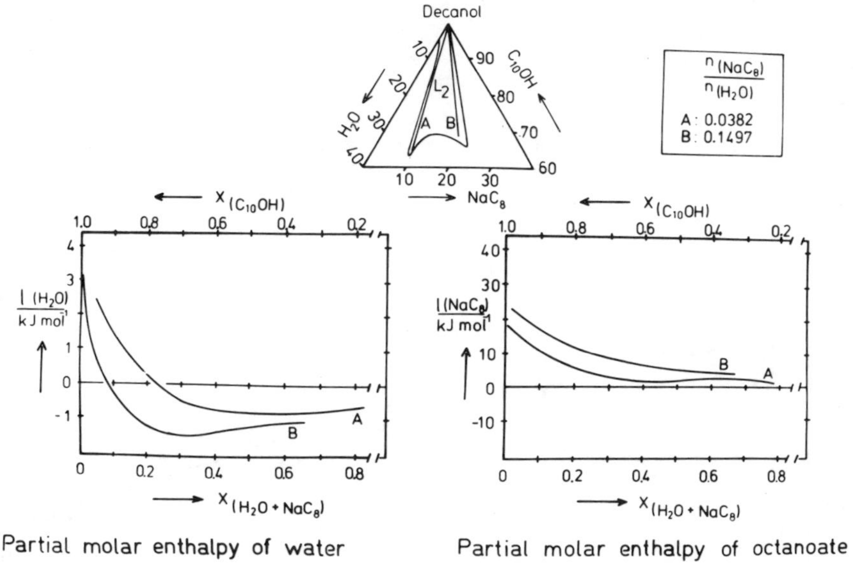

Figure 5. The partial molar enthalpy of water (left-hand diagram), and octanoate (right-hand diagram) in L_2-solutions.
Curves A correspond to the ratio 0.038 moles of soap per mole of water.
Curves B correspond to the ratio 0.150 moles of soap per mole of water. Concentrations are expressed in mole fractions.

emulsions is characterized by their spectrometric properties. For example, the shift of the antisymmetric stretching band of water at about 3500 cm^{-1} changes stepwise and can be explained by the formation of two different types of micellar aggregates.[15]

In the lower part of the three-component phase region of L_2 rather large aggregates are formed as reflected by X-ray scattering.[12] This is valid both in the corner rich in water and the one most rich in octanoate.

The L_2 aggregates rich in water sediment on ultracentrifugation. Molecular weights found were about 16000 dalton in the water-rich part (the base of the 0.039 section plane) and about 12000 dalton in the water-poor part (the base of the 0.092 section plane). In the three-component system poorest in water (the base of the 0.180 section plane) no sedimentation was found.

As Friberg and others have shown, the particles in L_2 solutions also scatter light.[14] The scattering obviously originates from the strongly polar water-rich internal parts of the inverted micelles and not from the kinetic units including their apolar 'palissade layers', which must have almost the same optical density as the intermicellar decanolic liquid.

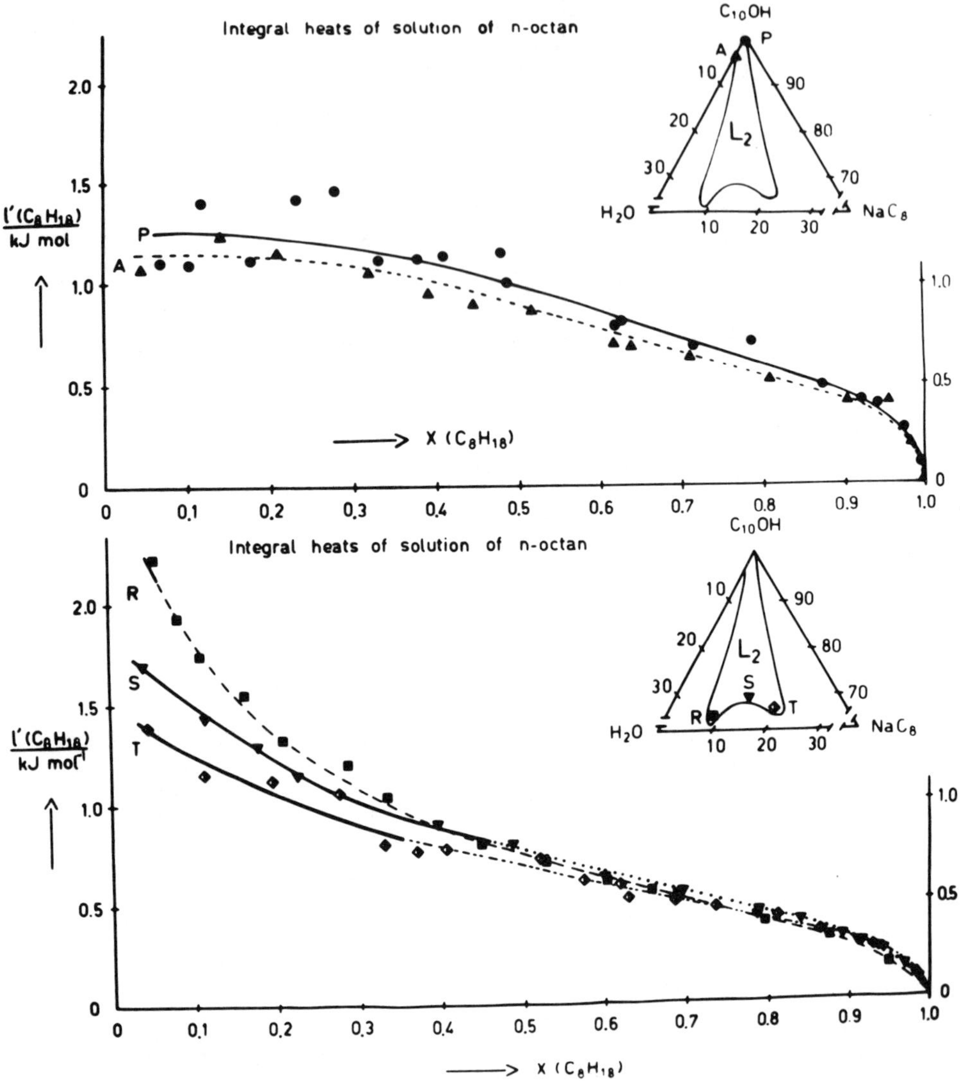

Figure 6. The apparent heat of solution of octane in L_2 solutions of different composition as indicated in the triangular phase diagrams. Concentrations are expressed in mole fraction octane.

CONCLUSIONS

It may be pointed out that the system discussed above is quite analogous to the system water-potassium oleate-pentanol-benzene discussed by Friberg.[11] All the observations reported here are in agreement with the model above with three different types of solutions L_2.

I The first case of L_2 solutions, the region with nearly ideal solution is characterized by the mutual solubility of decanol and octane. The systems bind only small amounts of water and octanoate. This situation may be valid up to the solubility of water in decanol, i.e. 0.5 mole of water per mole of decanol. If there is more water present than is necessary for hydration of the soap, the water may, according to its partial density, have almost the same properties as in a pure liquid state. On the other hand, only completely hydrated soap can be bound in these solutions, and this amount of soap is limited by the amount of water present.

II The region for the formation of the second types of L_2, the microemulsions w/o proper, requires relatively high concentrations of water and soap. Inverted micelles with the hydrophobic parts of the soap molecules in their external part and a polar internal environment resembling a concentrated aqueous electrolyte solution characterize these systems. The formation of inverted micelles is favoured by their ability to take up in their external 'shells' completely apolar substances such as hydrocarbons. In doing so the hydrophobity of the external shells increases and finally the shells can no longer exist in contact with the aqueous internal environment of the inverted micelles. At certain contents of hydrocarbon the microemulsion is thus disintegrated and an aqueous soap solution separates from the system.

III The third types of L_2 solution is characterized by rather high molar ratios of soap-water, more than one mole of soap per ten moles of water. The interactions between the components in these systems leads according to X-ray scattering to the formation of large aggregates, but polar inhomogenities containing ionized groups and water are not formed to the extent necessary for light scattering.[13] Because of the low water content in the aggregates their density may be almost the same as the density of the solvent and they do not sediment on ultracentrifugation. At the high concentration of the strongly amphiphilic octanoate the aggregates formed obviously are capable of binding almost infinite amounts of octane to the small amounts water present.

On the other hand, in the direction of higher concentrations of soap the region for this third type of L_2 solution is limited by the requirement that at least the first hydrate water must be present, i.e. about 5 moles of water per mole of ionic surfactant.[12]

We believe that these three types can be obtained in all homogeneous four component solutions water in oil stabilized by surfactants.

ACKNOWLEDGEMENTS

We wish to thank Professor P. Stenius and Dr. J. B. Rosenholm for constructive discussions. Financial support from the Finnish Research Council for Natural Sciences is gratefully acknowledged.

REFERENCES

1. T. P Hoar and J. H. Schulman, Nature (London) 152, 102 (1943).
2. C. E. Cooke and J. H. Schulman in "Surface Chemistry", P. Ekwall, K. Groth and V. Runnström-Reio, Editors, Munksgaard, Copenhagen (1965)
3. N. P. Fedoseeva, L. A. Kochanova and E. D. Shchukin, Fiz. Khim. Poverkh Yavlenii, Pasplavakh 25-29, U. N. Eremenko, Editor, "Naukova Dunka", Kiev USSR (1971).
4. S. Friberg and I Buraczewska in "Micellization, Solubilization and Microemulsions," K. L. Mittal, Editor, Vol. 2, pp. 791-799, Plenum Press, New York 1977.
5. H. F. Eicke, J. Colloid Interface Sci. 52, 164 (1975).
6. H. F. Eicke, in "Micellization, Solubilization and Microemulsions," K. L. Mittal, Editor, Vol. I, pp. 429-443, Plenum Press, New York 1977.
7. A. S. Kertes and H. Gutman in "Surface and Colloid Science," E. Matijevic, Editor, Vol 8, pp. 193-272, Wiley, N. Y. 1976.
8. A. S. Kertes in "Micellization, Solubilization and Microemulsions," K. L. Mittal, Editor, Vol. 1, pp. 445-466, Plenum Press N.Y. 1977.
9. W. Geffcken, Zeitschrift für Phys. Chem. 155, No. 7, 25 (1931).
10. P. Ekwall, I. Danielsson and P. Stenius in "Surface Chemistry and Colloids," MTP Intern. Rev. Sci., Phys. Chem. Ser. 1, M. Kerker, Editor, Butterworths, London 1972.
11. I. Danielsson, J. B. Rosenholm, P. Stenius and S. Backlund, Prog. Colloid Polymer Sci. 61, 1 (1976).
12. P. Ekwall and L. Mandell, Acta Chem. Scand. 22, 699 (1968).
13. B. Svens and M. Turpeinen, Prog. Colloid Polymer Sci. 56, 30 (1975).

14. S. Friberg and E. Sjöblom, J. Colloid Interface Sci., submitted for publication.
15. J. B. Rosenholm and J. E. Österholm, J. Colloid Interface Sci., submitted for publication.

PHASE BEHAVIOR OF MICROEMULSION SYSTEMS WITH EMPHASIS ON EFFECTS OF PARAFFINIC HYDROCARBONS AND ALCOHOLS

J. G. Dominguez* , G. P. Willhite and D. W. Green

Department of Chemical and Petroleum Engineering

University of Kansas, Lawrence, Kansas 66045

Quaternary phase diagrams of systems containing deoiled Witco TRS 10-80 (a commercial alkylaryl sulfonate), brine, water or oil soluble alcohol and paraffinic hydrocarbons were studied by locating phase boundaries of microemulsions in pseudo ternary planes of constant sulfonate to hydrocarbon ratio or constant sulfonate to brine ratio. At moderate sulfonate concentrations, four separate microemulsion regions were identified. The fourth region encompassed the greatest composition range and was studied extensively. This region was confined by linear phase boundaries on pseudo ternary planes of constant surfactant to hydrocarbon or constant surfactant to brine ratios. Slopes of these phase boundaries were related to hydrocarbon type, alcohol type, salinity and sulfonate to hydrocarbon or sulfonate to brine ratio. A model based on the composition of the interface between the internal and external phases of the microemulsion and the thermodynamics of phase equilibria was developed to explain the linear phase boundaries.

INTRODUCTION

Microemulsions are being evaluated in processes designed to displace oil from depleted petroleum reservoirs[1]. In these oil recovery processes, a microemulsion is injected into a porous medium containing oil and water. The microemulsion solubilizes and/or

* Present address: ECOPETROL, Bogota, D. E., Columbia, South America.

displaces the oil and water as it flows through the porous media. In the process, mixing between the microemulsion and reservoir fluids occurs and this mixing causes changes in the composition of the microemulsion which must ultimately lead to separation into two or more phases[2-4]. Adsorption of surface active constituents in the microemulsion onto the porous media also contributes to changes in microemulsion composition. These factors have stimulated interest in understanding the phase behavior of microemulsion systems at different compositions.

Microemulsions of interest in oil recovery applications have five distinct components (alcohol, hydrocarbon, surfactant, water and sodium chloride). Water and sodium chloride are frequently treated as a pseudo-component, reducing the microemulsion system to four components. In this study, the definition of a microemulsion proposed by Healy and Reed[5] will be adopted with slight modification. A microemulsion is defined as a "thermodynamically stable, translucent, micellar-solution of oil and water that may contain electrolytes and one or more amphiphilic compounds".

The phase behavior of a four component system may be studied in a variety of manners. If the phase behavior is desired at intervals of 5% change in composition, several hundred equilibrium samples would be required. Phase boundaries would be determined by interpolation between points adjacent to the boundaries. A pseudoternary diagram where two components such as sulfonate and alcohol are present in a fixed ratio can be constructed by this method with 100 equilibrium samples located at desired composition intervals[6]. Another method is based on estimation of phase boundaries from material balance calculations[7]. All of these techniques either require a large number of samples to define phase behavior and/or yield results which define the microemulsion behavior for a limited region of concentrations. There is a need for methods to describe phase behavior in terms of quantitative models.

One such model for microemulsions was proposed by Bowcott and Schulman[8] who investigated microemulsion systems by titrating dispersions of hydrocarbon, water and surfactant to transparency with alcohol. They interpreted the data using a model describing the distribution of alcohol between the internal phase, an interphase and external phase in the microemulsion. The model assumes the alcohol is distributed between the three phases while the surfactant is only present in the interphase. According to this model, a transparent oil continuous microemulsion can be diluted by maintaining a constant ratio of hydrocarbon to alcohol in the continuous phase. The total alcohol in the system (n_a) was described by Equation 1.

$$n_a = n_{ai} + n_{aw} + k_i n_o \tag{1}$$

where

n_{ai} = moles of alcohol in the interphase
n_{aw} = moles of alcohol in the water phase (internal)
n_o = moles of hydrocarbon in the external phase

Experimental data for systems containing hexanol, benzene, potassium oleate and water were obtained by titrating samples with fixed ratios of water to surfactant. The data revealed the existence of a linear relationship between the moles of hydrocarbon present in a sample and the moles of alcohol required to reach the point of transparency, supporting the concepts of the model.

The objective of the research presented in this paper was to determine if the approach developed by Bowcott and Schulman could be extended to define phase behavior in microemulsion systems of interest in oil recovery applications. In the process of this research, the effects of alcohol type, salinity and hydrocarbon type on the phase behavior of microemulsions were investigated.

METHODS AND MATERIALS

The procedure used to investigate phase behavior of microemulsions was based on titrating along dilution paths where the ratio of sulfonate to hydrocarbon or sulfonate to brine was held constant. Figure 1a illustrates a plane of constant sulfonate to hydrocarbon ratio containing a representative dilution path for systems prepared with preferentially water soluble alcohols. Point A represents the starting composition for one dilution path. Dilution was done by adding brine and titrating the system to transparency. The term "preferentially water soluble" means that alcohol preferentially partitions into the water phase at the temperature, pressure, salinity and other conditions of the experiment. Dilution paths for oil soluble alcohols remained in planes of constant sulfonate to brine ratio as in Figure 1b and began at Point C on the zero hydrocarbon-alcohol line. Oil was the diluent for these systems.

Dilution paths for both water and oil soluble alcohols were generated in a similar manner although the starting points were on opposite sides of the quaternary diagram. The procedure will be illustrated with isopropyl alcohol (IPA) as the cosurfactant. A dispersion of surfactant in hydrocarbon was placed in a 10 ml or 20 ml stoppered graduated cylinder. A small amount of brine was added, the sample was shaken vigorously and placed in a constant temperature bath to equilibrate. The number, volumes and macroscopic characteristics of the equilibrium phases were recorded. If the system was turbid or separated into two phases, it was titrated to transparency with IPA. Otherwise, more brine was added. This procedure was continued until the water content of the sample was on the order of 90% or more by volume or it was not possible to obtain a microemulsion by addition of alcohol.

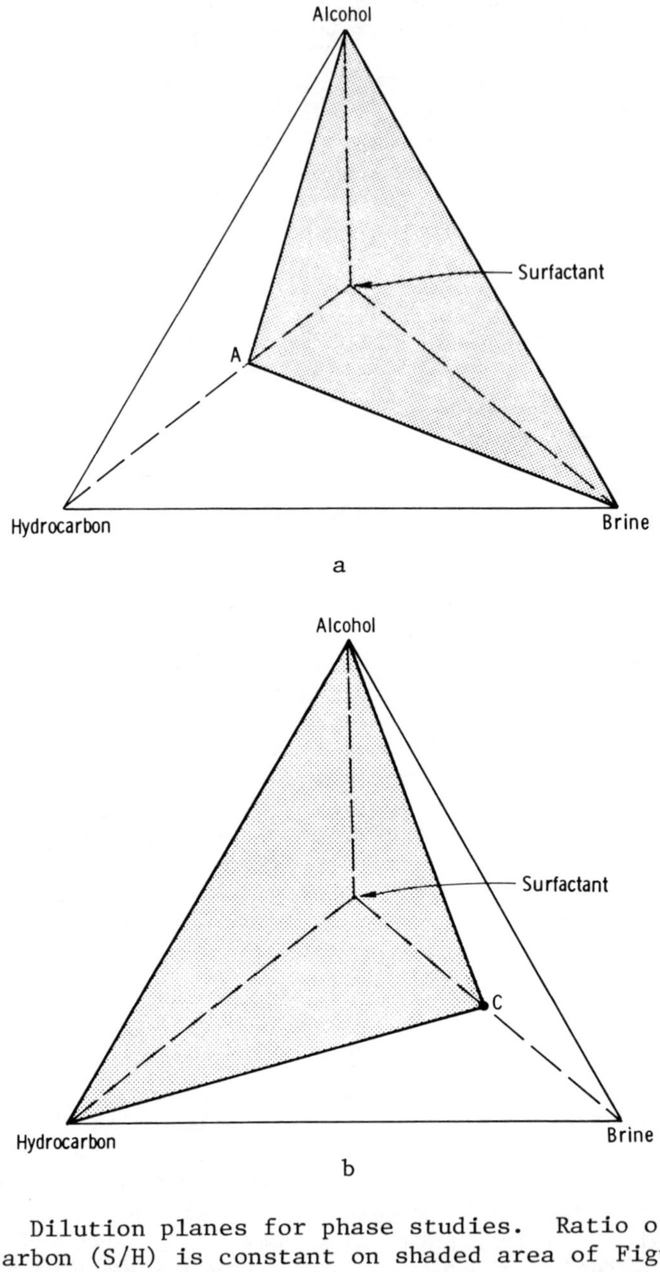

Figure 1. Dilution planes for phase studies. Ratio of sulfonate to hydrocarbon (S/H) is constant on shaded area of Figure 1a (top). Ratio of sulfonate to brine (S/B) is constant on shaded area of Figure 1b (bottom).

Phase boundaries for single phase transparent microemulsion regions were sharp. Compositions at phase boundaries were determined within a few microliters of alcohol. Most samples gave evidence of phase separation or phase stability after water or alcohol was added. An equilibration time of 24 hours was found adequate to determine phase separation or phase stability for most systems studied. Longer times were allowed for samples with low water content and high apparent solution viscosity.

Stability of single phase transparent microemulsions was investigated by interrupting the experiments at or near compositions where the phase boundary had been crossed. Thirty samples were left in the constant temperature bath for periods ranging from several weeks to 2 months without evidence of phase separation. A few samples were left undisturbed for several months without visible change.

The stability of multiphase systems was not studied in as many samples as the single phase transparent microemulsions. Phase volumes in multiphase regions above the upper boundary of the transparent microemulsion region reached equilibrium rapidly and were observed to be stable over periods of 1 to 2 months in the few samples which were studied. Multiphase regions at alcohol compositions less than those required to obtain transparent microemulsions equilibrated slowly. Small changes in phase volumes were sometimes observed with time. In these samples, the relative volume of each phase was large. It was concluded that the system would remain multiphase even if sufficient time was allowed for phase volumes to equilibrate.

Thermodynamic stability of selected samples was determined from phase behavior before and after elevating the temperature of the microemulsion. In all samples examined, the microemulsions returned to the same state after the samples reached thermal equilibrium at the initial temperature. Optical anisotropy was not determined. Viscosity and electrical resistivity data were obtained on selected samples[9].

Deoiled Witco TRS 10-80, a commercial high molecular weight alkyl aryl sulfonate, was the surfactant in all experiments[9]. The average equivalent weight of the sulfonate was 426.5. Analysis by high pressure liquid chromatography[10] indicates that TRS 10-80 contains about 89% monosulfonates and 11% polysulfonates by mass. All other materials were high purity[9].

RESULTS

Water Soluble Alcohols

Dilution paths for water soluble alcohols were studied extensively. The same general trends were observed for all systems. A typical dilution path is presented in Figure 2. Figure 2 relates the amount of IPA required to obtain a microemulsion when a sample containing 0.448 ml of TRS 10-80 and 2.0 ml of n-octane was diluted with brine (10.6K mg/l NaCl). The data points define the lower boundary of the microemulsion region. A transparent microemulsion region was found above this phase boundary. In general, multiphase systems were observed at all alcohol concentrations less than the data points shown. Low alcohol content microemulsions were found in some systems[9]. Similar dilution paths were found using n-hexane, n-heptane, n-octane, n-nonane as well as mixtures of n-hexane and n-doecane and n-hexane and n-octadecane.

The alcohol-brine data shown in Figure 2 can be represented by five regions which characterize the dilution process. These are shown schematically in Figure 3. In Region 1, water is solubilized without adding alcohol. Region 1 is usually narrow and is followed by Region 2 where it is necessary to add relatively large quantities of alcohol in order to titrate the system to transparency. Region 3 is characterized by solubilization of water with little or no addition of alcohol. At low sulfonate concentrations, Region 3 does not exist and the interval between Regions 2 and 4 is multiphase. In Region 4, a linear relationship was found between the alcohol and brine necessary to maintain a microemulsion. Transition to Region 5 occurs when a water phase drops out. The resulting aqueous phase is in equilibrium with an emulsion or microemulsion phase.

Results and other data for Regions 1 and 2 are described elsewhere[9]. Region 3 was studied extensively using IPA. Figure 4

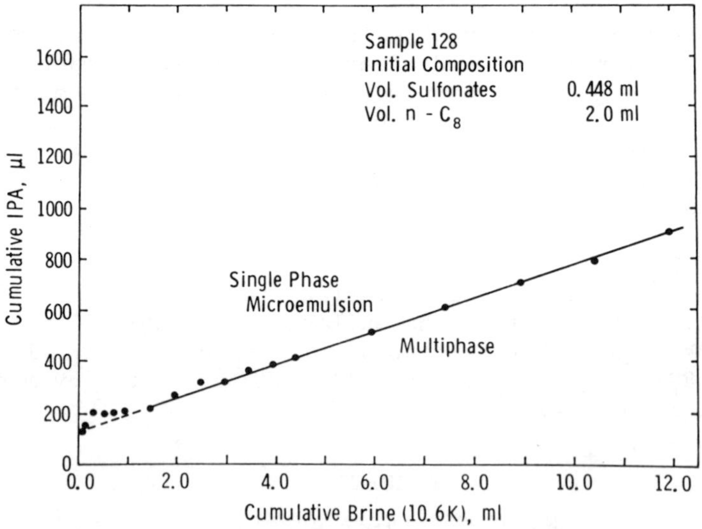

Figure 2. Alcohol-brine data defining the lower boundary of microemulsions along the dilution path.

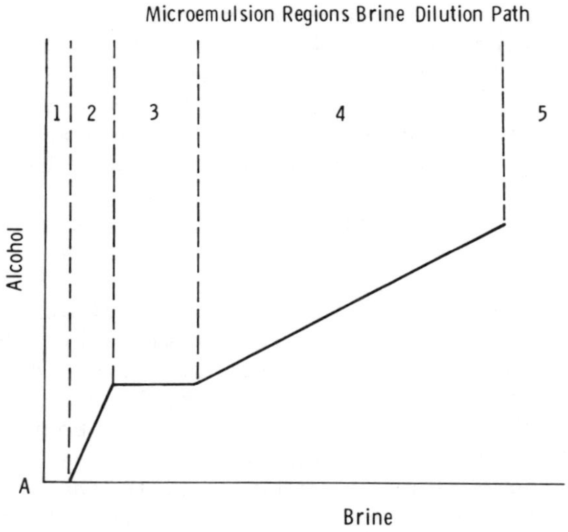

Figure 3. Characteristic microemulsion regions along the lower boundaries for brine dilution paths.

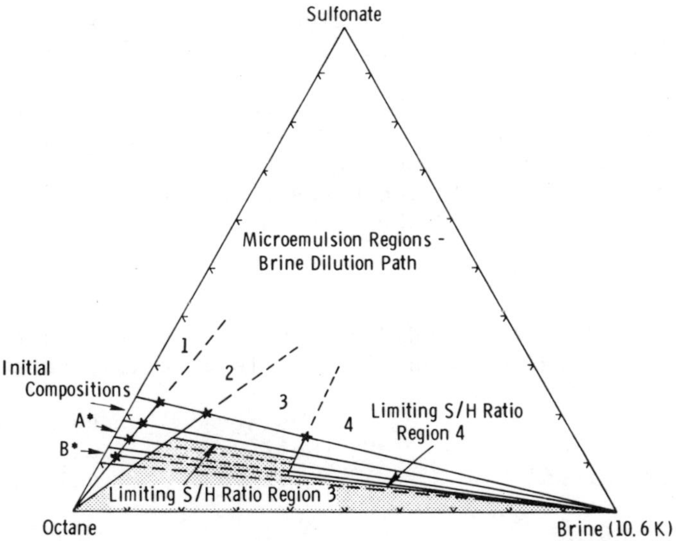

Figure 4. Limiting S/H ratios for Regions 3 and 4 for TRS 10-80, octane, brine (10.6K NaCl) IPA system.

shows the projection of the extent of Regions 1, 2, and 3 on the zero IPA concentration ternary diagram for six dilution paths when the hydrocarbon was n-octane. The solid lines on each dilution path indicate where transparent microemulsions were found as illustrated in Figure 2. The shaded area identifies multiphase systems. Up to four phases were observed in this multiphase region. Point A* on Figure 4 is the minimum sulfonate/octane ratio for which Region 3 could be obtained. Also shown on Figure 4 is Point B*. Point B* is the critical sulfonate concentration below which it is not possible to form single phase microemulsions characteristic of Region 4. These critical sulfonate ratios are functions of hydrocarbon type and salinity. Table 1 summarizes the values of A* and B* estimated from data for the IPA-10.6K brine dilution paths.

Region 4 was studied extensively because of its presence over a broad range of concentrations, particularly where the microemulsion oil displacement process might occur. It was discovered that there was an upper boundary to Region 4 in the range of sulfonate concentrations studied. The upper boundary can be reached by titrating alcohol into a microemulsion initially near the lower boundary of Region 4. Some alcohol can be added to the microemulsion while the system remains as a single phase. Further addition of alcohol leads to a phase boundary where the system separates into two phases, a microemulsion phase in equilibrium with an essentially pure hydrocarbon phase. The upper boundary for Region 4 is shown in Figure 5 for one system. The alcohol necessary to expel the hydrocarbon from the microemulsion is also a linear function of the amount of brine in the sample.

The linear relationships between IPA and brine at the lower and upper phase boundaries of the single phase microemulsion region were found for all systems studied. Figures 6 and 7 show the lower and upper boundaries on dilution paths where the sulfonate to n-heptane ratios vary from 0.126 to 0.297 volume/volume.

Table I. Critical Sulfonate-Hydrocarbon Ratios for Existence of Microemulsions in Regions 3 and 4. IPA-10.6K Brine Systems.

Hydrocarbon	Point A* (Sulf/Hydro vol/vol)	Point B* (Sulf/Hydro vol/vol)
n-C6	.145	.063
n-C7	.196	.093
n-C8	.196	.129
n-C9	.254	.200
n-C10	.314	.228
n-C11	--	.293

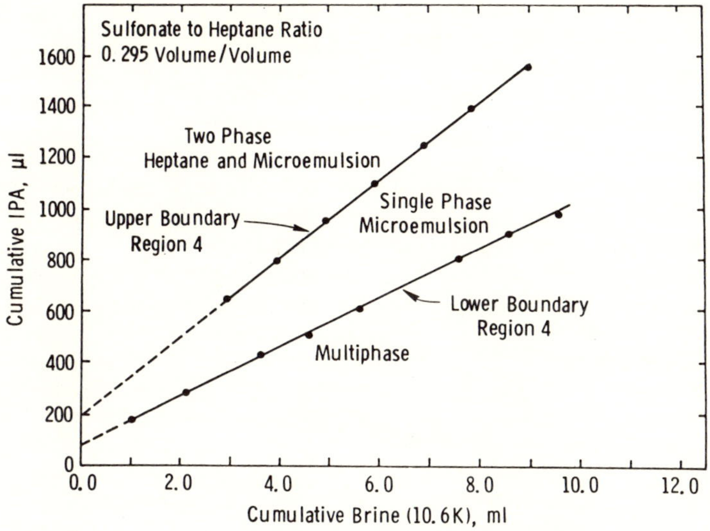

Figure 5. Upper and lower microemulsion boundaries for n-heptane along the brine dilution path.

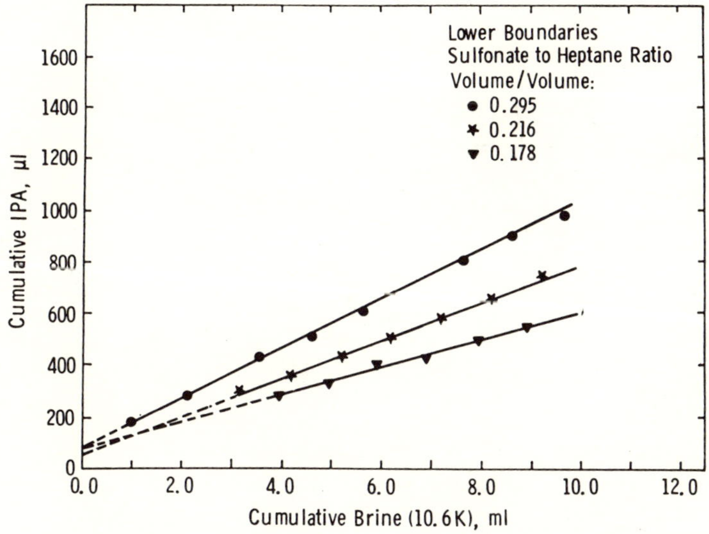

Figure 6. Effect of sulfonate to heptane ratio on the lower phase boundaries of Region 4.

The effects of molecular weight on the lower phase boundary are shown on Figure 8, a series of dilution paths where the ratio of sulfonate to hydrocarbon volumes is 0.215. Figure 9 contains similar data for hexane, octane, and nonane for the upper boundary of Region 4. The slope of the straight lines representing the phase boundaries decreases as the molecular weight of paraffinic hydrocarbons increases. Binary mixtures of paraffinic hydrocarbons behave similarly to pure hydrocarbons. For mixtures, the slopes and intercepts of the straight lines which define the lower boundaries of Region 4 have values which lie between the corresponding values of these parameters for the constituents of the mixture.

Figure 10 depicts the effect of alcohol type on the upper boundary of Region 4. For the same amount of water, more ethanol than IPA or propanol is required to reach the upper boundary of Region 4. Salinity also has a strong effect on the upper boundary of Region 4. Figure 11 depicts the effect of salinity on the upper boundary of an IPA-octane system. The effects of alcohol and salinity were not examined in detail at the lower phase boundary.

Figure 12 portrays the phase behavior of heptane-TRS 10-80 on a S/H dilution plane. Region 4 is the narrow slice designated M on the diagram. Other S/H diagrams are available[9]. Reference 11 discusses quaternary phase behavior in detail for the nonane TRS 10-80 system.

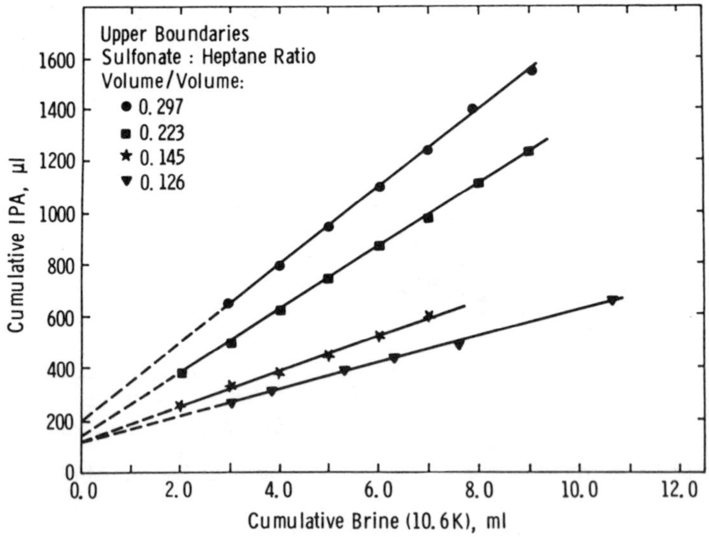

Figure 7. Effect of sulfonate to heptane ratio on the upper phase boundaries of Region 4.

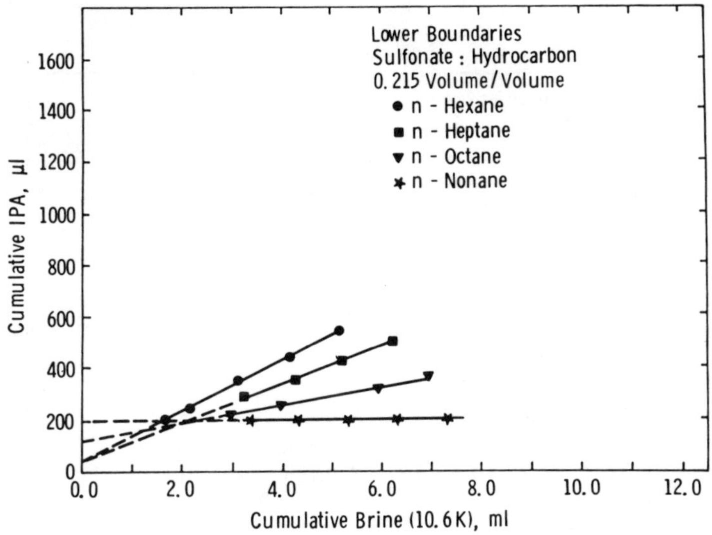

Figure 8. Effect of hydrocarbon type on the lower phase boundaries of Region 4.

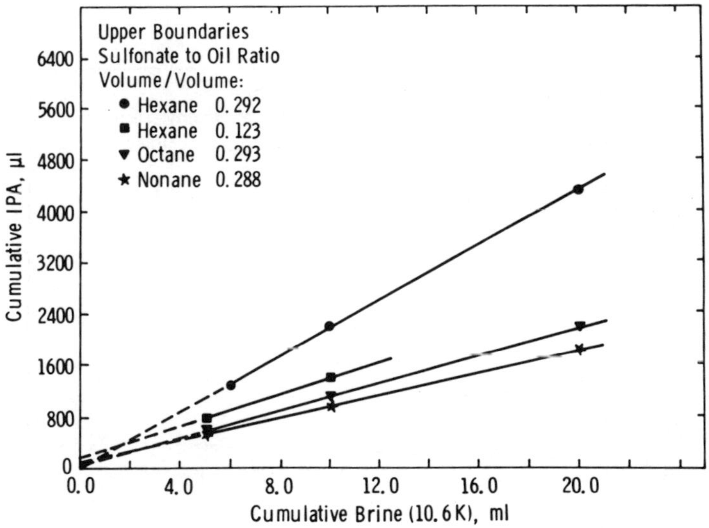

Figure 9. Effect of hydrocarbon type on the upper phase boundaries of Region 4.

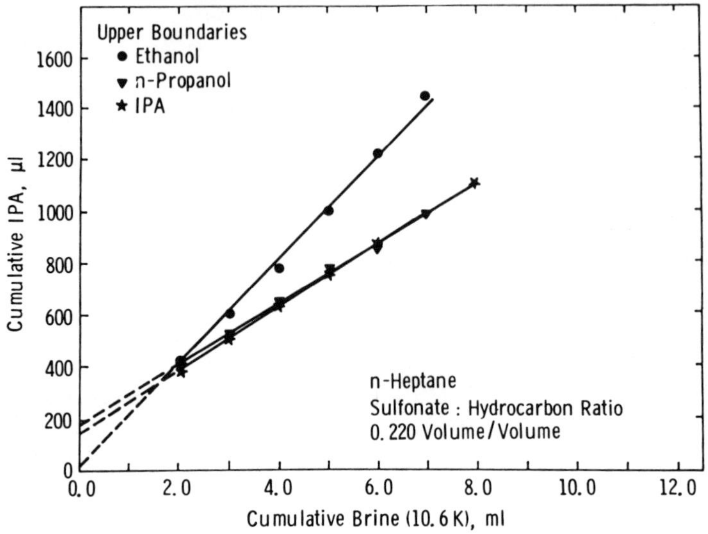

Figure 10. Effect of alcohol type on upper phase boundaries of Region 4.

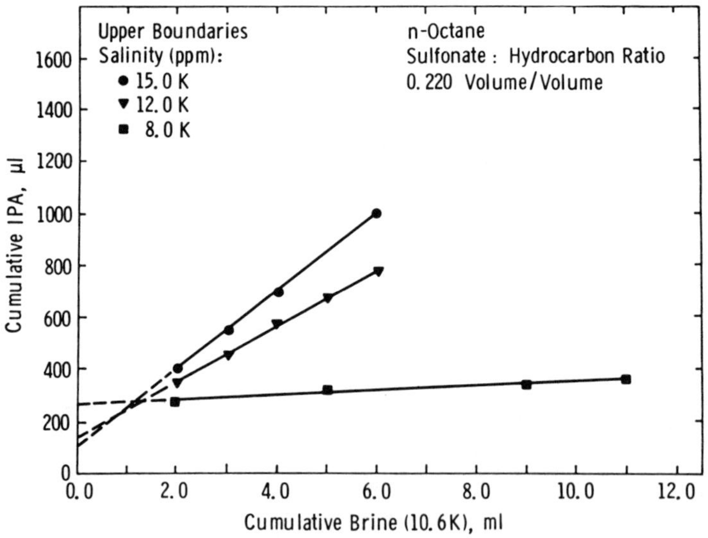

Figure 11. Effect of salinity on upper phase boundaries of Region 4.

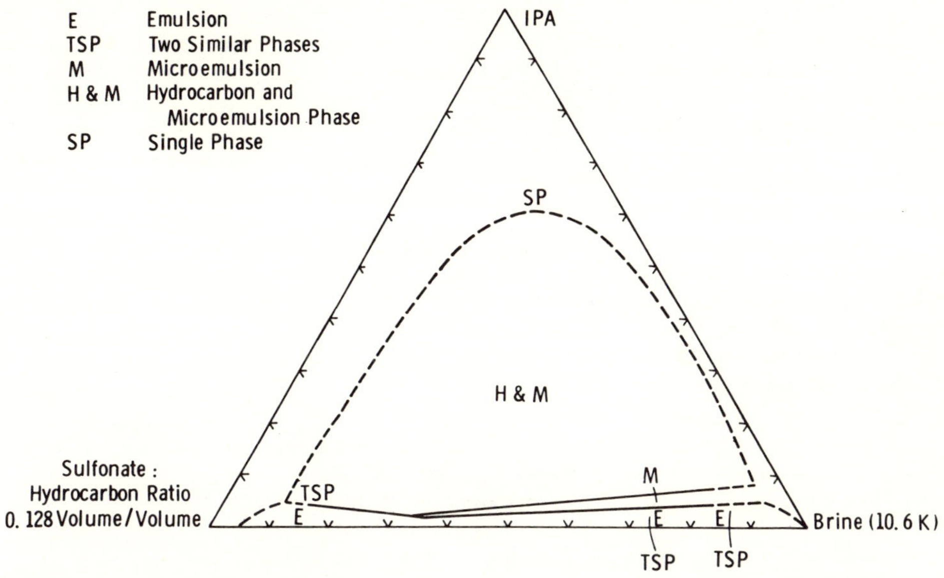

Figure 12. Pseudo ternary phase diagram for the dilution plane where the ratio of sulfonate to n-heptane is constant at 0.128 volume/volume.

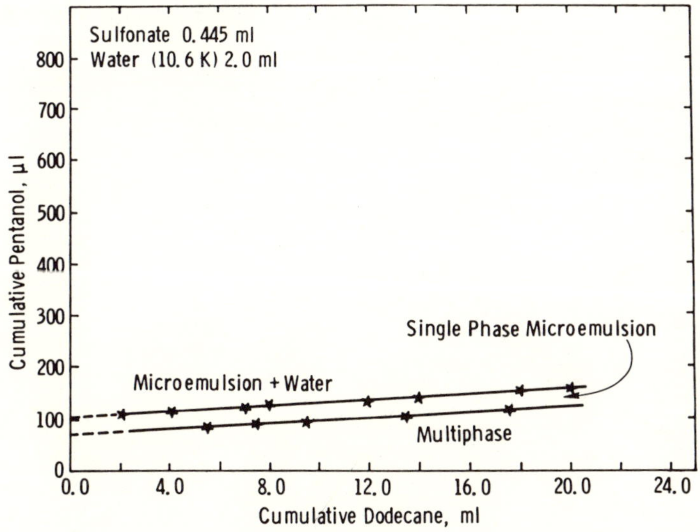

Figure 13. Phase boundaries for Region 4' along the n-pentanol-dodecane dilution path when sulfonate to brine ratio is constant.

Oil Soluble Alcohols

Microemulsions prepared with preferentially oil soluble alcohols were obtained using methods similar to those applied to study preferentially water soluble alcohols. The stock solution consisted of purified TRS 10-80 and a brine. Hydrocarbons were used to dilute the system and the phase boundaries were determined by titration with preferentially oil soluble alcohols.

The existence of five different regions along the dilution path was confirmed with a few samples. Characteristics of these regions were similar to the characteristics of the five regions defined in Figure 4 for water soluble alcohols. In the following discussion regions obtained with preferentially oil soluble alcohols are denoted with an apostrophe.

Figure 13 shows the lower and upper boundaries of Region 4' for a system that contains 0.445 ml of TRS 10-80 and 2.0 ml of brine (10.6K mg/l of NaCl), pentanol and dodecane. The transparent microemulsion is bounded above and below by multiphase regions. The lower and upper boundaries represent linear relationships between the alcohol required to obtain a microemulsion and the amount of hydrocarbon in the system.

The main difference between systems prepared with preferentially water soluble alcohols and preferentially oil soluble alcohols is that at the upper boundary of Region 4' the systems separ-

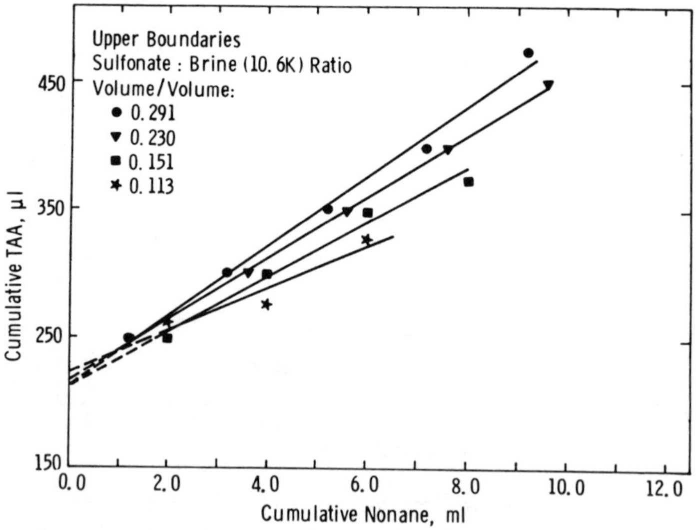

Figure 14. Effect of sulfonate to brine ratio on the upper boundaries of Region 4'.

ate into a microemulsion phase in equilibrium with an almost pure water phase. Region 5' is a two phase region where microemulsions are in equilibrium with an excess oil phase.

Other parameters were varied to study the lower and upper phase boundaries. Results for the upper phase boundaries are presented in Figures 14-17. The slope of the upper phase boundary increases with sulfonate to brine ratio as in Figure 14 for the TAA-nonane system. Figure 15 shows the effect of hydrocarbon type on the characteristics of the upper boundary of Region 4' while Figure 16 shows that a decrease in the polarity of the alcohol decreases the amount of alcohol necessary to reach the upper boundary of Region 4'. Figure 17 shows that, all other parameters being the same, a decrease in salinity increases the amount of alcohol necessary to reach the upper boundary of Region 4'.

DISCUSSION

The alcohol-brine volumes which define the lower boundary of microemulsion Region 4 fit a straight line whose slope and intercept are functions of salinity, hydrocarbon type, alcohol type and surfactant-to-oil ratio. The upper alcohol-brine boundary of Region 4 is also a straight line whose parameters vary with these same variables. Analogous results were obtained in Region 4' when the alcohols used were oil soluble.

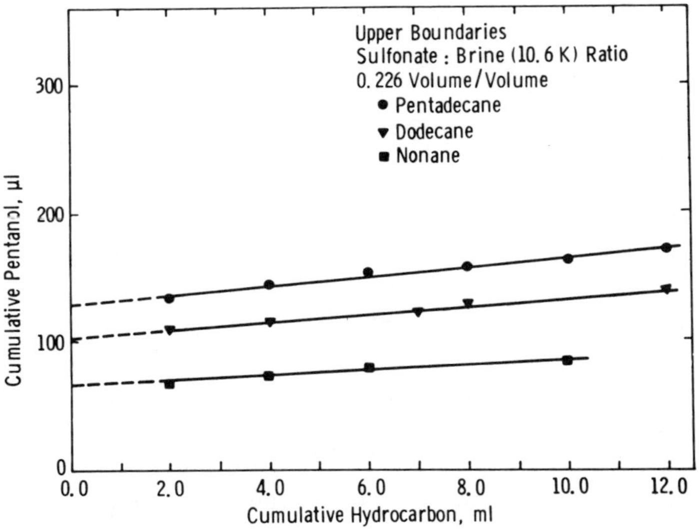

Figure 15. Effect of hydrocarbon type on upper boundaries of Region 4' for systems prepared with n-pentanol.

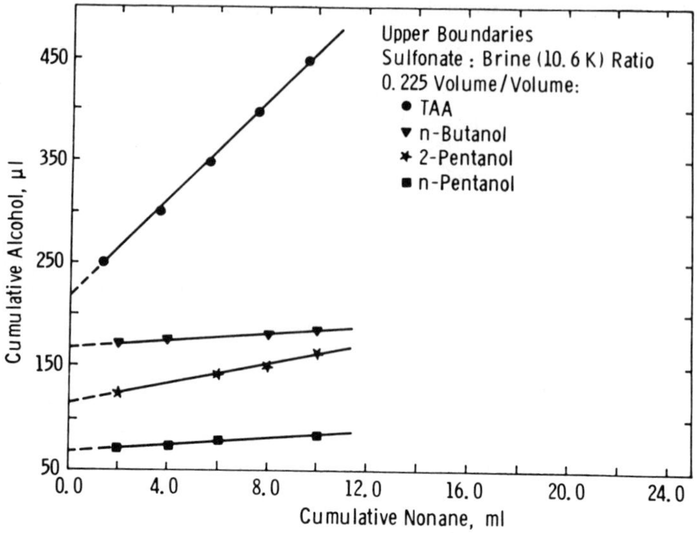

Figure 16. Variation of upper phase boundaries with alcohol type in Region 4'.

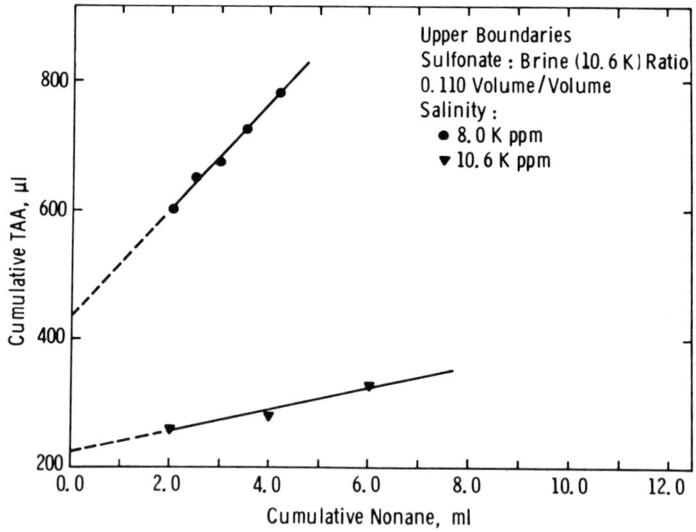

Figure 17. Influence of electrolyte concentration on the upper boundaries of Region 4'.

Slopes of the phase boundaries are shown in Tables II and III for representative systems. Slopes K and K' refer to the upper boundaries of Regions 4 and 4' while k and k' are the slopes for the lower boundaries of Regions 4 and 4'. The intercepts of these lines, discussed later in this paper, $V_{ai} + V_{ao}$, $V'_{ai} + V'_{ao}$, $V_{ai} + V_{aw}$, and $V'_{ai} + V'_{aw}$ represent the amounts of alcohol at the interface and solubilized in the internal phase.

Correlation of these slopes and intercepts with sulfonate to hydrocarbon ratio as in Table II permits prediction of phase boundary locations at intermediate concentration for a particular system where salinity and alcohol type are fixed. Point B* in Table I defines the lowest sulfonate/hydrocarbon ratios where Region 4 can exist for the IPA, 10.6K brine, TRS 10-80 systems. That is, at Point B* the slopes k and K are equal.

Variation of slopes with alcohol type, hydrocarbon type and salinity are illustrated in Tables II-VI. The data indicate the dependence of the phase boundaries of Regions 4 and 4' on these parameters. Although these systems were not investigated as ex-

Table II. Parameters of the Straight Lines Defining the Upper and Lower Boundaries of Region 4 for IPA-10.6K Brine-Heptane Systems.

Upper Boundary

Sulf./hept. (vol/vol)	K μl/ml. brine	$V_{ai} + V_{ao}$ (μl)	V_{ai} (μl)
.297	150.3	198	191
.223	97.0	142	136
.145	67.0	122	116
.126	50.4	116	111
.112	31.4	138	135

Lower Boundary

	k μl/ml. brine	$V_{ai} + V_{ao}$ (μl)	V_{ai} (μl)
.295	96.0	74	70
.216	72.9	50	46
.178	52.7	70	66
.144	35.5	85	82

Table III. Parameters of Straight Lines Defining the Upper Boundary of Region 4' - 10.6K Brine.

System	Sulf./brine (vol/vol)	K' μl/ml.	$V'_{ai} + V'_{aw}$ (μl)	V'_{ai} (μl)
TAA-Nonane	.291	27.5	212	165
	.230	24.0	217	162
	.151	21.3	213	140
	.113	16.5	223	147
Pentanol-Dodecane	.449	3.60	146	146
	.229	2.76	103	103

Table IV. Effect of Hydrocarbon Type on K' and V'_{ai} for a Sulfonate/Brine (10.6K) Ratio of 0.225 volume/volume. Alcohol is n-Pentanol.

Hydrocarbon	K' (μl/ml hydr.)	$V'_{ai} + V'_{aw}$ (μl)	V'_{ai} (μl)
Nonane	1.67	67	67
Dodecane	2.76	103	103
Pentadecane	3.55	128	128

Table V. Effect of Alcohol Type on K' and V'_{ai} for Samples Prepared in Nonane With a Sulfonate to Brine (10.6K) Ratio of .225 (vol/vol).

Alcohol	K' (μl/ml)	$V'_{ai} + V'_{aw}$ (μl)	V'_{ai} (μl)
TAA	24.0	217	162
n-Butanol	1.8	167	167
2-Pentanol	4.73	115	115
n-Pentanol	1.67	67	67
n-Hexanol	1.37	45.5	45.5

Table VI. Effect of Salinity on Parameters of Straight Lines Defining Upper Boundaries of Regions 4 and 4'.

System	Salinity (mg NaCl/l)	K (μl/ml brine)	$V_{ai} + V_{ao}$ (μl)	V_{ai} (μl)
IPA-Octane	8000	9.2	263	262
S/H=0.225 vol/vol	12000	107	138	132
	15000	149.3	102	93
		K' (μl/ml hydrocarbon)	$V'_{ai} + V'_{ao}$ (μl)	V'_{ai} (μl)
2-Pentanol-Nonane	5000	17.4	256	256
S/B=0.225 vol/vol	10600	4.73	115	115
TAA-Nonane	10600	24.0	217	162
S/B=0.225 vol/vol	12000	17.6	188	148
S/B=0.111 vol/vol	8000	82.6	436	281
	10600	16.5	223	147

tensively as the IPA, 10.6K brine systems, similar correlations of slopes with sulfonate/brine ratio or sulfonate/hydrocarbon ratio are suggested from the data.

The usefulness of these correlations lies in the fact that phase boundaries for Regions 4 or 4', on dilution paths where the ratios of sulfonate/hydrocarbon or sulfonate/brine are constant, can be located with a few data points and can be represented with a relatively simple model. The model corresponding to the boundaries is developed in the next section.

Development of a Model For Upper and Lower Phase Boundaries of Regions 4 and 4'

Figure 18 is a schematic representation of one type of a hydrocarbon in water microemulsion which is probably characteristic of Region 4[8]. Other micellar shapes have been identified[12-15] and may be present in Region 4. No specific assumptions were made concerning geometric shape or roughness of the interface.

The model considers the hydrophilic and the lipophilic phases to be separated by an interface whose main components are the amphiphilic molecules. This point of view is sustained by several investigators[16-19] with the exception of some recent literature[20] which postulates cosolubilization for some microemulsions. Alcohol added to the microemulsion is distributed between the internal

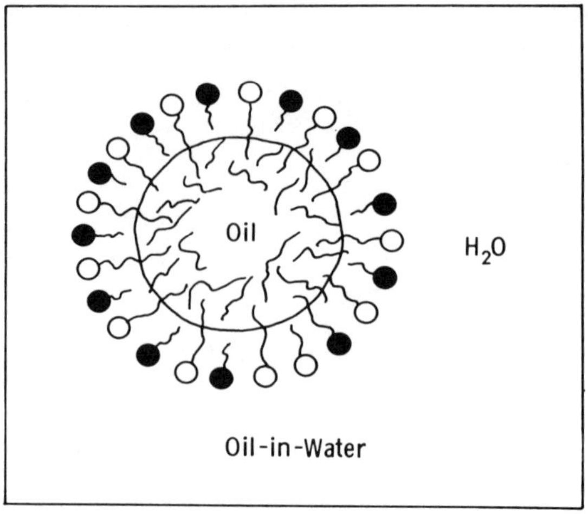

Figure 18. Schematic representation of an oil in water microemulsion with sulfonate and alcohol forming the interface.

phase (hydrocarbon), the interface and the external phase (water) according to the material balance defined by Equation 2.

$$N_a = N_{ao} + N_{ai} + N_{aw} \tag{2}$$

where

N_a = total moles alcohol in the system
N_{ao} = moles of alcohol in the hydrocarbon phase
N_{ai} = moles of alcohol at the interface
N_{aw} = moles of alcohol in the water phase

The development of a model for microemulsions at the upper and lower phase boundaries will be illustrated using the upper boundary of Region 4.

The procedure used to study the upper boundary involved dilution of the microemulsion with water. Along each dilution path, the amounts of hydrocarbon and sulfonate are constant. All of the sulfonate is considered to be at the interface and all of the hydrocarbon to be solubilized. When water is added to the system, some of the alcohol at the interface and some dissolved in the oil is transported to the external water phase, changing the curvature of the interface. Depletion of alcohol in the micelle locates the system underneath the upper boundary of Region 4. Additional alcohol is required to reach the phase boundary.

The linear relationship between alcohol and brine volumes

along the upper boundary of Region 4 can be developed from thermodynamic principles. In this development it is assumed that the amounts of alcohol (N_{ai}) and sulfonate (N_{si}) at the interface represented in Figure 18 are constant for each S/H dilution path along the upper boundary of Region 4. The alkanes used as the hydrocarbons in this research are considered to be absent from the interface. This assumption may not apply in systems containing polar molecules. Prince[19] and Mukerjee et al[21] have different viewpoints on the location of benzene. Prince observes triglycerides are always present in the interface. The presence of hydrocarbons in the interface does not affect the development of the model described in this section as long as the number of these molecules in the interface is constant.

The chemical potential of the alcohol in the interface is

$$\mu_{ai} = \mu^{\circ}_{ai} + RT \ln \gamma_{ai} X_{ai} \tag{3}$$

where μ°_{ai} is the standard chemical potential of alcohol at the interface. The activity coefficient γ_{ai} is constant along the upper boundary because the mole fraction of alcohol,

$$X_{ai} = \frac{N_{ai}}{N_{ai} + N_{si}} \tag{4}$$

remains fixed by the assumed configuration of the surfactant/alcohol interface. Thus, the chemical potential of alcohol in the interface must be constant on the upper boundary of Region 4, when pressure and temperature are fixed.

Since the system is at equilibrium, the chemical potentials of alcohol in the external phase, interface and internal phase must be equal. That is,

$$\mu_{ao} = \mu_{ai} = \mu_{aw} \tag{5}$$

or

$$\mu_{ai} = \mu^{\circ}_{ao} + RT \ln \gamma_{ao} \quad X_{ao} = \mu^{\circ}_{aw} RT + \ln \gamma_{aw} X_{aw} \tag{6}$$

where the γ's are the activity coefficients for the respective phases.

The standard chemical potentials in Equations 3 and 6 are functions of temperature and pressure but not composition. A constant value of μ_{ai} along the upper boundary infers that the activity, $a_w = \gamma_{aw} X_{aw}$, is constant when temperature and pressure are fixed. The mole fraction of alcohol in the external phase is

$$X_{aw} = \frac{N_{aw}}{N_{aw} + N_w} \tag{7}$$

when the amounts of sulfonate and hydrocarbon are neglected. It follows that

$$N_{aw} = \left(\frac{a_w}{\gamma_{aw} - a_w}\right) N_w \tag{8}$$

where

$$a_w = e \left(\frac{\mu_{ai} - \mu^\circ_{ai}}{RT}\right) \tag{9}$$

If the external phase is ideal ($\gamma_{aw} = 1.0$) or γ_{aw} is constant which is reasonable at low alcohol concentrations,

$$N_{aw} = K_i \; N_w \tag{10}$$

Substitution of these relationships into Equation 2 yields Equation 11.

$$N_a = N_{ao} + N_{ai} + K_i \, N_w \tag{11}$$

Equation 11 may also be written in terms of volumes. Equation 12 represents the data obtained in the laboratory

$$V_a = V_{ai} + V_{ao} + K \, V_w \tag{12}$$

where K is adjusted for conversion of K_i from moles to volume.

Equation 12 predicts that a plot of alcohol volume vs. water volume along the upper boundary of Region 4 is a straight line whose intercept is $V_{ai} + V_{ao}$ and whose slope, K, is the ratio of the amount of alcohol in the water to the amount of water. Analogous equations can be derived for the upper and lower boundaries of Region 4' and for the lower boundary of Region 4. Equation 13 is the expression for the upper boundary of Region 4'

$$V_a = V'_{ai} + V'_{aw} + K' \, V_o \tag{13}$$

The agreement of the models represented by Equations 12 and 13 with the experimental data shown in Figure 2, and Figures 5-17 demonstrates the consistency of the hypothesized structure of the interface with the requirements of phase equilibria.

The amounts of alcohol at the interface (V_{ai} or V'_{ai}) in Tables II-VI were estimated by computing the V_{ao} or V'_{aw} from equilibrium distribution data[9].

The data in Tables II-VI and the models represented by Equations 3 - 13 were also used to compute the change in standard free energy that occurs when an alcohol molecule is transported from one fluid phase to the interface of a microemulsion. This analysis and a discussion of the results are presented in Reference 9.

SUMMARY AND CONCLUSIONS

The following observations and conclusions are based on the analysis of experimental data for quaternary systems composed of TRS 10-80 (a petroleum sulfonate), brine, water or oil soluble alcohols and normal paraffin hydrocarbons.

Four microemulsion regions were identified in systems diluted with the brine or hydrocarbon and titrated to transparency with a water soluble alcohol in planes of constant sulfonate to hydrocarbon ratio. Similar regions were observed for titrations in planes of constant sulfonate to brine ratio for oil soluble alcohols. Critical sulfonate to hydrocarbon ratios for the existence of microemulsions were found for Regions 3 and 4 in systems containing isopropanol. These ratios increased as molecular weight of the hydrocarbon increased.

At the sulfonate and alcohol concentrations studied, the principal microemulsion regions (4 or 4') have linear upper and lower phase boundaries (volume basis) for dilution paths where the ratios of sulfonate to hydrocarbon or sulfonate to brine were constant. The slopes of these phase boundaries were shown to change with salinity, alcohol type and hydrocarbon type.

A model which predicts linear phase boundaries for Regions 4 or 4' was developed from a hypothesized configuration of sulfonate and alcohol at the interface. The model is consistent with the thermodynamics of phase equilibria. This model is more general than an analogous model proposed by Bowcott and Schulman for spherical w/o microemulsions because no assumption was made regarding the shape of the interface.

ACKNOWLEDGEMENTS

This investigation was supported by the Tertiary Oil Recovery Project at the University of Kansas. The Witco Chemical Company supplied sulfonate samples.

NOMENCLATURE

k	slope of lower boundary of Region 4, μl alcohol/ml brine
k'	slope of lower boundary of Region 4', μl alcohol/ml brine
k_i	mole alcohol/mole hydrocarbon
K	slope of upper boundary of Region 4, μl alcohol/ml brine
K'	slope of upper boundary of Region 4', μl alcohol/ml oil

V_{ai} volume of alcohol at the interface in Region 4, μl
V'_{ai} volume of alcohol at the interface in Region 4', μl
V_{ao} volume of alcohol solubilized in the oil phase in Region 4, μl
V_{aw} volume of alcohol solubilized in the water phase in Region 4', μl
V_o total volume of oil, ml
V_w total volume of water, ml

REFERENCES

1. W. B. Gogarty and W. C. Tosch, J. Pet. Tech., 20, 1407-1414. (1968).
2. R. N. Healy and R. L. Reed, Soc. Pet. Eng. J., 17, 129-139. (1977).
3. R. N. Healy, R. L. Reed and C. W. Carpenter, Soc. Pet. Eng. J., 15, 87-103 (1975).
4. J. A. Davis and S. C. Jones, J. Pet. Tech., 20, 1415-1428. (1968).
5. R. N. Healy and R. L. Reed, J. Pet. Tech., 14, 491-505. (1974).
6. B. L. Wickert, M.S. Thesis, Department of Chemical and Petroleum Engineering, University of Kansas (1978).
7. R. N. Healy, R. L. Reed and D. G. Stenmark, Soc. Pet. Eng. J., 16, 147-160 (1976).
8. J. E. Bowcott and J. H. Schulman, Z. Electrochem., 59, 283-288. (1955).
9. J. G. Dominguez, Ph.D. Dissertation, University of Kansas (1977).
10. D. R. Zornes, G. P. Willhite and M. J. Michnick, Soc. Pet. Eng. J., 18, 207-218 (1978).
11. B. L. Wickert, G. P. Willhite, D. W. Green and S. L. Black, Paper No. 45d, presented at Symposium on Interfacial Phenomena in Chemical Flooding Processes, AIChE 85th National Meeting, Philadelphia, Pennsylvania (1978).
12. D. O. Shah, A. Tamjeedi, J. W. Falco and R. D. Walker, Jr., AIChE J., 18, 1116-1120 (1972).
13. K. Shinoda, T. Nagagawa, B. Tamamushi and T. Isemura, Editors, "Colloidal Surfactants", Academic Press, New York, 1963.
14. D. Stigter, J. Colloid Interface Sci., 23, 379 (1967).
15. P. Mukerjee, in "Micellization, Solubilization, and Microemulsions", K. L. Mittal, Editor, Volume 1, pp. 171-194, Plenum Press, New York, 1977.
16. P. A. Windsor, Chem. Rev., 68, 1-40 (1968).
17. L. E. Scriven, Nature, 26, 123 (1976).
18. S. Friberg, I. Lapezynska, and G. Gillberg, J. Colloid Interface Sci., 56, 19. (1976).
19. L. M. Prince, in "Microemulsions: Theory and Practice", L. M. Prince, Editor, pp 48-56, Academic Press, New York, 1977.
20. D. O. Shah, R. D. Walker, Jr., W. C. Hsieh, N. J. Shah, S. Dwivedi, J. Nelander, R. Pepinsky and D. W. Deamer,

Paper number SPE 5815, presented at Improved Oil Recovery Symposium of the Society of Petroleum Engineers of AIME, Tulsa, Oklahoma (1976).
21. P. Mukerjee, J. R. Cardinal and N. R. Desai, in "Micellization, Solubilization, and Microemulsions", K. L. Mittal, Editor, Volume 1, pp 241-261, Plenum Press, New York, 1977.

AN ELECTRICAL CONDUCTIVITY MODEL OF W/O-MICROEMULSIONS

Hans-Friedrich Eicke and Andres Denss

Institute of Physical Chemistry

University of Basel, CH-4056 Basel, Switzerland

A simple, straight-forward physical model of the electrical conductivity in W/O-microemulsions is suggested and applied to water/AOT/benzene systems. The model is essentially based upon two processes: (i) a dissociation of individual surfactant molecules within the inverted micellar aggregates and (ii) a transfer of charges (cation or anion) to another (originally neutral) micellar entity. The physical situation is taken to be represented by a phase equilibrium with respect to the exchangable charged species between the droplet pseudo-phase and the solution phase consisting of a dilute solution of charged aggregates in the non-polar solvent. The experimental results are fairly well represented by the theoretically derived conductivity equation which provides a clear insight into the underlying physical processes.

INTRODUCTION

Not unexpectedly, conductometric and dielectric loss measurements belong to the earliest investigations of emulsions and, particularly, microemulsions, since variations of the overall resistances and of the complex dielectric permitivities are evident. Hanai[1], for example, has covered these early investigations in a review. Also more recent studies appeared with respect to this subject[2-6]. Apart from the papers which are mostly concerned with technical aspects of emulsions, a large number of publications interested in the theoretical background can be traced back to the classical works of Lorentz[7], Lorenz[8], Maxwell[9], and Wagner[10].

However, many instances have been reported of considerable deviations from the predictions based upon classical models[1,11]. These refer not only to technical emulsions but also to the so-called microemulsions which are thermodynamically stable and possess, accordingly, more reproducible structures.

Thus facing this situation, theoretical considerations as to the effect of solubilized water on the electrical conductivity may still be worthwhile in order to check whether simple models are adequate to interpret the observed physical phenomena.

EXPERIMENTAL

Purified Aerosol OT (AOT)[12] in benzene (0.83 mol dm^{-3}) was selected as a suitable system. The detergent concentration was specified by the demand to produce as high an excess of micelles compared with the monomers as is compatible with the condition of individual, free, entities, i.e. the mean distance between the aggregates must still be larger than the particle diameter. Higher detergent concentrations give rise to transitions to lyotropic liquid crystals.

The conductivity was determined with a Wayne-Kerr Universal Bridge, Type 221 at 1591.5 Hz and 25.00 ± 0.05°C, using a gold plated, cylindrical cell, Type MFL3/MS (WTW, Weinheim Germany). The reproducibility of the data (compared with those obtained from test measurements with distilled water of similar conductivity) was about ± 5%. The experimental results are shown in Fig. 1 where the conductivity is plotted against the amount of solubilized H_2O.

According to the above it can be assumed that, taking a critical micelle concentration of the system of about 10^{-3} mol dm^{-3} and the aggregation number to be 20, the concentration of the monomers is smaller by a factor of 40 as compared to that of the micelles. It is thus reasonable to suggest that the micellar aggregates are responsible for the observed conductivity even without added water. If a microemulsion is formed the tendency of the detergent material to be in the water/hydrocarbon interface is more pronounced.

MODEL

With regard to the charge production two processes have to be considered a priori: (i) A dissociation of AOT molecules inside the micellar entities which is thought to be independent of the medium the aggregates are embedded in, and (ii) A transfer of charges, i.e. of an anion or (less probably in this case) of a cation which stem from the dissociation of the detergent molecule inside the droplet, to another (originally neutral) micellar aggregate. This latter process is considered to represent a phase-transfer between the droplet pseudo-phase (built up by the ensemble of microemulsion droplets) and the solution phase consisting of a very dilute solution of charged micellar aggregates (produced by the just mentioned process) in the nonpolar solvent. The charge transfer will actually proceed in two steps: ion (droplet phase) → ion (nonpolar solvent) and ion (nonpolar solvent) → ion (resolubilized in micellar aggregate).

According to these two processes the following theoretical model is proposed:

The dissociation inside a microemulsion droplet can be described by

$$S_n \rightleftarrows \frac{n-1}{n} S_n^+ + \frac{1}{n} S_n^- \tag{1}$$

where it has been assumed that one surfactant molecule ($\frac{1}{n} S_n$) per microemulsion droplet (S_n) is dissociated. Applying the mass

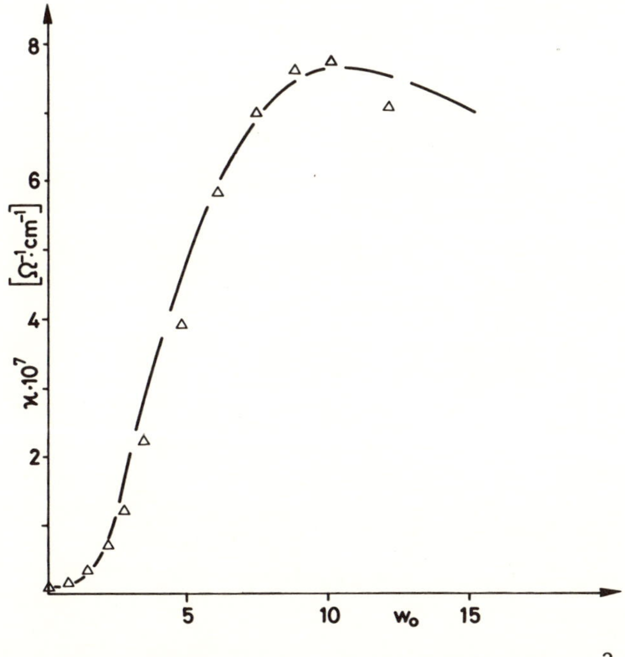

Figure 1. Specific conductivity (κ) of 0.83 mol dm^{-3} AOT in benzene at 25.00 ± 0.05°C versus amount of solubilized water w_o = $[H_2O]/[AOT]$. Experimental points (Δ), calculated curve through points (——) according to equation (11). Parameters: K^{I*}_{diss} = 6.8×10^{-14}, $z^2e^2/4\pi\varepsilon\varepsilon_0 kT\ 10^{-8} = 575$, $s_o = 4 \times 10^{-5}$ mol cm^{-3}, $\varepsilon = \alpha + \beta w_o$, $\alpha = 2$, $\beta = 0.1$, $R/10^{-8} = 14 + 22\ w_o$.

action law to the equilibrium of equation (1), yields

$$K^{I}_{diss} = \frac{[S^{+}_{n}]^{(n-1)/n}\,[S^{-}_{n}]^{1/n}}{[S_{n}]} \,. \qquad (2)$$

On physical grounds it has to be assumed that most probably the anion of an anionic surfactant (in the present case of AOT) will be trasferred. Therefore, considering the electroneutrality with respect to the droplet pseudo-phase (I), equation (2) is solved, for example, for the anion concentration within phase I, hence

$$[S^{-}_{n}]^{I} = K^{I}_{diss}[S_{n}] \qquad (3)$$

It should be noted that phase I is electroneutral: after a charge transfer the opposite charge remains solubilized in the micellar aggregate which now belongs (according to our convention) to phase II, i.e., the nonpolar solution phase.

According to the above, two states of the anion have to be viewed which are in equilibrium. Thus the electrochemical potentials ($\tilde{\mu}_a$) of the anions in the coexisting pseudo-phases must be equal:

$$\tilde{\mu}^{I}_{a} = \tilde{\mu}^{II}_{a}$$

or

$$\tilde{\mu}^{\ominus\, I}_{a} + kT \ln c^{I}_{a} = \tilde{\mu}^{\ominus\, II}_{a} + kT \ln c^{II}_{a}, \qquad (4)$$

The activities of the anions in the pseudo-phases I and II have been replaced by concentrations due to the low degree of dissociation. The ratio of the anion concentrations in both pseudo-phases follows from equation (4), i.e. with $c^{I}_{a} = [S^{-}_{n}]^{I}$,

$$\frac{c^{II}_{a}}{[S^{-}_{n}]^{I}} = e^{-\frac{\tilde{\mu}^{\ominus\, II}_{a} - \tilde{\mu}^{\ominus\, I}_{a}}{kT}} = e^{-\frac{\mu^{\ominus\, II}_{a} - \mu^{\ominus\, I}_{a}}{kT}} \cdot e^{-\frac{z\,e\,(\psi^{II}-\psi^{I})}{kT}} \qquad (5a)^{1)}$$

the $\mu^{\ominus}_{a}$'s and ψ's refer to the standard chemical potentials of the

---

1) Although the present discussion refers to the exchange of anions, the valency (z) has not been replaced by (-1) for the sake of generality of the model developed in this paper.

anions in the respective phases and the electrical potentials of the respective phases.

By combining equations (3) and (5a), the charge production within phase I is connected with a charge transfer between the two pseudo-phases. If it is assumed that most of the anions are resolubilized within micellar aggregates, then (to a first approximation) $c_a^{II} \cong [S_n^-]^{II}$.

$$c_a^{II} \cong [S_n^-]^{II} = K_{diss}^{I}[S_n]\, e^{-\frac{\mu_a^{\ominus\, II} - \mu_a^{\ominus\, I}}{kT}} \cdot e^{\frac{z\, e(\psi^{II} - \psi^{I})}{kT}} \qquad (5b)$$

The mass conservation demands

$$s_o = [S_n] + [S_n^+]^{II} + [S_n^-]^{II} \qquad (6)$$

if it is assumed, as discussed above, that to a first approximation the weighed-in concentration of detergent is essentially contained in the microemulsion droplets. Moreover, since the degree of dissociation is rather small the last two terms in equation (6) may reasonably be neglected. Accordingly, equation (5b) is modified to give

$$[S_n^-]^{II} = K_{diss}^{I\,*}\, s_o\, e^{-\frac{z\, e\, (\psi^{II} - \psi^{I})}{kT}} \qquad (7)$$

if the difference of the standard chemical potentials of the anions between the two pseudo-phases are combined with K_{diss}^{I}, indicated by K_{diss}^{I*}.

The difference of the electrical potentials between the two pseudo-phases is in the present case directly proportional to the charge Q of the spherically assumed micellar aggregate divided by the capacity C of a sphere, thus

$$\psi^{II} - \psi^{I} \cong \frac{Q}{C} = \frac{z\, e}{4\pi\varepsilon\varepsilon_o\, R} \qquad (8)^{2)}$$

where R is the radius of the spherical droplet and ε the dielectric

2) A constant term ($\Delta\psi_o$) corresponding to zero excess charge (no charge transfer) has been neglected.

permittivity of the solution phase, ε_o the absolute permittivity. Therefore, equation (7) can be written

$$[S_n^-]^{II} = K_{diss}^{I*} \; s_o \; e^{-\frac{z^2 e^2}{4\pi\varepsilon \varepsilon_o R kT}} \tag{7a}$$

The specific electrical conductivity κ is defined by

$$\kappa = 2 \, c_j \, F \, \bar{u} \tag{9}$$

where c_j is the ionic concentration in mol cm^{-3}, F the Faraday constant, and $\bar{u}$ the mean mobility $\frac{1}{2}(u_+ + u_-)$ of the oppositely charged droplets. This last term is equal to the ratio of the velocity of the particles and the field strength. It can be replaced, accordingly, by

$$\bar{u} = \frac{z\,e}{\rho} = \frac{z\,e}{6\pi\,\eta\,R} \tag{10}$$

where the friction ρ is determined by Stoke's law. (η is the viscosity of the solution). Now substituting c_j and $\bar{u}$ in equation (9) by equations (7a) and (10), respectively, one finally obtains (N_A = AVOGADRO's number)

$$\kappa = \frac{z^2 e^2 N_A K^*_{diss} \; s_o \; e^{-\frac{z^2 e^2}{4\pi\varepsilon \varepsilon_o R kT}}}{3\,\pi\,\eta\,R} \tag{11}$$

RESULTS AND DISCUSSION

R and ε are dependent on the amount of solubilized water in the microemulsion. The effect on the permittivity is rather weak which is also verified by dielectric increment measurements. We, therefore, write $\varepsilon = \alpha+\beta w_o$ where α denotes the macroscopic dielectric constant of the over-all solution without added water, i.e. about 2, while β describes the dependence of ε on w_o. However, R is linearly dependent on $w_o=[H_2O]/[AOT]$, the number of water molecules per AOT molecule. This follows from the assumption that R is proportional to the square root of the average number of surfactant molecules in the interface, i.e. $(\bar{n}_{AOT})^{\frac{1}{2}}$, which is equivalent to saying that $\bar{n}_{AOT}$ is proportional to the spherical water/hydrocarbon interface. The dependence of $\bar{n}_{AOT}$ on the amount of solubilized water has already been derived[13,14], and shown to be approximately given by

$$\bar{n}_{detergent} \cong \left(\frac{cmc}{12}\right)^3 \cdot r_o^3 \cdot \frac{e^{6(\frac{\theta}{T})}}{(\frac{\theta}{T})^6} \cdot v_{H_2O}^2 \cdot w_o^2, \tag{12}$$

hence, $R \cong \text{const}\ w_o$ (at T = constant). In the present case it is suitable to write $R = R_o + \text{const}\ w_o$, where R_o is the radius of an AOT micelle in benzene with added water.

r_o is the shortest distance between the centre of the surfactant dipole and the spherical interface (polar droplet core (ε_2) /nonpolar solvent (ε_1)), θ, a characteristic temperature, $=[(\varepsilon_2 - \varepsilon_1)/\varepsilon_1(\varepsilon_1 + \varepsilon_2)]\mu_{app}^2/r_o^3 k$. The apparent dipole moment (μ_{app}) corresponds to the surfactant molecule built in the detergent layer of the droplet. v_{H_2O} is the volume of a water molecule, and k is the Boltzmann constant.

From equation (11) it is seen that two effects are counteracting. With growing droplet size due to the solubilization of water, the exponential term in the nominator is strongly increasing; whereas, with larger droplet radii, the influence of the denominator gradually dominates. This latter effect reduces the total conductivity again.

Equation (11) allows, actually, an even more evident interpretation of the underlying physical processes: the exponential factor depends on the ratio of the electrical potential energy and the thermal energy of the particles. It thus describes the probability that an ion pair formed by two oppositely charged micellar aggregates dissociates in these nonpolar solvents. Hence, the total conductivity can be considered to be determined by two dissociation processes, namely, a dissociation of single surfactant molecules in phase I and a dissociation of ion pairs in phase II and a viscosity effect due to increasing droplet sizes with the amount of solubilized water.

The agreement between the experimental plot shown in Figure 1 and the theoretically calculated specific conductivity according to the above proposed model is quite satisfactory. Since the model contains no restrictions as to the solubilized phase volume, it should be valid (in the framework of the above introduced assumptions) also for large degrees of solubilization, thus justifying the title of this paper.

The aim of this contribution is to show that a relatively simple, straight-forward physical picture (with a minimum of restrictive assumptions) describing dissociation and charge transfer processes is compatible with the experimental results. It does not by any means claim to be generally applicable but wants to stimulate other work in the microemulsion area.

ACKNOWLEDGMENT

This work is part of project No. 2.718-0.77 of the Swiss National Science Foundation.

REFERENCES

1. T. Hanai, in "Emulsion Science", P. Sherman, Editor, Academic Press, New York, 1968.
2. M. Clausse, and P. Sherman, C.R. Acad. Sci., Ser. C 279, 919 (1974).
3. H. F. Eicke, and C. W. Shepherd, Helv. Chim. Acta 57, 1951 (1974).
4. R. A. Mackay, C. Hermansky, and R. Agarwal, in "Colloid and Interface Science", M. Kerker, Editor, Vol. II, p.289, Academic Press, New York, 1976.
5. M. Clausse, R. J. Sheppard, C. Bond and C. G. Essex, ibid. Vol. II, p. 233.
6. M. Clausse, P. Sherman and R. J. Sheppard, J. Colloid, Interface Science, 56, 123 (1976).
7. H. A. Lorentz, Ann Wied, 11, 70 (1880).
8. L. Lorenz, Ann Wied, 9, 641 (1880).
9. J. C. Maxwell, "Treatise on Electricity and Magnetism," Dover, New York, 1959.
10. K. W. Wagner, Arch. Elektrotech. 2, 371 (1914).
11. S. S. Dukhin, in "Surface and Colloid Science", E. Matijević, Editor, Vol. 3, pp. 83-165, Wiley Interscience, New York 1971.
12. A. Denss, Ph.D. Thesis, University of Basel, 1977
13. H. F. Eicke, J. Colloid Interface Science, 52, 65 (1975).
14. H. F. Eicke, and J. Rehak, Helv. Chim. Acta 59, 2883 (1976).

REACTIONS IN MICROEMULSION MEDIA

Roland E. Barden and Smith L. Holt*

Department of Chemistry, The University of Wyoming

Laramie, Wyoming 82071

As defined by L. M. Prince, microemulsions are spherical aggregates of oil or water dispersed in the other liquid and stabilized by an interfacial film of one or more surfactants such that the droplets range in diameter from 10 to 200 nm. Since "bulk" water and "bulk" oil coexist in the same solution, a microemulsion is a suitable solvent for chemical reactions involving water-soluble species (e.g. small ions) and water-insoluble species (e.g. large organic molecules). The only constraint imposed on this system is that the organic molecule must be capable of entering the interfacial film so that the reactants can come in contact with each other. Thus the organic reactant must posses a polar group such as a hydroxyl or amino group so that, in the context of microemulsion chemistry, it can function as a cosurfactant. Except for this constraint, microemulsions are very attractive as solvents, particularly when one desires to investigate the influence of interfacial phenomena on chemical processes. Microemulsions feature a very high content of interfacial area per unit volume. The ultra-small size of the dispersed droplets frequently leads to transparent solutions, thereby permitting a chemical reaction to be analyzed by UV-visible spectroscopy as well as by potentiometry and a number of other spectroscopic methods. The utility of a microemulsion as a host for a chemical reaction is not generally appreciated. Only a couple of laboratories have investigated chemical reactions in microemulsions. Most published work has been concerned

*Chemistry Department, University of Georgia, Athens, GA 30602

with the interaction of transition metal ions with large organic molecules

INTRODUCTION

The influence of surfactant solutions on various chemical processes has been investigated rather extensively in the last 10-15 years. The great majority of published studies have been performed with aqueous micellar solutions (for recent reviews, see References 1-3). Most workers have been primarily interested in the catalytic properties of micellar solutions. Other phenomena, such as the reactivity of functional groups in various interfacial environments, have also been investigated.[4,5] In many studies of this kind the micellar solution is considered to be a model system for proteins or enzymes.[6,7]

Inverse micelles, which form when suitable amounts of a detergent are dissolved in a non-polar solvent, have also been investigated as solvents for chemical reactions. According to Fendler et. al.[8], inverse micellar solutions may have some advantages over aqueous micellar solutions as models for protein. When small amounts of water are solubilized in the inverse micellar solution, the system becomes analogous to a protein in that both feature water-accessible binding sites consisting of several polar functional groups surrounded by a hydrophobic region.[8] Compared to aqueous micellar solutions, the inverse micellar solution has not been widely adapted as a model system; most of the published studies have come from Fendler's group.[9,10]

Microemulsions, a third type of surfactant solution, are stable dispersions of one liquid in another in the form of spherical droplets.[11,12] The emulsified droplets are sufficiently small ($<0.14\mu$) so that transparent solutions can be obtained. These solutions are characterized by a large amount of interfacial area per unit volume: also, the dispersed phase may constitute a significant portion of the total system volume. Such a system is well suited for investigating the interaction between water soluble ions (e.g. transition metals) and organic molecules that are sparingly soluble in water. Chemical processes in these solutions can be investigated by a number of techniques, including UV-visible, IR, NMR, CD and EPR spectroscopy and potentiometry.

Microsmulsions were initially investigated by Schulman and coworkers.[13-16] The physical chemistry of these solutions has not been completely elucidated and most of published work on microemulsions, even at the present time, describes attempts to remedy this deficiency.[17-19] Microemulsions are generally composed of water, hydrocarbon, an ionic surfactant, and a cosurfactant.[11,12] For example, the microemulsion used in much of our work consists of water droplets dispersed in hexane; the stabilizing surfactant is hexadecyltrimethylammonium perchlorate and 2-propanol is the co-surfactant. To a degree in systems where the surfactant concentration is relatively high (∿ 10% by weight) such a solution may be thought of as an inverse micellar solution containing solubilized water. Some workers prefer the terms "swollen micellar solution"[20] or "micellar emulsion"[21] for these systems, rather than microemulsion. In our own work, however, we have a bulk encapsulated phase as well as a bulk continuous phase, consequently microemulsion is the proper term to apply.

Microemulsions are extraordinary solutions in some respects and they are therefore used in a number of important industrial applications.[11,12] Cosmetic and pharmaceutical products based on these solutions are valued for their stability (and "appearance"). Other microemulsions are important to the water-based floor-polish and paint industries, the cleaning fluids industry, and so on. More recently, microemulsions have been applied to tertiary oil recovery.[23,24] In spite of these notable contributions in industrial chemistry, microemulsions have not been a popular subject of investigation by scientists in academia, except for a small number of physical chemists. Only a few chemists have exploited the extraordinary properties of a microemulsified solution in areas of chemistry not directly related to industrial applications. In particular, efforts to investigate microemulsions as media for chemical reactions have thus far been reported only by our group and by Mackay's group.[25] It is this latter area of microemulsion chemistry to which this review addresses itself.

MICROEMULSIONS AS A HOST FOR CHEMICAL REACTIONS

Reactions Involving Porphyrins and Metals

There is considerable ongoing research centered around porphyrins and metallo-porphyrins primarily because of their importance in biological systems. While the vast bulk of studies have been carried out in systems which are not microemulsions, in fact microemulsions are quite attractive for the study of porphyrin-metalloporphyrin chemistry. The reasons for this are several fold. First, regardless of the type of microemulsion (e.g. oil or water disperse) used, the porphyrin can be chosen such that it is soluble in the oil phase while the metal ion is of necessity soluble in the aqueous phase. This insures that the metal ion incorporation can only occur at the interface thus limiting the number of possible mechanisms for metallation. In such a system the effect of anionic, cationic or nonionic interfacial environments on metal ion incoroporation can be studied. Secondly, a metalloporphyrin of appropriate design can be encapsulated in either a hydrophobic droplet (utilizing an oil-in-water microemulsion) or a hydrophilic droplet (utilizing a water-in-oil microemulsion). It is then possible to effect chemical reactions involving these metalloporphyrins while they reside in a variety of biochemically relevant environments. Finally, a metalloporphyrin designed to orient itself at an interface may serve to eliminate one or more of the problems experienced in other model system, e.g. the irreversible dimerization reaction in hemoglobin model systems:

$$2Fe^{II}P + O_2 \rightarrow PFe{-}O_2{-}FeP \xrightarrow{2Fe^{II}P} 2(PFe^{III}{-}O{-}Fe^{III}P).$$

Studies on metal ion incorporation into tetraphenylporphine (TPP) have been published by Letts and Mackay.[26] These authors utilized benzene in water (o/w) microemulsions stabilized by either soap or detergent (Table I). The metal ions Mg(II), Mn(II), Zn(II), Co(II) and Cu(II) were examined. Of these only Cu(II) was incorporated into TPP. The rate of incorporation was found to vary, however, depending on the nature of the surfactant and the type of cofactor (a Lewis base added to aid in proton removal or complex with the metal) (Table II). It was found that, in general, insertion could be effected in the presence of anionic surfactants but not in the presence of the cationic surfactant cetylpyridinium bromide. The single exception was the inhibition of the reaction in the sodium cetyl sulfate (SCS) microemulsion when 2,2'-bipyridine or ethylenediamine was present as the cofactor.

Table I. Constitution of Microemulsions Used by Letts and Mackay

Component	Proportions, wt %		
	Sodium Cetyl Sulfate (SCS)	Cetylpyridinium Bromide (CPB)	Potassium Oleate
Water	54.54	54.45	54.70
Benzene	6.12	5.73	8.21
Cyclohexanol	23.49	21.62	24.61
Surfactant	15.85	18.20	12.48

Adapted from Ref. 26, with permission.

A detailed study of the incorporation was carried out using quinoline as the cofactor. The reaction was found to be first order in $TPPH_2$, second order in quinoline and first order in Cu(II). The experimental rate law was found to be $-d\ln TPPH_2/dt = (k[Cu(II)] + k')[Q]^2M^{-2}sec^{-1}$ where $k = 1.3 \times 10^4 M^{-3}sec^{-1}$ and $k' = 42$. Extending these investigations it was found that k_{obsd} was inversely

Table II. Rate of Incorporation of Copper (II) by Tetraphenylporphine in Benzene-Water-Cyclohexanol-Surfactant Microemulsions

Surfactant	Cofactor	$10^3[Cu^{2+}]$,M	$t_{1/2}$,hr
Potassium oleate	None	10	0.58
Sodium cetyl sulfate	2,2'-Bipyridine or ethylenediamine	10	No reaction
	None	10	14.5
	Ammonia	10	11
	Octadecyl acetate (10^{-2}M)	6.0	6.5
	Albumin (0.6 wt %)	0.1	7.0
	Quinoline(10^{-3}M)	6.0	0.023

Adapted from Ref. 26, with permission.

proportional to the third power of the phase volume, which was interpreted to indicate that the Cu(II) is bound to the droplet surface.

In a later study Letts and Mackay[27] investigated the effect of the addition of triphenyl phosphine (Ph_3P) on the incorporation of Cu(II) into TPP. Using chemical analyses and optical and electron paramagnetic resonance spectroscopy they determined that the Ph_3P stabilized the formation of a Cu(II)-TPP complex in the interphase region of the benzene microdroplet. Two additional Cu(II)-TPP species were isolated as detergent aggregates. It was suggested that the latter two species are intermediates in the formation of CuTPP. The suggested reaction sequence is shown in Figure 1.

Letts and Mackay[26,27] apparently chose a o/w microemulsion as a solvent for their studies because of the need to solubilize a metal ion and an organic molecule simultaneously. Neither the metal ion nor $TPPH_2$ are inherently surface active and thus capable of entering the interfacial film. This shortcoming may be partially offset by attracting the metal ion to the water-side of the interfacial film with electrostatic forces. However, no incorporation was observed in the absence of added cofactor (Lewis base), and thus the cofactor must play a critical role in bringing Cu(II) and $TPPH_2$ together so they can interact. Letts and Mackay[26] suggested that the cofactor acts as a catalyst by complexing the Cu(II), aiding in the removal of protons from the porphyrin, or both. Their data and arguments clearly favor the complexation postulate. The authors of this review suggest that the cofactor is a type of phase transfer catalyst. In other words, incorporation becomes possible only when the cofactor-metal complex enters the "oily"

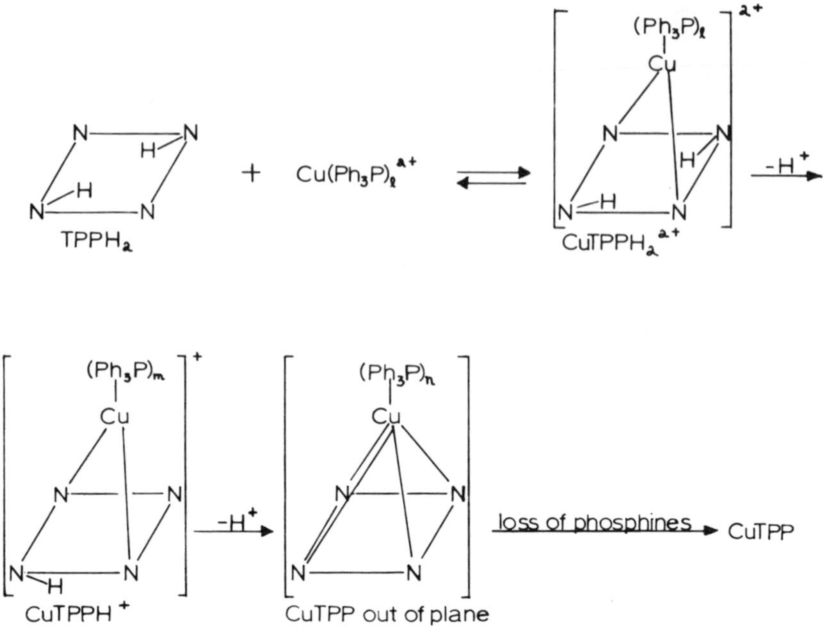

Figure 1. Proposed intermediates in the reaction between Cu^{2+}, Ph_3P and $TPPH_2$. Reproduced from Reference 27 with permission.

portion of the interfacial film and $TPPH_2$ and Cu(II) come into contact with each other. The metal ion specificity of the process apparently depends on the nature of the cofactor·metal complex and the ability of $TPPH_2$ to extract metal ion from this complex, as suggested by Letts and Mackay.[26]

Jones and Mackay[28] have studied the photodegradation of chlorophyll in an o/w microemulsion composed of SCS, 1-pentanol, mineral oil and phosphate buffered water. Chlorophyll is an excellent molecule for studies in a microemulsion because it contains a somewhat polar head group and a long non-polar tail. Thus chlorophyll should be capable of entering an interfacial film. Investigation of the optical absorption spectrum of chlorophyll in the microemulsion indicated that the molecule was indeed located in the interface.[28] When photolyzed with white light the solubilized chlorophyll undergoes photodegradation. This process is first order in pigment concentration. The rate of the photodegradation was retarded by oxygen, which is consistent with a mechanism involving cleavage of the porphyrin ring. Added oxidants or reductants accelerated the rate of the photodegradation, but adding a complete redox system (both oxidant and reductant) prevented the photodegradation. Both oil soluble and water soluble redox agents were effective in the latter studies, implying that the redox reactions take place in the interfacial film.

Work in the authors' laboratories has focused on the incorporation of transition metal ions into protoporphyrin IX.[29] A detergentless w/o microemulsion composed of hexane, water, and 2-propanol has been used in most experiments.[30] (Detergentless microemulsions are discussed in greater detail below.) In some cases small amounts of a cationic detergent, hexadecyltrimethylammonium perchlorate, was added to the system. Preliminary results indicate that Cu(II) is rapidly incorporated into protoporphyrin IX in the detergentless microemulsion. The reaction is complete in about 5 minutes under the conditions tested. However, no incorporation is observed over 24 hr if the cationic detergent is added to the microemulsion. The mechanism of incorporation appears to be quite complex and further studies will be required in order to elucidate the rate law for this process.

Reactions Involving Amino Alcohols and Metals

A rather complete study of the interaction of Cu(II) with the side chains of selected N^{α}-dodecanoyl-amino alcohols has been carried out in the authors' laboratories.[31-33] The w/o microemulsion used in these studies was composed of hexane, water, 2-propanol and hexadecyltrimethylammonium perchlorate. Certain compositions of these four chemicals were shown to be microemulsions by ultracentrifugation and conductivity studies (Figure 2).[30] A relatively low amount of detergent was added to our system compared to the usual formulation for a microemulsion as described in the literature. Added detergent was shown to enhance the stability of the system in the presence of reactants. However, we did not want to crowd the interface with detergent and thereby prevent the ligand from entering the interfacial film. Thus the compromise position was to add a modest amount of detergent.

The L-amino acids of interest were chemically modified to achieve two goals. The first goal was to ensure that the ligand would function as a cosurfactant, i.e. enter the interfacial film. The second goal was to chemically block the α-amino and α-carboxyl groups so that only the functional group of interest, i.e. that in the side chain, would be free to interact with the metal ions. Thus the α-amino group was acylated with dodecanoic acid to form an amphipathic molecule, and then the α-carboxyl group was reduced to convert the amino acid to an amino alcohol.

In our studies complex formation was observed between Cu(II) and each of the five N-acyl-amino alcohols tested.[31-33] The properties of the complexes were assessed by potentiometry and by UV-visible and EPR spectroscopy. Table III lists the ligand:metal ratios of limit complexes and, where measurable, the $\log_{10}$ of formation constants for the different combinations of Cu(II) and ligand. Table IV lists EPR parameters for Cu(II) complexes of the five amino alcohols studied.

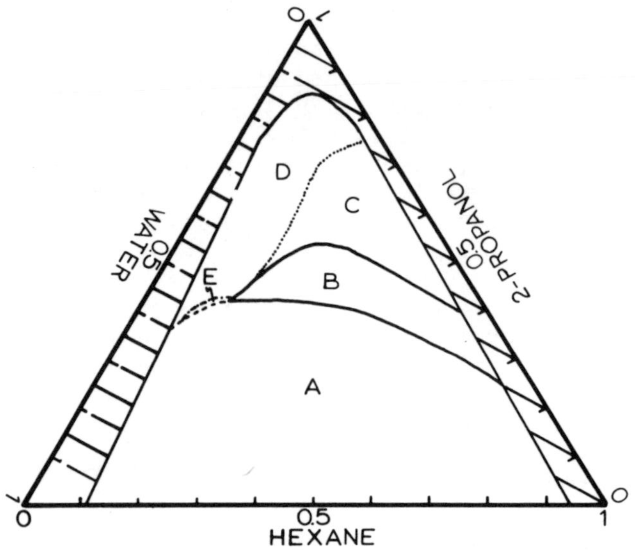

Figure 2. Ternary phase diagram for the hexane, water and 2-propanol system in the presence of relatively small amounts of hexadecyltrimethylammonium perchlorate. Region A includes unstable, opaque macroemulsions; Region B, stable transparent microemulsions; Region C, appears to contain small H-bonded aggregates of water and 2-propanol; Region D, includes "normal" ternary solutions. Reproduced from Ref. 30 with permission.

The Cu(II) complexes with the side chains of histidinol and lysinol exhibit a reasonable stability although they are of different stoichiometry. The limit complex for the Cu(II)/histidinol system has a ligand to metal ratio of 2:1.[31] We concluded that the Cu(II) was chelated by N$^{\alpha}$-dodecanoyl-L-histidinol through an imidazole nitrogen and the amide carbonyl oxygen. This conclusion was based on a comparison of the absorption spectrum of the histidinol complex with the spectra of simpler Cu(II) complexes in which Cu(II) had been shown to coordinate to two N's and two O's. Such a conclusion also was consistent with the EPR data (Table IV), which in turn bear a remarkable similarity to the EPR data reported by Lindskog and Nyman for Cu(II)-substituted human carbonic anhydrase.[34] Clear evidence of motional restraints in the EPR spectra, ultracentrifugation studies, and the solubility properties of the Cu(II)·ligand complex indicated that the 2:1 complex is indeed located in the interfacial domain of the microemulsion.

In the Cu(II)/lysinol system the limit species is a CuL_4^{2+} complex in which four ε-amino groups are bound to Cu(II) in a square-planar geometry.[32] The EPR data obtained for this complex (Table IV) are quite similar to those reported for bicarbonate-

Table III. Stoichiometry and Formation Constants of Cu(II) Complexes of N^{α}-Dodecanoyl-Amino Alcohols

Ligand	Limit Complex[a] ML_x, x =	$\log_{10}$ Formation Constant K_1	K_2	K_3	K_4
histidinol	2	4.28	2.66		
lysinol	4	6.13	5.66	4.97	3.93
glutaminol	1	0.23			
methioninol	2[b]				
tryptophanol	2				

a. Determined by potentiometric and/or EPR measurements.
b. ML_x complex was identified, but it may not be a true limit species.
c. Data from Ref. 31-33.

Table IV. EPR Parameters of Cu(II) Complexes of N^{α}-Dodecanoyl-Amino Alcohols

Ligand	g_m	$g_{\parallel}$	$g_{\perp}$	$A_{\parallel}$ (G)	A_N(G)
histidinol	2.12	2.32		130	
lysinol		2.25	2.07	170	15
glutaminol		2.36		140	
methioninol		2.32		135	
tryptophaol		2.31		155	

Data from Ref. 31-33.

free, Cu(II) substituted transferrin (for which $g_{\|} = 2.205$, $g_{\perp} = 2.05$, $A_{\|} = 210G$ and $A_N = 12G$).[35] This is in accord with the postulate that Cu(II) in transferrin is coordinated to four nitrogens in a planar array.[35]

Complexes of Cu(II) with the methioninol, glutaminol, and tryptophanol derivatives are much weaker than the complexes with the side chains of histidinol and lysinol.[32,33] In fact the weakly interacting side chains had to be "forced" to interact with Cu(II) by significantly decreasing the amount of water (and detergent) in the microemulsion. The limit species for glutaminol was the CuL^{2+} complex (Table III), and the suggested ligand site was the carbonyl oxygen of the amido group.[32] No limit species was identified in the methioninol system, although both CuL^{2+} and $CuL_2{}^{2+}$ species were observed.[32] The limit $CuL_2{}^{2+}$ species in the Cu(II)/tryptophanol system was very weakly formed; a ligand (N^{α}-dodecanoyl-L-tryptophanol) to metal mole ratio of 100:1 was required to completely eliminate the CuL^{2+} species.[33] In the latter system there is a similarity between the EPR parameters of the Cu(II) complex formed in the microemulsion (Table IV) and the EPR parameters of a metalloprotein. In this case the data are similar to that obtained for bicarbonate-containing Cu(II)-transferrin ($g_{\|} = 2.312$, $A_{\|} = 156$ G).[35]

An investigation of the interaction of Co(II) and Zn(II) with the side chains of N^{α}-dodecanoyl-L-histidinol and N^{α}-dodecanoyl-L-lysinol is in progress in our laboratories.[36] Preliminary results suggest that the complexes with Co(II) are tetrahedral in nature with a maximum of three ligands coordinated to each metal. Presumably, the fourth position is occupied by a water molecule.

The microemulsion is an excellent medium for determining the effect, if any, of an interfacial environment on metal-ligand interactions. A number of investigators have reported that surfactant solutions caused a significant change in the rate of certain chemical reactions.[1,2] In our work the properties of metal·ligand complexes have been measured under equilibrium conditions. Overall the available body of data is very small thus the following general conclusions must be regarded as tentative. Formation constants measured in microemulsions tend to be similar to the formation constants of analogous systems measured in aqueous solutions. Also, the spectral data for complexes in microemulsions are usually comparable to those of analogous complexes as measured in water, although a few exceptions have been observed. On the other hand, the stoichiometry of complexes may be influenced by the interfacial environment; a strongly interacting pair such as Cu(II) and the side chain of lysinol exhibits "normal" stoichiometry, but more weakly interacting pairs may not. Overall, the interfacial environment does not appear to have a drastic effect on the physical properties of transition metal complexes.

In the w/o microemulsion a transition metal interacts with a ligand which extends from an essentially hydrophobic shell into a polar "pocket". This arrangement is similar to that which exists at the metal binding site in metalloproteins. Thus the w/o microemulsion is potentially a suitable model for investigating metal complexes of biological interest. A few cases of remarkable similarity between the physical properties of a metal·side chain complex in the microemulsion and those of a metalloprotein have been observed, as pointed out (vide ante).

Other Reactions in Microemulsions

Mackay, Letts, and Jones have investigated acid-base equilibria and dye adsorption phenomena in o/w microemulsions stabilized with ionic detergents.[25] The acid-base studies with 1-methyl-4-cyanoformylpyridinium oximate showed that appropriate acid-base equilibrium studies can provide the necessary corrections for use of buffers in o/w microemulsions. Their studies also showed that a water soluble dye, crystal violet, was adsorbed primarily in the "oily" portion of the interfacial film. Analysis of the reaction between the dye and added hydroxide ion revealed a large medium effect on the second order rate constant.

Perhaps the first intentional use of a microemulsion as a host for a chemical reaction was the work of Stoeckenious, Schulman and Prince.[37,38] In these studies, OsO_4 was fixed into double bonds of alkyds in the oil phase of o/w microemulsions. Subsequent treatment and analysis by electron microscopy led to clear evidence of the existence of very small dispersed droplets in microemulsions.

O-nitrosophenol type ligands function as potent transition metal chelators. A biological example is ferroverdin, which consists of three molecules of an organic chelating agent, p-ethenylphenyl 3-nitroso-4-hydroxybenzoate, bound to Fe(II).[39] The ligand apparently is selective for Fe(II) since the natural product, as isolated from a strain of Streptomyces, contains this metal. We are synthesizing the ligand and measuring formation constants, and other properties, of complexes with a variety of metals in an attempt to gain some insight into the selectivity of the ligand for Fe(II).[40] Microemulsions are an excellent solvent for these studies.

DETERGENTLESS MICROEMULSIONS

On the basis of ultracentrifugation and conductivity data and visual examination, certain ternary compositions of hexane, water and 2-propanol were shown to be w/o microemulsions, even though a soap or detergent was not present.[30] A ternary phase diagram was prepared for this system (Figure 3). Detergentless microemulsions were discovered in the course of developing a suitable w/o microemulsion for investigating metal·ligand complexes in an interfacial environment (vide ante).

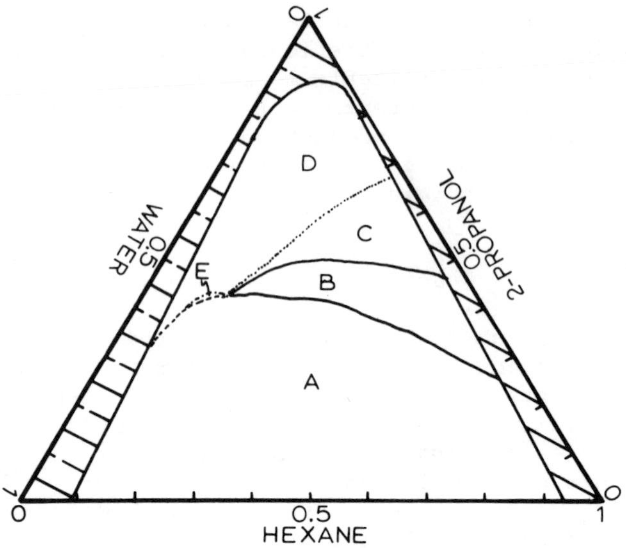

Figure 3. Ternary phase diagram for the hexane, water and 2-propanol system in the absence of soap or detergent. See the legend for Figure 2. Reproduced from Ref. 30 with permission.

We are making a vigorous effort to expand our knowledge of detergentless microemulsions since it seems probable that they could serve as inexpensive solvents for certain chemical reactions of industrial interest. Our efforts thus far have shown that toluene, but not benzene, can replace hexane as the oil phase.[41] Other studies have shown that ^{1}H NMR is a useful analytical tool for determining the nature of different phases; indeed, "bulk" water can be detected in the w/o (detergentless) microemulsion with this tool.[42] We are also investigating the solubility of salts such as NaCl and KOH in the ternary systems, and at the same time determining the effect of added salt on the phase boundaries.[42,43] The ability of detergentless w/o microemulsions to solubilize organic material is also of interest, thus we have initiated an investigation of the efficiency of these systems as solvents for extracting hydrocarbons from Utah tar sands.[44]

CONCLUDING COMMENTS

The available data, though limited, demonstrate clearly that microemulsions are attractive solvents for certain types of chemical reactions. The authors of this review sincerely hope that new investigators become interested in exploring the potential of these systems. The novice in this field should be aware that a microemulsion cannot be formulated with just whatever combination of oil, water, detergent and cosurfactant seems convenient. Considerable preliminary work is required to establish that a given system is indeed a microemulsion. Physical methods for making such a determination have been described.[12,30] In addition, one must determine whether the microemulsion is o/w or w/o; methods for doing this have been described by Dreher and Sydansk.[45]

As stated earlier, a microemulsion is especially attractive as a solvent for reactions in which one (or more) of the reactants is ionic and water soluble and one is organic and only sparingly soluble in water. It is noteworthy that the two groups publishing most of the work in this area chose, quite independently, to study the interaction of metal ions and organic ligand. Mackay's group uses o/w microemulsions with relatively large amounts of detergent, and at least some of their work has focused on rates of chemical reactions. In contrast, we have used w/o microemulsions with or without relatively small amounts of detergent, and thus far our work has focused on the properties of metal·ligand complexes under equilibrium conditions. Thus the efforts of the two groups have not overlapped, rather they are complementary.

ACKNOWLEDGEMENTS

The authors' research with microemulsions has been supported by the following agensies: National Science Foundation, The University of Wyoming, Marathon Oil Company, Industrial Fund of the Rocky Mountain Institute for Energy and Environment. R.E.B. is the recipient of a Research Career Development Award from NIH. The essential contribution of our students (G. D. Smith, B. A. Keiser, N. F. Borys, G. K. Lund, and D. L. Varie) to our research efforts is gratefully acknowledged. Also, we wish to acknowledge the following "surface active chemists": K. D. Dreher, who introduced us to the wonders of microemulsions; P. Mukerjee, for many helpful discussions about surfactant chemistry; L. M. Prince, the remarkable clarity of his writing has greatly facilitated our entry into a new area of research.

REFERENCES

1. E. H. Cordes, Editor, "Reaction Kinetics In Mivelles," Plenum Press, New York, 1973.
2. J. H. Fendler and E. J. Fendler, "Catalysis in Micellar and Macromolecular Systems, "Academic Press, New York, 1975.
3. C. A. Bunton, Progr. Solid State Chem., 8, 239 (1973).
4. P. Heitman, Eur. J. Biochem., 5, 305 (1968).
5. P. Heitman, R. Husung-Dublitz, and H. J. Zunst, Tetrahedron, 30, 4137 (1974).
6. C. Gitler and A. Ochoa-Solano, J. Am. Chem. Soc., 90, 5004 (1968).
7. A. Kupfer, C. Gani, and S. Shaltiel, Biochem. Biophys. Res. Commun., 79, 1004 (1977).
8. E. J. Fendler, S. A. Chang, J. H. Fendler, R. T. Medary, O. A. El Seoud, and V. A. Woods, in "Reaction Kinetics in Micelles," E. Cordes, Editor, p. 127, Plenum Press, New York, (1973).
9. W. L. Hinze and J. H. Fendler, J. Chem. Soc., Dalton Trans., 1469 (1976).
10. J. H. Fendler, Accounts Chem. Res., 9, 153 (1976).
11. L. M. Prince, in "Emulsions and Emulsion Technology," K. J. Lissant, Editor, Part I, p. 125, Marcel Dekker, New York, 1974.
12. L. M. Prince, Editor, "Microemulsions: Theory and Practice" Academic Press, New York, 1977.
13. T. Hoar and J. H. Schulman, Nature, 152, 102 (1943).
14. J. H. Schulman and J. A. Friend, J. Colloid Sci., 4, 497 (1949).
15. J. H. Schulman and D. P. Riley, J. Colloid Sci., 3, 383 (1948).
16. J. E. Bowcott and J. H. Schulman, Z. Electrochem., 59, 283 (1955).
17. L. M. Prince, J. Colloid Interface Sci., 52, 182 (1975).
18. E. Ruckenstein and J. C. Chi, J. Chem. Soc., Faraday Trans., 71, 1690 (1975).
19. D. G. Rance and S. Friberg, J. Colloid Interface Sci., 60. 207 (1977).
20. K. Shinoda and H. Kunieda, J. Colloid Interface Sci., 42, 381 (1973).
21. A. W. Adamson, "Physical Chemistry of Surfaces," 2nd ed., p. 519, Interscience, New York, (1967).
22. S. Friberg, Chem. Tech., 6, 124 (1976).
23. T. M. Doscher, Chem. Tech., 7, 232 (1977).
24. V. K. Bansal and D. O. Shah, in "Microemulsions: Theory and Practice," L. M. Prince, Editor, p. 149, Academic Press, New York, 1977.
25. R. A. Mackay, K. Letts and C. Jones, in "Micellization, Solubilization, and Microemulsions," K. L. Mittal, Editor, Vol. 2, p. 801, Plenum Press, New York, 1977.
26. K. Letts and R. A. Mackay, Inorg. Chem. 14, 2990 (1975).
27. K. Letts and R. A. Mackay, Inorc. Chem. 14, 2993 (1975).
28. C. E. Jones and R. A. Mackay, J. Phys. Chem. 82, 63 (1978).

29. B. A. Keiser, R. E. Barden and S. L. Holt, Unpublished data, (1978).
30. G. D. Smith, C. E. Donelan and R. E. Barden, J. Colloid Interface Sci. 60, 488 (1977).
31. G. D. Smith, B. B. Garrett, S. L. Holt, and R. E. Barden, J. Phys. Chem. 80, 1708 (1976).
32. G. D. Smith, B. B. Garrett, S. L. Holt, and R. E. Barden, Inorg. Chem. 16, 558 (1977).
33. G. D. Smith, R. E. Barden and S. L. Holt, J. Coord. Chem., in press.
34. S. Lindskog and P. O. Nyman, Biochim. Biophys. Acta 85, 462 (1964).
35. R. Aasa and P. Asin, J. Biol. Chem. 243, 2399 (1968).
36. B. A. Keiser, G. D. Smith, R. E. Barden, and S. L. Holt, Unpublished data (1978).
37. J. H. Schulman, W. Stoeckenius, and L. M. Prince, J. Phys. Chem., 63, 1677 (1959).
38. W. Stoeckinius, J. H. Schulman, and L. M. Prince, Kolloid Z., 169, 170 (1960).
39. S. C. De Sanctis, D. Grdenic, N. Taylor and D. Crowfoot-Hodgkin, Proc. Roy. Soc., Ser B. 184, 121 (1973).
40. D. V. Hertzler, D. E. Linn, S. L. Holt and R. E. Barden, Unpublished data, (1978).
41. G. K. Lund, S. L. Holt and R. E. Barden, Unpublished data, (1978).
42. B. A. Keiser, D. L. Varie, R. E. Barden and S. L. Holt, Unpublished data, (1978).
43. N. F. Borys, S. L. Holt and R. E. Barden, Unpublished data, (1978).
44. D. King and R. E. Barden, Unpublished data, (1978).
45. K. D. Dreher and R. D. Sydansk, J. Pet. Tech., 1437 (1971).

REACTIONS IN MICROEMULSIONS: PHOSPHATE ESTER HYDROLYSIS

C. Hermansky and R. A. Mackay

Department of Chemistry, Drexel University

Philadelphia, PA 19104

As part of our continuing study of the use of microemulsions as media for the investigation of interactions and reactions at microscopic oil-water interfaces, we have examined the reaction of p-nitrophenyl diphenyl phosphate with hydroxide and fluoride ion. This reaction is known to be catalysed by aqueous cationic micelles, and to serve as a basis of comparison we have employed a hexadecane in water microemulsion stabilized by cetytrimethyl ammonium bromide (CTAB) and 1-butanol as cosurfactant. The reaction is first order in ester and first order in base, as it is in both solution and aqueous micelles. The second order rate constant k_2 was measured over a phase volume ($\emptyset$) range of approximately 15-85%. For these compositions the value of k_2 varied by only a factor of three, decreasing with increasing $\emptyset$ to a minimum at 50%, and then increasing again. Since the ester and base are located in the droplet and aqueous regions, respectively, the values of k_2 should be multiplied by a factor of $\emptyset(1-\emptyset)$ to account for the effective concentration of reactants. These corrected rate constants do not vary significantly over the entire range of compositions, and are constant to within ±10% for $25\% \leq \emptyset \leq 85\%$. Based on effective concentration, the intrinsic rate constant in the microemulsion is found to be an order of magnitude greater than in aqueous CTAB. For the reaction of the phosphate ester with sodium hydroxide, the nucleophile is actually the butoxide ion. No trace of product resulting from attack of hydroxide is obtained.

INTRODUCTION

Microemulsions are optically transparent, stable, isotropic dispersons of oil in water or water in oil. They are most commonly stabilized by a mixture of a surfactant and a cosurfactant, usually a medium chain alcoho. Examination by low angle x-ray[5], light scattering[6], ultracentrifugation[7], electron microscopy[2] and viscosity measurements[8] have shown that microemulsions contain spherical droplets having diameters in the 10-60 nm range. The formation of the microemulsion is spontaneous[9,10] and it is at least mechanically stable. For oil in water (o/w) systems of the type examined here, the internal structure may be described as a stable collection of "oil" microdroplets in an aqueous continuous phase. These systems are very useful for the study of chemical reactions at oil-water boundaries due to the high volume fraction (20-80%) occupied by the disperse phase, and the very high interfacial area ($\sim 10^9 cm^2/L$).

We have investigated the reaction of p-nitrophenyl diphenyl phosphate with hydroxide and fluoride ions since extensive studies of these reactions have been conducted in aqueous cetyltrimethyl ammonium bromide (CTAB) micelles.[11] In order to provide a basis for comparison, we have utilized a hexadecane in water microemulsion stabilized by CTAB and 1-butanol.

EXPERIMENTAL

Materials

The preparation and purification of p-nitrophenyl diphenyl phosphate was carried out according to the method of Gulick and Geske.[12] The melting point after recrystalization from hexane was 49-50°C. The CTAB (Eastman Kodak Co., technical grade) was purified by recrystallization from methanol.[13] Diphenyl chlorophosphonate (99%) and diphenyl phosphate (Aldrich Chemical Corporation) were used as received. Diphenyl ethylphosphate was produced in ethanol through the reaction of sodium ethoxide with diphenyl chlorophosphonate.

Microemulsion Preparation

The oil in water microemulsions were prepared by mixing surfactant, alcohol, oil and water in the proportions shown in Figure 1. Stirring was required only to speed formation of the clear microemulsion. The psuedo three component phase map shown in figure 1 was determined by titration. Initial compositions of surfactant (CTAB + butanol) and oil were titrated with water to determine the clear and turbid regions. Initial compositions of surfactant and water were similarly titrated with oil. In general, addition of small amounts of electrolyte (≲ .01M) or organic substance have a negligible effect on the phase boundaries. All of the compositions employed in the kinetic studies, shown by the dashed line in figure 1, were clear and isotropic.

Kinetics

The formation of the p-nitrophenoxide was followed spectrophotometrically at 400 nm using a Cary-14 spectrophotometer fitted with a temperature controlled cell holder. The extinction coefficient of the p-nitrophenoxide ion in the CTAB microemulsion is 1.8 x $10^4 M^{-1} cm^{-1}$ irrespective of water content. A 1 cm cuvette was filled with 2.5 ml of microemulsion, .01-.06 M in sodium hydroxide or fluoride, and equilibrated in the cell holder. Ten microliters of a .01 M solution of p-nitrophenyl diphenyl phosphate in dioxane was added to the cuvette from a 25 microliter syringe (Lab-Crest) and this solution immediately agitated. The kinetic run was started within 20 seconds after addition of the phosphate. With

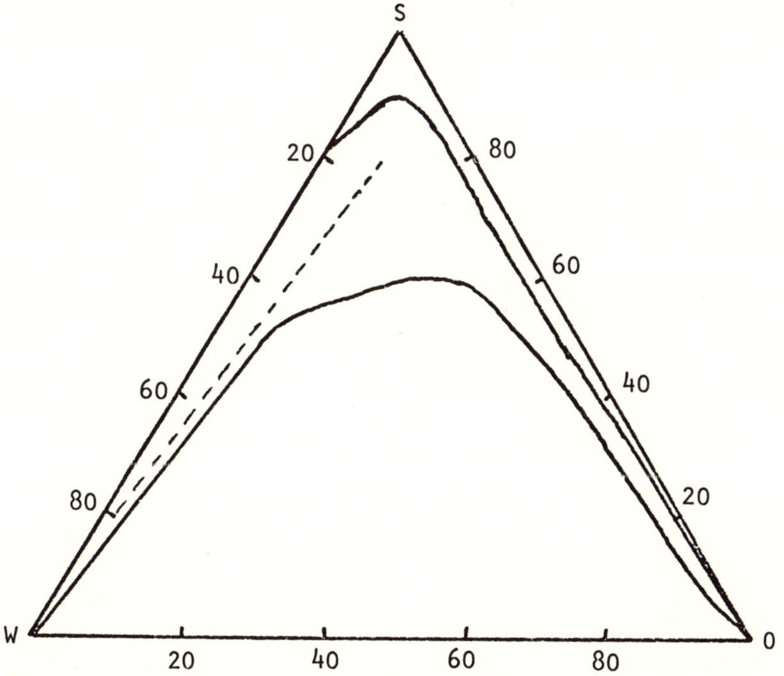

Figure 1. Pseudo-three component phase map of water/hexadecane/CTAB/1-butanol. The outlined area shown is the o/w microemulsion. Composition is given in weight percent. w = water, o = hexadecane and s = surfactant (50 wt. % CTAB + 50 wt. % 1-butanol). w + o + s = 100 wt. %. The dashed line corresponds to the 15-85% phase volume Ø range used in kinetic study.

fluoride, .03 M agueous borate buffer (pH 9) was used in place of the water to prevent hydrolysis of the p-nitrophenoxide ion. The hydroxide or fluoride ion concentration was always at least three orders of magnitude greater than the phosphate ester concentration (5×10^{-5}M). Activation enthalpies were determined by measuring the rate constant at four temperatures in the range 15-45°C. The activation enthalpies for the hydroxide and fluoride reactions in aqueous CTAB are approximately 14 kcal $mole^{-1}$.[11]

RESULTS AND DISCUSSION

Kinetic semilogarithmic plots of the absorbance at 400 nm vs time were linear over at least 75% of the reaction. The psuedo first order rate constants k_1 obtained from the slope of these plots were independent of the initial p-nitrophenyl diphenyl phosphate concentration. Both the fluoride and hydroxide reactions in the microemulsion were found to be first order in nucleophile as previously reported for solution and aqueous CTAB micelles.[11] The values of the second order rate constants k_2 measured over a phase volume ($\emptyset$)[14] range of approximately 15-85% (Figure 1) varied by a factor of three, decreasing with increasing $\emptyset$ to a minimum at 50% water, and then increasing again. The data are given in Table I.

Table I. Rate constants for reaction of p-nitrophenyl diphenyl-phosphate with hydroxide and fluoride in a CTAB/butanol/hexadecane o/w microemulsion at 25°C (vide text).

	hydroxide			
$\emptyset^a$	$k_2{}^b$(rel)	$k_{2,\emptyset}{}^c$(rel)	$k_2{}^b$(rel)	$k_{2,\emptyset}{}^c$(rel)
.79	2.3	1.9	4.1	2.8
.70	1.5	1.2	1.7	1.5
.58	1.1	1.1	1.2	1.2
.47	1.0	1.0	1.0	1.0
.36	1.0	0.9	1.1	1.0
.25	1.2	0.9	1.4	1.0
.16	1.8	0.9	1.2	1.1

a) Phase volume; initial composition 10% oil, 90% emulsifier (50% CTAB, 50% butanol).
b) Second order rate constant relative to the value at $\emptyset = 0.5$ (0.13 and 0.045 M^{-1} sec^{-1} for OH^- and F^-, respectively).
c) Each rate constant multiplied by a factor of $\emptyset(1-\emptyset)$; vide text.

Since the oil soluble ester and water soluble nucleophile are located in the droplet and aqueous regions respectively, the values of k_2 were corrected to reflect the effective concentration of reagents. The nucleophile (X^-) located in the aqueous phase, has an effective concentration of $(X^-)/(1-\emptyset)$. If distributed evenly in the drop, the effective concentration of the phosphate ester (P) is given by $(P)/\emptyset$. Designating the second order rate constant based on these effective concentrations as $k_{2,\emptyset}$ its value is given in Equation (1).

$$k_{2,\emptyset} = k_2\emptyset(1-\emptyset) \tag{1}$$

The values of $k_{2,\emptyset}$ are included in Table I.

The intrinsic rate constant (k_{2i}) is the actual value for the reaction in the oil-water interface. The value of k_{2i} depends upon the actual concentration(s) averaged over the location(s) in which the reaction takes place. However, k_{2i} should be directly proportional to $k_{2,\emptyset}$. The constancy of the values of $k_{2,\emptyset}$ in the microemulsion suggest that the intrinsic rate constant does not change when the system is diluted with water.

The rate constant for the hydroxide and fluoride reactions in the microemulsion were conpared with those in aqueous CTAB. If the intrinsic rate constant in both systems is the same then $k_2(\text{micelle})/k_2(\text{microemulsion}) \cong \emptyset_{ME}(1-\emptyset_{ME})/\emptyset_{micelle} \approx 250$. The maximum experimental value of this ratio is about 30. This order of magnitude difference cannot be explained in terms of surface potential (ψ) since this would require that $\psi_{ME} > \psi_{micelle}$ by more than 50 mv, while it is expected that the reverse order should hold. The microemulsion drop's surface, being composed of both charged surfactant and uncharged cosurfactant molecules, should have a surface potential less than that of an aqueous micelle composed of the same surfactant. It may be that the interfacial polarity of the microdroplet is less than that of the micelle at their respective reaction surfaces. The measured activation enthalpies ($\Delta H^{\neq}$) for the fluoride reaction are consistent with this view, being about 14 and 10 kcal mol^{-1} for aqueous CTAB and microemulsion, respectively.

The activation enthalpy for hydroxide in the microemulsion is also lower than aqueous CTAB being about 8 and 14 kcal $mole^{-1}$, respectively. Since $\Delta H^{\neq}$ is about the same for both nucleophiles in the micelle, it seems odd that they differ in the microdroplet. Further, when the nonionic surfactant B200 (Olin Chemical) is used in place of CTAB, the value of k_2 for fluoride decreases by a factor of approximately 20 as expected, while an increase is observed for hydroxide. The reaction of hydroxide and alcohol produces alkoxide ion, which has been shown to be a very effective nucleophile in micellar catalysis.[15] A product analysis (vide infra) showed this mechanism to be operative in the microemulsion.

Product Analysis

Attempts to analyze the small amounts of product in the presence of large amounts of surfactant, oil and alcohol by means of this layer chromatography have been unsuccessful to date. Since the presence of the phenoxide group interfers with in situ ultraviolet spectral analysis, diphenyl chlorophosphenate was employed in place of the p-nitrophenyl diphenyl phosphate. If the reaction is with hydroxide, the product will be diphenyl phosphate while diphenylbutyl phosphate will result from reaction with butoxide as shown in Equation (2).

$$(C_6H_5O)_2\text{-}\overset{O}{\overset{\|}{P}}\text{-}Cl \begin{cases} \xrightarrow{OH^-} (C_6H_5O)_2\text{-}\overset{O}{\overset{\|}{P}}\text{-}O^- \\ \xrightarrow{OR^-} (C_6H_5O)_2\text{-}\overset{O}{\overset{\|}{P}}\text{-}OR \end{cases} \qquad (2)$$

The spectra of these two products[16] in the microemulsion were compared with that of the actual reaction product, clearly showing that the alkyl ester is formed. The spectra are shown in Figure 2.

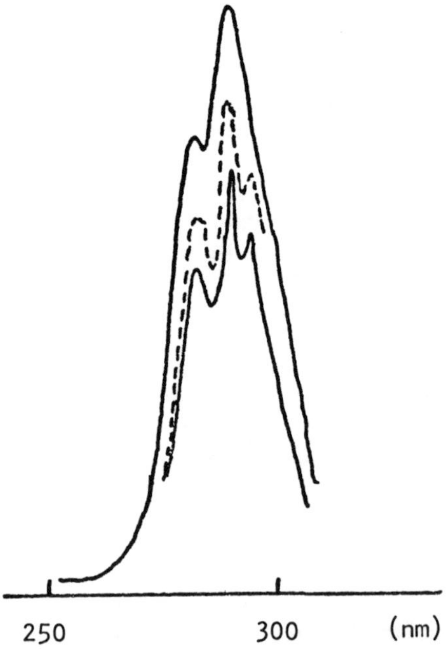

Figure 2. Spectra of diphenylphosphate (upper solid), diphenylethylphosphate (lower solid) and diphenylchlorophosphonate reaction product (dashed line) with hydroxide in a CTAB/butanol/hexadecane o/w microemulsion.

All of the necessary control experiments were performed to preclude other possible reaction sequences (e.g. - reaction of hydroxide with with the chlorophosphonate followed by attack of the phosphate anion on butanol, etc.). Quantitative spectral analysis showed that the butoxide ester reaction product accounted for all of the initial chlorophosphonate reactant. This mechanism is also consistant with the results using nonionic surfactant. The Olin B200 is of the polyoxyethylene type, and contains a terminal hydroxyl group which can also react with hydroxide to form a nucleophile.

With fluoride, similar spectral analysis confirms that the product is the expected fluorophosphonate.

SUMMARY

The reaction between phosphate ester and fluoride or hydroxide is first order in each. The second order rate constant, when corrected for the effective concentration of ester and nucleophile, is independent of phase volume over the range of 25-80%. The intrinsic rate constant in the microdroplet is greater than in the micelle, probably due to a difference in interfacial polarity. Product analysis for the hydroxide reaction in the microemulsion shows that butoxide is the nucleophile.

REFERENCES and NOTES

1. J.H. Schulman, W. Stoeckenius and L.M. Prince, J. Phys. Chem., 63, 1977 (1959).
2. W. Stoeckenius, J.H. Schulman and L.M. Prince, Kolloid Z., 169, 170 (1960).
3. L.M. Prince, J. Colloid Interface Sci., 52, 182 (1975).
4. P. Ekwall, L. Mandell and K. Fontell, J. Colloid Interface Sci., 33, 215 (1970).
5. J.H. Schulman and D.P. Riley, J. Colloid Sci., 3, 383 (1948).
6. J.H.Schulman and J.A. Friend, J. Colloid Sci., 4, 1988 (1971).
7. J.E.L. Bowcott and J.H. Schulman, Z. Electrochem., 59, 283 (1955).
8. J.E.L. Bowcott, Ph.D. Dissertation (Cambridge, 1957).
9. W.C. Tosch, S.C. Jones and A.W. Adamson, J. Colloid Interface Sci., 31, 297 (1969).
10. S. Levine and K. Robinson, J. Phys. Chem., 76, 876 (1972).
11. C.A. Bunton and L. Robinson, J. Org. Chem., 34, 773 (1968).
12. W.M. Gullick and D.H. Geske, J. Am. Chem. Soc., 88, 2928 (1966).
13. P. Mukerjee and K.J. Mysels, J. Org. Chem., 77, 2937 (1955).
14. The volume fraction occupied by the droplets (phase volume $\emptyset$) is calculated from the composition of the microemulsion as $\emptyset$ = 1-wg, where w is the weight fraction of water and g is the specific gravity of the microemulsion.

15. C.A. Bunton, L. Robinson and M. Stam, J. Am. Chem. Soc., 92, 7393 (1970).
16. The spectrum of diphenyl ethyl phosphate was used to simulate that of diphenyl butyl phosphate since the former could be obtained more cleanly. They both have the same near uv spectra.

Part VI
Adsorption at Interfaces

RHEOLOGICAL PROPERTIES OF FLUID INTERFACES

F.C. Goodrich

Inst. of Colloid and Surface Science
Clarkson College of Technology
Potsdam, New York 13676

The status of interfacial rheology as a branch of fluid mechanics is reviewed. The surface viscosity coefficients which enter into the boundary conditions needed to solve problems in fluid mechanics involving a free interface are suggested to be examples of capillary excess transport coefficients in the same sense that the familiar adsorption concentrations Γ of Willard Gibbs are excess thermodynamic properties whose values depend upon a dividing surface convention.

Experimental equipment needed to measure surface rheological properties is discussed with particular emphasis upon the properties of longitudinal surface waves. It is stressed that entirely erroneous results are obtained if the investigator neglects the mechanical coupling of the interface with the adjacent bulk fluids.

INTRODUCTION

Although the pronounced effect of oil slicks in damping out capillary ripples was observed in antiquity, interfacial rheology as an analytic discipline dates back to the researches of Stokes, Kelvin, and Rayleigh. After a period of quiescence, the subject at the present time is experiencing a revival of interest, among whose contributors are Scriven, Levich, Hansen, Mann, Slattery, Van den Temple, the Lucassens, Schechter, Wasan, and their collaborators. Much of what I have to say will be taken from the publications of this latter group.

Dating from the early experiments of Langmuir[1] and continuing into the present, a great deal of experimental work was performed without adequate hydrodynamic analysis of the fluid motions involved. Explicitly it was the custom down to about fifteen years ago to treat the fluid interface as a two-dimensional hydrodynamic body divorced from mechanical contact with the adjacent bulk fluid phases. This procedure results in an enormous simplification of the mathematics involved, but except in the case of extremely viscous or extremely elastic surface films, the results are worthless in the interpretation of experimental data. Beginning about fifteen years ago, hydrodynamic analyses began to appear in the literature in which the obvious was recognized: the interface is not mechanically divorced from the bulk phases, and bulk phase viscous drag upon the interface plays an essential role in determining the fluid motion. In this review I shall discuss only that recent work in surface rheology in which this interaction between interface and bulk is adequately recognized in the supporting mathematics.

SURFACE SHEAR VISCOSITY

Newtonian models of motion at a plane interface require the introduction of two coefficients of surface viscosity, one for dilation of the interface and the other for shear in the plane of the interface. The measurement of either is facilitated by experimental designs which suppress the motion associated with the other, and for surface shear viscosity this is accomplished by two instruments currently in use. The older of the two is the channel viscometer of Burton, Mannheimer, and Schechter,[2,3] illustrated in Figure 1.

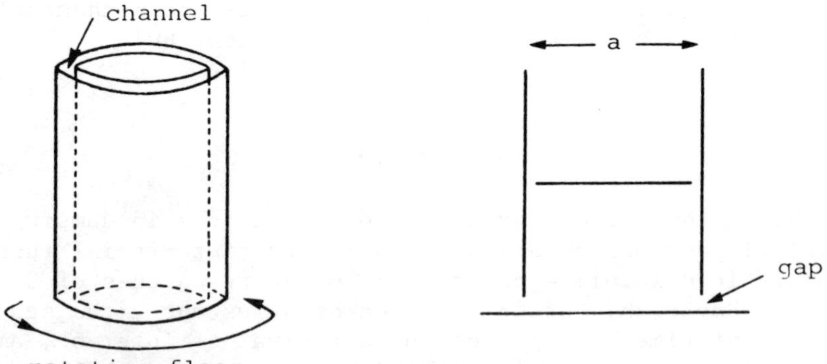

Figure 1. Channel surface viscometer of Schechter, Burton, and Mannheimer.

A circular channel of width a is filled with the two phase system, say air/water or oil/water. The floor of the channel is separated from its cylindrical walls by a narrow gap in such a way that the floor may be rotated at a steady rate beneath the fluid interface entrained in the channel. The fluid motion thus generated is communicated by viscous drag from the moving floor through the lower bulk phase to the interface, and through it into the upper phase. At steady state, a dust particle floating in the interface at the center of the circular channel will be observed to move along it at a steady velocity. Let v_m^o be the velocity of this dust particle when the interface is free from surface active materials. Then if in the presence of surface active materials the centerline, interfacial velocity under the same experimental conditions of temperature, channel depth, and floor rotation rate be v_m, the surface shear viscosity of the contaminated interface is

$$\eta = \frac{a}{\pi}(\mu^I + \mu^{II})\left(\frac{v_m^o}{v_m} - 1\right)$$

in which μ^I and μ^{II} are the bulk shear viscosities of the respective phases.

In the channel surface viscometer the motion is generated remote from the interface and communicated to it through the bulk phases. In the surface viscometer of Goodrich, Allen, and Poskanzer,[4,5] the motion is generated in the interface and dissipated into the bulk phases. The design is sketched in Figure 2 in which a cylindrical vessel of radius a is divided into upper

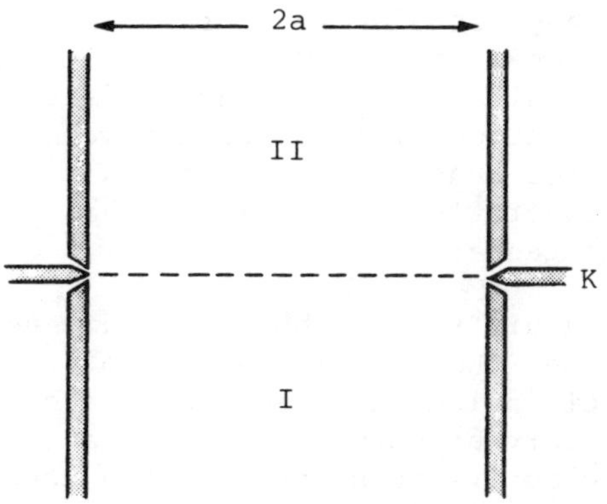

Figure 2. Knife edge surface viscometer of Goodrich, Allen, and Poskanzer.

and lower portions, each containing a different bulk phase. Into the narrow, circular slot which separates the two halves is fit a sharp knife edge K free to rotate about the axis of the cylinder. With the knife edge in contact with the perimeter of the interface and rotating at a steady period P_K, the motion is propagated into the interior of the vessel by viscous drag forces. A dust particle floating in the interface near the axis of the cylinder will pick up this motion and revolve about the axis in a circular orbit. Let P_o be the period of this orbit when the interface is free from surface active substances and P be its period under the same experimental conditions after surface active substances have been injected into the system. Then the surface shear viscosity is

$$\eta = 0.5631\ (\mu^I + \mu^{II})aP_K\left(\frac{1}{P} - \frac{1}{P_o}\right)$$

The instruments of Schechter-Burton-Mannheimer and of Goodrich-Allen-Poskanzer have been used to follow viscometrically changes in surface structure for insoluble and for soluble adsorption films.[6-12]

SURFACE DILATIONAL VISCOSITY

The viscometers of section 2 shear the interface without dilating it. The ideal surface dilational viscometer would dilate the interface isotropically without shearing it. This ideal design has yet to be constructed, and instead most workers have relied on rectilinear geometries in which the fluid surface in a Langmuir trough is compressed or expanded at various rates by means of movable barriers. Shear is always present under these circumstances, and the careful worker either has to assure himself that its effects are negligible or else estimate them separately from the type of experiment reported in section 2. To date hardly anyone has troubled to be this careful, and many of the values of dilational viscosity reported in the literature must be sums of both dilational and shear effects. Because the experimental determination of dilational viscosity is less widely understood than is the case for shear viscosity, I will devote this section to a theoretical analysis of what I believe to be the optimum rectilinear geometry.

Consider a Langmuir trough whose long dimension is oriented along the x axis. Let the movable barrier of the trough execute small amplitude oscillations of frequency ν about $x = 0$. By analogy with the theory of sound waves, one anticipates in the presence of surface active substances that a longitudinal wave will be propagated along x in which the surface density of adsorbed molecules is subjected to periodic compressions and rarefactions. The longitudinal wave will be damped in space and in time due to (1) irreversible processes taking place within the interface (2) viscous dissipation within the bulk substrate. Because the surface chemist is interested in (1) he has historically generally neglected (2), a serious error; for upon more careful investigation it turns out that in very many cases (2) is dominant.

The strain introduced into the surface by a barrier oscillating along the x axis is nonisotropic, and it follows that the stress may also be expected to be nonisotropic. The particular significance of this remark to experimental work is that a surface pressure measuring device such as a Wilhelmy plate suspended into the surface at x = L will register values which depend upon the orientation of the plate. Only if surface shear elasticity and viscosity are negligible will the pull on the plate be independent of its orientation. I shall attempt to make these remarks quantitative in the following.

Let the xy plane be the plane of the interface, and let the z axis be erected normal to the interface, positive in the gas phase. The diagonal components of the surface strain tensor are s_{xx} and s_{yy}, and a Newtonian hypothesis applied to the interface then leads to the constitutive relations

$$\begin{aligned} \gamma_{xx} &= \gamma + (\varepsilon_1 - \varepsilon_2)(s_{xx} + s_{yy}) + 2\varepsilon_2 s_{xx} \\ \gamma_{yy} &= \gamma + (\varepsilon_1 - \varepsilon_2)(s_{xx} + s_{yy}) + 2\varepsilon_2 s_{yy} \end{aligned} \tag{1}$$

for the diagonal components of the elastic part of the surface stress tensor. Here ε_1 is the elastic modulus for isotropic dilation of the interface, ε_2 is the elastic modulus for shear, and γ is the equilibrium surface tension. It is convenient to rewrite Equation (1) in terms of a surface pressure tensor

$$\begin{aligned} \Pi_{xx} &= \gamma - \gamma_{xx} = -(\varepsilon_1 - \varepsilon_2)(s_{xx} + s_{yy}) - 2\varepsilon_2 s_{xx} \\ \Pi_{yy} &= \gamma - \gamma_{yy} = -(\varepsilon_1 - \varepsilon_2)(s_{xx} + s_{yy}) - 2\varepsilon_2 s_{yy} \end{aligned} \tag{2}$$

From Equations (2) and remembering that the rectilinear geometry of the Langmuir trough requires $s_{yy} = 0$, we have the nonisotropic situation

$$\Pi_{xx} = -(\varepsilon_1 + \varepsilon_2)s_{xx} \quad ; \quad \Pi_{yy} = -(\varepsilon_1 - \varepsilon_2)s_{xx} \tag{3}$$

or in other words a Wilhelmy plate suspended perpendicular to the long axis of the trough will in general exhibit greater variations in surface pressure than a Wilhelmy plate suspended parallel to this axis. The viscous part of the surface stress tensor is constructed in an analogous fashion, whence for the rectilinear strains generated in the Langmuir trough we replace Equations (3) by

$$\Pi_{xx} = -\left[(\varepsilon_1 + \varepsilon_2) + (\kappa + \eta)\frac{\partial}{\partial t}\right] s_{xx}$$

$$\Pi_{yy} = -\left[(\varepsilon_1 + \varepsilon_2) + (\kappa - \eta)\frac{\partial}{\partial t}\right] s_{xx} \qquad (4)$$

in which κ is the coefficient of dilational surface viscosity and t is time. It is apparent from Equations (4) that only in the absence of shear moduli $\varepsilon_2 = \eta = 0$ will the surface stress be isotropic $\Pi_{xx} = \Pi_{yy}$. On the other hand, one could exploit this difference to effect separate determinations of dilational and shear effects, for from Equations (4)

$$\frac{1}{2}(\Pi_{xx} + \Pi_{yy}) = -\left(\varepsilon_1 + \kappa\frac{\partial}{\partial t}\right) s_{xx}$$

$$\frac{1}{2}(\Pi_{xx} - \Pi_{yy}) = -\left(\varepsilon_2 + \kappa\frac{\partial}{\partial t}\right) s_{xx} \qquad (5)$$

The use of Equations (5) in a longitudinal wave experiment will now be discussed.

THE LONGITUDINAL SURFACE WAVE

The general theory of longitudinal waves has been reviewed by the Lucassens,[13,14] and for analytic details the reader is referred to their papers. The key points in the hydrodynamic investigation are the following. I idealize the Langmuir trough to be infinitely long and infinitely deep. In the substrate water the fluid velocity vector satisfies the linearized Navier-Stokes equations.

$$\rho\frac{\partial v_x}{\partial t} = \mu\left[\frac{\partial^2 v_x}{\partial x^2} + \frac{\partial^2 v_x}{\partial z^2}\right]$$

$$\rho\frac{\partial v_z}{\partial t} = \mu\left[\frac{\partial^2 v_z}{\partial x^2} + \frac{\partial^2 v_z}{\partial z^2}\right] \qquad (6)$$

Here, v_x and v_z are respectively the horizontal and vertical components of the velocity vector, ρ is the density of the water, and

μ is its bulk shear viscosity. Because the water is incompressible, the velocity components are related by

$$\frac{\partial v_x}{\partial x} + \frac{\partial v_z}{\partial z} = 0 \qquad (7)$$

Equations (6) and (7) must be solved subject to boundary conditions. Because the motion is generated locally by the oscillating barrier and is destroyed by viscous dissipation, we must have both velocity components vanish as $x \to \infty$ and $z \to -\infty$. Furthermore, at the barrier (here idealized to be a mathematical line oscillating about $x = 0$ at $z = 0$), the horizontal component v_x must match the horizontal velocity of the moving barrier.

More importantly, over the free interface at $z = 0$ the velocity components must satisfy a boundary condition which expresses the mechanical coupling of the interface to the bulk substrate. In the general theory of capillary ripple motion, there are two such boundary conditions, but because we emphasize in this work the longitudinal wave, the important boundary condition involves the horizontal velocity component only.

$$\frac{\partial}{\partial x} \Pi_{xx} + \mu \frac{\partial v_x}{\partial z} = 0 \quad \text{at} \quad z = 0 \qquad (8)$$

Writing ξ for the horizontal component of the surface displacement vector, then at the surface $z = 0$, $v_x = \partial\xi/\partial t$ and $s_{xx} = \partial\xi/\partial x$. Substituting from Equations (4) into Equation (8) we get

$$\left(\alpha + \beta \frac{\partial}{\partial t}\right) \frac{\partial^2 \xi}{\partial x^2} = \mu \frac{\partial v_x}{\partial z} \quad \text{at} \quad z = 0 \qquad (9)$$

in which $\alpha = \varepsilon_1 + \varepsilon_2$ and $\beta = \kappa + \eta$.

The second boundary condition which enters into the general theory of capillary ripple motion[13] involves the normal velocity component v_z, and it is satisfied to a good approximation for the longitudinal wave if at the interface

$$|v_z| << |v_x| \quad \text{at} \quad z = 0 \qquad (10)$$

Equation (10) emphasizes the fact that for the longitudinal wave the motion is dominated by its horizontal component.

A simple solution to Equations (6-9) which represents a wave traveling along the positive x axis from the origin to the right is

$$\xi = A \exp i(kx - \omega t)$$

$$v_x = - i\omega A \exp(mz + i(kx - \omega t)) \tag{11}$$

$$v_z = - \frac{k}{m}\omega A \exp(mz + i(kx - \omega t))$$

in which $\omega = 2\pi\nu$. Equation (7) is satisfied automatically for any values of the constants k and m, and Equations (6) are satisfied if

$$\mu(m^2 - k^2) + i\rho\omega = 0 \tag{12}$$

v_x and v_z vanish as $x \to \infty$ if k has a positive imaginary part, and vanish as $z \to -\infty$ if m has a positive real part. Because of Equation (10), we must also have $|m|>>|k|$, and this fact permits us to neglect k^2 in Equation (12) and to write an explicit solution for m.

$$m = (\rho\omega/\mu)^{1/2} \exp(-i\pi/4) \tag{13}$$

Finally, the boundary condition, Equation (9), is satisfied if

$$(\alpha - i\beta\omega)k^2 = i\mu\omega m = (\rho\omega^3\mu)^{1/2} \exp(i\pi/4) \tag{14}$$

As is conventional in rheological investigations, I define a loss angle ϕ by

$$\tan\phi = \beta\omega/\alpha \tag{14}$$

in terms of which

$$\alpha - i\beta\omega = \alpha e^{-i\phi}/\cos\phi \tag{16}$$

Then combining Equations (14) and (16), k is explicitly

$$k = \left[\frac{\rho\omega^3\mu}{\alpha^2}\cos^2\phi\right]^{1/4} \exp i\left(\frac{\pi}{8} + \frac{1}{2}\phi\right) \tag{17}$$

From an examination of Equations (13) and (17), it is apparent that our approximation $|m|>>|k|$ will be valid if the circular frequency ω is sufficiently small and the elasticity α sufficiently large. This confirms one's intuitive feeling that the longitudinal wave will be favored over the generation of capillary transverse ripples only if the oscillation frequency of the barrier is kept low.

The results obtained so far are for a traveling, longitudinal wave. Because it is a simple experiment to dip a Wilhelmy plate into a conventional Langmuir trough, it is tempting to interpret the experimental results as those due to a wave traveling outward to the plate from the oscillating barrier; but such an interpretation ignores the fact that the plate itself interferes in the motion, sending back a reflected wave to the barrier. It is preferable to use the experimental design shown in Figure 3 in which a standing wave pattern is generated in the trough by two oscillating barriers moving 180° out of phase. At the stagnant point midway between the barriers is inserted a Wilhelmy plate. If the plate is positioned as shown, then the variable response measured is Π_{xx}. If the plate is rotated 90°, the response is Π_{yy}. I consider the first case.

Let the plate be positioned at x = 0 and the two barriers at $x = \pm L$. Then two traveling waves are symmetrically superposed and at any point x

$$\xi = A\, e^{-i\omega t} \frac{\sin kx}{\sin kL} \tag{18}$$

From Equation (4) one derives for the response of the plate

$$\Pi_{xx} = -\alpha \frac{A}{L} \frac{1}{\cos\phi} \frac{kL}{\sin kL} e^{-i(\phi+\omega t)} \tag{19}$$

Because k from Equation (17) is a complex number, the function kL/sin kL is also complex. Let it be written in polar coordinates

$$\frac{kL}{\sin kL} = \Lambda e^{i\chi} \tag{20}$$

The computation of Λ and χ from the rheological parameters is outlined in the appendix. Substituting Equation (20) into Equation (19) we have

$$\Pi_{xx} = -\alpha \frac{A}{L} \frac{\Lambda}{\cos\phi} \exp i(\chi - \phi - \omega t) \tag{21}$$

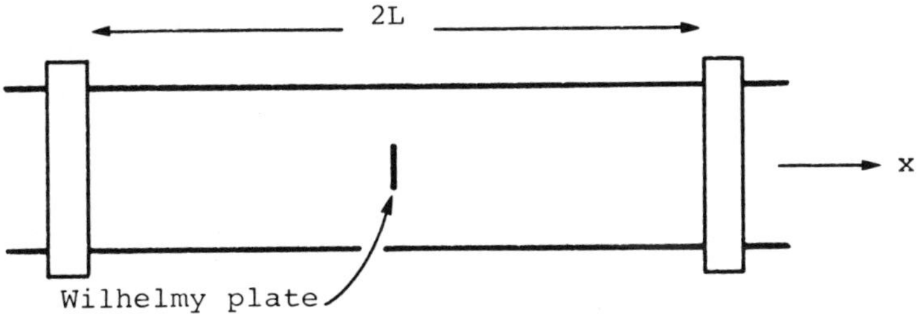

Figure 3. Recommended design of a Langmuir trough for the study of longitudinal surface waves. In the orientation shown, the Wilhelmy plate measures Π_{xx}. Rotated through 90°, the Wilhelmy plate measures Π_{yy}.

For computational purposes, it is convenient to take the real parts of Equations (18) and (21). The oscillations of the barriers and the surface stress response are then

$$\xi = \pm A \cos \omega t \qquad \text{at } x = \pm L$$
$$\Pi_{xx} = -\alpha \frac{A}{L} \frac{\Lambda}{\cos\phi} \cos(\chi - \phi - \omega t) \qquad \text{at } x = 0 \tag{22}$$

whence the amplitude of the surface stress oscillations is $\alpha A\Lambda/L \cos\phi$ and the phase displacement is $\chi - \phi$. These relations predict a hysteresis loop if Π_{xx} is plotted parametrically against ξ. The area H of such a loop is

$$H = \oint \Pi_{xx} d\xi$$
$$= \frac{A^2\alpha}{L} \frac{\pi\Lambda}{\cos\phi} \sin(\chi - \phi) \tag{23}$$

after integration over a complete cycle of the motion.

H has the dimensions of energy per unit distance along the y axis, but it does not represent work losses within the system, for the displacement ξ is measured at one location and the response Π_{xx} at another. H could, in fact, even be negative, depending upon the phase angle $\chi - \phi$.

If an identical analysis is carried out for the stress component Π_{yy}, then the right-hand sides of Equations (21, 22) are valid for Π_{yy} provided that α is interpreted to be $\varepsilon_1 - \varepsilon_2$ and ϕ defined by Equation (15) is calculated from $\beta = \kappa - \eta$. The quantities Λ and χ, however, are computed for both Π_{xx} and Π_{yy} from the procedures described in the appendix.

CALCULATIONS

It is well to use Equations (22, 23) in some practical calculations to demonstrate how they predict the expected experimental behavior. Let us suppose that a monolayer, soluble or insoluble, is in place upon the Langmuir trough and that the barriers are oscillated with a frequency ν so that $\omega = 2\pi\nu$. Then we use Equations (22) to plot Π_{xx} parametrically against ξ for selected values of t. Explicitly if the trough is such that L = 20 cm, A = 1 cm, $\nu = 0.1$ sec^{-1} and the monolayer has the properties $\alpha = \varepsilon_1 + \varepsilon_2 = 10$ dyne cm^{-1}, $\beta = \kappa + \eta = 0$, then with water as the substrate ($\rho = 1$ g cm^{-3}; $\mu = 0.01$ poise), the hysteresis loop of Figure 4 is obtained. From the form of the loop, it is apparent that Π_{xx} and ξ are nearly in phase, meaning that the monolayer is not far from a state of perpetual equilibrium. Evidently, the time period ν^{-1} = 10 sec. of the oscillations is large compared to the time needed for the longitudinal wave to travel the distance L.

Keeping the same monolayer, we now increase the frequency to ν = 0.28 sec^{-1}. The hysteresis loop is altered to that sketched in Figure 5. The area is now much larger, and Π_{xx} and ξ are nearly 90° out of phase, so that ν^{-1} = 3.6 sec is commeasureate with the time needed for the longitudinal wave to travel from barrier to blade. Raising the frequency to ν = 0.45 sec^{-1} we get the curve of Figure 6. Π_{xx} and ξ are approximately 180° out of phase and the area has diminished.

These results are summarized by the plots in Figure 7 in which the area H calculated from Equation (23) is plotted as a function of frequency ν for selected values of β. The areas of the loops in Figures 4, 5, 6 fall as points on the curve β = 0, which is also that curve which displays the sharpest maximum. We arrive at the important conclusion that the detection of a monolayer hysteresis loop is no evidence per se that the monolayer possesses any surface viscosity whatsoever, and indeed, other things being equal, the presence of surface viscosity actually serves to diminish the area of a hysteresis loop. These remarks

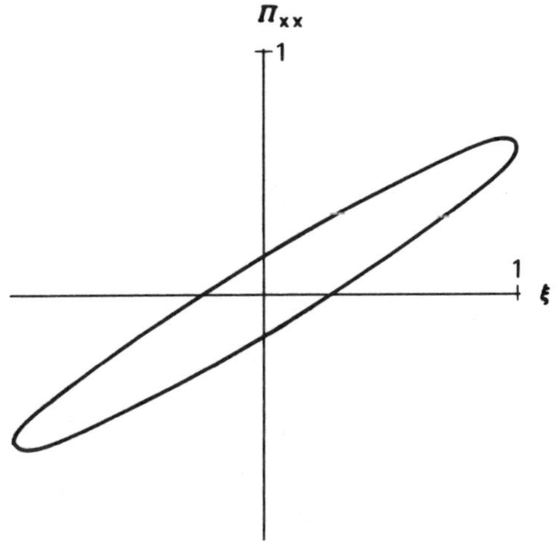

Figure 4. Low frequency hysteresis loop on water. A = 1 cm; L = 20 cm; α = 10 dyne cm^{-1} = 10 milli Newton m^{-1}; β = 0; ν = 0.10 sec^{-1}.

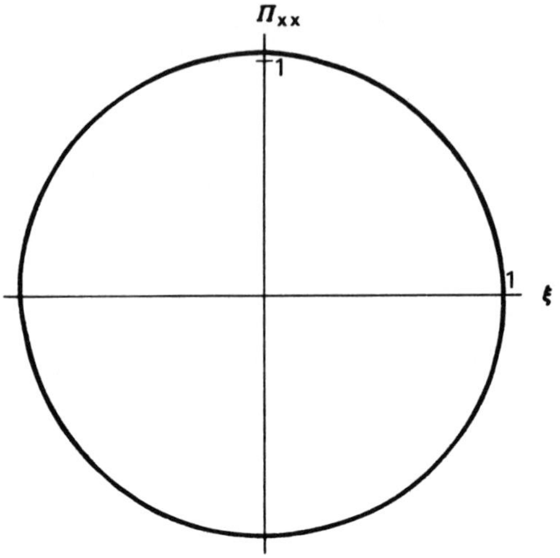

Figure 5. Resonance frequency hysteresis loop. As in Figure 4, but with $\nu = 0.28\ \text{sec}^{-1}$.

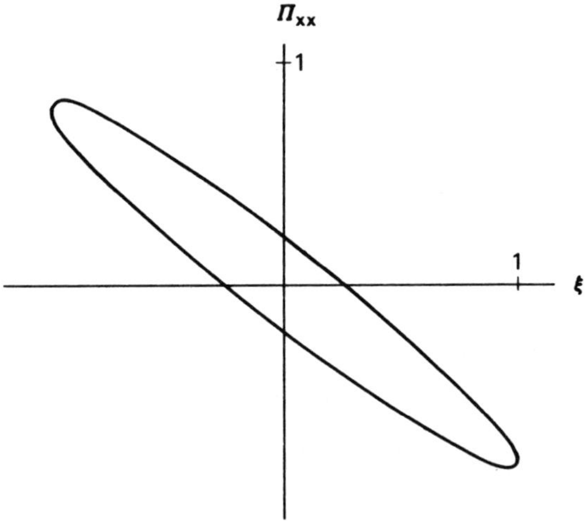

Figure 6. High frequency hysteresis loop. As in Figure 4, but with $\nu = 0.45\ \text{sec}^{-1}$.

emphasize the essential role played in the experiments by the viscosity of the substrate. For $\beta = 0$ all hysteresis effects are to be assigned to the substrate, and the decline in hysteresis area with increasing surface viscosity must mean that the extra viscous losses in the interface are overcompensated by a drop in the concomitant viscous losses occurring in the substrate. All that experiments in surface rheology can ever measure is a composite blend of both effects.

A reduction in surface elasticity α would shift the plots of Figure 7 to the left. In general the frequency ν_{max} of the resonance maximum depends sensitively on α and only in a minor way upon β, being given approximately by the dimensionless group

$$(\omega^3\rho\mu/\alpha^2)^{1/4}\ L = 3$$

whence an initial estimate for iterative calculations leading to the determination of α from experimental data is

$$\alpha = 1.75\ L^2(\nu^3_{max}\rho\mu)^{1/2}$$

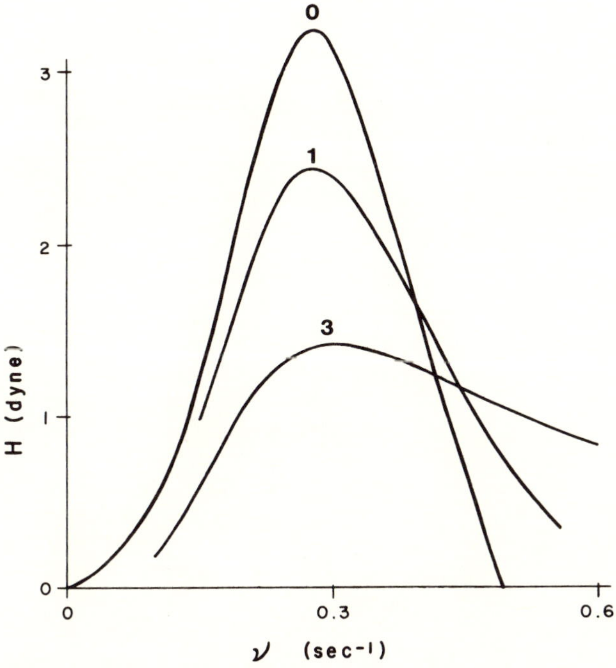

Figure 7. Area H of a hysteresis loop as a function of frequency for selected values of the surface viscosity β = g sec^{-1}. A = 1 cm; L = 20 cm; α = 10 milli Newton m^{-1}.

The amplitude H_{max} of the resonant absorption maximum is the parameter most sensitive to β, and in any case a simultaneous measurement of both ν_{max} and H_{max} is sufficient data for the calculation of the rheological parameters α and β. As suggested in section 3, analogous hysteresis plots based on Π_{yy} instead of Π_{xx} would be necessary in order to separate dilational from shear effects.

SURFACE VISCOSITY AS A CAPILLARY EXCESS TRANSPORT PROPERTY

I shall now change subjects and pose the fundamental problem of how surface viscosities are to be interpreted. That they exist there can be no doubt, and they have already proved their empirical worth in casting light upon surface structure.[6-12] Theories based upon explicit, gaseous, monolayer models have been proposed,[15,16] all of them valid only for monolayers so dilute that present experimental devices are too insensitive to test the predictions.

In unpublished work of my own I have attempted to generalize the capillary thermodynamics of Willard Gibbs valid for the static interface to cases in which the fluid interface is in motion. As in the work of Gibbs, the capillary transition layer is taken to be diffuse, and this real interface is compared with a fictitious model in which the two phases retain bulk phase properties right up to a mathematical discontinuity or dividing surface. Gibbs showed how this dividing surface in the model could be positioned in such a way as to define capillary excess quantities such as surface free energies, entropies, adsorption concentrations, etc. Precisely the same program is available for the moving interface, and the objective of the analysis is to derive rheological boundary conditions such as Equation (8) from the general equations of mass, momentum, and energy transport in a two phase system with a diffuse interface.

It turns out that the boundary conditions used in the hydrodynamic analysis of those fluid flows generated in experimental equipment of the sort discussed in sections 2 and 4 are derivable from the theory only if a dividing surface is introduced into the moving interface in such a way that by comparison with the real system, the fictitious one has zero excess volume and zero excess mass. These conventions happily coincide with one of Gibbs' most popular conventions for the static interface and thus constitute a smooth generalization from thermodynamics to fluid mechanics. As a result of this convention, a model system having the same mass and volume as the real one will exhibit capillary excess transport properties, among which are the surface viscosity coefficients κ and η. The formalism is such that κ and η are expressible as integrals over the molecular distribution functions used in nonequilibrium statistical mechanics, so that the path is open to a molecular theory of surface viscosity based upon first principles; but because molecular distribution functions in liquids are so imperfectly known, it will doubtless be a long time before reliable numerical predictions are forthcoming.

REFERENCES

1. I. Langmuir and V. J. Schaefer, J. Am. Chem. Soc. 59, 2400 (1937).
2. R. J. Mannheimer and R. S. Schechter, J. Colloid Interface Sci. 25, 434 (1967); 27, 324 (1968); 32, 195 (1970); 32, 212 (1970); 32, 225 (1970).
3. R. J. Mannheimer and R. A. Burton, J. Colloid Interface Sci. 32, 73 (1970).
4. F. C. Goodrich, L. H. Allen and A. Poskanzer, J. Colloid Interface Sci. 52, 201 (1975).
5. A. Poskanzer and F. C. Goodrich, J. Colloid Interface Sci. 52, 213 (1975).
6. L. Gupta and D. T. Wasan, Ind. Eng. Chem. Fund. 13, 26 (1974).
7. V. Mohan, B. Malviya and D. T. Wasan, Can. J. Chem. Eng. 54, 515 (1976).
8. V. Mohan, L. Gupta and D. T. Wasan, J. Colloid Interface Sci. 57, 496 (1976).
9. H. C. Maru, V. Mohan and D. T. Wasan, Chem. Eng. Sci. (1979), in press.
10. L. Wei and J. C. Slatter, in "Colloid and Interface Science," M. Kerker, Editor, Vol. IV, p. 399, Academic Press, New York, 1976.
11. A. M. Psokanzer and F. C. Goodrich, J. Phys. Chem. 79, 2122 (1975).
12. D.W. Goupil and F. C. Goodrich, J. Colloid Interface Sci. 62, 142 (1977).
13. E. H. Lucassen-Reynders and J. Lucassen, Adv. Colloid Interface Sci. 2, 347 (1969).
14. J. Lucassen and M. van den Tempel, Chem. Eng. Sci. 27, 1283 (1972).
15. E. R. Cooper and J. A. Mann, J. Phys. Chem. 77, 3024 (1973).
16. J. C. Slatter, Int. J. Multiphase Flow 4, 171 (1978).

APPENDIX

We are to find the quantities Λ and χ defined by

$$\frac{kL}{\sin kL} = \Lambda e^{i\chi}$$

in which the complex wave number k is defined by Equation (17). For simplicity write $kL = r\, e^{i\theta}$ where

$$r = \left[\frac{\rho\omega^3\mu}{\alpha^2}\cos^2\phi\right]^{1/4} L \quad \text{and} \quad \theta = \frac{\pi}{8} + \frac{1}{2}\phi$$

ϕ is the loss angle $\tan\phi = (\kappa + \eta)\omega/\alpha$. It is elementary to show that

$$\sin kL = \sin(r\cos\theta)\cosh(r\sin\theta) + i\cos(r\cos\theta)\sinh(r\sin\theta)$$

Recasting this equation into polar coordinates and dividing the result into $r\, e^{i\theta}$ we easily identify

$$\Lambda = r/[\sin^2(r\cos\theta)\cosh^2(r\sin\theta) + \cos^2(r\cos\theta)\sinh^2(r\sin\theta)]^{1/2}$$

$$\chi = \theta - \arctan[\cot(r\cos\theta)\tanh(r\sin\theta)]$$

ULTRA-LOW INTERFACIAL TENSION AND ITS IMPLICATIONS IN TERTIARY OIL RECOVERY

J. C. Morgan, R. S. Schechter and W. H. Wade

The University of Texas at Austin

Austin, Texas 78712

The large variations found in the physical and chemical properties of both petroleum oil and its porous medium have led to a diversity of recovery techniques. By design or in practice, many of these methods rely on reducing the oil-water interfacial tension to extremely low values, often to 10^{-3} dyne/cm or less, in order to mobilize oil trapped by capillary forces. The majority of such low tension systems utilize surfactants or surfactant mixtures, and it is upon these systems that this review concentrates.

Publications have tended to fall into separate groups dealing with low or high surfactant concentrations. This distrinction is made because at the lower concentrations, usually less than 2 g/l, phase volume changes due to mass transfer during eqilibration are absent or not readily observable. At higher concentrations, usually 30 g/l or more, phase volume changes are both observable and all-important. The higher surfactant concentration studies, which are more directly relevant to most proposed enhanced oil recovery methods, show that interfacial tensions in the useful range of 10^{-3} dyne/cm or less are usually associated with the formation of a third, microemulsion phase containing almost all the surfactant, plus solubilized water and hydrocarbon.

The same empirical rules governing optimum parameter values for low tensions appear to apply in both the high and low surfactant concentration regimes.

In fact, agreement is often quantitative, which leads to the conclusion that division on the concentration basis is largely artificial. The few studies which bridge the concentration gap support this.

Proposed explanations of the existence and manipulation of low tensions and associated microemulsion phases are reviewed. Theoretical and experimental results suggest that surfactant micelle behavior is one key to understanding and predicting low tensions.

INTRODUCTION

Present trends in world-wide energy supply and demand are certainly leading towards a shortfall stemming primarily from exhaustion of proven oil reserves. New technology or perhaps development of coal may provide long-term solutions to this problem, but in the meantime there has been a significant commitment to increasing the efficiency of recovery from established oil reservoirs. The potential contribution of this enhanced oil recovery (EOR) may be demonstrated from the U. S. situtation, where 300 billion barrels, or 67% of the original oil in place, is not considered economically recoverable by primary or secondary (water-flooding) techniques.[1-3] Of this, estimates of probable EOR potential are usually in the range 25[3] to 60[1] billion barrels. The rate of EOR production will depend on further development and refinement of recovery techniques and, of course, on oil price[4], but the tentative estimate of Doscher[5] of 10^6 barrels/day by 1990 (one-eighth of present U. S. production) does not seem unrealistic.

The variations found in crude oil compositions and viscosities, plus the wide range of reservoir rock porosity, permeability and composition, have led to a diversity of potentially successful EOR techniques. The most important include miscible floods (using alcohols, carbon dioxide, liquid petroleum gas or surfactants), immiscible surfactant floods, emulsion floods, alkaline floods, polymer floods, high pressure gas injection, and thermal processes (in-situ combustion, steam floods, etc.). All of these, together with important combinations of the different techniques, have been tested in pilot floods with varying degrees of success. The ultimate relative importance accorded to each method varies from author to author, with perhaps greatest emphasis placed on surfactant methods in general[1], carbon dioxide floods[5], and thermal recovery, the latter being in widespread use even at present[6].

One factor that most of the EOR techniques listed above have in common is that they involve one or more immiscible displacement processes. For these, the interfacial tension between displacing and displaced phases will determine in part the displacement effectiveness, and it is this facet of oil recovery which initiated our present interest in ultra-low interfacial tensions. Therefore, it is appropriate to describe the mechanism of immiscible displacement in order to identify those EOR processes which rely on tension reduction to increase immiscible displacement from porous media.

Immiscible Displacement Processes

The high pressure required to force a non-wetting phase through a small capillary was first noted by Jamin[7], and subsequently quantified by Gardescu,[8] Calhoun,[9] and Muskat.[10] Detailed treatments of this subject have been given in a number of recent reviews[11-14], and so only a brief outline is necessary here.

A trapped, non-wetting, residual oil ganglion (Figure 1) remaining after water-flooding may be modeled as in Figure 2. For the simplest case, with advancing and receding contact angles Θ_2 and Θ_1, both zero, and with the same interfacial tension γ at both oil-water interfaces, the pore constriction will prevent movement of oil in the direction of the applied pressure gradient unless this pressure difference is in excess of[8,11]

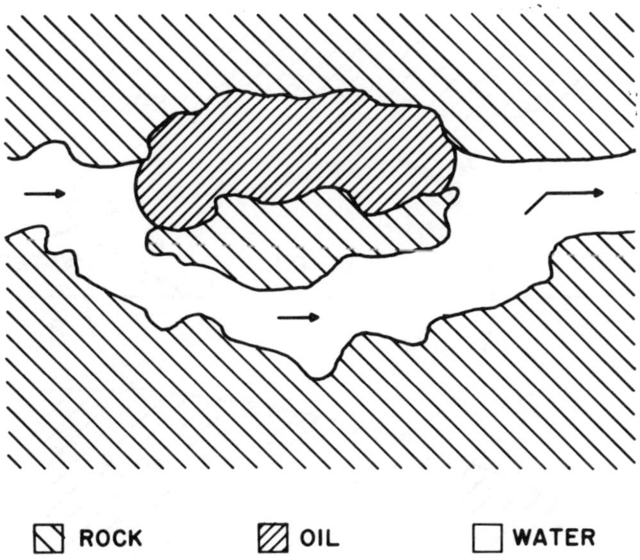

Figure 1. By-passed Ganglion of Residual Oil Trapped by Capillary Forces in a Pore Restriction.

$$\Delta P = P_2 - P_1 = 2\gamma \left\{ \frac{1}{R_1} - \frac{1}{R_2} \right\} \qquad (1)$$

With this model, assuming a practical oil reservoir applied pressure gradient of 1-2 psi/ft (2.14 - 4.2 x 10^6 dyne/cm^3)[15,16] the value of γ required to mobilize oil can be estimated. This depends only on the non-uniformity of the porous medium (the difference in r_1 and r_2) and on the length L of the trapped ganglion. Given typical values of these parameters[11,13] calculation shows that γ must be reduced from its usual value of between 10 and 30 dyne/cm to less than 0.1 dyne/cm[13] and probably to the vicinity of .001 dyne/cm[12,17].

Core displacement studies which demonstrate this importance of interfacial tension include those of Taber[11] and Wagner and Leach[22]. The latter is unusual in that liquid/vapor mixtures near the critical point are used, thus avoiding possible tension changes within the core due to adsorption losses when surfactants are used. Their conclusion, in line with results of core floods with surfactant systems, is that at practical flood rates, significant displacement of residual, non-wetting phase begins at tensions less than approximately .07 dynes/cm. A considerably lower tension than this would be necessary for useful recovery, of course, and we will adopt Melrose and Brandner's[12] estimate of 10^{-3} dyne/cm or less as the "ultra-low tension" required for near complete displacement.

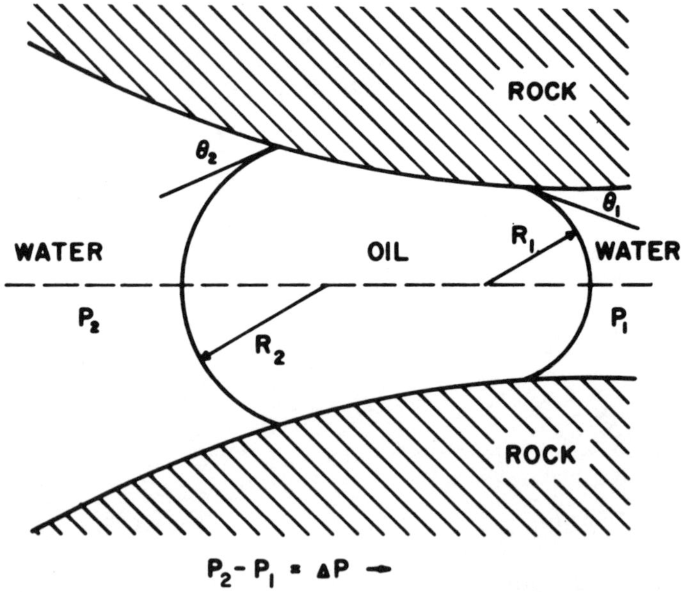

Figure 2. Model of Trapped Oil Ganglion.

In more general terms, Taber[11] refers to a critical value of the ratio ($\Delta P/\gamma L$) which must be exceeded before displacement occurs. This critical value increases with increasing permeability of the porous medium[18]. Taber's ratio may be made dimensionless by including the effective permeability to the displacing phase in the numerator. A number of alternative forms of this dimensionless capillary number have been developed (see Stegmeier[14]) which use the concept of competition of viscous and capillary forces in describing immiscible displacement. Several[17,19-21] have as their important element ($u\mu/\gamma$) where μ is the viscosity of the displacing phase and u is its Darcy velocity. Displacement may be effected by increasing the viscous force (increase μ or u) or by decreasing the capillary force (decrease γ).

Many EOR methods may be categorized on this basis, as a brief consideration of their displacmeent mechanisms shows. Immiscible surfactant floods generally aim to reduce γ to low values (as in (17)). Alkaline floods produce surfactants in situ, and hence lower γ[23-26] (though viscosity[25] may also be important). Polymer floods rely on increasing the sweep efficiency and to a lesser extent on increasing the viscous drag by increasing the waterflood viscosity[26].

Other EOR methods have perhaps less clear-cut mechanisms. A miscible surfactant flood has, effectively, a zero γ, but such a flood might be expected to degenerate by slug dilution to a multiphase, immiscible flood[28]. Recovery is then basically by a low tension mechanism, but mass transfer behavior such as oil swelling or oil solution may be important[14]. Alcohol and carbon dioxide floods usually depend on similar mass transfer mechanisms leading towards miscibility,[14] but an immiscible carbon dioxide displacement process utilizing the low interfacial tensions near the critical point has been described by Rosman and Zana[29]. Thermal methods generally work mainly by reducing the viscosity of the crude oil,[6] and do not fit into this scheme because they do not usually free oil trapped by capillary forces. Further details of the above and other EOR techniques may be found in the literature (14,26,30), the only purpose of this cursory listing being to demonstrate that achievement and control of low interfacial tensions are important in a number of areas.

Apart from a few publications involving nearly miscible phases of similar composition,[22,29,31,32] interest in ultra-low tensions (defined as less than 10^{-3} dyne/cm here) has been limited almost entirely to systems containing surfactants. Our present purpose is to integrate this literature as far as possible, and then to examine proposed explanations of the low tension state.

Ultra-low Tension Surfactant Systems

Harkins and Zollman[33] reported the first low hydrocarbon/water γ (.04 dyne/cm on addition of oleic acid) as far back as 1926. Uren and Fahry[34] concluded there was an inverse relationship between waterflood effectiveness and γ in 1927, and the first surfactant waterflood patent was issued to Atkinson[35] in the same year. Interest then lapsed until revived in the 1950's by Calhoun and coworkers[36,37]. Other particularly relevant early publications dealing with the influence of γ on oil recovery have been listed by Hill _et al._[38]

Reports of ultra-low tensions are now fairly commonplace, and may be divided usefully into two groups. The first deals with relatively low surfactant concentration systems, usually 2 g/l or less, where phase volume changes due to mass transfer during equilibration and tension measurement are not readily observable. The second body of tension measurements is the higher-concentration systems, typically 30 g/l or more. Here phase volume changes during equilibration may be large, and are linked to the tension data obtained. We will deal with each group of results individually, and then discuss the extent to which such a division is justifiable.

As most of the surfactants proposed for EOR have been made by sulfonating crude oil (petroleum sulfonates) or some other hydrocarbon feedstock, interest is focussed upon sulfonates, but some other types of surfactants are discussed where appropriate. Different authors have used the pendant drop method,[39-41] the sessile drop method,[42-44] or the spinning drop technique[45-47] to measure low interfacial tensions. All these may be used for tensions down to 10^{-4} dyne/cm, although the smallest reported tensions measured by pendant drop are on the order of 10^{-2} dyne/cm.

Low Tensions with Low Surfactant Concentrations

(a) Influence of the Nature of the Oil Phase

Interfacial tensions have been reported to be affected by a large number of parameters. Remarkably, a minimum in interfacial tension is often found at some value, with tensions rising steeply at slightly lower and higher parameter values. In the example of Figure 3, the tension minimum using a crude oil is seen as a function of surfactant concentration (after Wilson and Bradner[48]). Varying the concentration of the electrolyte, sodium chloride, at constant surfactant concentration also gives a tension minimum with the crude oil. These two variable effects may be economically combined as in Figure 4, by Wilson, Murphy and Foster[49]. This shows that for a given crude oil, the petroleum sulfonate has a

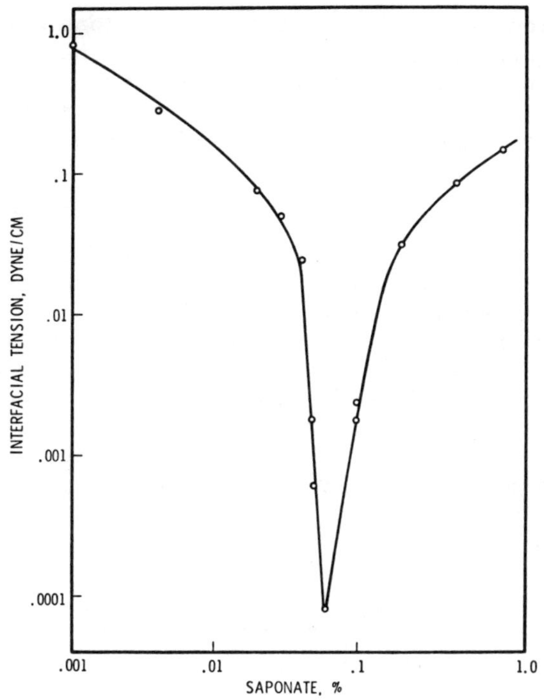

Figure 3. Tension Minimum Obtained with a Crude Oil as Surfactant Concentration is Increased.

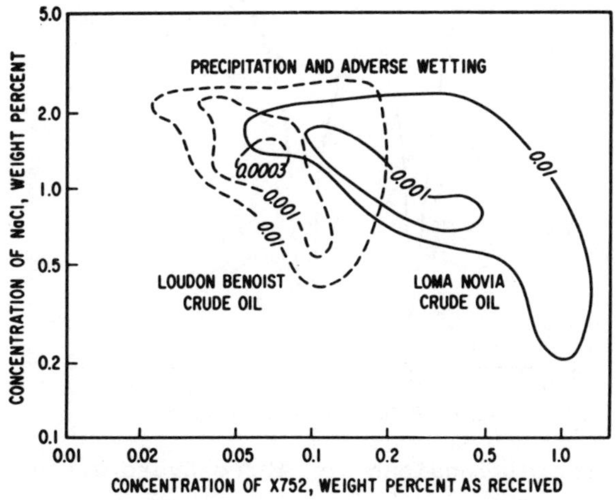

Figure 4. Low Tension Regions for Crude Oils Contour Lines Show Constant Interfacial Tension.

distinct low tension region. If ultra-low tensions are considered (less than 10^{-3} dyne/cm), this region is seen to be elongated. For instance the London Benoint crude oil gives ultra-low tensions at a 0.1% surfactant, 0.75% NaCl, whereas at lower surfactant concentrations significantly higher NaCl concentrations are required. Figure 4 also shows that the ultra-low tension region is dependent on the crude oil used.

In a series of investigations of the effect of changing oil phase nature, Wade and coworkers[50-52] replaced the crude oil by pure hydrocarbons of known structure. In Figure 5[53] tensions are shown for a fixed aqueous phase composition containing 2 g/l of the petroleum sulfonate, TRS 10-80 and 10 g/l NaCl against the homologous series of n-alkanes, n-alkyl benzenes and n-alkyl cyclohexanes. Ultra-low tensions are observed with sharp tension minima. The number of alkyl carbons in the hydrocarbon at the tension minimum (n_{min}) may be used to identify the minimum position in each case.

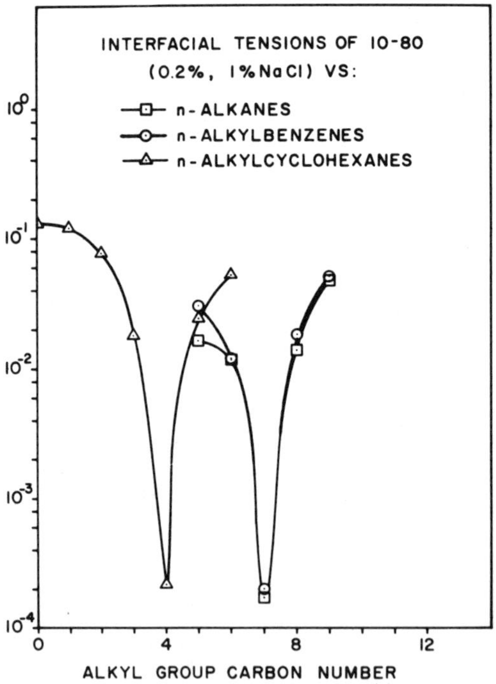

Figure 5. Interfacial Tensions for Three Hydrocarbon Homologous Series.

With each hydrocarbon series, it is found that the tension minimum can be moved by changing among other things, the nature of the surfactant. In Figure 6[52] an increasing mole fraction of C_{15} o-xylene sulfonate in the surfactant mixture gives an increase in the average surfactant equivalent weight, and this results in an increase in n_{min} with each hydrocarbon series.

In Figure 5, with TRS 10-80 as the surfactant, we see that heptane, heptyl benzene and butyl cyclohexane are equivalent in the sense that they all give tension minima with the same surfactant formulation. This equivalency is virtually independent of the nature of the surfactant phase, being duplicated, for example, with a o-xylene sulfonate mixture of equivalent weight 395 in Figure 6.

Comparisons such as this, combined with a study of hydrocarbon mixing rules[51], have produced the concept of the equivalent alkane carbon number (EACN)[52]. For instance, as heptyl benzene is equivalent to heptane, the EACN of heptyl benzene is 7. Similarly, the EACN of butyl cyclohexane is 7.

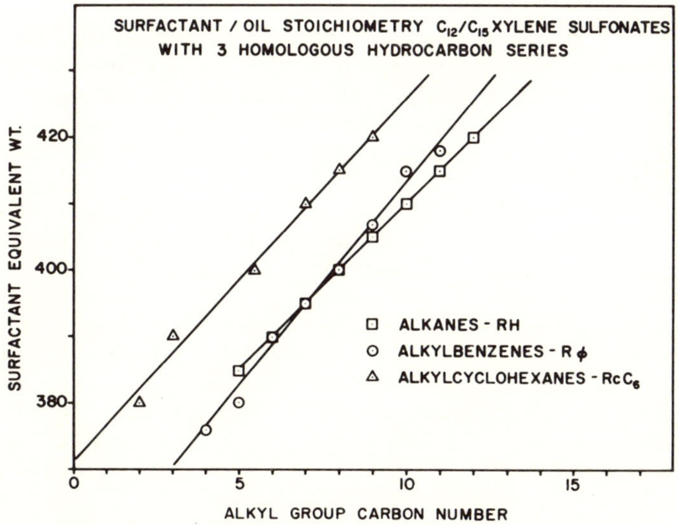

Figure 6. Correlation of Minimal Interfacial Tensions for Alkyl-Group Carbons Numbers vs. Surfactant Equivalent Weight for Mixtures of Two Synthetic Sulfonates.

Mixtures of hydrocarbons average very simply on a mole fraction basis[51]. Thus an equimolar mixture of hexane and decane will give a minimum tension against the same surfactant phase as octane. The mixture, therefore, has an EACN of 8. Any pure or mixed hydrocarbon may be assigned an EACN by comparison with alkanes. For mixtures containing up to twenty-nine components[52] EACN has been calculated, provided the EACN of each component is known, from

$$(\text{EACN})_{\text{mixture}} = \Sigma_i \ (\text{EACN})_i X_i \qquad (1)$$

where Xi is the mole fraction of the ith component of the mixture.

As all the components of any specific crude oil have never been identified, Equation 1 cannot be used to calculate the EACN of a crude oil. However, by comparison with alkanes the indications are that many crude oils have EACN's in the 6-9 range[52]. This information is helpful when choosing pure hydrocarbons for use as crude oil substitutes in tension phase studies. Crude oils, apart from being malodorous, are usually very dark, which can make observation of phase volume changes difficult. Moreover they are sometimes so viscous that equilibrium drop shapes during tension measurement are attained very slowly. Hence pure hydrocarbons, or synthetic oil mixtures[28], have been used in a number of parameter studies which have provided much basic information applicable to crude oils.

It may be noted that if the hydrocarbon molecular weight is increased by adding alkyl groups, then the surfactant formulation for optimum low tension behavior of changed considerably. Thus a surfactant of higher molecular weight becomes necessary in Figure 6. However, if a phenyl group is added to heptane (or any other alkane) there is very little change in the required surfactant formulation. This implies that it is the aliphatic content of a crude oil which determines its tension behavior, and that the aromatic content has a near negligible influence.

As further implication of the EACN work as summarized by equation 1 is that components of low EACN will have a large effect on the crude oil tension properties. Particularly important is that the EACN of a crude oil will depend quite strongly on the amount of dissolved hydrocarbon gas present (especially methane). This can be quite high for a "live" oil (oil at reservoir conditions). Unless sampling is done very carefully, however, much of this gas may be lost. If allowance is not made for this difference between "live" and "dead" crude oil, the wrong formulation for oil recovery will be obtained from laboratory tests.

(b) Influence of the Nature of the Surfactant (Sulfonates)

It is usually the case, as in Figure 6, that an increase in the average sulfonate equivalent weight leads to an increase in n_{min}. This is attributable to an increase in the length of the major alkyl chain in the average surfactant molecule, as has been demonstrated with studies of homologous surfactant series[54].

Studies of surfactant mixtures show that they tend to average on a mole fraction basis with regard to tension behavior[54] in the same way as did hydrocarbon mixtures. Thus if n_{min} for each surfactant component is known, a mixture will have an n_{min} according to

$$(n_{min})_{mixture} = \Sigma_i (n_{min})_i X_i \qquad (2)$$

where X_i is the mole fraction of the ith component.

Equation (2) has been shown to apply to multicomponent surfactant mixtures[54], and to mixtures of two components providing each is fairly complex, such as a petroleum sulfonate or an o-xylene sulfonate. It usually does not apply for mixtures of isomerically pure sulfonates unless at least four different species are mixed[55,56].

More detailed information on surfactant structure effects has been obtained from comparison on monoisomeric surfactants. Studies of alkyl benzene sulfonates (generic structures as in Figure 7) showed as expected, the n_{min} generally increases with the total number of alkyl carbons in the surfactant[54,56-58]. Additionally, however, the positon of attachment of the benzene ring to the chain

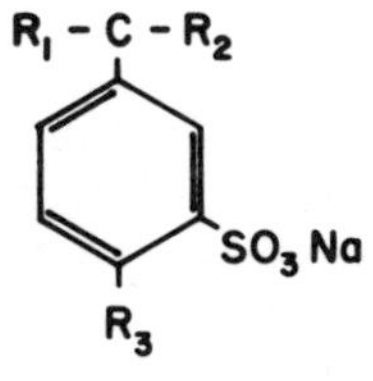

SURFACTANT GROUP	R_3 ALKYL CHAIN LENGTH	PREFERRED ALKANE
I	$R_3 \ll R_1 + R_2$	10
II	$R_3 < R_1 + R_2$	<5
III*	0	12.5

*Sulfonate group now in para position

Figure 7. Three Structures Studied by Doe et al.[56-58].

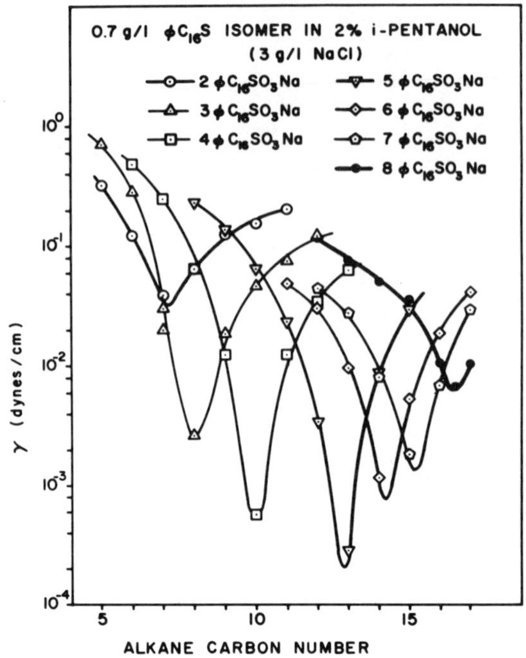

Figure 8. Alkane Scans for Surfactants of Different Molecular Structures in 2% iso-pentanol at 3 g/l NaCl.

has a very strong influence on n_{min}. Figure 8 shows this for the isomers of phenyl hexadecane sulfonate (a group III surfactant, with $R_1+R_2+1 = 16$ in Figure 7). Here n_{min} is lowest for the 2-isomer and increases towards the mid-chain isomer, 8-phenyl hexadecane sulfonate.

Results obtained with some sixty alkyl benzene sulfonates of known structure may be summarized by saying that at fixed molecular weight, branching of alkyl chain will almost always increase n_{min}. All types of branching are, however, not equal in effect. In general, splitting the main alkyl chain to give polysubstitution in the benzene ring (e.g. type III → type I or II in Figure 7) is the most efficient way to increase n_{min}.

This may be of importance when considering ways to minimize surfactant adsorption loss onto reservoir rock, which can be an economically crippling factor. The surfactant formulation must have an n_{min} value equal to the EACN of the crude oil. As n_{min} increases with both the total alkyl carbon number and with branching efficiency, using the most efficiently branched structure allows use of the lowest possible surfactant molecular weight. In general, adsorption decreases with increasing molecular weight, so this approach could be advantageous in selecting surfactants.

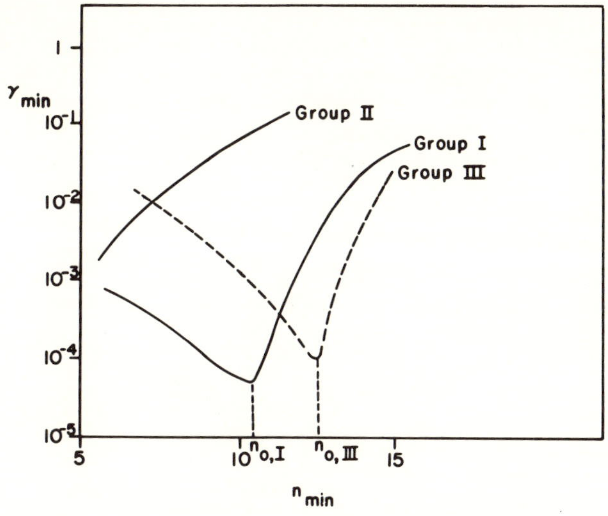

Figure 9. The Three Types of Alkane Preference Curves.

However, study of n_{min} shifts tells only part of the story. For successful oil recovery, a tension of 10^{-3} dyne/cm or less is mandated, and lowest tensions (at n_{min}) given by many surfactant formulations are considerably above this. In Figure 8, for instance, only the 4,5 and 6 isomers given minimum tension (γ_{min}) which are sufficiently low. This behavior has been shown to be governed by both hydrocarbon and surfactant structure, with other parameters such as salinity, presence of alcohol, - etc., having lesser importance. First we will consider just one structural type of surfactants, the group III class of Figure 7. These were the original monosubstituted linear alkyl benzene sulfonates studied by Doe et al[57,58]. Values of γ_{min} obtained for various values of ($R_1 + R_2 + 1$) and different ratios of $R_1:R_2$ were found to follow a fixed line of γ_{min} versus n_{min}. Changing n_{min} by varying the salinity and concentration of alcohol present produced more data points on the same γ_{min}/n_{min} curve, which is given in Figure 9. Figures 8 and 9 show that for a group III structure surfactant, γ_{min} will be ultra-low providing that n_{min} is near 12 on the alkane scale. Alkanes distant from this value have never been found to give ultra-low tensions with any group III surfactant, no matter how the tension optimization is carried out.

That surfactant structure also has an effect on γ_{min} is shown from the γ_{min}/n_{min} curves obtained when alkyl groups are substituted para to the main alkyl chain. Group I surfactants, with para groups not larger than propyl, give ultra-low tensions when formulated so that n_{min} is at or near decane. Group II surfactants, with larger para alkyl groups, do not give ultra-low tensions against any of the liquid alkanes, but the trend in Figure 9 suggests that they might do so if n_{min} was just below 5.

These results with alkanes seem to be qualitatively applicable to crude oils, judging from some preliminary results[56] but tensions obtained with crude oils of a given EACN are somewhat higher than those obtained against their equivalent alkanes.

(c) Effect of Surfactant Concentration

For monoisomeric sulfonates, changing the surfactant concentration has little effect on n_{min}, though γ_{min} is often increased as the concentration is decreased[59,60]. When the concentration is moved down through the critical micelle concentration (taken as the break-point in the surface tension/concentration curve) γ_{min} jumps to high values of 0.1 dyne/cm or more, and the distinct hydrocarbon preference is lost.

For complex surfactants such as petroleum sulfonates, there is the added complication that n_{min} increases when the overall concentration is decreased. This shift in n_{min} accelerates on approaching the c.m.c., where the low tension is again lost[59]. Obviously a shift in n_{min} with surfactant concentration is a difficult effect to allow for, but in practice such a shift is likely to be encountered because surfactant adsorption and dilution will continuously lower the surfactant concentration. It would appear that use of such surfactants in low concentration systems could lead to difficulties in tension control, particularly as some petroleum sulfonates solutions have been found to change with time, with n_{min} decreasing over a period of months[61].

(d) Effect of the Electrolyte

No sulfonate has ever been reported as giving a low tension in the absence of added electrolyte. Instead, many sulfonates will give a tension minimum at one particular "optimal" salinity with a fixed hydrocarbon phase[48,49]. In fact, the value of this optimal salinity for low tension, S*, is commonly used instead of n_{min} to characterize a surfactant formulation, particularly with studies at higher surfactant concentrations. When comparing results of n_{min} studies with optimum salinity data, it is helpful to remember that if some parameter change such as alcohol addition increases n_{min}, this is equivalent to a decrease in S* with a fixed hydrocarbon phase. More directly, an increase in salinity will increase n_{min}.

Although some reservoir brines have sodium chloride concentrations low enough to create no problems, other range up to 20% by weight or more. These highly concentrated brines often contain significant amounts of di-valent cations, particularly calcium and magnesium. The typical commerical petroleum sulfonate precipitates at a lower sodium chloride concentration, ∿4% being the common solubility limit. Equivalent monoisomeric sulfonates often precipitate even earlier. Sulfonates are far less tolerant of divalent cations than of monovalent cations[(62-64)].

Precipitation of surfactant is not the only problem associated with divalent ions. Ion-exchange (calcium or magnesium for sodium) between brine and a sodium sulfonate is possible[(65,66)], and this could change n_{min} for the surfactant, thus terminating low tension displacement. In addition, divalent ions can cause a catastropic increase in sulfonate adsorption losses[(63,66-68)].

A number of approaches have been proposed to solve, or at least avoid, the above problems. The first is avoidance by conditioning the reservoir to prevent contact of sodium sulfonate with divalent ions. This can be done by precipitating calcium and magnesium ions as carbonates[(64,69)], by using, for example, a sodium carbonate solution. Alternatively, a sequestering agent such as sodium tri-polyphosphate[(38)] can be used, which avoids, presumably, any injectivity/permeability problems caused by a solid precipitate. Divalent ions can also be removed by a preflush with a pure sodium chloride brine[(70,71)] but this can only be successful if no soluble sources of divalent ions, such as gypsum, are present[(71)]. Although preflushes have succeeded in field tests[(70)], they commonly do not condition the resevoir adequately[(15)] - in particular, the connate water may be incompletely displaces[(69)].

The second approach is to find surfactants that can tolerate high salinities and divalent ions but still give low tensions. Although some sulfonates, such as polybutene sulfonates[(67)] and alkyl tetralin sulfonates[(55)], have high salinity and high calcium tolerances, emphasis in this direction has been focussed on non-ionic surfactants[(72)], and non-ionic/anionic surfactant mixtures. If a successful surfactant were to be found, the cation exchange problem could be virtually eliminated by making the calcium/sodium and the calcium/magnesium ratios the same in the surfactant flood formulation as in the connate water[(73)].

(e) Other Parameters of Importance

The majority of surfactant systems described in the

literature or proposed for actual oil recovery contain a low molecular weight alcohol, typically in the range propanol to pentanol. The alcohol was intended to increase surfactant solubility, but has a strong effect on tension behavior. Systematic studies have shown that addition of a higher molecular weight, oil soluble alcohol decreases the optimum salinity for low tension (dealt with in the following section on high surfactant concentration systems) and increases n_{min} for most sulfonates[59]. A lower molecular weight alcohol has less effect on tension behavior, and may even move n_{min} for a high molecular weight sulfonate downwards[54].

It has been shown that n_{min} will decrease with increasing temperature[53], and also with solution age for some petroleum sulfonates[61]. The effect of pressure is not known at this time, except that hydrocarbon/water tensions in the absence of surfactant tend to rise with pressure[74]. Shear rate has been reported as a variable of importance. Szabo[75] found that a petroleum sulfonate solution gave an increased tension after shear degradation. The polymer used for viscosity control is always liable to interact with the surfactant, particularly with sulfonates, and this can lead to significant loss of surfactant by an entrapment mechanism[76]. Specific effects of polymer invasion of the surfactant slug on surfactant solution/crude oil tensions are not known, however.

Finally, pH could conceivably have an appreciable effect on tension behavior. Certainly n_{min} for non-ionic surfactants can be fairly sensative to pH changes[72], but little has been published for sulfonates. Caustic floods rely on reaction of the alkali with natural acids in the crude oil to form interfacially active compounds[23-26]. These natural surfactants can give ultra-low tensions, and a tension minimum may be found as a function of pH[23]. Certainly pH will have a profound influence on the oil recovery process, because sulfonate adsorption decreases sharply above the point of zero charge of the reservoir rock, e.g.[77], and because oil-water interfacial viscosity and emulsion stability (see, 78,79) are important factors which may also be pH dependent.

High Surfactant Concentration Systems - Tension and Phase Behavior

The low surfactant concentration studies yield much information on factors affecting crude oil/surfactant solution tensions, but many systems developed for EOR are intended for use at higher surfactant concentrations, typically 30-100 g/l. For these systems, tension behavior is best discussed in the context of their phase behavior.

Many details of the phase behavior characteristic of surfactant EOR systems of current interest were first described by Winsor[80,81]. In recent publications, frequent use has been made of pseudo-ternary phase diagrams in explanation of the observed phenomena. This approach has been adopted, for example, by Robbins[82] in discussion of the work of Shinoda *et al*[83-85] on non-ionic surfactant systems, and by Reed *et al*[13,28,86] for sulfonate systems.

As EOR systems commonly contain at least five components (oil,water, electrolyte, surfactant and cosurfactant such as alcohol) representation on a ternary phase diagram requires some grouping to give three "pseudo-components". Thus water and electrolyte may be grouped as brine, oil is invariably the second component, and surfactant plus alcohol is sometimes chosen as the third[13,86,87]. This choice of pseudo-components can lead to problems if the alcohol to surfactant ratio in any phase is at all dependent on the overall water to oil ratio, or upon the total surfactant concentration. Salter[88] has preferred to incorporate the alcohol into both the brine and oil pseudo-components in the ratio indicated by alcohol partitioning between these phases. This is based on the assumption, inferred from the work of Tosch *et al*[89], that the presence of surfactant has very little effect on partitioning of alcohol. A more detailed approach to the problem of chosing truly independent pseudo-components has been given by Fleming and Vinatieri[90]. In Figure 10, a series of idealized pseudo-ternary phase diagrams is presented with brine, oil and surfactant as the pseudo-components. Alcohol has not been allocated here, but could be included with the surfactant, split between brine and oil, or probably even left out completely without affecting the basic type of phase behavior observed. Diagram (a) is at the lowest electrolyte level of the series. Phase behavior is very simply for this system. At high surfactant concentrations there is a single phase region, below which a two phase region exists. A formulation whose initial composition lies in the latter will separate to give, at equilibrium, a phase at each end of the composition tieline through point x. The upper phase is nearly pure oil, and the lower phase is a microemulsion of composition y containing practically all of the surfactant and brine plus a significant amount of solubilized oil.

As the electrolyte concentration is increased, the amount of solubilized oil in the microemulsion increases. With many systems, a three phase region may be encountered at some higher salinity. Here the microemulsion is in equilibrium with excess brine and oil phases, both of which usually contain very little surfactant. When the salinity is only just high enough for the initial composition x to lie in the three phase region,

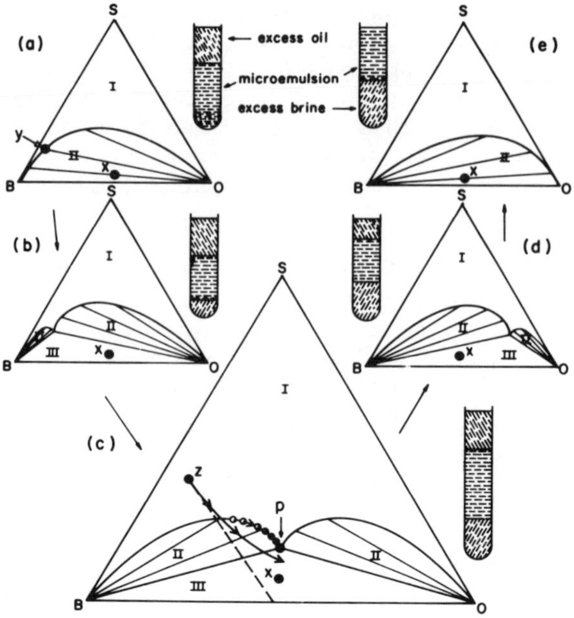

Figure 10. Idealized Pseudo-ternary Phase Diagrams for a Surfactant/Brine/Oil System with Salinity Increasing from (a) to (e).

as in Figure 10(b), the excess brine phase is smaller than the excess oil phase, and the microemulsion is brine-rich. As the salinity increases further, the excess phases become more nearly equal in volume as in (c), with microemulsion (middle phase) then containing equal volumes of solubilized oil and water. Further salinity increases give (d) and then the two phase system (e), where the surfactant has been driven into the oil phase, taking some solubilized water with it.

From the interfacial tension viewpoint, two kinds of interfaces are now of importance, that between microemulsion(m) and excess oil(o), and that between microemulsion and excess brine(w). In fact, for three phase systems, three interfacial tensions are measurable; γ_{om}, γ_{mw} and γ_{ow}. Of these γ_{ow}, between excess brine and oil phases has attracted little attention. Reed and Healy[13] mention that γ_{ow} is high for at least some systems which give very low values of γ_{mw} and γ_{om}. Similar observations have been made by the present authors with several systems in which the surfactant concentration in both excess phases is very low.

Reed and Healy[13] have shown that as the volume of oil, V_o, solubilized into the microemulsion incereases, γ_{om} decreases. As the volume of water V_w solubilized into the microemulsion increases, γ_{mw} decreases. These trends are shown in Figure 11. V_s being the volume of surfactant in the microemulsion phase. The point where the tension curves cross is referred to by Reed and Healy as the optimum salinity for interfacial tension, C. This is said to be the optimal situation because for an efficient flood, the microemulsion slug displacing the oil bank must be displaced itself by drive water. Therefore, both γ_{om} and γ_{mw} must be kept low simultaneously. The point where the solubilization curves cross is refered to as the optimum salinity for phase behavior, C_ϕ, and this corresponds to the symmetrical ternary diagram of Figure 10(c). As indicated by Figure 11, values of C_ϕ and C_γ are invariably in close proximity, so close that C_γ is associated with the symmetrical-type phase diagram.

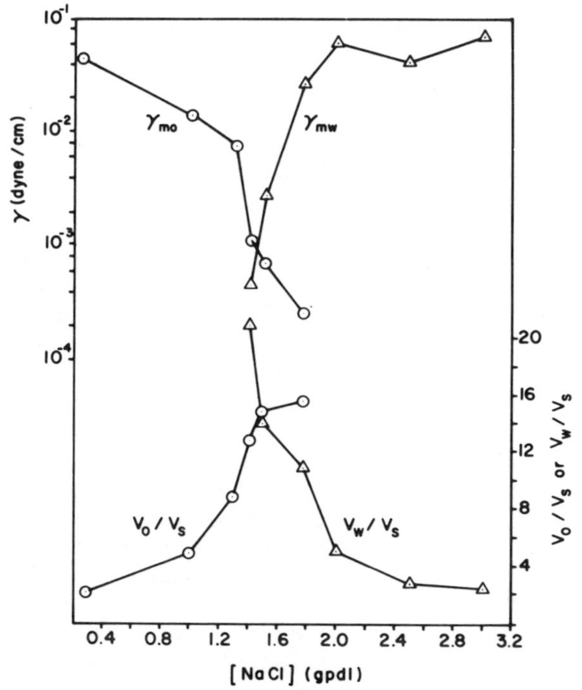

Figure 11. Interfacial Tensions and Solubilization Parameters for a System with 3% (total) of C_{12} o-xylene S(monoethanolamine salt) plus Tertiary amyl alcohol in ration 63:37 against a Synthetic Oil.

It is of some interest to trace the progress of a hypothetical surfactant flood relying on this optimization of tension behavior. Take the injected slug composition as z in Figure 10(c), there being some oil included in it. At first oil and brine are displaced miscibly, and are incorporated into the slug. Ideally, this should just dilute the slug on a straight line from z toward the oil/brine reservoir composition, but surfactant losses and incorportion of displaced connate water presumably will lead to a curved path as shown. Totally miscible displacement will cease when the multiphase boundary is reached. If, as indicated, the left-hand two phase region is entered, then brine will begin to separate out, and the microemulsion composition will continue to change along with the dotted line until point p. Any further brine and oil contacted by the microemulsion will then be displaced immiscibly by the low tension mechanism.

The likelihood of a flood being an economic success is increased if the efficient miscible displacement portion can be prolonged. Depression of the single phase/multiphase boundary will achieve this, and Baviere[91] has indicated that the boundary is at its lowest with a phase diagram of the type shown in Figure 10(c). The second criterion is that the immiscible displacement stage must be at ultra-low values of γ_{mo} and γ_{mw} (requiring the same type of phase diagram). Unfortunately, a large number of parameters influence the phase behavior and hence the tension behavior, so that in practice it is difficult to maintain ideal conditions throughout the lifetime of a flood.

A number of essentially equivalent techniques have been used to study the influence of system parameters on phase and tension behavior. The first involves a salinity scan, changing the phase diagram in the sequence (a) to (e) in Figure 10. At constant surfactant and alcohol concentration the salinity scan will identify C_γ (and C_ϕ) as in Figure 11. Changes in C_γ can then be followed for various parameter changes. Reed and Healy[13] have found that C_γ decreases with the alkyl chain length of the surfactant used, and with decreasing temperature. C_γ decreases if the alcohol molecular weight is increased. The same dependences of C_γ and C_ϕ on surfactant and alcohol molecular weights have been reported by Puerto and Gale[92]. Salter[88], and Jones and Dreher[93] have found the same trends in C_ϕ with alcohol addition. In addition, Hsieh and Shah[94] found C_γ to increase with increasing hydrocarbon molecular weight. Salager <u>et al</u>[95] have recently ordered many of these parameters in an empirical formulation of considerable generality.

The second approach, that of Shinoda and co-workers[83-85], replaces salinity scans with temperature as the independent variable. Robbins[82] has correlated their data with ideal ternary phase diagams, and concluded that for the non-ionic surfactants used by Shinoda et al, an increase in temperature corresponds to changing the phase diagram type in the sequence (a) to (e) of Figure 10. This is the reverse of the response of sulfonates to increased temperature. The effect of different system parameters on the phase inversion temperature (corresponding to passing through the Figure 10(c) situation) gives information for non-ionic surfactants which is equivalent to C_γ studies.

The marked similarity between parameter dependences of C_γ and n_{min} respectively for high and low concentration sulfonate systems has led to a number of investigations of possible links between the two regimes[59,94,96]. The most direct way to do this is to compare alkane or salinity scans for exactly the same systems at different surfactant concentrations. Comparisons of this type have shown that for mono-isomeric sulfonates, the low tension cross over point, with γ_{om} equal to γ_{mw}, occurs at the same alkane carbon number as n_{min} for the system at much lower surfactant concentration[59]. For broad spectrum sulfonates, n_{min} measured at low concentrations is higher than the high concentration cross-over point, as would be expected from the concentration dependence of n_{min}. Further studies showed that the parameter dependences of n_{min} and the cross-over point were to a large extent quantitatively as well as qualitatively comparable[59,95]. This should mean that, at least for most sulfonate systems, n_{min} parameter dependences found at low surfactant concentrations should indicate tension and phase behavior of the system at high concentrations, and vice versa.

Theories of Low Interfacial Tension

A completely satisfying explanation of the low tension state on a molecular scale has not yet been proposed, but it is worth noting briefly some of the ideas which have been published to date.

Phenomenological studies have provided a considerable amount of information, and it is now know that sharp interfacial tension minima may be seen with a variety of surfactant molecular structures as a function of many different parameters. Interfacial tension minima seen in two-phase micellar systems as a function of surfactant concentration have been considered by Franses, Bidner and Scriven[97] in terms of mixed micellization phenomena. They conclude that a single surfactant in two phases cannot have, ordinarily, a maximum in chemical potential as a function of concentration. Therefore, no minimum in γ can be seem (n_{min} is concentration independent). With two or more surfactant species present, however, the micelle composition can vary with total surfactant concentration, and this can lead to a minimum of γ at a concentration above the c.m.c. It is worth noting that low tensions do, in fact, vanish below the c.m.c.[59], which supports this approach.

Antoniewicz and Rodriquez[98] have devloped a model of the hydrocarbon-water-surfactant system in which the surfactant molecules are confined to a latice in the interface. The free energy of the surface phase can be calculated by considering surfactant molecule/interface interaction plus lateral interactions. Values can be assigned to the interaction energy parameters involved by a best fit procedure so that the model then gives the sharp minimum in γ seen as a function of alkane carbon number.

Wade et al[59] have attempted to correlate the observed dependences of n_{min} on various surfactant parameters with the ways in which these parameter changes affect surfactant standard chemical potential in the aqueous and hydrocarbon phases. Surfactant partitioning data for three phase systems lend some support to this approach. In similar vein is the comment of Reed and Healy[13] that C_γ might correspond to the salinity where the lipophile-oil and hydrophile-water interaction energies are about equal. These authors go on to suggest that when these interaction energies are both large and equal interfacial activity is high. Tensions observed at C_γ are then lower than with equal but lower interaction energies.

As mentioned earlier, the presence of surfactant micelles (or some alternative form of aggregate) is a necessary condition for a low interfacial tension. Results with system at surfactant concentrations high enough for observation of phase volume changes show that a maximum in solubilization corresponds to the lowest tension[13,86]. Thus suggests that swollen micellar state is associated with low tensions. Miller et al[99] believe that low tensions do, in fact, result from phase separation of micellar solutions into a "micelle-rich" phase and a "micelle-lean" phase. Their calculations indicate that the micelles must swell appreciably in order to reach the diameter of at least 100 Å required before phase separation and the resulting low tension can occur. This would explain the known association of middle phase microemulsions with low tensions and the theory does predict tensions in reasonable agreement with the results of Healy et al[86] for this type of system.

Miller et al[99] suggest that the interfacial tensions should be, approximately, the product of the interfacial thickness and the average excess free energy per unit volume of interface. The latter becomes practically small in the large micelle situation because the number of interacting particles is drastically reduced.

They also suggest that the interfacial thickness is proportional to the micelle diameter to a first approximation. The approach of Fleming[100] is simlar to this in some respects. Fleming uses a schematic density profile of the interface plus application of scaling theory to give the result that the tension should be proportional to kT/Σ^2. A low tension is then associated with a large value of Σ, which is a correlation length associated with interfacial thickness. Fleming's interpretation of low tensions was developed initially for a liquid/vapor interface near critical point and may be applied qualitatively to low interfacial tension created by surface active agents. If so, it may be attractive to identify the correlation length Σ with the micelle diameter, both being a measure of interfacial thickness and both, when large, suggested to be associated with a low interfacial tension.

ACKNOWLEDGEMENTS

This research has been supported by grants from the National Science Foundation, The Robert A. Welch Foundation, The Department of Energy and the following companies: Gulf Research and Development Company, Pittsburgh, Pennsylvania; Chevron Oil Field Research, LaHabra, California; Continental Oil Company, Ponca City, Oklahoma; Shell Oil's Bellaire Research Center, Houston, Texas; Amoco Production Company, Tulsa, Oklahoma; Sun Oil Company, Richardson, Texas; Witco Chemical Corporation, Petrolia, Pennsylvania; Mobil Res. and Dev., Dallas, Texas; Atlantic Richfield Res. and Dev., Dallas, Texas; Exxon Production Research, Houston, Texas; Stepan Chemical Company, Northfield, Illinois; Ashland Chemical, Columbus, Ohio; Union Oil of California, Brea, California; and British Petroleum, Limited, Sunbury-on-Thames, England.

REFERENCES

1. T. M. Geffen, World Oil, 177(5), 84 (1973).
2. M. B. Roy, C. W. Tucker and C. J. Lakey, presented at the 52nd Fall Meeting of SPE-AIME, Denver, Colorado, 1977.
3. J. M. Sharp, presented at the 50th Fall Meeting of SPE-AIME, Dallas, Texas, 1975.
4. W. H. Wade, Oil and Gas J., p. 160 (1975).
5. T. M. Doscher and F. A. Wise, presented at the SPE-AIME Improved Oil Recovery Symposium, Tulsa, Oklahoma, 1976.
6. D. N. Dietz, presented at the 50th Fall Meeting of SPE-AIME, Dallas, Texas, 1975.
7. J. M. Jamin, Compt. Rend., 50, 172, 311, 385 (1960).
8. I. I. Gardescu, Trans. AIME, 136, 351, (1930).
9. J. C. Calhoun, Jr., "Fundamental of Reservoir Engineering," U. of Oklahoma Press, Norman, Oklahoma, p. 134, (1953).
10. M. Muskat, "Physical Principles of Oil Production," McGraw-Hill Company, New York, p. 290, (1949).

11. J. J. Taber, Soc. Pet. Eng. J., 9, 3, (1969).
12. J. C. Melrose and C. F. Brandner, J. Canadian Pet. Tech., 13, 54, (1974).
13. R. L. Reed and R. N. Healy, in "Improved Oil Recovery by Surfactant and Polymer Flooding," D. O. Shah and R. S. Schechter, Editors, p. 383 Academic Press, New York, 1977.
14. G. L. Stegemeier, ibid, p. 55.
15. R. N. Healy, R. L. Reed and C. W. Carpenter, Soc. Pet. Eng. J., 15, 87, (1975).
16. R. W. Parsons, J. Pet. Tech., 26, 550, (1974).
17. W. R. Foster, J. Pet. Tech., 25, 205, (1973).
18. J. J. Taber, J. C. Kirby and F. U. Schroeder, presented at 71st National AIChE Meeting, Dallas, Texas, 1972.
19. T. F. Moore and R. L. Slobod, Producers Monthly, 20(10), 20, (1956).
20. E. G. LeFebre du Prey, Soc. Pet. Eng. J., 6, 247, (1966).
21. A. Abrams, Soc. Pet. Eng. J., 15, 437, (1975).
22. O. R. Wagner and R. O. Leach, Soc. Pet. Eng. J., 6, 335, (1966).
23. H. Y. Jennings, Jr., Soc. Pet. Eng. J., 15, 197, (1975).
24. C. E. Cooke, Jr., R. E. Williams and P. W. Kolodzie, J. Pet. Tech., p. 1365, (1974).
25. C. E. Johnson, Jr., presented at the 50th Fall Meeting of SPE-AIME, Dallas, Texas, 1975.
26. L. A. Wilson, Jr., in "Improved Oil Recovery by Surfactant and Polymer Flooding," D. O. Shah and R. S. Schechter, Editors, p. 1, Academic Press, New York, 1977.
27. R. O. Leach, O. R. Wagner, W. H. Wood and C. F. Harpke, J. Pet. Tech., p. 206, (1962).
28. R. N. Healy and R. L. Reed, Soc. Pet. Eng. J., 17, 129, (1977).
29. A. Rosman and E. Zana, presented at the 52nd Fall Meeting of SPE-AIME, Denver, Colorado, 1977.
30. R. G. Larson and G. J. Hirasaki, presented at the 51st Fall Meeting of SPE-AIME, New Orleans, Louisiana, 1976.
31. D. Atack and O. I. Rice, Disc. Faraday Soc., 15, 210, (1953).
32. J. W. Cahn and J. E. Hilliard, J. Chem. Phys., 28, 258, (1958).
33. W. D. Harkins and H. Zollman, J. Am. Chem. Soc., 48, 69, (1926).
34. L. C. Uren and E. H. Fahmy, Petroleum Division, AIME, 318, (1927).
35. H. Atkinson, U. S. Patent No. 1,651,311, (1927).
36. E. Ojeda, F. W. Preston and J. C. Calhoun, Jr., Prod. Monthly, 18(2), 20, (1953).
37. J. Paez, P. Reed and J. C. Calhoun, Jr., Bull. Pennsylvania State U., University Park, No. 64, 115, (1954).
38. H. J. Hill, J. Resiberg and G. L. Stegemeier, J. Pet. Tech., 25, 186 (1973).

39. J. M. Andreas, E. A. Hauser and W. B. Tucker, J. Phys. Chem., 42, 1001, (1938).
40. H. Y. Jennings, Jr., Rev. Sci. Instrum., 28, 774 (1957).
41. V. Schoettle and H. Y. Jennings, Jr., Rev. Sci. Instrum., 39, 386, (1968).
42. G. Quincke, Pogg. Ann., 160, 337, (1877).
43. C. F. Brandner and J. C. Melrose, Presented at the Div. Pet. Chem., Am. Chem. Soc., Atlantic City, New Jersey, D33-D40, (1965).
44. L. I. Osipow, "Surface Chemistry," Reinhold Publishing Co., New York, 1962.
45. V. Vonnegut, Rev. Sci. Instrum., 13, 6, (1942).
46. H. M. Princen, I. Y. Z. Zia and S. G. Mason, J. Colloid Interface Sci., 23, 99, (1967).
47. J. L. Cayias, R. S. Schechter and W. H. Wade, in "Adsorption at Interfaces," K. L. Mittal, Editor, p. 234, ACS Symposium Series No. 8, American Chemical Society, Washington, D.C., 1975.
48. P. M. Wilson and C. F. Brandner, presented at 165th National ACS Meeting, Dallas, Texas, (April 1973).
49. P. M. Wilson, C. L. Murphy and W. R. Foster, presented at the SPE-AIME Improved Oil Recovery Symposium, Tulsa, Oklahoma, 1976.
50. J. L. Cayias, R. S. Schechter and W. H. Wade, J. Colloid Interface Sci., 59, 31, (1977).
51. L. Cash, J. L. Cayias, G. Fournier, D. MacAllister, T. Schares, R. S. Schechter and W. H. Wade, J. Colloid Interface Sci., 59, 39, (1977).
52. R. L. Cash, J. L. Cayias, R. G. Fournier, J. K. Jacobson, T. Schares, R. S. Schechter and W. H. Wade, Soc. Pet. Eng. J., 16, 351, (1976).
53. J. C. Morgan, R. S. Schechter and W. H. Wade, in "Improved Oil Recovery by Surfactant and Polymer Flooding," D. O. Shah and R. S. Schechter, Editors, pp. 101-117, Academic Press, New York, 1977.
54. W. H. Wade, J. C. Morgan, J. K. Jacobson and R. S. Schechter, Soc. Pet. Eng. J., 17, 122, (1977).
55. P. H. Doe, unpublished work, (1976).
56. P. H. Doe, M. El-Emary and W. H. Wade, presented at the ACS Symposium on Chemistry of Oil, Anaheim, California, 1978.
57. P. H. Doe, R. S. Schechter and W. H. Wade, J. Colloid Interface Science., 59, 525, (1977).
58. P. H. Doe, M. M. El-Emary, R. S. Schechter and W. H. Wade, J. Am. Oil Chem. Soc., 54(12), 570, (1977); 55(5), 505 (1978); and 55(5), 513 (1978).
59. W. H. Wade, J. C. Morgan, R. S. Schechter, J. K. Jacobson, and J. L. Salager, Soc. Pet. Eng. J., 18, 242 (1978).
60. J. C. Morgan, J. Jeffries, R. S. Schechter and W. H. Wade, in preparation.

61. R. L. Cash, J. L. Cayias, M. Hayes, D. J. MacAllister, T. Schares and W. H. Wade, J. Pet. Tech. p. 985, (1976).
62. L. W. Holm and V. A. Josendal, Oil and Gas J., 158, (1972).
63. E. W. Malmberg and L. Smith, in "Improved Oil Recovery by Surfactant and Polymer Flooding," D. O. Shah and R. S. Schechter, Editors, p. 275, Academic Press, New York, 1977.
64. G. G. Bernard, J. Pet. Tech., p. 179, (1975).
65. G. A. Pope, L. W. Lake and F. Helfferich, presented at the 52nd Fall Meeting of SPE-AIME, Denver, Colorado, 1977; also SPE paper 6725, ibid, (1977).
66. L. W. Lake and F. G. Helfferich, presented at the 52nd Fall Meeting of SPE-AIME, Denver, Colorado, 1977.
67. H. R. Froning and L. E. Treiber, presented at the SPE-AIME Improved Oil Recovery Symposium, Tulsa, Oklahoma, 1976.
68. H. S. Hanna and P. Somasundaran, in "Improved Oil Recovery by Surfactant and Polymer Flooding," D. O. Shah and R. S. Schechter, Editors, p. 253, Academic Press, New York, 1977.
69. S. A. Pursley, R. N. Healy and E. I. Sandvik, J. Pet. Tech., 25, 793, (1973).
70. M. S. French, G. W. Keys, G. L. Stegemeier, R. C. Ueber, A. Abrams, and J. H. Hill, J. Pet. Tech., 25, 195, (1973).
71. L. K. Strange and W. B. Cloud, presented at the SPE-AIME Improved Oil Recovery Symposium, Tulsa, Oklahoma, 1976.
72. M. Hayes, presented at 53rd Fall Meeting of SPE-AIME, Houston, Texas, 1978. Ph.D. Dissertation.
73. H. J. Hill. F. G. Helfferich, L. G. Lake, J. Resiberg, and G. A. Pope, J. Pet. Tech., 1336 (1977).
74. N. Matubayasi, K. Motomura, S. Kaneshira, M. Nakamura, and R. Matuura, Bull. Chem. Soc., Japan, 50(2), 523 (1977).
75. M. T. Szabo, presented at the 52nd Fall Meeting of SPE-AIME, Denver, Colorado, 1977.
76. S. P. Trushenski, in "Improved Oil Recovery by Surfactant and Polymer Flooding," D. O. Shah and R. S. Schechter, Editors, p. 555, Academic Press, New York, 1977.
77. P. Somasundaran and D. W. Fuerstenau, J. Phys. Chem., 70, 90, (1966).
78. R. J. R. Cairns, D. M. Grist and E. L. Neustadter, paper presented at the Symposium on "Theory and Practice of Emulsion Technology," Brunel University, England, 1974.
79. A. T. Bourgoyne, Jr., B. H. Caudle and O. K. Kimbler, Soc. Pet. Eng. J., p. 60, (1972).
80. P. A. Winsor, Trans. Faraday Soc., 44, 376 (1948).
81. P. A. Winsor, "Solvent Properties of Amphiphilic Compounds," Butterworts, London, 1954.
82. M. L. Robbins, presented at the Improved Oil Recovery Symposium in SPE-AIME, Tulsa, Oklahoma, 1976.
83. K. Shinoda and S. Friberg, Adv. Colloid Interface Sci., 4, 281, (1975).

84. K. Shinoda and H. Kunieda, J. Colloid Interface Sci., 42, 381, (1973).
85. H. Saito and K. Shinoda, J. Colloid Interface Sci., 32, 647, (1970).
86. R. N. Healy, R. L. Reed and D. G. Stenmark, Soc. Pet. Eng. J., 16, 147, (1976).
87. L. W. Holm, in "Improved Oil Recovery by Surfactant and Polymer Flooding," D. O. Shah and R. S. Schechter, Editors, p. 453, Academic Press, New York, 1977.
88. S. J. Salter, presented at the 52nd Fall Meeting of SPE-AIME, Denver, Colorado, 1977.
89. W. C. Tosch, S. C. Jones and A. W. Adamson, J. Colloid Interface Sci., 31, 296, (1969).
90. P. D. Fleming and J. E. Vinatieri, J. Chem. Phys., 66, 3147, (1977).
91. M. Bairere, presented at the 51st Fall Meeting of SPE-AIME, New Orleans, Louisiana, 1976.
92. M. C. Puerto and W. W. Gale, Soc. Pet. Eng. J., 17, 193, (1977).
93. S. C. Jones and K. D. Dreher, presented at the 50th Fall Meeting of SPE-AIME, Dallas,Texas, 1975.
94. W. C. Hsieh and D. O. Shah, presented at the SPE-AIME Symposium on Oil field and Geothermal Chemistry, LaJolla, California, 1977.
95. J. L. Salger, E. Vasquez, J. C. Morgan, R. S. Schechter and W. H. Wade, presented at the SPE-AIME Improved Oil Recovery Symposium, Tulsa, Oklahoma, 1978.
96. W. H. Wade, J. L. Salager, E. Vasquez, M. El-Emary, C. Koukounis and R. S. Schechter, this proceedings volume, pp. 801-816.
97a. J. E. Puig, E. I. Frances, H. T. Davis, W. G. Miller and L. E. Scriven, SPE Preprint 7055, SPE-AIME Improved Oil Recovery Symposium, Tulsa, Oklahoma, April 16-19, 1978.
b. E. I. Frances, H. T. Davis, W. G. Miller and L. E. Scriven, Symposium on Chemistry of Oil Recovery, 175th ACS National Meeting, Anaheim, California, March 13, 1978.
c. L. E. Scriven, D. R. Anderson, M. S. Bidner, H. T. Davis, and C. D. Manning, SPE Symposium on Improved Oil Recovery, Tulsa, Oklahoma, March 22-24, 1976.
d. E. Franses, M. S. Bidner and L. E. Scriven, in "Micellization, Solubilization and Microemulsions, K. L. Mittal, Editor, p. 855, Plenum Press, New York, 1977.
98. P. R. Antoniewicz and R. Rodriquez, J. Colloid Interface Sci., 64, 320, (1978).
99. C. A. Miller, R-N. Hwan, W. J. Benton and T. Fort, Jr., J. Colloid Interface Sci., 61, 664, (1977).
100. P. D. Fleming, manuscript to be published.

SOLUTION CHEMISTRY OF SURFACTANTS AND THE ROLE OF IT IN ADSORPTION AND FROTH FLOTATION IN MINERAL-WATER SYSTEMS

P. Somasundaran and K.P. Ananthapadmanabhan

Henry Krumb School of Mines
Columbia University
New York, NY 10027

Adsorption of surfactants on minerals and froth flotation can be expected to be determined in addition to the aqueous chemistry of minerals and the interactions between the surfactant and the dissolved inorganic species also by the solution chemistry of surfactants. The role of solution chemistry becomes important particularly due to the dependence of the type and concentration of surfactant species on solution conditions such as pH. In particular, hydrolyzable surfactants such as fatty acids and amines can undergo various associative interactions to form ionomolecular complexes such as acid-soap in the appropriate pH range. Equilibrium species distribution diagrams that have been computed recently from literature data and estimates of energy of interactions between molecules for two typical surfactants, namely, oleic acid and amine, are reviewed in this paper, and the role of various complexes in determining interfacial processes such as flotation and surface tension lowering is considered. Formation of certain ionomolecular complexes is found to coincide with observed conditions of maximum surface activity as measured by surface tension, surface tension decay rate and flotation.

INTRODUCTION

Adsorption of surfactants on the mineral surface from an aqueous medium and the resultant hydrophobicity of it are strongly influenced by the surface chemical and electrokinetic properties of the solid as well as by the solution chemistry of surfactants. The flotation of mineral particles caused by the attachment of air bubbles to particles and their subsequent levitation, on the other hand, is determined by the degree of hydrophobicity of the two interfacial regions (solid/liquid and liquid/gas), which in turn are affected by, among other things, the adsorption density of the surfactant as well as the orientation of the adsorbed surfactant molecules. The overall process of flotation is governed by a large number of such factors, but most importantly, it can be expected to be influenced by the solution chemistry of the surfactants. Nevertheless, the role of surfactant solution chemistry in flotation has received only limited attention in the past. It is the aim of this paper to discuss the nature of chemical equilibria of certain common surfactants in solution and evaluate their influence on flotation. Particularly the type of complexes that can result from the association of various species under different conditions and their potential role in flotation will be considered here. It is however realized that a complete quantitative treatment incorporating all the possible interactions among surfactant and mineral species will have to await the availability of relevant thermodynamic data for such interactions.

CHEMICAL EQUILIBRIA IN SURFACTANT SOLUTIONS

The behavior of surfactant species in solution is determined essentially by the properties of their polar heads and hydrophobic tails and the resultant tendency of the solvent to accommodate them under various conditions. For example, a weakly acidic surfactant RH will exist as ions (R^-) at high pH values, neutral molecules at low pH values and may form an ionomolecular complex (RHR^-) in the intermediate pH range.[1-11] As the surfactant concentration is increased, micellisation or precipitation will occur in solution, depending upon the Kraft point of the system. In addition to this, surfactant species can also undergo associative interactions to form other aggregates such as the R_2^{2-} dimer even in sub-micellar solutions,[5-8,10-18] depending upon the nature of hydrophilic and hydrophobic parts of the surfactant species. As the surface activities of aggregate species as R_2^{2-} or R_2H^- will be different from those of the monomers, R^- or RH, one can expect flotation of minerals using them to be dependent upon the solution conditions, such as pH and surfactant concentration.

In this paper, the above mentioned associative interactions between surfactant species are discussed and the possible role of resultant complexes in flotation is examined in detail. Also the role of micellisation, hemi-micellisation--a process analogous to micellisation at the solid/liquid interface--and precipitation are discussed with the help of examples from the literature whenever possible.

Associative Interactions in Surfactant Solutions

Surfactants have been in general considered in the past to exist as monomers up to a particular concentration and above that to aggregate to form micelles or to precipitate. A number of properties of surfactant solutions such as conductivity,[12] molar volume,[14] osmotic coefficient,[17,18] hydrolysis,[2,4] etc. have, however, been reported to exhibit deviations from their expected ideal behavior below the critical micelle concentration (CMC). For example, specific conductivity of certain surfactant solutions below CMC has been found to undergo positive deviations from the behavior expected on the basis of the Debye-Hückel-Onsager relationship. Such deviation could be accounted for by considering the formation of dimers and other multimers which will have a higher electrophoretic mobility owing to their lower hydrodynamic resistance as compared to an equivalent number of monomers.[12] There have been attempts to account for the deviations in other properties also to such aggregation in aqueous phase and to estimate the thermodynamic constants for association complexes from the data obtained for such properties as a function of concentration.[5-8,14,15] However, some of the above deviations can also arise from possible artifacts that can exist under the experimental conditions used.

Association of surfactants is mainly due to the "hydrophobic bonding" (i.e. chain-chain interaction) between their non-polar parts.[7,13] It is widely accepted that the hydrocarbon molecules enhance the water structure around it.[19,20] Under such conditions, association of monomers can be expected to decrease the number of water molecules in such an ordered state.[21,22] The resultant increase in entropy would favor the formation of multimers. Following this concept, Nemethy and Scheraga[21] had formulated a statistical thermodynamic procedure for the estimation of hydrophobic free energy involved in the association of proteins. In subsequent works, Scheraga and co-workers extended their investigation to the study of the contributions of hydrophobic bonding energy to the dimerization of fatty acids.[23] In another approach, Bangs[7] assumed that the changes in interfacial energy accompanying the changes in interfacial area due to dimerization to be entirely due to the bonding between the associating species. The change in interfacial area during dimerization was estimated using molecular models and the corresponding change in interfacial energy was obtained by assuming the surface energy of a molecule to be the same as that at oil/water interface.[7] It might be interesting to note that the estimates of hydrophobic energy for dimerization by Scheraga and co-workers[23] and Bangs[7] were in good agreement with each other.

In addition to hydrophobic interactions, that of the polar or ionic heads with various solvent and solute species will also influence the formation of complexes. For example, the formation of a doubly charged dimer (R_2^{2-}) will be hindered by charge/charge repulsion.[12] Formation of an acid-soap dimer (R_2H^-) between an ion and a molecule, on the other hand, is more probable, because of the absence of charge/charge repulsion and the possibility of polar/ionic head interaction through hydrogen bonding, if the ionic and polar heads are placed at the same end of the dimer.[6,7,10,11]

It must be noted here that the formation of higher multimers such as trimers or tetramers also can cause deviations in solution properties. It is, however, difficult to distinguish the effects of higher multimers from dimers at this stage. On the other hand, higher multimers cannot be expected to exist in significant amounts, because of the accentuated repulsion between the ionic heads which would now have to be placed closer to one another compared to that for the case of a doubly charged dimer. It is therefore assumed for further analysis that higher multimers such as trimers or tetramers are not present in the system.

Based upon the above considerations, the associative interactions that are likely to occur in two major surfactant systems, i.e. potassium oleate and dodecylamine solutions are discussed below.

Oleate solutions. Formation of a 1:1 complex between potassium oleate and oleic acid has been considered as early as in 1927.[24] Subsequent studies by McBain,[1] Ekwall,[2] Mukerjee,[6] and others[25-27] have provided evidence for such associations in oleic acid systems. On the basis of data available at present for this system the following chemical equilibria can be written for oleate solutions.

$$RCOOH(\ell) \rightleftarrows RCOOH(aq) \qquad pK_{sol} = 7.6 \tag{1}$$

$$RCOOH \rightleftarrows RCOO^- + H^+ \qquad pK_a = 4.95 \tag{2}$$

$$2RCOO^- \rightleftarrows (RCOO)_2{}^{2-} \qquad pK_D = -4.0 \tag{3}$$

$$RCOO^- + RCOOH \rightleftarrows (RCOO)_2H^- \qquad pK_{AD} = -4.95 \tag{4}$$

$$Na^+ + (RCOO)_2H^- \rightleftarrows (RCOO)_2HNa \qquad pK_{SAS} = -9.35^{8} \tag{5}$$

The value of pK_a of oleic acid shown above is that obtained by Jung[8] by extrapolation of the pK_a values of short chain fatty acids.

Analysis of the literature values showed that the dimerization constant (K_D) for oleate ions varied over 3 to 4 orders of magnitude.

The value chosen here is again that obtained by Jung[8] assuming a linear relationship between the logarithm of solubility and the hydrocarbon chain length.

It is possible to estimate the equilibrium constant for the ionomolecular complex (acid-soap), since the extra stability of the acid-soap over the dimer will be essentially due to the absence of charge/charge repulsion and possible hydrogen bonding between the ionic and polar heads, as shown below.

$$\Delta G^{o}_{R_2{}^{2-}} = \underset{(-)}{\Delta G^{o}_{C-C}} + \underset{(+)}{\Delta G^{o}_{Elec.}} + \underset{(+)}{\Delta G^{o}_{KE}} \qquad (6)$$

$$\Delta G^{o}_{R_2H^-} = \underset{(-)}{\Delta G^{o}_{C-C}} + \underset{(-)}{\Delta G^{o}_{H}} + \underset{(+)}{\Delta G^{o}_{KE}} \qquad (7)$$

$$\Delta G^{o}_{R_2H^-} = \underset{(-)}{\Delta G^{o}_{H}} - \underset{(+)}{\Delta G^{o}_{Elec.}} + \Delta G^{o}_{R_2{}^{2-}} \qquad (8)$$

$$K_{AD} = \mathrm{Exp}\left(-\frac{\Delta G^{o}_{R_2H^-}}{RT}\right) \qquad (9)$$

where ΔG^{o}_{C-C}, $\Delta G^{o}_{Elec.}$, ΔG^{o}_{KE} and ΔG^{o}_{H} represent the free energy change due to the chain-chain interaction, charge/charge repulsion, kinetic energy changes and the hydrogen bonding respectively. By estimating the ionic repulsion energy and the hydrogen bonding energy, one can obtain K_{AD}, provided the formation constant for $R_2{}^{2-}$ is known. Mukerjee[6] estimated on this basis the value of K_{AD} to be thirty times that of K_D, by assuming a 4A° separation between the ionic heads in a dimer and 1000 cal/mole for the hydrogen bonding. The value of K_{AD} shown in equation (4) was obtained in our analysis by assuming a 13.8 A° separation between ionic heads. The latter value of distance of separation is obtained from molecularly scaled models.[7]

It must be pointed out here that the evaluation of charge/charge repulsion involves the use of a value for the dielectric constant of the medium surrounding the charges which is expected to be lower than that of pure water. However, in our treatment[11] as well as the one earlier by Mukerjee,[6] a dielectric constant of 78 for water has been used.

Using equations (1-5), and the mass balance equation:

$$C_T = C_{RCOOH} + C_{RCOO^-} + 2C_{(RCOO)_2{}^{2-}} + 2C_{(RCOO)_2H^-} \qquad (10)$$

where C_T is the total surfactant concentration, it is possible to determine the activities of the individual species and their distri-

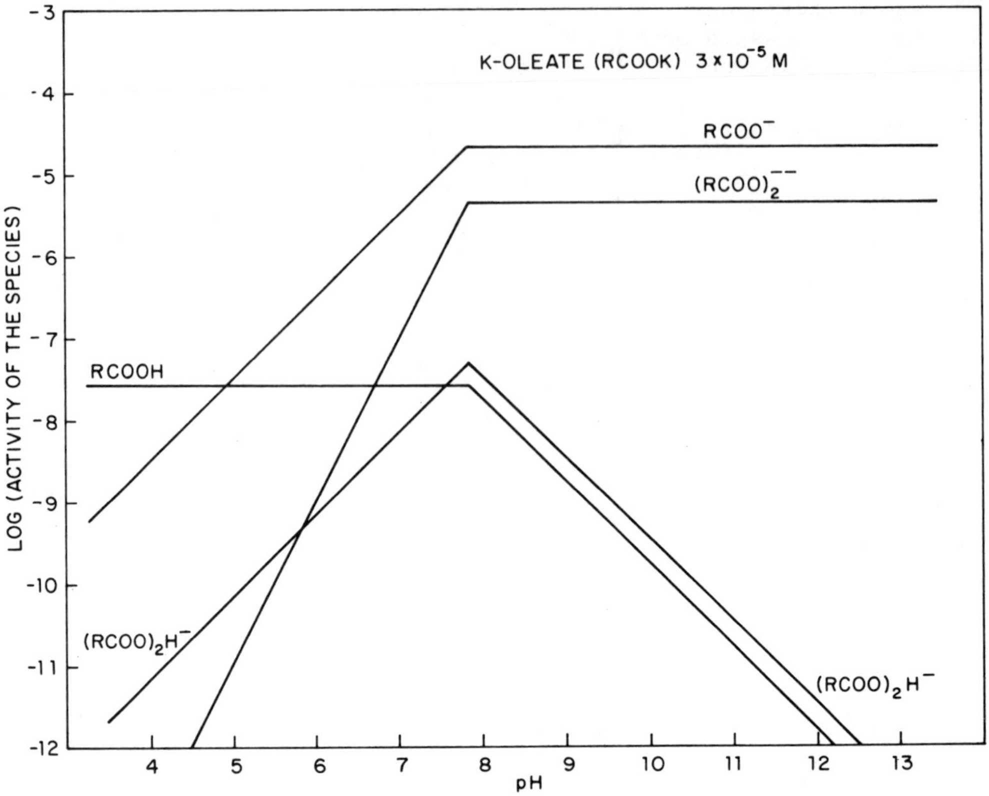

Figure 1. Oleate species distribution diagram as a function of pH. Total oleate concentration = 3×10^{-5} M.

bution, as a function of solution conditions such as pH below the precipitation limit of the acid-soap salt. A typical oleate speices distribution diagram at a total oleate concentration of 3×10^{-5} M is shown in Figure 1 as a function of pH. It is to be noted from this diagram that (1) a maximum in the activity of acid-soap ($RCOOH.RCOO^-$) occurs at pH 7.8, (b) precipitation of neutral oleic acid (RCOOH) occurs at pH 7.8, (c) activities of the ionic monomer and the ionic dimer increase up to pH 7.8 and remain practically constant above it.

The significance of these observations to flotation is discussed in a later section.

Dodecylamine solutions. Hydrolyzable cationic surfactants such as dodecylamine can also undergo associative interactions similar to that discussed for the oleate system. The possible chemical equilibria in this system are:

$$RNH_3^+ \rightleftarrows RNH_2 + H^+ \qquad pK'_a = 10.63 \qquad (11)$$

$$2RNH_3^+ \rightleftarrows (RNH_3)_2{}^{2+} \qquad pK'_D = -2.08 \qquad (12)$$

$$RNH_3^+ + RNH_2 \rightleftarrows (RNH_2.RNH_3)^+ \qquad pK'_{AD} = -3.12 \qquad (13)$$

$$RNH_2(\ell) \rightleftarrows RNH_2(aq) \qquad pK'_{sol} = 4.69 \qquad (14)$$

The dimerization constant for dodecylamine hydrochloride used here is assumed to be the same as the one obtained by Mukerjee for dodecylamine thiosulfate.[17] The K'_{AD} constant for the amine-aminium complex formation was estimated in the same manner as that described for the oleate system. The mass balance equation for this system can be written as:

$$C_T = C_{RNH_2} + C_{RNH_3^+} + 2C_{(RNH_3)_2{}^{2+}} + 2C_{(RNH_2.RNH_3^+)} \qquad (15)$$

Species distribution diagrams have been determined as a function of pH for two different concentrations of dodecylamine hydrochloride (see Figures 2 and 3). The total concentrations of amine have been chosen in such a way that one (5×10^{-5}M) is above the

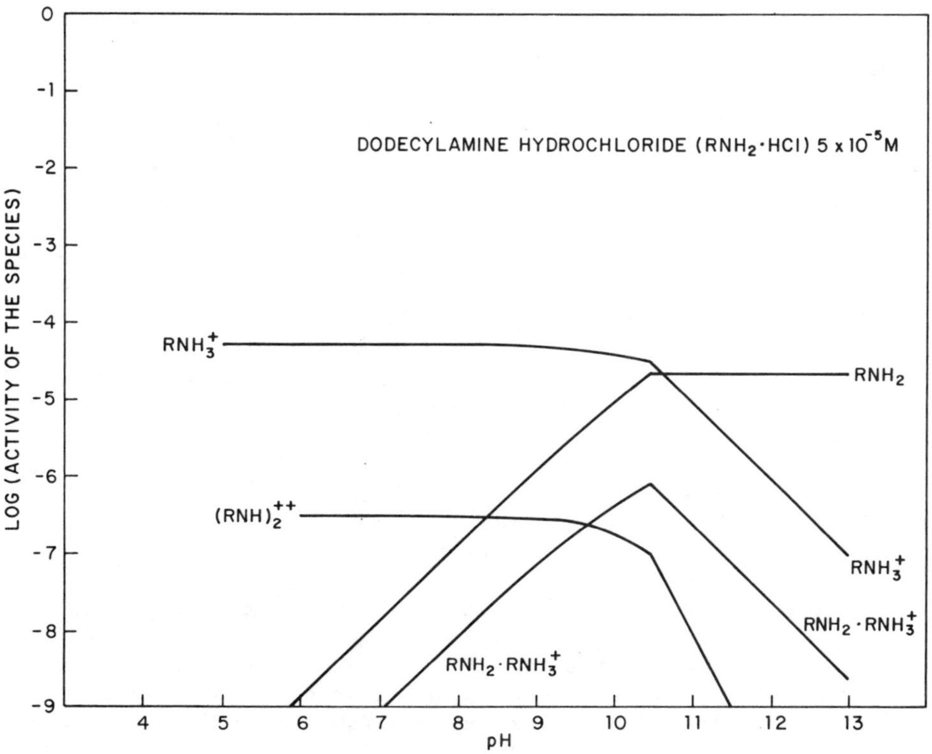

Figure 2. Dodecylamine species distribution diagram as a function of pH. Total amine = 5×10^{-5}M.

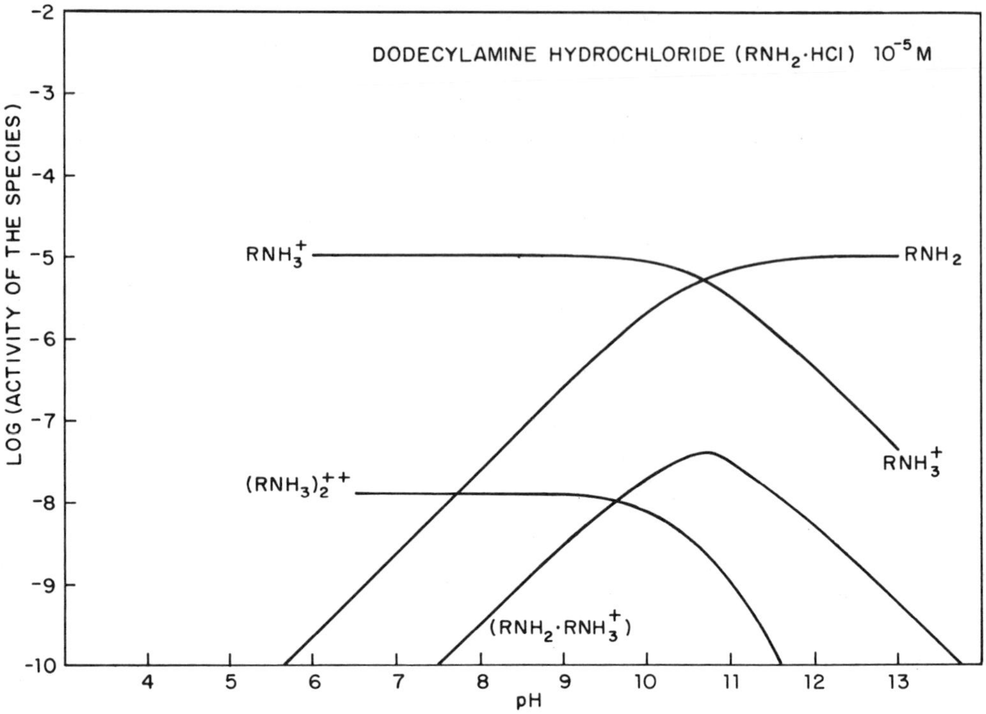

Figure 3. Dodecylamine species distribution diagram as a function of pH. Total amine = 10^{-5}M (below solubility limit).

precipitation limit of the neutral dodecylamine and the other (10^{-5}M) is below it. It is to be noted that the pH of precipitation often coincides with the pH of maximum complex formation and this makes it difficult to distinguish between the roles of these two phenomena. By conducting tests at the above two concentrations, the effects of precipitation can be distinguished from those of complex formation. A comparison of Figures 2 and 3 reveals that, apart from precipitation, the pH of maximum amine-aminium complex has shifted from higher pH (10.9) to lower pH (10.4) values with increase in the total dodecylamine concentration. The implications of these observations are discussed in a later section.

SURFACE ACTIVITIES OF OLEATE AND DODECYLAMINE SOLUTIONS

Based on their charge and molecular size, the surface activities of various oleate and dodecylamine species in solution can be expected to be different. For example, ionomolecular complexes, $RCOOH.RCOO^-$ and $RNH_2.RNH_3^+$ will have a higher surface activity compared to their corresponding ionic monomers. Similarly, charge considerations will again make ionomolecular complexes more surface active than the corresponding dimers. On the other hand, a direct comparison of the surface activities of dimer and the ionic monomer is difficult because of the opposing effects of their molecular size and charge. At low surface coverages, it is possible that the dimers can adsorb at the air/liquid interface with an inverted 'U' shaped configuration, thereby allowing the ionic heads to be in solution and the hydrocarbon chains in air, provided the chain is sufficiently long to bend around. At high surface coverages, on the other hand, it is reasonable to expect the adsorption of dimer with its ionic heads at the opposite ends to be less probable than the adsorption of individual ionic monomers. On the contrary, adsorption of such dimers at the solid/liquid interface can be feasible, as it would orient hydrophilic ends towards the mineral as well as the bulk solution.

Surface properties of oleate and dodecylamine solutions obtained from surface tension results are shown in Figures 4 and 5[9,28] as a function of pH. Comparison of Figure 4 with Figure 1 and Fig-

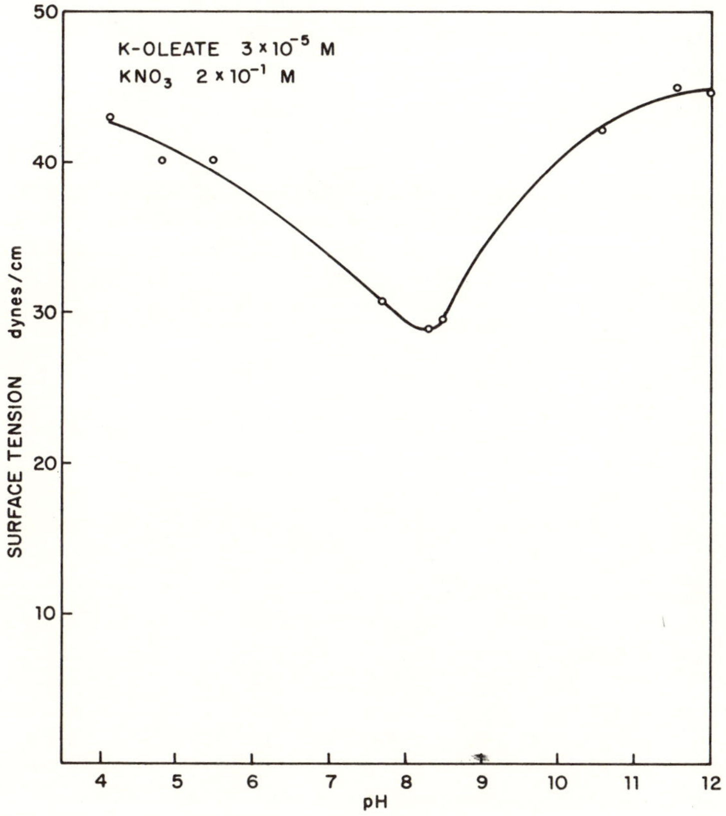

Figure 4. Surface tension of potassium oleate solution as a function of pH. Total oleate = 3×10^{-5} $\underline{M}$.

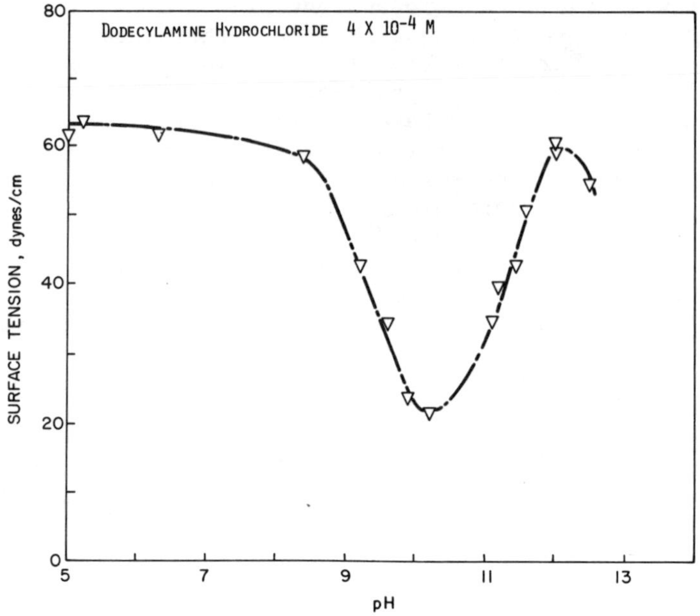

Figure 5. Surface tension of dodecylamine solution as a function of pH. Total amine = 4×10^{-4}M.

ure 5 with Figure 2, clearly shows that the minimum in surface tension in both cases occurs in the pH region where the maximum in ionomolecular complex activity and the precipitation edge of the neutral molecule also occur in solution. These observations are, thus, in accordance with the expected surface activities of different species considered above.

In the light of the above discussion, the flotation dependence of minerals using oleic acid and dodecylamine is discussed below.

FLOTATION USING OLEATE

Typical results obtained for the dependence of flotation of hematite using oleate is shown in Figure 6.[9] The sharp maximum in flotation at pH 8 is seen to correspond to that where the surface tension for the same total concentration of oleate is minimum. Also, pH of maximum flotation coincides with the pH of maximum acid-soap formation (see Figure 7). These observations indicate a possible correlation between flotation and the activities of these species in solution. In addition, changes in concentration of other species, and in properties of the mineral such as the interfacial potential, can also cause accountable differences in the flotation behavior.

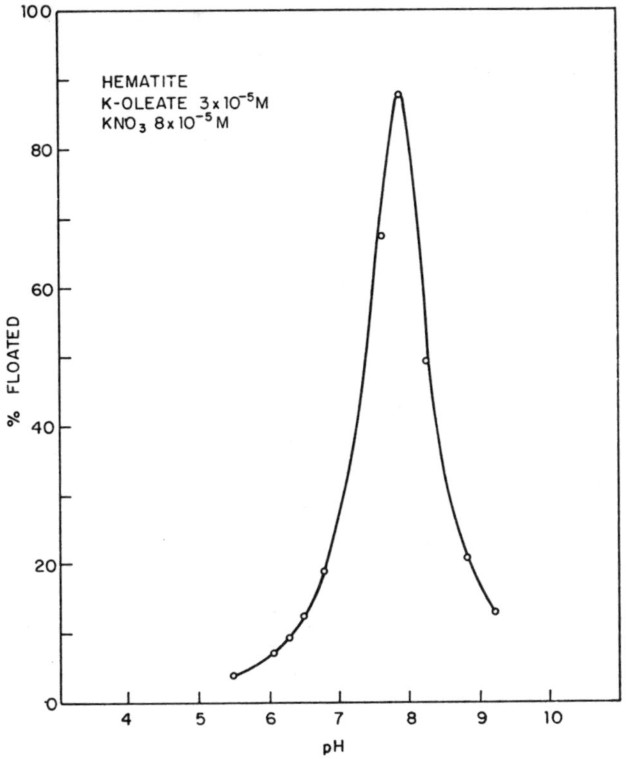

Figure 6. Hallimond cell flotation of hematite as a function of pH.

Taking all such factors into consideration the following mechanism is proposed for the flotation of hematite using oleate. (The role of various Fe-oleate complexes can be incorporated into this scheme only when thermodynamic data for these complexes become available):

Increase in flotation with decrease in pH in the alkaline pH range is attributed to:

a) increase in the acid-soap concentration and its consequent increase in adsorption by electrostatic interactions of hydrogen bonding.

b) increased adsorption of the acid-soap due to also the increase in the number of positive sites on the mineral

c) possibly, increased adsorption of the negatively charged oleate monomer and the oleate dimer due to the increase in the number of positive sites on the mineral, and

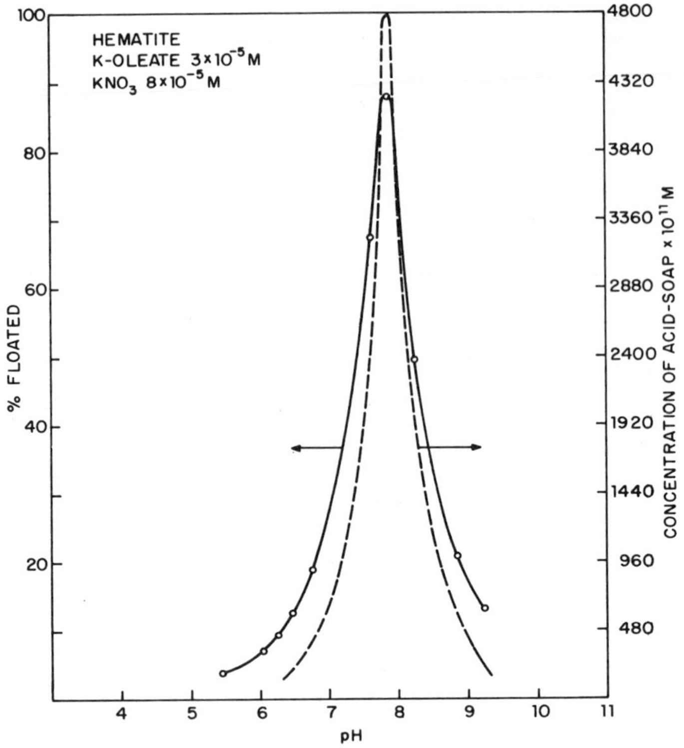

Figure 7. Correlation of hematite flotation with the acid-soap concentration.

d) increased adsorption of neutral oleic acid due to hydrogen bonding with surface hydroxyl groups or co-adsorption between the ionic species.

The decrease in flotation with decrease in pH below pH 8 is attributed in a similar manner to

a) a decrease in concentration of the acid-soap and consequent decrease of its adsorption on hematite

b) the effects of decreases in concentrations of oleate monomers, oleate dimers, and the acid-soap dimer on their electrostatic interaction with the hematite. This effect should, however, be minimal since the logarithmic decrease in the concentration of the species with decrease in pH will be mostly offset by a similar increase in the concentration of the positive surface sites.

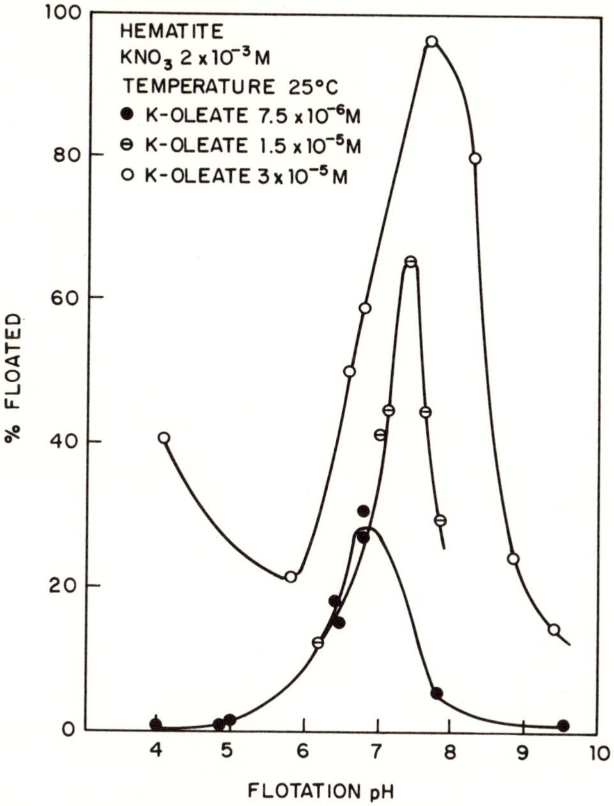

Figure 8. Hematite flotation as a function of pH. Total oleate = 7.5×10^{-6} M(●), 1.5×10^{-5}M(θ) and 3×10^{-5}M(O).

It is to be noted that the above flotation mechanisms based on the solution chemistry of oleate can also explain the dependence of pH of maximum flotation of hematite on the concentration of total oleate species in solution (see Figure 8). The pH of maximum acid-soap formation and the onset of oleic acid precipitation has been calculated at various oleate concentrations and is given in Figure 9. It can be clearly seen that this parameter also follows the same trend with oleate concentrations as the pH of maximum flotation giving further support to the proposed mechanism based on oleate solution chemistry. The strong dependence of flotation of minerals on the oleate chemistry can also be seen from the results of Polkin and Najfonow[29] (see Figure 10) where the maximum in flotation for a number of minerals of significantly different surface chemical and electrochemical properties occurs in the pH range of 7 to 8. Again, the possible role of acid-soap which forms in maximum amounts in this region needs to be noted.

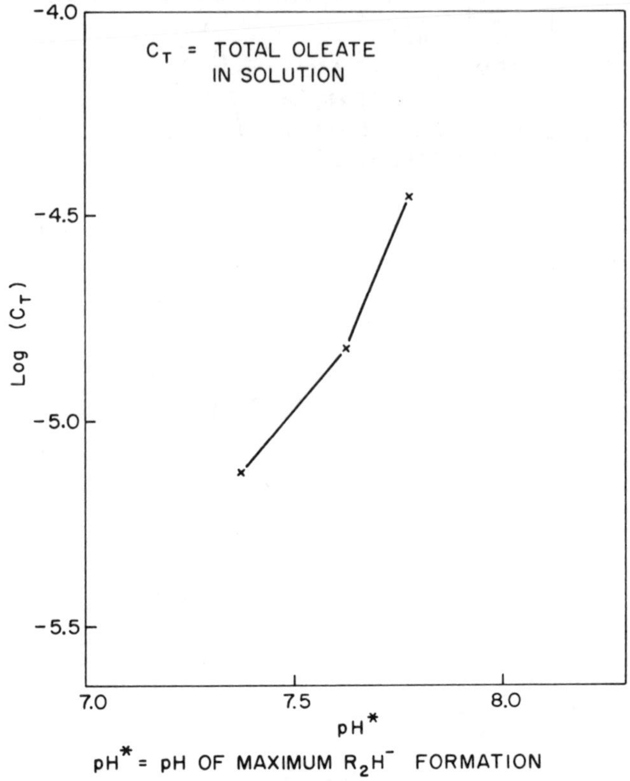

Figure 9. Total oleate concentration vs. pH of maximum acid-soap formation.

FLOTATION USING DODECYLAMINE

Flotation using amines usually exhibits a maximum around pH 10-11. Typical results obtained for the flotation of quartz using 10^{-5} and 5×10^{-5} mole/l dodecylamine solutions using a Hallimond cell are given in Figures 11 and 12. The pH of maximum flotation at 5×10^{-5} mole/l is found to correspond to the pH of formation of maximum amounts of aminium dimer and amine-aminium complex which also coincides with the pH of onset of amine precipitation. At 10^{-5} mole/l, however, there is no precipitation of dodecylamine and in this case the pH of maximum flotation corresponds simply to that of the pH of the ionomolecular complex formation. In this case, it is thus possible to distinguish between the role of the collector complexes and that of the neutral molecule precipitation. These observations fully support the proposed mechanism based on the formation of complexes between collector species.

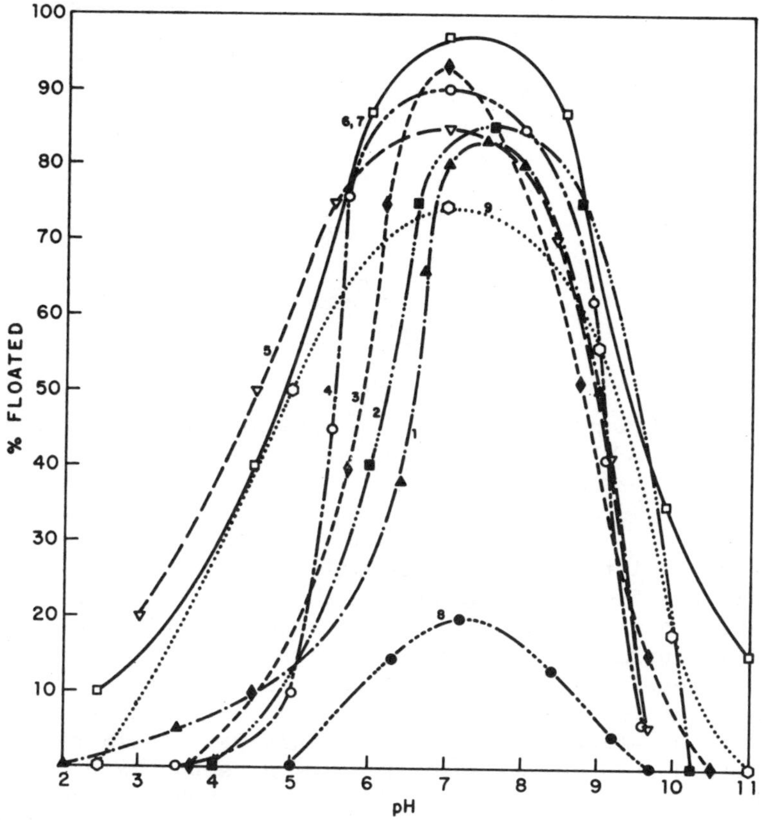

Figure 10. Flotation recovery of minerals as a function of pH. Collector oleic acid (1000 gms/ton). (1) Columbite (2) Zircon (3) Tantalite (4) Ilmenite (5) Rutile (6) Garnet (7) Tourmaline (8) Albite (9) Perovskite (from Reference 29).

ROLE OF DIMERS IN FLOTATION

The discussion above indicates that the role of association complexes in governing the flotation properties of minerals using hydrolyzable surfactants such as oleic acid and dodecylamine can be important. In the case of strongly ionizable surfactants such as sulfonates and sulfates, appreciable amounts of ionomolecular complexes can be present only at very low pH values (<2). On the other hand, depending upon the hydrocarbon chain interaction and the ionic repulsion involved in the formation of multimers, dimers and other multimers can be present under most pH conditions.

As mentioned earlier, adsorption of dimers at the solid/liquid interface can also lead to an energetically compatible situation.

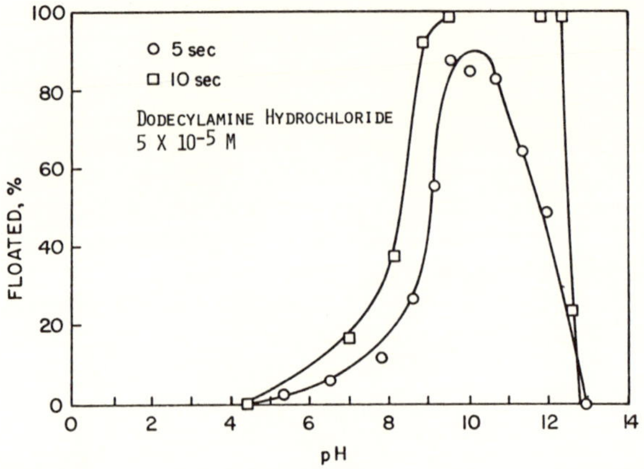

Figure 11. Hallimond cell flotation of quartz as a function of pH. Dodecylaminehydrochloride = 5 x 10^{-5}M.

From the point of view of flotation, adsorption of doubly charged dimers with the polar heads at the opposite ends at the solid/liquid interface may not be suitable, as this would render a "hydrophilic surface" to solution and thus would affect the flotation deleteriously. In fact, such effects could possible contribute to the decrease in mineral flotation often observed at higher surfactant concentrations. In the past, this was attributed to a number of factors such as the adsorption of a second layer of surfactant with a reverse orientation, decrease in bubble size and the saturation of the bubble/solution and the solid/liquid interfaces with surfactants, creating incompatibility with the hydrophobic surface of the mineral.

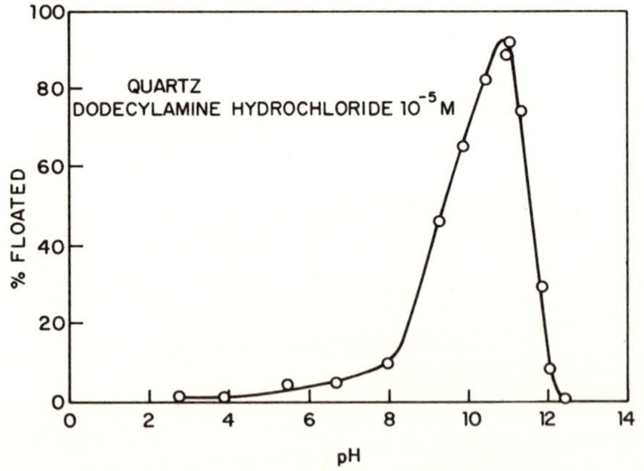

Figure 12. Hallimond cell flotation of quartz as a function of pH. Dodecylaminehydrochloride = 10^{-5}M.

HEMI-MICELLIZATION AND MICELLIZATION

Hemi-micellization is a phenomenon that is analogous to the micelle formation, occurring at the solid/liquid interface as a result of the lateral interactions between the adsorbed molecules. A schematic diagram of hemi-micelle formation is given in Figure 13. Free energy involved in the removal of hydrocarbon chains from an aqueous environment upon hemi-micelle formation can be expected to contribute towards increased adsorption of the surfactant at the solid/liquid interface. Such interactions at the solid/liquid interface lead to marked changes in interfacial parameters such as adsorption density, zeta potential, flotation, etc. A typical example is given in Figure 14 where the results for such interfacial parameters obtained for dodecylsulfonate/alumina systems are given as a function of sulfonate concentration.[30] Flotation data for quartz using alkyl ammonium acetate (see Figure 15) also provide additional support for such behavior.[31] In fact, this flotation dependence can be made use of conveniently to obtain the free energy involved in hemi-micellization.

In a system such as quartz/alkylamine where only electrostatic and lateral interaction forces are operative, the Stern-Graham equation can be written as:[32]

$$\Gamma_i = 2rC.\mathrm{Exp}\left[\frac{(-W'_e + n\phi')}{kT}\right] \qquad (16)$$

where Γ_i is the adsorption density, W'_e is the electrostatic interaction between the mineral and the surfactant molecule, ϕ' is the energy involved in the removal of a single 'CH_2' group from aqueous solution to the hemi-micelle and 'n' is the number of 'CH_2' groups in the surfactant molecule, k is the Boltzmann constant and T is

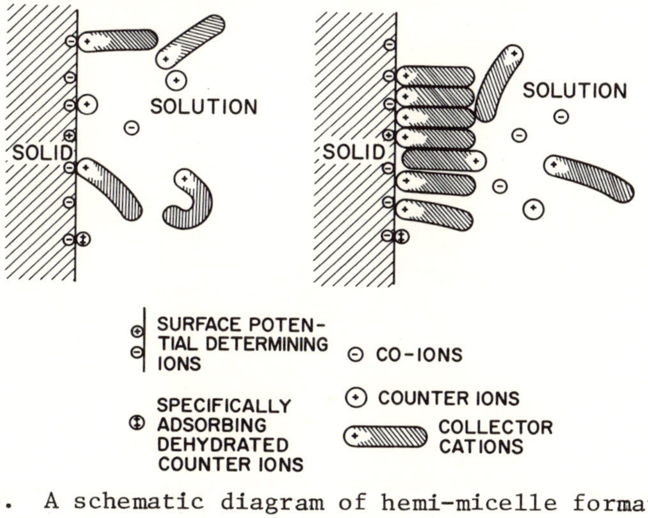

Figure 13. A schematic diagram of hemi-micelle formation.

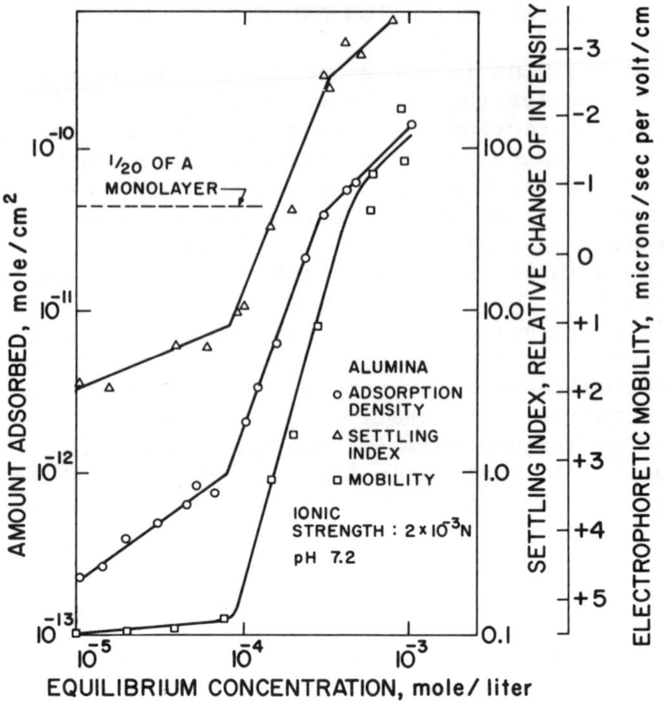

Figure 14. Adsorption density of dodecylsulfonate, electrophoretic mobility and settling rate of alumina-sodium dodecylsulfonate system as a function of the concentration of sodium dodecylsulfonate. (Reproduced by permission of the University of California.)

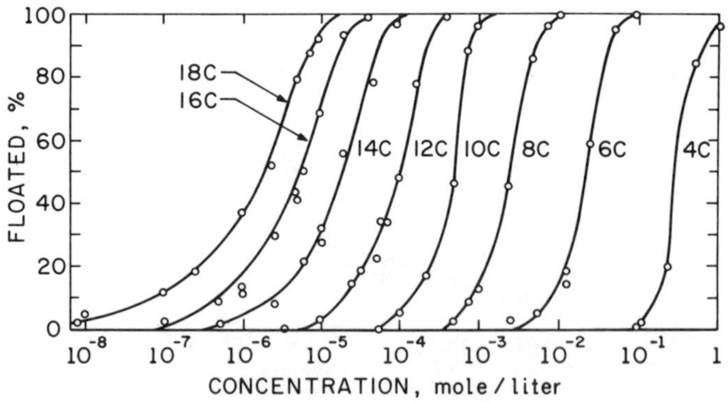

Figure 15. The effect of alkyl chain length on the flotation of quartz in alkylammonium acetate solutions.[31]

the absolute temperature.

At the concentration C_{HM}, when hemi-micelles begin to form,

$$C_{HM} = \frac{\Gamma'}{2r} \mathrm{Exp}\left[\frac{(W'_e - n\phi')}{kT}\right] \tag{17}$$

or

$$\ln C_{HM} = \ln\left(\frac{\Gamma'}{2r}\right) + \frac{W'_e}{kT} - \frac{n\phi'}{kT} \tag{18}$$

Thus, a plot of log C_{HM} vs. n should be a straight line with a slope $\left(\frac{-\phi'}{kT}\right)$ which can be used to evaluate ϕ'. Fuerstenau et al[32] obtained a concentration parameter by extrapolating the linear rising portion of flotation recovery vs. log concentration curve and assuming it to be proportional to C_{HM}. This parameter was then plotted as a function of the number of carbon atoms and ϕ' the energy involved in transferring $-CH_2-$ groups from aqueous phase to hemi-micelles was computed (see Figure 16). The value of ϕ' so obtained is 1 kT per $-CH_2-$ group which is quite comparable to the energy gain due to micellisation in bulk solution (see Figure 17).

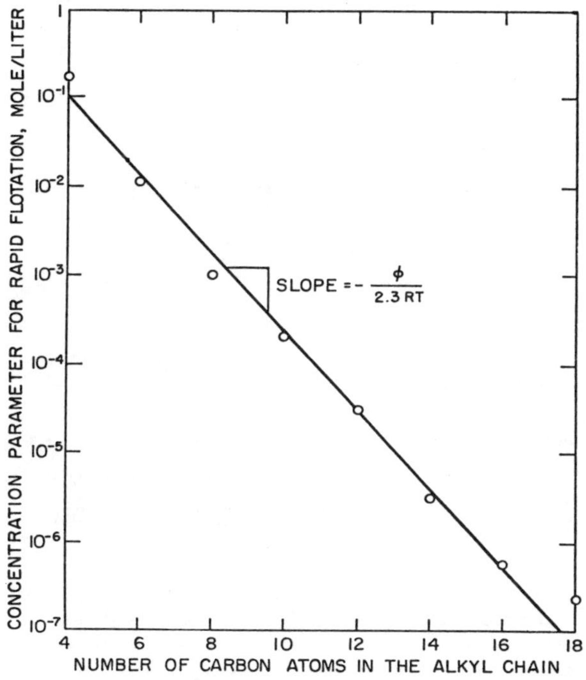

Figure 16. The effect of chain length on the concentration parameter of quartz with alkylammonium acetates[31].

Micelle formation also has been known to influence the adsorption of surfactants at the solid/liquid interface. Micelles themselves are believed to be non-surface active. However, exclusion of micelles from the interfacial region either due to the solvation characteristics of the solid and the surfactant[34,35] or due to the charge/charge repulsion of the micelle from the solid surface[36] can conceivably yield maxima in adsorption isotherms. Adsorption from micellar solutions has been discussed elsewhere.[34,35]

PRECIPITATION

Interaction of surfactants with the counter ions in the system, leading to precipitation is not uncommon in flotation systems. In fact, on the basis of an extensive study of the solubility products of a number of cationic soaps of common fatty acids, du Rietz[37,38] has suggested the point of precipitation to be a requirement for incipient flotation. Fuerstenau and Miller,[39] using a homologous series of aklyl sulfonates have also recently obtained a direct correlation between calcite flotation and the solubility product of calcium salt. On the other hand, excessive precipitation (probably due to the supersaturation of the corresponding counter ions in the bulk solution) in the bulk has been found also to adversely affect the flotation.[40] For example, addition of calcium nitrate to a calcite/potassium oleate system around pH 10 decreases the calcite flotation

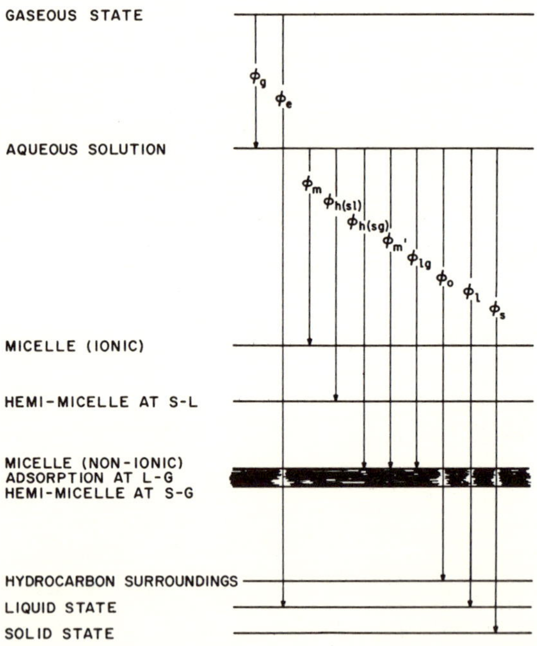

Figure 17. Schematic diagram for free energy transfer of $-CH_2-$ groups from aqueous solution to various environments.[33]

significantly; this has been attributed to the depletion of surfactant owing to precipitation.[40]

It is often considered that while precipitates nucleated on the solid surface and thus 'physically adsorbed' on the surface can cause flotation, the bulk precipitates themselves may not act as collectors.[41] The adsorption density (or, more strictly, the apparent adsorption density) obtained under precipitation conditions can be quite high, if the nucleation of the precipitates can occur at the solid surfaces. The adsorption results obtained for calcite/oleate system shown in Figure 18 illustrate this point as the apparent sharp increase in slope of the adsorption isotherm above 10^{-4}M of oleate can be seen to correspond to the precipitation limit of calcium oleate in the bulk.[40]

CONCLUDING REMARKS

Flotation is a complex phenomenon governed by the properties of the three interfaces, namely, solid/liquid, liquid/gas and solid/

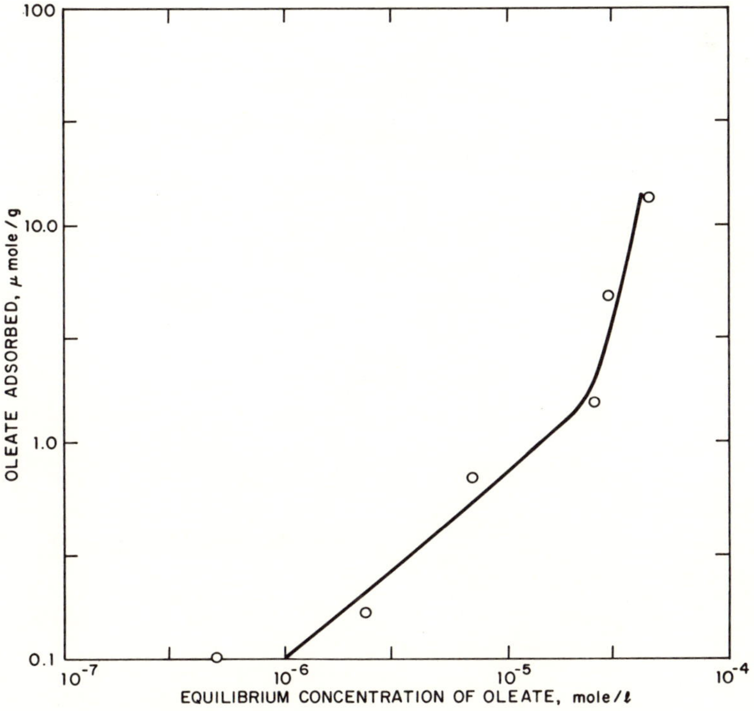

Figure 18. Adsorption isotherm of potassium oleate on calcite at a natural pH of 9.6.[40]

gas. Attachment of air bubbles to particles results from the favorable energy balance created by the adsorption of surfactants at various interfaces. Adsorption in turn is controlled by, among other things, the solution chemistry of surfactants including their associative interactions such as micellization premicellar aggregation and precipitation. Adsorption studies at the solid/liquid and liquid/air interfaces, coupled with the study of other interfacial properties, such as electrokinetic potential as a function of relevant variables such as surfactant concentration and pH, have yielded useful information on mechanisms of adsorption and therefore the dependence of flotation on such solution conditions. Thus, the results obtained for surface tension and flotation in systems containing hydrolyzable surfactants such as oleic acid and dodecylamine as a function of pH, along with the data estimated for activities of various surfactant species, have thrown considerable light on the importance of the role of solution chemistry. Premicellar association, hemimicellar association at solid/liquid interfaces, precipitation, and even micellisation have a role to play in determining surfactant adsorption on minerals and flotation. A complete quantitative understanding of the surfactant mineral interaction will, however, be possible only when the thermodynamic data for all relevant reactions between various surfactant species and dissolved mineral species become available.

ACKNOWLEDGMENT

Support of the National Science Foundation (ENG-76-80139) is gratefully acknowledged.

REFERENCES

1. J.W. McBain and H. McHan, J. Am. Chem. Soc., 70, 3838 (1948).
2. P. Ekwall, Kolloid Z., 92, 141 (1940).
3. J. Stauff, Physik. Chem., 183A, 55 (1938).
4. J. Lucassen, J. Phys. Chem., 70, 1824 (1966).
5. D. Eagland and F. Franks, Faraday Soc., 61, 2468 (1965).
6. P. Mukerjee, J. Phys. Chem., 69, 2821 (1965).
7. L.B. Bangs, "Surfactant Dimers and Their Adsorption," Ph.D. Dissertation, MIT, (1964).
8. R.F. Jung, "Oleic Acid Adsorption at the Goethite-Water Interface," M.S. Thesis, Univ. Melbourne, 1976.
9. R.D. Kulkarni and P. Somasundaran, in "Adv. in Interfacial Phenomena on Particulate/Solution/Gas Systems, Applications to Flotation Research," P. Somasundaran and R.B. Grieves, Editors, AIChE Symp. Series, No. 150, 124 (1975).
10. P. Somasundaran, K.P. Ananthapadmanabhan and R.D. Kulkarni, Paper presented at the XIIth Intn'l. Minl. Proc. Congr., Sao Paulo, Brazil, 1977.
11. K.P. Ananthapadmanabhan, P. Somasundaran and T.W. Healy, Paper presented at the 107th Ann. AIME Meeting, Denver, 1978.

12. P. Mukerjee, K.J. Mysels and C.I. Dulin, J. Phys. Chem., 62, 1390 (1958).
13. P. Mukerjee, Adv. Colloid Interface Sci., 1, 241 (1967)
14. F. Frank and H.T. Smith, J. Phys. Chem., 68, 3581 (1964).
15. E. Eagland and F. Franks in "Proc. IVth Intn'l. Congr. on Surface Active Substances," Brussels, Vol. 2, p. 535, London (1964).
16. R. Smith and C. Tanford, Proc. Nat. Acad. Sci. USA, 70, 289 (1973).
17. P. Mukerjee, J. Phys. Chem., 62, 1404 (1958).
18. H.F. Walton, E.N. Heibert and E.H. Scholtes, J. Colloid Sci., 1, 385 (1946).
19. H.S. Frank and M.W. Evans, J. Chem. Phys., 13, 507 (1945).
20. H.S. Frank and W.Y. Wen, Disc. Farady Soc., 24, 133 (1957).
21. G. Nemethy and H.A. Scheraga, J. Phys. Chem., 66, 1773 (1962).
22. G. Nemethy and H.A. Scheraga, J. Chem. Phys., 36, 3401 (1962).
23. E.E. Schrier, E.M. Pottle and H.A. Scheraga, J. Am. Chem. Soc., 86, 3444 (1964).
24. J.W. McBain and A. Stewart, J. Chem. Soc., 1392 (1927).
25. E.D. Goddard, S. Goldwasser, G. Golikeri and H.C. Kung in "Molecular Association in Biological and Related Systems," E.D. Goddard, Editor, Adv. Chem. Ser. No. 67, 1968.
26. H.C. Kung and E.D. Goddard, J. Colloid Interface Sci., 29, 242 (1969).
27. H.C. Kung and E.D. Goddard, Kolloid Z. Z. Polym., 232, 812 (1969).
28. P. Somasundaran, Intn'l. J. Mineral Proc., 3, 35 (1976).
29. S.I. Polkin and T.V. Najfonow in "Intn'l. Mineral Proc. Congr." Vol. I, p. 307, N. Arbiter, Editor, Gordon and Breach Sci., New York, 1965.
30. P. Somasundaran, T.W. Healy and D.W. Fuerstenau, J. Colloid Interface Sci., 22, 599 (1966).
31. P. Somasundaran, "The Effect of van der Waals Interaction Between Hydrocarbon Chains on Solid-Liquid Interfacial Properties," Ph.D. Dissertation, Univ. California, Berkeley, California (1964).
32. D.W. Fuerstenau, T.W. Healy and P. Somasundaran, Trans. AIME, 229, 321 (1964).
33. I.J. Lin and P. Somasundaran, J. Colloid Interface Sci., 37, 731 (1971).
34. P. Somasundaran and H.S. Hanna, in "Proc. SPE Symp. on Improved Oil Recovery," p. 241, Apr. 16-19, Tulsa, Oklahoma (1978).
35. H.S. Hanna and P. Somasundaran, Paper presented at the SPE-AIChE Jt. Symp. on Interfacial Phenomena in Chemical Flooding Processes, AIChE Meeting, Philadelphia, June 4, 1978.
36. P. Mukerjee and A. Anavil in "Adsorption at Interfaces," K.L. Mittal, Editor, p. 107, ACS Symp. Ser. No. 8, 1975.
37. C. du Rietz, Paper presented at the XIth Intn'l. Mineral Proc. Congr., Cagliari, paper 13, 1975.

38. C. du Rietz in "Progress in Mineral Dressing," Trans. IVth Intn'l. Mineral Dressing Congr., Stockholm, 1957, Pub. Almquist and Wiksell,
39. M.C. Fuerstenau and J.D. Miller, Trans. AIME, 238, 153 (1967).
40. K.P. Ananthapadmanabhan and P. Somasundaran, Paper presented at the 106th Ann. AIME Meeting, Atlanta, 1976.
41. D.R. Nagaraj and P. Somasundaran, unpublished results (1976).
42. P. Somasundaran, J. Colloid Interface Sci., 31, 559 (1960).

INTERFACIAL TENSION AND PHASE BEHAVIOR OF PURE SURFACTANT SYSTEMS

W. H. Wade, E. Vasquez, J. L. Salager, M. El-Emary,
C. Koukounis, and R. S. Schechter
The University of Texas at Austin

Austin, Texas 78712

Most surfactant systems studied in relation to their potential value in enhanced oil recovery are composed of complex mixtures such as petroleum sulfonates or alkylxylene sulfonates. Although recent studies have shown that the low interfacial oil/water tensions given by the above surfactants, there has been no systematic studies of phase behavior with such a comparison attempted.

In this study, interfacial tension and phase behavior properties are compared for two surfactants: a monoisomeric, and an isomerically mixed commercial alkyl aryl sulfonate toward this end.

Provided that a suitable formulation of the amphiphile/brine/oil alcohol system is found, numerous surfactants can give low interfacial tensions in the 10^{-3} dyne/cm range, and exhibit three-phase behavior with the production of a middle phase microemulsion.

By scanning one of the formulation parameters, one observes the same quality of transition for both surfactants: the minimum tension and three-phase formation are tightly coupled phenomena; the partition coefficient of the surfactant changes by several orders of magnitudes and solubilization is maximum in the transition region. In three-phase systems the partition coefficient of the surfactant, i.e., the ratio of its concentrations in excess oil and excess water phases, is near unity. Since the concentration of the surfactant in these excess phases is very low, actually of the same order of magnitude as the critical micelle concentration in a similar aqueous environment, it is possible to express the optimum conditions in terms of an equality of the standard chemical potentials of the surfactant in both phases; these potentials can be affected by a change in any formulation variable. The effect of a perturbation of any system parameter (salinity, oil nature, alcohol type and concentration, surfactant type, and temperature) can be explained as an unbalance of this condition, and may be compensated by a proper change of any other formulation parameter.

Hydrocarbon mixing rules and the Equivalent Alkane Carbon Number concept are found to hold for pure surfactants as well as for petroleum sulfonates.

For isomerically pure surfactant, the optimum formulation is independent of the surfactant concentration, as opposed to the so-called concentration shift of commercial products which seems to be a mixture property.

The similarity of the observed behavior of pure surfactants and commercial mixtures is explained by remarkably simple linear mixing rules, and is illustrated by the co-partitioning of a binary surfactant mixture.

INTRODUCTION

In the past few years a number of publications from this laboratory have explored the parameters controlling surfactant generated oil/water low interfacial tensions (LIFT). These studies were conducted at relatively low surfactant concentrations to avoid solubilization and phase behavior complications characteristic of higher surfactant concentrations. One of the interesting, early findings was that complex oil phases such as crude oils of interest to the petroleum industry are not required to obtain LIFT. In fact, crude oils can be replaced by pure, monoisomeric alkanes.[1] However, it was discovered that a given surfactant system exhibited a remarkable preference for a particular alkane, alkylbenzene or alkycyclohexane if LIFT was obtained.[2] This specificity gave rise to the concept of equivalent alkane carbon number (EACN) in which the tension behavior of octane, say, is equivalent to octylbenzene or butylcyclohexane. It was found, moreover, that the EACN of a hydrocarbon mixture was the mole average value of the EACN's of all the compounds present in the mixture. These scaling rules for hydrocarbons have been tested using binary[3] and more complex mixtures containing up to 29 components.[4] Further studies have included the effect of added electrolyte,[2] surfactant molecular weight[5] and alcohol cosurfactant[6] on the preferred alkane. Systematic trends were observed providing the basis for designing surfactant systems for use with a particular crude oil.

Recently, the influence of surfactant structure has been assessed.[7-10] These studies have resulted in a classification of various sulfonated alkyl aryl structures into groups, each being most effective against certain alkanes.

Moreover, a number of papers published by industrial researchers interested in oil recovery appeared.[11-14] Their systems utilized high surfactant concentrations (>1wt%) and always consisted of complex oil phases and commercial surfactants. For such systems multiphase (>2) equilibrium systems were commonly observed. Nevertheless their studies on the effect of surfactant molecular weight[12,13] electrolyte concentration[13] and alcohol cosurfactants[14] on multiphase formation revealed trends remarkably similar to those observed for low surfactant concentration (two-phase) systems. Minimal LIFT values for a particular system were always attained for three-phase systems and the concept of optimal electrolyte concentration for such behavior was developed.

Our recent studies[6,15] on phase behavior have demonstrated that complex oil phases can be modeled by monoisomeric hydrocarbons and that the concept of optimal salinity proposed by Healy and Reed[11] can be quantitatively related to the preferred alkane carbon number (ACN) or the EACN for the oil phase. In these studies and those of others, more or less complex surfactant mixtures were employed.

The purpose of the present study is to show that phase behavior and LIFT are intimately related and that the scaling rules developed previously will apply even when the surfactant is a pure monoisomeric species.

EXPERIMENTAL

Interfacial Tension Studies

Interfacial tensions were measured at 27°C using the spinning drop interfacial tensiometer as described elsewhere.[1]

Phase Behavior Studies

Aqueous phases containing surfactant (see below), electrolyte (NaCl), and alcohol (sec butanol) were contacted with the appropriate oil phase in stoppered test tubes. After gentle shaking every two hours for twelve hours, they were allowed to stand at constant temperature ($25\pm1^{\circ}C$) until phase volumes became time independent for two days. The volume fraction of aqueous to oil phase (WOR) initially was always four.

Chemicals

The behavior of two surfactants is compared here. The first is a commercial preparation of Exxon made by alkylating o-xylene with propylenetetramer followed by sulfonation and subsequent neutralization with a base such as NaOH. Although the starting materials and process must produce a large ensemble of surfactant species, this material is undoubtedly much less complex than petroleum or mahogany sulfonates, and will hereafter be abbreviated as Exxon #1. The second surfactant (abbreviated here UT #2) was produced in this laboratory by the flow chart given in Figure 1. Small amounts (<2%) of isomeric species arise in the acylation and sulfonation steps. This surfactant was chosen because earlier studies[4,7-10] showed it to be particularly well structured for minimal tension with a variety of crude oils, coupled with minimal surfactant molecular weight.

The oil phase hydrocarbons (n-alkanes, n-alkylbenezenes, and n-alkylcyclobutanes) employed in these studies ranged from reagent to pure grade. No complications from isomeric impurities would be expected[4] and none were found. The available distilled water was employed with reagent grade NaCl and sec butanol added as required. Concentrations are expressed in units of grams per deciliter (gpdl).

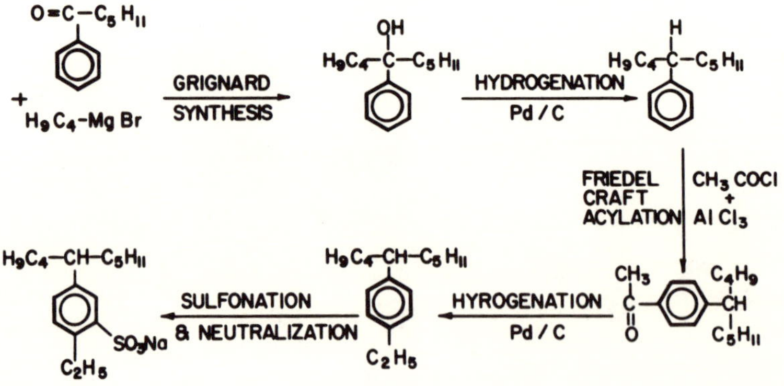

Fig. 1. The synthetic pathway for UT #1-5 (p-ethylphenyl) decane-sodium sulfonate.

Partition Coefficients

Surfactant concentration was measured using ultraviolet absorbance. The aqueous solutions were analyzed directly after diluting the more concentrated solutions with water to bring them on scale. If the surfactant analysis was for an alkane oil phase, the surfactant concentrations could be measured directly. Solutions too concentrated were diluted with chloroform. This procedure was used except when the oil was an alkylbenzene. In this case a more elaborate procedure is required since the ultraviolet spectrum of the surfactant is primarily due to the presence of the benzene ring. The surfactant (and perhaps some alkylbenzene) is first extracted from the aqueous solution using ethylbenzene. This is then dissolved in chloroform (Certified A.C.S.) and introduced into a silica gel column which is then flushed with chloroform. Once all the hydrocarbon has been removed, methanol is used to elute the surfactant. The surfactant concentration can be measured in methanol using U. V. techniques. The details of column preparation, sample preparation and collection are described by Vasquez.[16]

RESULTS AND DISCUSSION

Phase Behavior

In many of the remaining figures, data have been cast so as to facilitate comparison of the behavior of Exxon #1 and UT #2. For example each cross-hatched regime in Figures 2-4

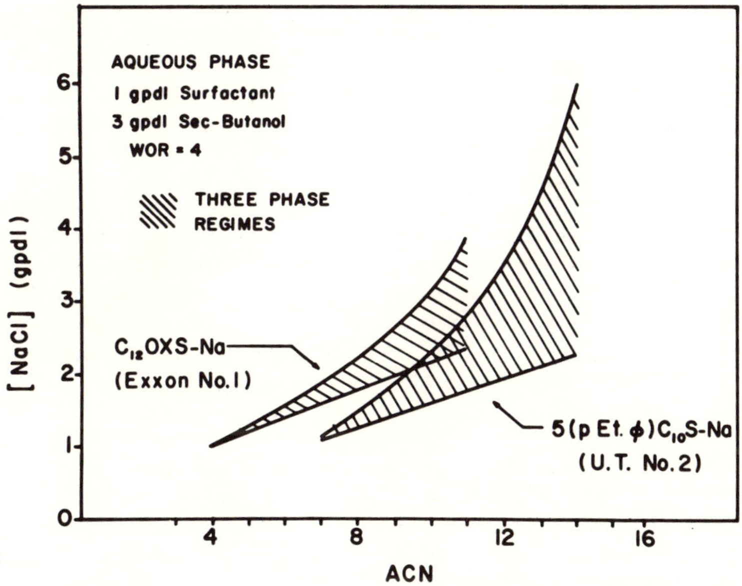

Fig. 2. Phase behavior with salinity and oil phase alkanes as variables.

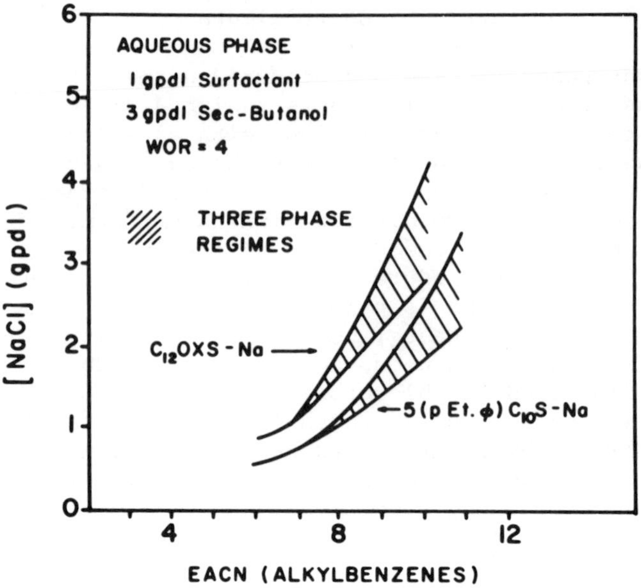

Fig. 3. Phase behavior with salinity and oil phase alkyl benzenes as variables.

delineates the coexistence of three phases. Above the upper boundary is a two phase regime with surfactant partitioned primarily into the oil phase. Below the lower boundary is another two phase regime but with surfactant in the aqueous phase. To calculate EACN in Figures 3 and 4, earlier interfacial tension studies dictated that the benzene ring made no contribution to oil phase equivalent alkane carbon number and cyclohexane was the equivalent of four alkyl carbons. Thus, for instance, octylbenzene and octylcyclohexane are assigned EACNs of 8 and 12 respectively. There is considerable similarity of the boundaries for the three phase regimes for the two surfactants. At low salinities (or EACN) the three phase regime vanishes, or strictly speaking, is not detectable. Conversely, the higher the salinity, the more tolerant is the three phase regime to variations in salinity (or EACN).

As was done earlier,[15] it is convenient to locate an optimal salinity, S*, by the mid-point in the salinity range for three phase coexistence with a particular hydrocarbon. When this is done for the phase behavior displayed in Figure 2, and S* plotted versus ACN in Figure 5, The typical logarithmic dependence is

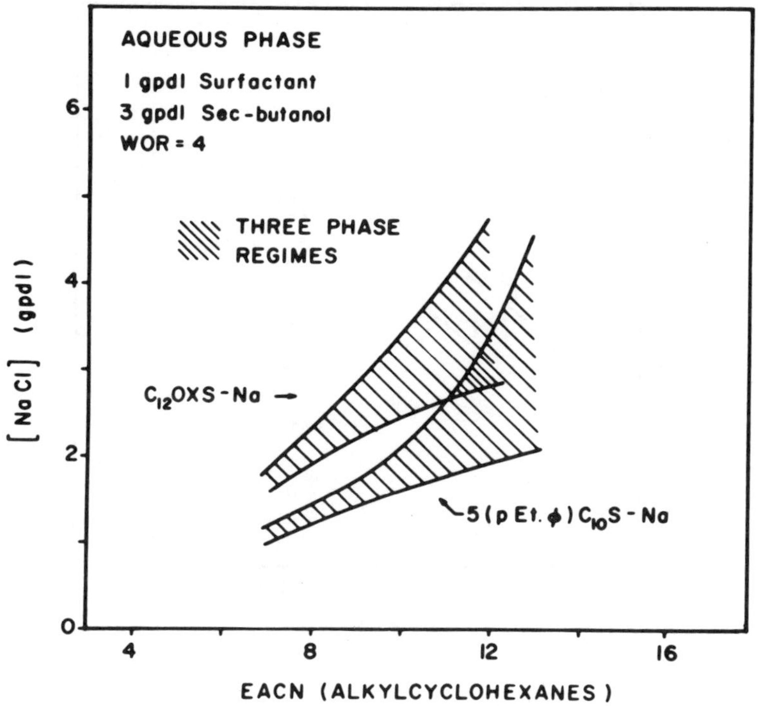

Fig. 4. Phase behavior with salinity and oil phase alkyl cyclohexanes as variables.

observed.[15] Displacement of the two data sets arises from a combination of surfactant molecular weight and structural effects. On the basis of molecular weight alone, one would expect the position of the data sets to be reversed.[5,12] Their actual relative positon is a clear demonstration of the molecular weight "effectiveness" of the UT #2 molecular structure. Both data sets quantitatively fit the earlier found relationship

$$\ln S^* = 0.16 \text{ (EACN)} + \text{const.} \tag{1}$$

with S* in units of gpdl. The slope has been found identical in value for all sulfonate surfactants studied in this laboratory for various oil phase compositions, surfactant concentration, or alcohol cosolvent type or concentration. As an example of the application of equation 1 and the earlier reported hydrocarbon scaling rules[4] to a variety of oil phase compositions, the data of Figure 6 show that the alkane and alkylcyclohexane data are coincident with some skewing for the alkylbenzene data.

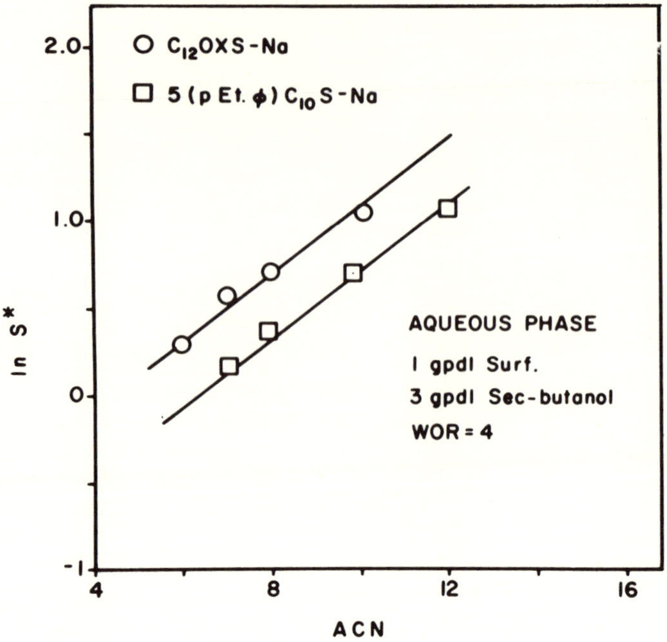

Fig. 5. The variation of optimal salinity, S*, with ACN.

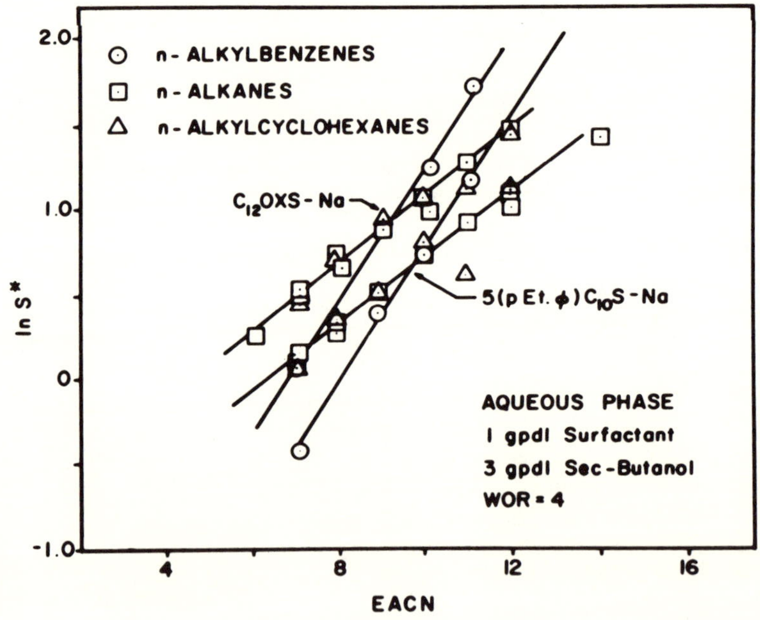

Fig. 6. The intercomparison of S* for the three homologous series of hydrocarbons.

Surfactant Partitioning

Surfactants of potential interest for LIFT investigations preferentially partition into the aqueous phase at low salinities and the oil phase at high salinities. For complex surfactants it has been found that equipartitioning is coincident with minimal interfacial tension.[6] The partition coefficient is here defined as

$$P = \frac{C_{s/o}}{C_{s/w}} \qquad (2)$$

with concentrations Cs/o (surfactant in oil) and Cs/w (surfactant in water) expressed in gpdl. Figure 7 shows that both UT #2 and Exxon #1 exhibit a pronounced preference for a particular phase depending on the salinity. Such a sharp dependence of the partition coefficient may be expected for UT #2 (a monoisomeric surfactant), but might not be expected for Exxon #1 since this surfactant is a complex mixture of surfactant species. The reason for this collective behavior is not yet understood, but it has been observed for all cases studied.

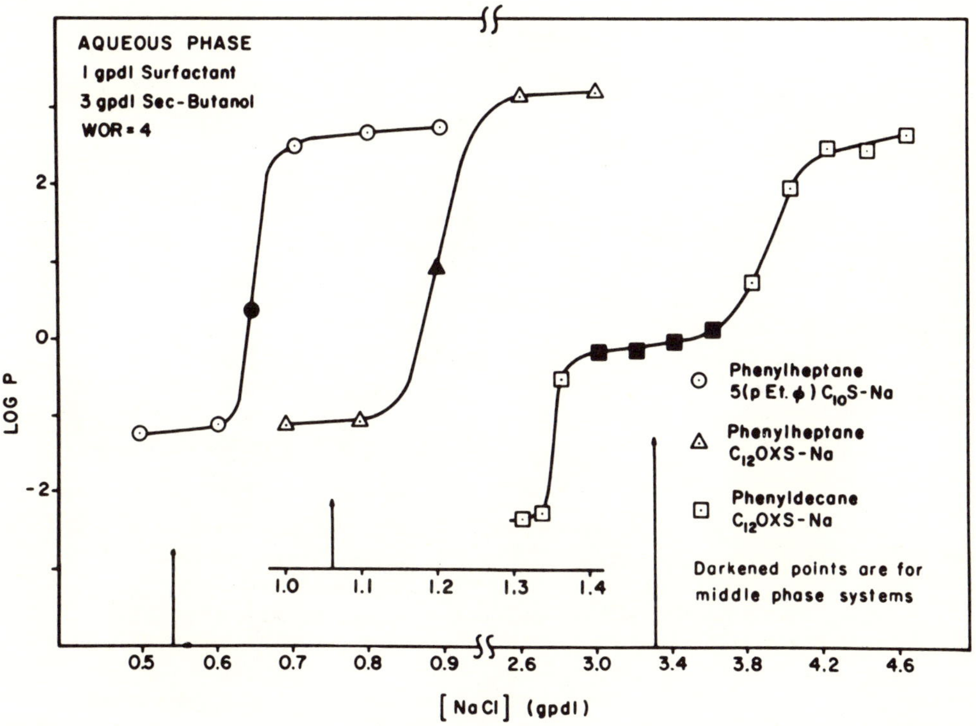

Fig. 7. Partition coefficients vs. salinity for various formulations.

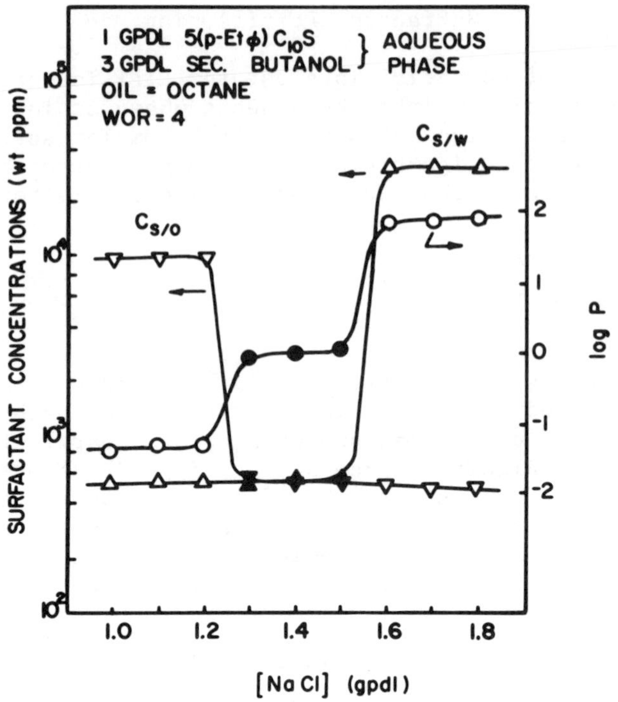

Fig. 8. The relation of absolute surfactant concentrations to partition coefficients.

The partition coefficients presented in Figure 7 apply to systems with middle phases as well as to upper and low phase microemulsions. Partition coefficients with middle phase formation are defined as the ratio of the concentration in the excess oil phase to that in the excess water phase. Both concentrations are, as shown in Figure 8, quite small, since most of the surfactant resides in the middle phase, but their ratio is very near unity. Thus one observes the P ≃ 1 is coincident with the three phase regime.

This result may be expected if it is asserted that middle phase formation requires a "properly balanced" surfactant. The fact that P ≃ 1 in the middle phase region has been observed previously for complex surfactants,[6] but these results also show that it is true for pure ones.

Figure 7 also shows that for a given surfactant system the range of salinities at which middle phases are observed increases with increasing EACN. Phenyldecane (EACN = 10) therefore shows a larger range over which P ≃ 1 than does Phenylheptane (EACN = 7).

The aqueous phase concentrations within the three phase regimes do not greatly exceed the CMC measured in the absence of oil with all other factors being the same. The trends over a range of salinities are shown in Figure 9. The concentration of surfactant in the aqueous phase is reduced to a value which is only 3 to 4 times the CMC. Furthermore, the limited data presented here indicate a correlation between Cs/w and CMC in the three phase regime.

Interfacial Tension

Figure 10 shows the interfacial tension of alkanes measured against aqueous solutions containing various concentrations of UT #2. Below the CMC (200 ppm for this aqueous phase composition), the more traditional oil/water tensions in the range of 0.1-10 dynes/cm are observed. For example, at 100 ppm, the tension is about 0.1 and independent of the composition of the oil phase. No alkane preference is seen. At higher surfactant concentrations, the sharp alkane preference, in this case for nonane, is observed and the minimum tensions are in the range of 5×10^{-3} dyne/cm. This again indicates, as previously noted, that micelles are needed to achieve ultralow tensions. Furthermore the lowest tensions are coincident with the conditions for middle phase formation. Figure

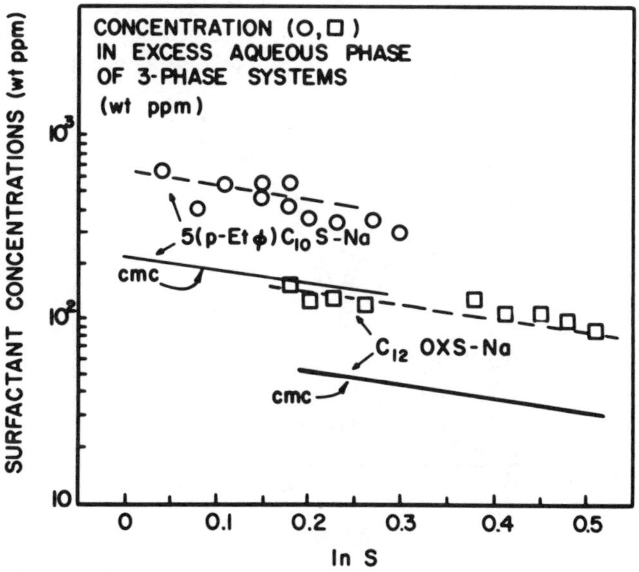

Fig. 9. The correspondence of residual aqueous phase surfactant concentration to CMC as a function of salinity.

5 shows that for a salinity of 1.6 gpdl, the preferred alkane for middle phase formation is nonane which corresponds to the alkane giving the minimum tension in Figure 10. These results suggest that indeed a middle phase which is too small in extent to be detectable may very well have been present during previous studies. Thus low tensions may very well result from the existence of a thick interface having the same or a similar structure as that of the middle phase microemulsion. This tentative proposal requires further investigation.

Middle phase formation at higher surfactant concentrations dictates the measurement of both oil/middle phase and water/middle phase tensions ($\gamma_{m/o}$ and $\gamma_{m/w}$). Two salinity/tension scans passing through the three phase envelopes are given in Figure 11. The character of these scans is typical of those reported for commercial surfactants.[15] No new features are added or lost which can be attributed to reduced surfactant complexity. Thus it should be possible to model the interfacial tension and phase behavior of a commercial surfactant by an appropriate monoisomeric species.

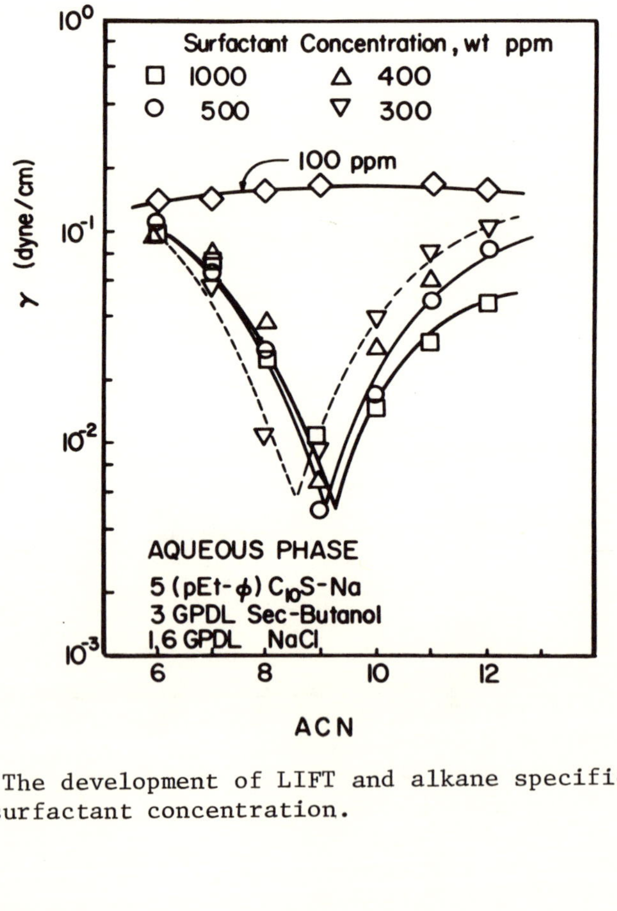

Fig. 10. The development of LIFT and alkane specificity as related to surfactant concentration.

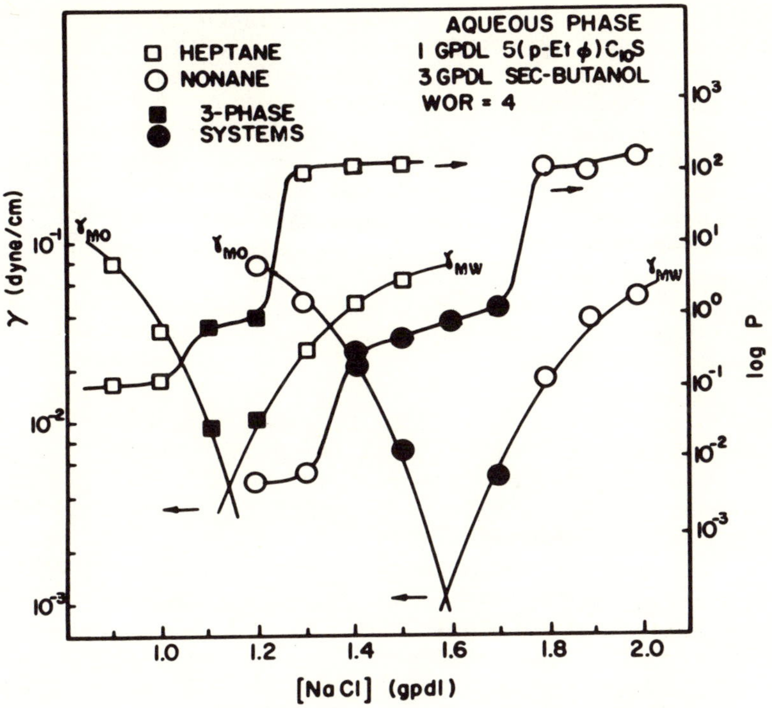

Fig. 11. The relation of LIFT and partitioning.

Chemical Potential and LIFT

The evidence is increasingly comprehensive that the condition for minimal interfacial tension or optimal salinity for middle phase formation corresponds to equal partitioning of surfactant between oil and water. With the required equilibrium constraint of uniformity of surfactant chemical potential throughout the system, one obtains

$$\mu^o_{s/o} + RT\ln C_{s/o}a_{s/o} = \mu^o_{s/w} + RT\ln C_{s/w}a_{s/w} \tag{3}$$

Where μ^o is the surfactant standard chemical potential in oil (s/o) or water (s/w) and a is the activity coefficient. Assuming that the activity coefficients are near unity and taking P = 1 gives

$$\mu^o_{s/o} = \mu^o_{s/w} \tag{4}$$

as the thermodynamic condition for low tension or optimal salinity state.

In this study and many of those referenced earlier, a host of variables have been identified which one would expect to affect either $\mu^o_{s/o}$ or $\mu^o_{s/w}$ or both. Both $\mu^o_{s/o}$ and $\mu^o_{s/w}$ will be a function of temperature, pressure, alcohol cosurfactant concentration (at least for isopropanol, sec-butanol and isobutanol which are sensibly partitioned into both phases), and surfactant structure. $\mu^o_{s/w}$, but not $\mu^o_{s/o}$, will be influenced by salinity, alcohol concentration (for species of lower molecular weight than those cited above), and surfactant molecular weight (with constant structure). $\mu^o_{s/o}$, but not $\mu^o_{s/w}$, will be affected by oil EACN (or ACN) and alcohol concentration (increasingly important as the molecular weight increases from n-butanol to pentanol isomers and then to hexanol).

To illustrate optimal salinity in terms of chemical potentials, a chemical potential scale/salinity plot is hypothesized in Figure 12. The $\mu^o_{s/w}$ is shown as monotomically increasing with salinity, whereas $\mu_{s/o}$ is considered constant (since salt is effectively insoluble in oil). Optimal salinity is the crossing point for the two lines. Remembering the generality equation (1), leads to the requirement the $\mu^o_{s/o}$ increases with increasing EACN of hydrocarbon phase molecular weight. Higher molecular weight alcohols always lower S* of necessity by lowering $\mu^o_{s/o}$. The lowest molecular weight alcohols slightly increase S* by lowering $\mu^o_{s/w}$. Increased surfactant molecular weight per se always reduces optimal salinity by increasing $\mu^o_{s/w}$ (there is probably a relatively minor influence on $\mu^o_{s/o}$). Studies on a variety of sulfonate surfactants show that

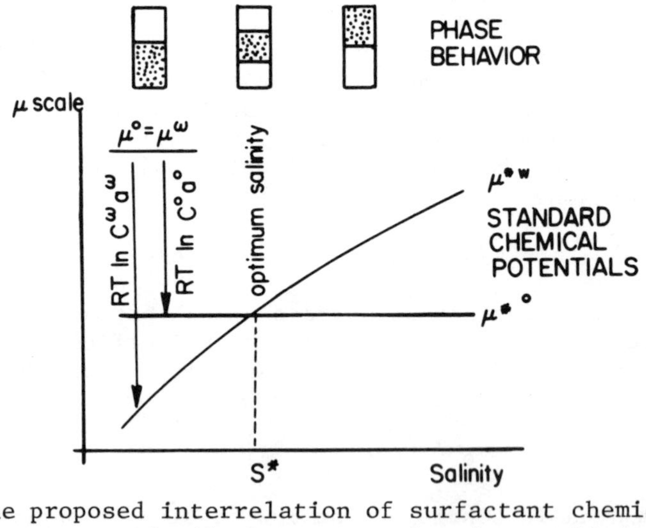

Fig. 12. The proposed interrelation of surfactant chemical potential in the aqueous and oil phases as related to salinity.

increased branching of the tail structure markedly increases S* probably by both lowering $\mu^{o}_{s/w}$ and raising $\mu^{o}_{s/o}$. Temperature increases S* (except for non-ionics) probably affecting both $\mu^{o}_{s/o}$ and $\mu^{o}_{s/w}$. Since one can think of generating the three phase regime by increasing the salinity to the point where surfactant is salted-out of the aqueous phase optimally, then increasing the hydrophile/lipophile balance increases S*.

ACKNOWLEDGEMENTS

This research has been supported by grants from the National Science Foundation, the Robert A. Welch Foundation, the Energy Research and Development Administration, the Department of Health, Education and Welfare, and following companies: Amoco Production Company, Tulsa, Oklahoma; Atlantic Richfield Research and Development Department, Dallas, Texas; Chevron Oil Field Research, La Habra, California; Continental Oil Co., Ponca City, Oklanoma; Exxon Production Research, Houston, Texas; Gulf Research and Development Co., Pittsburgh, Pennsylvania; Mobil Research and Development Corp., Dallas, Texas; Shell Oil's Bellaire Research Center, Houston, Texas; Stepan Chemical Co., Northfield, Illinois; Sun Oil Co., Richarson, Texas; Tenneco Oil, Houston, Texas; United States Department of the Interior, Bureau of Mines, Bartlesville, Oklahoma; Witco Chemical Corp., Petrolia, Pennsylvania.

REFERENCES

1. J. L. Cayias, R. S. Schechter and W. H. Wade, in "Adsorption at Interfaces," K. L. Mittal, Editor, ACS Symposium Series, No. 8, p. 234, American Chemical Society, Washington, D. C., 1975.
2. R. L. Cash, J. L. Cayias, G. R. Fournier, J. K. Jacobson, C. A. LeGear, T. Schares, William H. Wade and R. S. Schechter, in "Detergents in the Changing Scene," p. 1, published by American Oil Chemists Society, Champaign, Illinois, 1977.
3. R. L. Cash, J. L. Cayias, G. R. Fournier, D. MacAllister, T. Schares, W. H. Wade and R. S. Schechter, J. Colloid Interface Sci., 59, 39, (1977).
4. R. S. Schechter, J. L. Cayias and W. H. Wade, Soc. Pet. Eng. J., 16, 351, (1976).
5. J. K. Jacobson, J. C. Morgan, R. S. Schechter and W. H. Wade, J. Pet. Technol., 17, 122, (1977).
6. W. H. Wade, R. S. Schechter, J. C. Morgan, J. K. Jacobson and J. L. Salager, Soc. Pet. Eng. J., p. 242, (August 1978).
7. P. H. Doe, M. El-Emary, R. S. Schechter and W. H. Wade, presented at the Symposium on Chemistry of Oil, March 12-17, 1978, ACS Division of Petroleum Chemistry, Anaheim, California. (To be published)
8. P. H. Doe, M. El-Emary, R. S. Schechter and W. H. Wade, J. Am. Oil Chem. Soc., 54, 570, (1977).

9. P. H. Doe, M. El-Emary, R. S. Schechter and W. H. Wade, J. Am. Oil Chem. Soc., 55, 505, (1978).
10. P. H. Doe, M. El-Emary, R. S. Schechter and W. H. Wade, J. Am. Oil Chem. Soc., 55, 513, (1978).
11. R. N. Healy and R. L. Reed, Soc. Pet. Eng. J., 14, 491, (1974).
12. P. M. Wilson, C. L. Murphy and W. R. Foster, presented at the Fourth SPE-AIME Symposium on Improved Oil Recovery, Tulsa, Oklahoma, March 22-24, 1978.
13. M. C. Puerto and W. W. Gale, presented at the Fourth SPE-AIME Symposium on Improved Oil Recovery, Tulsa, Oklahoma, March 22-24, 1978.
14a. W. C. Hsieh and D. O. Shah, presented at the Symposium on Oil Field and Geothermal Chemistry, La Jolla, California, June 1977.
b. S. C. Jones, and D. K. Dreher, Soc. Pet. Eng. J., p. 161 (June 1976).
c. S. J. Salter, presented at the 52nd Annual Fall Technical Conference of Society of Petroleum Engineers, Denver, Colorado, October 1977.
15. J. L. Salager, (1978) Ph.D. Dissertation. The University of Texas at Austin, Austin, Texas.
16. E. Ortiz de Vasquez, (1978) M.Science Thesis, The University of Texas at Austin, Austin, Texas.

THE ROLE OF SURFACTANTS ON THE COALESCENCES OF EMULSION DROPLETS

I. B. Ivanov*, R. K. Jain, P. Somasundaran

School of Engineering and Applied Science
Columbia University
New York, N. Y. 10027

T. T. Traykov

Department of Chemistry, High Institute for Teachers
Shumen, Bulgaria

The coalescence of droplets and their life-time are shown to depend strongly on the surfactant properties and concentration. The following more important effects are predicted: 1) With pure liquids the energy is mainly dissipated in the droplets and the velocity of thinning, V, should not depend on the film viscosity. 2) The surfactant partition coefficient should play a crucial role on the emulsion stability. When it is soluble in the continuous phase, the surface mobility and the rate of thinning should be small and the flow in the droplet(s) could be disregarded; when the surfactant is soluble in the droplet(s), it should have no effect on the surface mobility and hence on the rate of thinning which must be much higher than it would be in the former case. 3) While the rate of thinning virtually should not depend on the surface viscosity, even values as small as 10^{-7} kg. s^{-1} would be sufficient to consider the interfaces as tangentially immobile with respect to the wave motion. 4) The film profile and hence the critical thickness at which the rupture occurs, should not depend on factors affecting to the same extent both the thinning and the wave motion. 5) The effect of the surfactant on the life-time of the droplets is mainly due to its influence on the velocity of thinning rather than on the critical thickness of rupture.

*On leave from the Department of Physical Chemistry, University of Sofia, Bulgaria.

INTRODUCTION

The stability of emulsions with high surfactant concentration has been generally considered to result from repulsion forces generated by surfactant layers coating the droplets[1,2]. The droplets in these emulsions are separated by a very thin film whose thickness (of the order of 10 nm or less) remains essentially without change with time. With lower surfactant concentrations. however, the films rupture at much higher thickness (of the order of several tens of nanometers[3,4]) referred to as the critical thickness[5] and the droplets coalesce. The film rupture presumably is due to the spontaneous growth, under the action of the negative disjoining pressure, of the surface disturbances which are always present in real systems. A convenient measure of the stability of these thin films is their life-time, t_ℓ, i.e., the time duration between the initiations of the movement of the droplets towards each other and their coalescence. Although t_ℓ is relatively small (it ranges from a fraction of a second to a few tens of seconds[6]) the time needed for all droplets in an emulsion to coalesce can be much larger if the droplets' concentration is low. Therefore, the observed (low) stability of these types of emulsions has a kinetic rather than a thermodynamic origin. The kinetic stability of the emulsions can play an important role in many technological processes, e.g., in the oil recovery, transportation and processing. The particle-droplet attachment in emulsion flotation can be treated very much in the same way as that in droplet's coalescence in emulsions of low stability.

The process of coalescence of the emulsion droplets can be conveniently split into two stages: (a) mutual approach of the slightly deformed droplets to the distance between them when a virtually plane parallel film forms (the gap width is then around 200 nm[5]) and (b) thinning of the film to the critical thickness of rupture, h_{cr}, which is around 50nm[3,4,5]. The velocity of droplets motion during the stage (a) is relatively high[7] so that the lifetime is essentially determined by the stage (b)[11].

The hydrodynamic behavior of systems with liquid/liquid interfaces is known to depend strongly on the liquid flow in both phases as well as on the properties of the surfactant[9,10,11]. A theory relevant to the real systems should ideally account for all these effects whose coupling complicates tremendously the mathematical problems involved. This might be the reason why most of the publications in this area involve analysis of the stability (against surface disturbances) of non-thinning films with liquid/liuqid interfaces. Vrij, Lucassen et al.[12,13] studied the stability of liquid films sandwiched between two semi-bounded liquids. The effect of the presence of an insoluble surfactant on the interfaces was accounted for by introducing the surface elasticity but without any detailed consideration of the surfactant transportation. Patzer and Homsy[14] conducted a similar analysis for a thin flim bounded by two spherically concentric liquid phases in the absence of any surfactant. Jain and Ruckenstein[15] in their stability analysis of an unbounded film with one liquid/liquid and one solid/liquid interface were the only ones to account for the effects associated with a soluble surfactant: surface elasticity, surface viscosity and surface and bulk diffusion.

The above works provided important information on the time constant of the disturbances growth and its dependence on the viscosity ratio of the liquids, the surface tension, the disjoining pressure and surfactant properties. However, they did not account for two important features of the films in real emulsion: these films are radially bounded and more importantly, their average thickness is decreasing with time. As shown previously for foam films[16,17] misleading conclusions for the influence of the surfactant on the rupture of the film can be reached if the latter effect is not taken into consideration. Moreover, the previous theories failed to make any predictions on the film life-time whose evaluation requires equation for the velocity of thinning (see above).

The recent theory of the thinning of emulsion films in the presence of soluble surfactants[18] enables one now to treat more consistently the problem of the disturbances growth and the relative influence of the various factors determining the life-time of the film. Many conclusions can be reached by analyzing the derived expressions for the velocity of thinning and the time constant of the surface disturbances growth. It is possible also to derive equations for the critical thickness of rupture of the film using the methods outlined elsewhere[16,17,18]. Because of the large number of factors involved this would lead however to huge untractable equations. On the other hand, many of those factors might be unimportant for a given system. This derivation is hence worthwhile only when a particular system is investigated experimentally and the exact values of its physico-chemical parameters are known.

The previous theoretical analysis[18] and experiments[6] have revealed that the partition coefficient of the surfactant between the liquid phases is of utmost importance in determining the velocity of thinning. Therefore in the present study of the disturbances growth, we have considered the surfactant to be soluble in both phases and have accounted for its transfer (surface and bulk diffusion) as well as for the surface viscosity. To simplify notations only one surfactant species is assumed to be present although the treatment can be easily generalized to a mixture of surfactants.

The paper is set up as follows: In the next section a general formulation of the hydrodynamic treatment of the thinning and rupture of emulsion films is given. It includes discussion of the major physical effects involved and the most important assumptions and approximations used. Section 3 summarizes briefly some theoretical results from References 18 and 19 concerning the film thinning. Section 4 deals with the theoretical analysis of the surface disturbances growth: a general dispersion equation and its simplified forms that are valid for some particular cases of practical importance are derived. The results from Sections 3 and 4 and their connection to the stability and the life-time of emulsion films are discussed in Section 5. The reader could read this section without going into the mathematical details of Sections 3 and 4. Those notations which are used throughout the whole paper are listed separately (in Section 6) and often are not explained in the text.

2. FORMULATION OF THE PROBLEM

We will be considering in this paper a system made of two identical droplets moving towards each other with the same velocity V/2 along the z-axis (see Figure 1).

We will make the following main assumptions:

1) The rheological behavior both of the bulk liquids and the adsorbed layers is Newtonian.

2) The flow is axisymmetric[17,20].

3) In the absence of surface disturbances the thinning film is plane-parallel[20].

4) Surfactant transfer from the film and the droplets onto the interfaces is diffusion controlled[17,18,23].

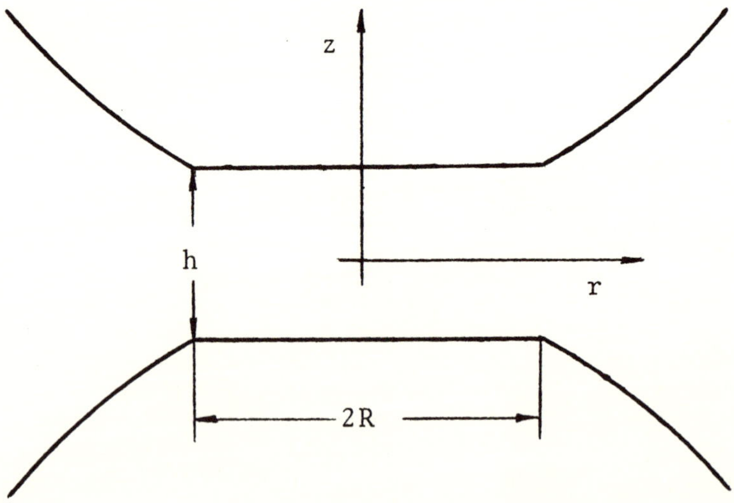

Figure 1. Sketch of a thin liquid film between two identical droplets. The surface disturbances are not shown.

5) The surfactant transfer is caused only by the liquid flow, i.e., with zero flow there is an equilibrium distribution of the surfactant in the system.

6) The surfactant concentrations Γ and c only slightly deviate from their equilibrium values Γ_o and c_o, i.e.[9,23]

$$|\Gamma-\Gamma_o| \ll \Gamma_o; \quad |c - c_o| \ll c_o \quad . \tag{1}$$

7) Thickness to radius ratio and Reynolds' number are small enough in the film so that the lubrication approximation can be used[18,21,25]. Peclet's number in the film is also assumed to be small.

8) Film thinning and surface disturbances can be treated separately[16,17,21].

9) The surface disturbances can be represented as the result of the superposition of infinite number of waves, i.e., the surface shape can be expanded in an infinite Fourier-Bessel's series. The wave amplitudes are small enough so that their hydrodynamic treatment can be carried out using the linearized wave theory and the linear stability analysis. In these cases the boundary conditions are to be applied at the undisturbed surface[9] and gravity can be neglected.

10) The liquid flow vanishes in the bulk of the continuous phase and in the droplets far away from the film surfaces so that the pressure, surfactant concentration etc. have their equilibrium values at r=R and $z=\pm\infty$[18,19,23].

11) All quantities are finite at r=0.

12) In the lubrication approximation the force balance is given by[17,20]

$$F = 2\pi\int_0^R (p^* - p^\ell)\, r\, dr \quad . \tag{2}$$

Because of the symmetry of the system all boundary conditions, referring to the film surfaces, will be written only for z = h/2. Bearing in mind that because of Assumption 2 all vectorial functions have only normal and radial components we can write the following system of equations and boundary conditions governing the flow and the surfactant transfer:

$$\frac{\partial \vec{v}}{\partial t} + (\vec{v}.\nabla)\vec{v} = -\frac{1}{\rho}\nabla p + \nu\nabla^2\vec{v}, \tag{3}$$

$$\nabla.\vec{v} = 0, \tag{4}$$

$$\frac{\partial c}{\partial t} + (\vec{v}.\nabla)c = D\nabla^2 c, \tag{5}$$

$$\frac{\partial p^*}{\partial r} = \mu^* \frac{\partial^2 v_r^*}{\partial z^2} \tag{6}$$

$$\frac{\partial p^*}{\partial z} = 0, \tag{7}$$

$$\nabla . \vec{v}^* = 0, \tag{8}$$

$$\text{a) } v_r = v_r^* = U, \quad \text{b) } v_z = v_z^* = \frac{1}{2}\left(\frac{\partial H}{\partial t} + U\frac{\partial H}{\partial r}\right) \text{ at } z = h/2 \tag{9}$$

$$\frac{\partial c^*}{\partial t} = D^* \nabla^2 c^*, \tag{10}$$

$$\mu^*\left(\frac{\partial v_r^*}{\partial z} + \frac{\partial v_z^*}{\partial r}\right) = \mu\left(\frac{\partial v_r}{\partial z} + \frac{\partial v_z}{\partial r}\right) + \mu_s \frac{\partial}{\partial r}(\nabla_r U)$$

$$+ \begin{cases} \dfrac{\partial \sigma_o}{\partial c_o} \dfrac{\partial c}{\partial r} & \text{(a)} \\ \dfrac{\partial \sigma_o}{\partial c_o^*} \dfrac{\partial c^*}{\partial r} & \text{(b)} \end{cases} \quad \text{at } z = h/2, \tag{11}$$

$$\frac{\partial \Gamma}{\partial t} + \Gamma_o \nabla_r U = -D^* \frac{\partial c^*}{\partial z} + D \frac{\partial c}{\partial z}$$

$$+ \begin{cases} D_s \dfrac{\partial \Gamma_o}{\partial c_o} \Delta_r c & \text{(a)} \\ D_s \dfrac{\partial \Gamma_o}{\partial c_o^*} \Delta_r c^* & \text{(b)} \end{cases} \quad \text{at } z = h/2, \tag{12}$$

$$p^* = p_o^* = p^\ell + \Pi \tag{13}$$

$$c^* = c_o^* \tag{14}$$

at $r = R$,

$$v_r = 0 \tag{15}$$

$$p = p_o \tag{16}$$

$$c = c_o \tag{17}$$

at $z \to \infty$,

where dot denotes scalar product, p^ℓ is the pressure in the bulk of the continuous phase and H(r) is the local thickness of the film.

Most of the above assumptions and equations have been discussed elsewhere. We shall give now only few additional comments that are for the present paper pertinent. Detailed analysis and discussion of Assumptions 4, 7, 8 and 12 will be presented in a forthcoming paper (see however Reference 21).

The tangential boundary condition (11) is a particular form of the bidimensional Navier-Stokes' equation[26]. More general formulation of it is given in References 26-29. Because of the cylindrical symmetry, μ_s in (11) stands for the sum of the surface shear and dilational viscosities which will be called further for brevity merely surface viscosity. According to the terminology of Maru et al.[29] this is the structural part of the surface viscosity while the last term, $\partial\sigma/\partial r$, in (11) accounts for what they call compositional surface viscosity i.e., for the effect of Marangoni-Gibbs[17].

The surfactant balance Equation 12 was first formulated phenomenologically by Levich[9] and recently derived on the basis of statistical mechanical principles by Brenner and Leal[30].

For convenience the last terms in Equations 11 and 12 were written both in terms of c_o and c_o^*. When the surfactant is soluble both in the film and in the droplets its concentrations c and c^* at $z = h/2$ at any given time are related through the equation $\Gamma(c) = \Gamma(c^*)$. By means of Assumptions 4 and 6 we thus obtain

$$\frac{\partial\Gamma_o}{\partial c_o}(c-c_o) = \frac{\partial\Gamma_o}{\partial c_o^*}(c^*-c_o^*) \qquad \text{at } z = h/2\ . \tag{18}$$

Equation 13 accounts for the fact that the disjoining pressure Π in an equilibrium film is the difference in pressures between the film and the bulk of the continuous phase[32]. The Equations 3-17 were written so that they apply both to the film thinning and wave motion. For either of those processes they can be further simplified. These simplifications will be discussed in Sections 3 and 4. However, we will not rewrite the equations that they lead to and will refer to general equations 3-17 during the derivation. Some additional boundary conditions used only for the wave motion will be discussed in the beginning of Section 4.

3. THINNING OF A PLANE-PARALLEL FILM

Equations 3-17 are further simplified as follows. If the liquid flow is caused by a time independent driving force all quantities should depend on time only through the thickness h. Hence, we can substitute in (3)[19]

$$\frac{\partial\vec{v}}{\partial t} = \frac{\partial\vec{v}}{\partial h}\ \frac{dh}{dt} = -V\,\frac{\partial\vec{v}}{\partial h}\ .$$

The local thickness H equals the thickness h of the plane-parallel film. Therefore (9b) will read

$$v_z = v_z^* = \frac{1}{2}\ \frac{dh}{dt} = -\frac{V}{2} \qquad \text{at } z = h/2. \tag{19}$$

Since Peclet's number is around 10^3 times larger than Reynold's number, the diffusion boundary layer approach can be used in (5) i.e., $\nabla^2 c \approx \partial^2 c/\partial z^2$. The derivative $\partial c/\partial t$ is neglected[18].

The solution of Equations 6-9 leads to:

$$v_r^* = -\frac{1}{2\mu^*}\left(\frac{h^2}{4} - z^2\right)\frac{\partial p^*}{\partial r} + U, \tag{20}$$

$$v_z^* = \frac{1}{2\mu^*}\left(\frac{h^2 z}{4} - \frac{z^3}{3}\right)\Delta_r p^* - z\nabla_r U, \tag{21}$$

$$p^* = p_o^* + \frac{3\mu^* V}{h^3}(R^2 - r^2) - \frac{12\mu^*}{h^2}\int_r^R U dr . \tag{22}$$

The derivative $\partial c^*/\partial t$ in (10) is of the order of the neglected convective terms $(\vec{v}^*.\nabla)c^*$ and can be neglected also.

The relative contribution of the surface viscosity term in (11) is of the order of $h\mu_s/6\mu^* R^2$ and can be neglected when $\mu_s < 10^{-4}$ kg. s^{-1} (see References 17 and 19). For a plane-parallel film $\partial v_z/\partial r = 0$ in (11).

Only two limiting cases of surfactant soluble in (a) the film, and (b) the drops, are considered. Then only the terms with c^* or c in (12) have to be kept respectively. The term $\partial\Gamma/\partial t$ is of the order of the neglected term $v_r\nabla_r\Gamma$ and can also be neglected.

The particular symmetry of the system suggest the following form of v_r:

$$v_r = U(r)f(\eta), \tag{23}$$

where $\eta = (z-h/2)(U/r\nu)^{1/2}$ is a dimensionless coordinate. Then in the case of surfactant soluble in the film Equations 11, 12, 20-23 lead to an algebraic equation for U/r:

$$\frac{U}{r} - \frac{V}{2h} + \frac{U}{r}(\varepsilon^f + \varepsilon^e) = 0 , \tag{24}$$

where

$$\varepsilon^f = -\frac{\Gamma_o(\partial\sigma_o/\partial c_o^*)}{3\mu^* D^*\left(1 + \dfrac{2D_s(\partial\Gamma_o/\partial c_o^*)}{D^* h}\right)} , \tag{25}$$

$$\varepsilon^e = - a_1\mu\, h(U/r\nu)^{1/2}/6\mu^* \tag{26}$$

with $a_1 = (df/d\eta)_{\eta=0}$. The solution of (24) is

$$U = Ar; \quad A = V/2h(1 + \varepsilon^f + \varepsilon^e). \tag{27}$$

Upon substituting (23) and (27) in (3) and (4) ordinary differential equation for $f(\eta)$ is obtained. Its numerical solution and the values of a_1 that it leads to were reported in Reference 19. Equations 2, 13, 22 and 27 allow the calculation of the ratio F/V, i.e., the friction coefficient. It is convenient to express this result as a ratio of the velocity of thinning, V, and its value, V_{Re}, for the same system with tangentially immobile surfaces, i.e., with U = 0:

$$\frac{V}{V_{Re}} = 1 + \frac{1}{\varepsilon^f + \varepsilon^e} \ . \tag{28}$$

In the case (b), surfactant soluble only in the droplets, the solution of (5) with the appropriate boundary conditions reveals that c does not depend on r, i.e., $\partial c/\partial r = 0$ in (11a). Hence the surfactant has no influence on the velocity of thinninng. Then the final solution for U and V is given again by (27) and (28) but with $\varepsilon^f = 0$.

An equation for V_{Re} was derived by Reynolds[33] for a film with zero disjoining pressure Π sandwiched between two rigid discs. Its application to films with fluid interfaces needs some comments. The radius, R, of a film formed between two identical drops of radii R_c or between a drop and a flat rigid surface is[20] $R^2 = FR_c/2\pi\sigma_0$. Then (2), (13) and (22) (with $V = V_{Re}$ and U = 0) lead to $V_{Re} = 2h^3(F-\pi R^2\Pi)/3\mu^*\pi R^4$ so that*

$$V_{Re} = \frac{2h^3\Delta P}{3\mu^* R^4}; \quad \Delta P = P_c - \Pi \tag{29}$$

Equation 29 holds also for a film formed in a biconcave meniscus[5,20] The more complicated case of a film between two drops of different radii and surface tensions is considered in References 21 22.

4. WAVE MOTION

Because of Assumption 8 in Section 2, when treating the growth of disturbances the film thickness, h, will be assumed to be constant i.e., the influence of the thinning on the wave motion will be neglected. The two flows will be coupled in Section 5 by means of a quasi-steady procedure. The problem becomes tractable and relatively simple equations are obtained with some additional simplifications and assumptions.

*For more detailed discussion of the driving force see Reference 20.

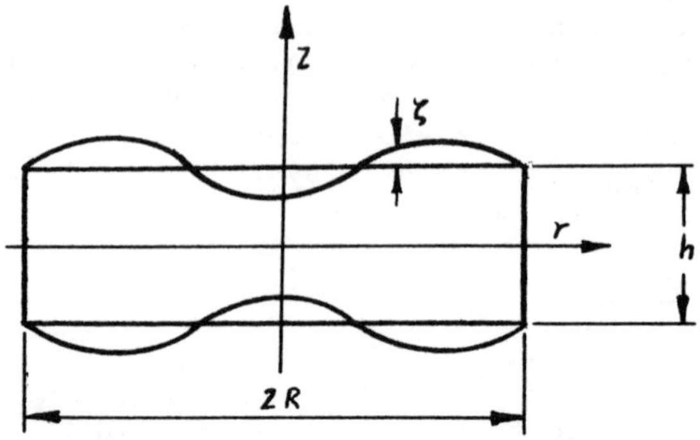

Figure 2. Symmetrical waves in a plane-parallel film.

We will be considering only symmetrical disturbances because they are the most efficient as far as the rupture of the films is concerned[16]. Then the local film thickness will be

$$H = h + 2\zeta \tag{30}$$

and (9b) reduces to

$$v_z = v_\zeta = \frac{\partial \zeta}{\partial t} \qquad \text{at } z = h/2. \tag{31}$$

The real film profile results from the superposition of an infinite number of waves but at each thickness including the critical thickness of rupture, one of the waves, called "critical" is dominating[16,17]. That is why in our treatment it will be assumed that ζ is determined only by one wave with wave number k_o.

The appropriate boundary condition for ζ is[21]

$$\zeta = 0 \quad \text{at } r = R. \tag{32}$$

Assumption 9 in Section 2, which is equivalent to say that

$$\text{a)} \quad \zeta \ll h \quad ; \qquad \text{b)} \quad k_o\zeta \ll 1 \tag{33}$$

enables us to neglect the convective terms $(\vec{v}.\nabla)\vec{v}$ and $(\vec{v}.\nabla)c$ in Equations 3 and 5 respectively. Then (see also (32))

$$\zeta = \zeta_o e^{\omega t} J_o(k_o r) , \tag{34}$$

where J_o is Bessel's function of first kind, zeroth order and ζ_o does not depend on t, r and h. A useful relation obeyed by ζ is

$$\Delta_r \zeta = -k_o^2 \zeta . \tag{35}$$

The critical wave is relatively long[16,35] and its angular velocity ω is small (see Reference 16) so that

$$\text{a) } k_o h \ll 1 \quad ; \qquad \text{b) } \omega h^2/\nu^* \ll 1. \tag{36}$$

Since (36a) is equivalent to the lubrication approximation and (36b) means that the time derivative $\partial \vec{v}^*/\partial t$ is negligible[16,17], we can use Equations 20 and 21 to account for the flow in the film. It should be borne in mind however that v_r^*, v_z^* and p^* are now only those parts of the respective quantities, which are associated with the wave. Because of the approximation (36a) the terms of the order of $k_o h$ appearing during the calculation will be neglected with respect to the unity.

The jump of the normal components p_{zz}^* and p_{zz} of the stress tensor associated with the surface disturbances is[21]

$$p_{zz}^* - p_{zz} = \sigma^f \Delta_r \zeta + 2(d\Pi/dh)\zeta, \quad \text{at } z = h/2 , \tag{37}$$

where

$$\sigma^f = \sigma_o + \frac{1}{2}\int_h^\infty \Pi \, dh \tag{38}$$

is the surface tension of the film[34].

The pressure p and the velocity components v_r and v_z vanish as $z \to \infty$.

Using standard procedures[9] it can be shown that the solution of Equations 3-5 reads

$$v_z = (\alpha_o Z_{k_o} + \alpha Z_k)\zeta, \tag{39}$$

$$v_r = -\frac{1}{k_o}(\alpha_o Z_{k_o} + \alpha \frac{k}{k_o} Z_k)\frac{\partial \zeta}{\partial r} , \tag{40}$$

$$p = \alpha_o \frac{\rho\omega}{k_o} Z_{k_o} \zeta , \tag{41}$$

where α_o and α are Fourier-Bessel's coefficients, $k = k_o(1 + \omega/\nu k_o^2)^{1/2}$ and

$$Z_{k_o} = \exp\{-k_o(z-h/2)\}; \; Z_k = \exp\{-k(z-h/2)\} . \tag{42}$$

In all cases of practical interest $\omega/\nu k_o{}^2 \ll 1$ so that a good and useful approximation is

$$k = k_o(1 + \omega/2\nu k_o^2) \quad . \tag{43}$$

Equations 39-41 suggest that Equations 20 and 21 can be put in the form $p^* = \beta\zeta$, $v_r^* = \tilde{v}_r^*(z)(\partial\zeta/\partial r)$, $v_z^* = \tilde{v}_z^*(z)\zeta$ and $U = B(\partial\zeta/\partial r)$. Then from (37-41) and (35) we obtain

$$\beta = - B\mu^* h + \alpha_o\rho\omega/k_o + 2\mu(\alpha_o k_o + \alpha k) + q \tag{44}$$

with

$$q = \sigma^f k_o^2 - 2(d\Pi/dh) \quad . \tag{45}$$

From (31), (34) and (39) we have

$$\omega = \alpha_o + \alpha \quad . \tag{46}$$

The kinematic boundary conditions $v_r = v_r^*$ and $v_z = v_z^*$ lead to:

$$\alpha = -(2\nu k_o^2/\omega)(Bk_o + \omega), \tag{47}$$

$$B = \frac{qh^2}{12\mu^*} + \frac{2\omega}{k_o^2 h}\{1 + \frac{\mu(k_o h)^3}{12\mu^*}(1 + \frac{\omega}{2\nu k_o^2})\} \tag{48}$$

The solutions of (5) and (10) have the form

$$c = \gamma Z_\ell \zeta \quad ; \qquad \ell^2 = k_o^2 + \omega/D \, , \tag{49}$$

$$c^* = \gamma^* \cosh(\ell^* z)\zeta \, , \qquad \ell^{*2} = k_o^2 + \omega/D^* \, , \tag{50}$$

where Z_ℓ is given by (42) (with ℓ instead of k) and the Fourrier Bessel's coefficient γ and γ^* are related through (18):

$$\gamma/\gamma^* = (\partial\Gamma_o/\partial c_o^*) \cosh(\ell^* h/2)/(\partial\Gamma_o/\partial c_o). \tag{51}$$

Then the boundary condition (9) yields

$$2\mu k_o B(1 + \frac{3}{4}\frac{\mu^*}{\mu}k_o h) + \mu k_o h(1 + \frac{\omega}{2\nu k_o^2})\omega + \frac{h}{2} q$$

$$= -Bk_o^2\mu_s + \begin{cases} (\partial\sigma_o/\partial c_o)\gamma & \text{(a)} \\ (\partial\sigma_o/\partial c_o)\gamma^* \cosh(\ell^* h/2) & \text{(b)} \end{cases} \tag{52}$$

With pure liquids the right-hand side of (52) is zero. The coefficients γ and γ^* are determined from (12):

$$Bk_o^2 \Gamma_o = D^*\gamma^*\ell^* \sinh(\ell^* h/2) + D\gamma\ell + \begin{cases} \gamma(\partial\Gamma_o/\partial c_o)(k_o^2 D_s + \omega) & \text{(a)} \\ \gamma^* \frac{\partial\Gamma_o}{\partial c_o^*} \cosh(\frac{\ell^* h}{2})(k_o^2 D_s + \omega). & \text{(b)} \end{cases} \tag{53}$$

In writing $\partial\Gamma/\partial t$ in terms of c or c^* Assumption 6 from Section 2 was used. The elimination of γ (or γ^*) from (52) and (53) leads to the dispersion equation we are looking for:

$$\omega\left(1 + \frac{3}{4}\frac{\mu^*}{\mu}k_oh + \frac{\mu_s + M}{2\mu}k_o\right)\left(1 + \frac{(k_oh)^3}{12}\frac{\mu}{\mu^*}\right)$$

$$= \omega^{(o)}\left(1 + \frac{3}{k_oh}\frac{\mu^*}{\mu} + \frac{\mu_s + M}{2\mu}k_o\right), \qquad (54)$$

where

$$\omega^{(o)} = -\,qh^3k_o^2/24\mu^* \qquad (55)$$

is the angular velocity of a wave in a foam film with tangentially immobile surfaces[13,16,17].

The term M in (54) arises from the last term in (52a)(or 52b)) and accounts for the effect of Marangoni-Gibbs. When the surfactant is soluble in both liquids, either of the following equivalent expressions* can be substituted for it:

$$M = -\frac{\Gamma_o(\partial\sigma_o/\partial c_o)}{Dk_o}\left(1 + \frac{k_oh}{2}\frac{D^*}{D}\frac{\partial\Gamma_o/\partial c_o}{\partial\Gamma_o/\partial c_o^*} + \frac{k_oD_s}{D}\frac{\partial\Gamma_o}{\partial c_o}\right)^{-1}, \qquad (56)$$

$$M = -\frac{2\Gamma_o(\partial\sigma_o/\partial c_o^*)}{D^*k_o^2h}\left(1 + \frac{2}{k_oh}\frac{D}{D^*}\frac{\partial\Gamma_o/\partial c_o^*}{\partial\Gamma_o/\partial c_o} + \frac{2D_s}{D^*h}\frac{\partial\Gamma_o}{\partial c_o^*}\right)^{-1}. \qquad (57)$$

When the surfactant is soluble in only one of the phases the appropriate equation (56 or 57) has to be used and the second term in parentheses has to be dropped. The quantity M has the dimension of surface viscosity and is, as a matter of fact, its compositional part[29]. Note however that it depends not only on the surfactant properties but also on h and k_o.

When writing the final Equations 56 and 57, we have neglected with respect to unity the terms $\omega/k_o^2 D$, $\omega/k_o^2 D^*$ (see Equations 49 and 50) and $\omega/D_sk_o^2$. This is equivalent to neglecting the time derivatives in (5), (10) and (12). Similarly, in (54) a term $\omega/2\nu k_o^2$ was also neglected. The latter is not equivalent however to neglecting $\partial\vec{v}/\partial t$ in (3) because $\partial\vec{v}/\partial t$ gives also other contributions to (54). The above approximations could be easily avoided at the expense of more complicated and less tractable final results.

Some simplified forms of the dispersion equation 54 are of particular interest. With intermediate viscosity ratio, more specifically with

$$(k_oh)^{-1} \gg \mu^*/\mu \gg k_oh \qquad (58)$$

---

*In order to prove the equivalency of (56) and (57) the relationship $\mu^*D^* \approx \mu D$ has to be used.

it leads to

$$\frac{\omega}{\omega^{(o)}} = \frac{1 + k_o^2 h(\mu_s + M)/6\mu^*}{\varepsilon_k^e + k_o^2 h(\mu_s + M)/6\mu^*} , \tag{59}$$

where

$$\varepsilon_k^e = k_o h\mu/3\mu^* . \tag{60}$$

For surfactant free emulsion $\mu_s = M = 0$ and

$$\omega = \omega^{(o)}/\varepsilon_k^e = qk_o h^2/8\mu , \tag{61}$$

which is the same as Equation 20 in Reference 13. Two other limiting forms of (54) for pure liquids are: (a) slightly viscous drops ($\mu^*/\mu >> (k_o h)^{-1}$):

$$\omega = 4\omega^{(o)}/(k_o h)^2 = qh/6\mu^* , \tag{62}$$

and (b) highly viscous drops ($\mu^*/\mu << (k_o h)^3$):

$$\omega = 4\omega^{(o)}/\varepsilon_k^e (k_o h)^2 = q/2k_o\mu . \tag{63}$$

It is noteworthy that similarly to the velocity of thinning of an emulsion film (see Section 5) ω in (61) and (63) does not depend on the film viscosity. The reason for it is that the energy in the drops is dissipated in a larger region of thickness $k_o^{-1} >> h$. Equation (63) was derived by neglecting in (54) the terms $3k_o h\mu^*/4\mu$ and $3\mu^*/\mu k_o h$. Since at this the terms with $\mu_s + M$ cancel out this equation is true also for a system containing surfactant. Indeed, since (63) is valid only for very viscous drops, the presence of the surfactant cannot affect the energy dissipation.

5. DISCUSSION

The hydrodynamic behavior and hence, the life-time of emulsion droplets depend on a number of parameters such as viscosity ratio, drop radius, surface activity and surface viscosity. Most of them can vary, depending on the system, with several orders of magnitude. Hence, the purpose of the present discussion will not be to study all the resultant possibilities, but to point out some of the most important effects that can be expected to affect the stability of emulsion. Most of these effects are not observed in macroscopic phases but appear in the film because of its thinness in other words because of the presence of disjoining pressure and the fact that the film thickness h is much smaller than the radial length scales of the processes of film thinning and wave motion, R and k_o^{-1} respectively.

The most interesting effects arise from the tangential mobility of the film interfaces. It is because of this that all final results in Section 3 and 4 were written as ratios of the velocity of thinning V or the angular velocity ω and the respective quantities V_{Re} and $\omega^{(o)}$ for the same system with tangentially immobile surfaces. Therefore the right-hand sides of those equations represent mobility factors, that take into account the relative increase of the respective quantity. This representation of the results has another advantage. As it will be shown in a subsequent paper[22] in the case when surface diffusion and viscosity can be neglected the mobility factor for the wave angular velocity, ω, of the foam and wetting films do not depend at all on the coupling of the film thinning and wave motion.

Although it is not clear as to what extent this inference will be applicable to the more complicated case considered in the present work, it is assumed that the results derived in Section 4 for the mobility factor of the angular velocity of waves in a non-thinning film will be relevant, at least qualitatively, to waves in a thinning film.

We shall discuss now the results for the film thinning, the wave motion and their influence on the film life-time.

Thinning of Emulsion Films

The velocity of thinning of an emulsion film with surfactant soluble in the continuous phase (the film) is given by Equation 28 where ε^f and ε^e (Equations 25 and 26) account for the role of the surfactant and the flow in the drops respectively. For a surfactant free system ($c_o = c_o^* = 0$) $\varepsilon^f = 0$ and Equations 26-29 lead to a simple expression for ε^e:

$$\varepsilon^e = \frac{h\mu^{1/3}}{\mu^*}\left(-\frac{a_1 h\rho\Delta P}{108\ R^2}\right)^{1/3} . \qquad (64)$$

With relatively thick films the influence of the disjoining pressure on the film thinning can be neglected so that $\Delta P \approx 2\sigma_o/R_c$. Typical values of the quantities involved in (64) which will be used for estimates throughout this Section are*

*Some of these values as well as other numerical values quoted hereafter can vary largely from system to system. Therefore, the conclusions drawn below on the grounds of numerical estimates should be considered only as a general trend. Some of them can turn out to be wrong for a particular system whose properties differ substantially from the above typical values.

(See Reference 6): $h = 100$ nm, $\rho = 10^3$ kg. m^{-3}, $R = 10^{-4}$m, $R_c = 10^{-3}$m, $\sigma_0 = 3.10^{-2}$ N.m^{-1} and $\mu \approx \mu^* \approx 10^{-3}$N.s.m^{-2}. Since $a_1 \approx -1$ (see Reference 19) the factor in parenthesis in (64) is nearly unity. Then $\varepsilon^e \approx 2 \times 10^{-4}$. Even with $\mu = 10^3\mu^*$ $\varepsilon^e << 1$ so that (28) yields for all practical purposes

$$V = V_{Re}/\varepsilon^e = (32\ h^5\Delta P^2/a_1^2\rho\mu R^4)^{1/3} \quad . \tag{65}$$

An interesting conclusion that Equation 65 leads to is that the velocity of thinning, V, does not depend on the film viscosity, μ^*. This is due to the very high mobility of the film interfaces which results in an intense flow in the drops where the main part of the energy is dissipated (for details see References 7 and 19).

For surfactants obeying Langmuir's isotherm

$$\Gamma_0 = \Gamma_\infty\ c_0/(a + c_0) \quad , \tag{66}$$

Equation 25 reads

$$\varepsilon^f = \frac{\Gamma_\infty^2\ k_B T c_0}{3D^*\ \mu^*(a + c_0)^2}\left(1 + \frac{2D_s\Gamma_\infty\ a}{D^* h(a + c_0)^2}\right)^{-1} . \tag{67}$$

For typical surfactants with moderate surface activity $\Gamma_\infty = 5.10^{-6}$ mol. m^{-2}, $a = 10^{-3}$ kmol. m^{-3}, $D^*\mu^* = 10^{-12}$ m.kg.s^{-2}, and $D_s/D^* \approx 10$*. Then with $c_0/a << 1$ we have

$$\varepsilon^f \approx \frac{10^4(c_0/a)}{1 + 10^3} \approx 10(c_0/a) \tag{68}$$

Therefore, even low surfactant concentrations will be enough to make $\varepsilon^f >> \varepsilon^e$. Then in the presence of surfactant (29) will become

$$V/V_{Re} = 1 + 1/\varepsilon^f \ . \tag{69}$$

In this case there is no dissipation of energy in the drops (V does not depend on the drop viscosity μ) and the film behaves like a film between two foam bubbles. The parameter ε^f accounts for the role of the gradient of surface tension due to the surfactant motion (effect of Marangoni - Gibbs).

The estimate (68) shows that at least at $c_0 \lessapprox a$ the surface diffusion flux overwhelmingly prevails on the bulk diffusion flux, so that (25) and (67) can be written as follows:

$$\varepsilon^f = -\frac{\Gamma_0(\partial\sigma_0/\partial\Gamma_0)h}{6\mu^* D_s} = \frac{\Gamma_\infty k_B T\ h}{6\mu^* D_s}\ \frac{c_0}{a} \quad . \tag{70}$$

The fact that in this case ε^f depends on Γ_0 and $\partial\sigma_0/\partial\Gamma_0$ means that

*This value of D_s was found for liquid/air interface[11,36,37]. It is expected to be lower at the liquid/liquid interface.

the surfactant behaves as an insoluble one and the mechanism of its supply to the interface is immaterial. Note that the surface diffusion term in (25) and (67) decrease as h increase and vanishes as $h \to \infty$. Indeed, for most processes involving capillary motion of the interface between two bulk liquids surface diffusion is immaterial[9].

With $c_o >> a$ the surface diffusion is negligible. Since bulk diffusion is less efficient in suppressing the surface tension gradient, in this concentration range $\varepsilon^f >> 1$ and $V \gtrapprox V_{Re}$. The latter statement is also true with $c_o \lessapprox a$ for surfactants whose surface diffusivity can be neglected. The limiting case of completely immobile surfaces, when $V = V_{Re}$, formally corresponds to $\varepsilon^f \to \infty$. Although under many circumstances the system can be very close to this situation it must be pointed out that this limit can never be reached with soluble surfactants. Indeed, ε^f, as defined by (67), exhibits a maximum at $c_o = a(1 + 2D_s\Gamma_\infty/aD^*h)^{\frac{1}{2}}$. The numerical value of ε^f at the maximum is very large ($\varepsilon^f \approx 3.10^2$) but still finite.

Totally different behavior is observed with surfactants soluble only in the drops. In this case the local surfactant concentration, c, does not depend on r and the surface tension gradient in (11) is zero. Therefore the Marangoni-Gibbs effect has no influence on the film thinning and the velocity of thinninng will be the same as for emulsion films from pure liquids (see Equation 65). Therefore, films with surfactant dissolved in the continuous phase will thin much slower than films in an emulsion whose continuous phase is a pure liquid.

Rupture of Emulsion Films

Let us assume again that the shape of the corrugated surface is determined only by one (critical) wave[8] described by Equation 34 (see also Figure 2). According to Equations 45, 54 and 55 the sign of the angular velocity, ω, is determined by the competition of two factors[8,39]: (a) the local capillary pressure due to the surface curvature (accounted for by the term $\sigma^f k_o^2$ in (45)) always gives a negative contribution to ω and hence damps the wave; (b) the variations of the disjoining pressure, Π, with the local thickness H can either damp the wave (with $d\Pi/dh < 0$) or increase its amplitude (with $d\Pi/dh > 0$). In the symmetrical system considered here the van der Waals' disjoining pressure is always negative (and $d\Pi/dh > 0$) so that it has a destabilizing effect on the wave motion.* However, since the absolute value

*If ω^{-1} is much greater than the relaxation time of the electrical double layer, the electrostatic contribution to Π can be accounted for by using the well known equilibrium expression[31].

of Π decreases with increasing h, at large thicknesses the capillary term $\sigma^f k_o^2$ will prevail and the wave will be damped. At smaller thicknesses the second term in (45) will be more important and the wave amplitude will be growing steadily until at some point the local thickness H becomes (virtually) zero and the film either ruptures or, at high surfactant concentrations, a black spot is formed. The instability of the wave will start at some transition thickness h_t, when $\omega = 0$, i.e., h_t can be calculated from the following expression:

$$q(h_t) = \sigma^f k_o^2 - 2 \left.\frac{d\Pi}{dh}\right|_{h_t} = 0. \tag{71}$$

The surface disturbances growth below h_t will depend on the value of ω. Let us restrict ourselves with the important case of intermediate viscosity ratio obeying the condition (58). There are both theoretical and experimental evidences[16,41] that the critical wave number is of the order of $5.10^5\ m^{-1}$ so that $k_o h < 0.1$. Then the parameter ε_k^e in (59), accounting for the energy dissipation in the drop should be also of the order of 0.1. With surfactant free systems both μ_s and M are zero and (59) reduces to (61), i.e., $\omega > \omega^{(o)}$. This increase of ω is obviously due to the surface mobility of the fluid/fluid interface which makes the growth of the disturbances easier.

If the surfactants are present in the system ε_k^e can be usually neglected so that the wave growth will not depend on the flow in the drops. It is easy to show that with surfactant soluble only in the film (see (25), (51) and (57))

$$Mk_o^2 h/6\mu^* \equiv \varepsilon^f\ . \tag{72}$$

With $c_o > a$ this term is expected to be much greater than unity and ε_k^e can be neglected. Only with $c_o/a < 10$ when μ_s is also very small[38] this term becomes lesser than unity (cf. (68)). When surface viscosity is present the energy dissipation in the drop is even less important: indeed, with surface viscosity as low as 2.10^{-7} kg.s^{-1} $\mu_s k_o^2 h/6\mu^*$ is of the order of 10 so that the surfaces behaves as almost tagentially immobile.

Surfactants soluble in the drops decrease the surface mobility even stronger. With the same diffusivities and surface activity the surface diffusion term in (56) is $k_o h$ times smaller than the respective term in (57) so that in this case the surface diffusion is less likely to be dominant. Since bulk diffusion is less efficient in decreasing the surface tension gradient the film surfaces are less mobile when the surfactant is soluble in the drop. Note however that the bulk diffusion term in (56) is $k_o h$ times greater than the respective term in (57)--this might lead under certain circumstances to rather high surface mobility.

The general conclusion we are led to is that small amounts of surfactant in either of the liquid phases are sufficient to damp the flow in the drops. However, the film surfaces can still be tangentially mobile provided that $c_o < a$: then the surfactant terms in (53) are smaller than 10 and $\omega > \omega^{(o)}$. The growth of the disturbances is faster under such conditions than in the case of tangentially immobile surfaces although it is considerably slower than for surfactant free systems. With $c_o > a$ the surfactant terms in (59) are much larger and the film behaves as though its surfaces were tangentially immobile.

The fact that increased surface mobility results in faster growth of the disturbances does not necessarily mean that in this case the film will rupture at higher thicknesses. As Vrij[40] pointed out reliable information on the film rupture can be obtained only if the evolution of the critical wave after the onset of the instability is taken into account. This can be done by means of the following quasi-steady procedure[16]. Since ω in Equation 54 is real, the liquid motion due to the surface disturbances will be an aperiodic one. Then ζ will depend on time only through h Therefore we can write

$$\frac{\partial\zeta}{\partial t} = \frac{\partial\zeta}{\partial h}\frac{dh}{dt} , \qquad (73)$$

or

$$\omega\zeta = -V\frac{\partial\zeta}{\partial h} . \qquad (74)$$

Integrating (74) we obtain

$$\ln\frac{\zeta(h)}{\zeta(h_t)} = -\int_{h_t}^{h}\frac{\omega}{V}\,dh . \qquad (75)$$

Therefore, ζ and hence, h_{cr}, are determined not only by ω but by the ratio ω/V and will not depend on any factor affecting both ω and V to the same extent.

The formulas for ω and V derived above along with the procedure outlined in[16,17] allows the calculation of ζ and h_{cr}. To avoid those complicated calculations we shall consider now only the inferences following from the inspection of the ratio ω/V for some particular systems.

For surfactant free systems Equation 61 and 65 yield

$$\left(\frac{\omega}{V}\right)/\left(\frac{\omega^{(o)}}{V_{Re}}\right) = \frac{\varepsilon^{e}}{\varepsilon_k^{e}} < 1 . \qquad (76)$$

Therefore, the surface mobility in this case favors more the film thinning than the disturbances growth and the critical thickness of rupture should be smaller than that of a film with tangentially immobile surfaces.

For the case when surfactant is soluble in the continuous phase and is present in large amounts the surface mobility is damped out and

$$(\frac{\omega}{V})/(\frac{\omega^{(o)}}{V})_{Re} = 1 \ . \qquad (77)$$

Therefore, the critical thickness in this case should be higher than in the former case. In other words the addition of surfactant to the continuous phase would increase the thickness of rupture.

When the surfactant is present in the drop in sufficiently high concentrations it reduces ω to $\omega^{(o)}$ but has not effect on the velocity of thinning. In this case we have

$$(\frac{\omega}{V}) \ (\frac{\omega^{(o)}}{V})_{Re} = \varepsilon^{e} < \frac{\varepsilon^{e}}{\varepsilon_{k}^{e}} \ . \qquad (78)$$

Therefore the surfactant should decrease the thickness of rupture with respect to its value for the surfactant free system.

It should be kept in mind that the above conclusions were drawn, first, without taking into account the influence of the thinning on the wave motion[35] (see Assumption 8 in Section 1) and, second, by assuming that the critical wave number is the same for systems with and without surfactants. Both assumptions can fail for surfactant free systems, and therefore, Equation 76 must be seen as a rough estimate indicating only the general trend that is expected.

The damping of the wave motion by the surfactant makes the results for surfactant containing systems more reliable. The comparison of (77) and (78) shows that the thickness of rupture should be higher when the surfactant is soluble in the film than when it is in the drops. Although reliable data to test extensively this theoretical prediction are still lacking, some results obtained in Reference 6 suggest that at least qualitatively the theory agrees with the experimentally observed trend. The critical thickness of benzene films containing lauryl alcohol formed between droplets of pure water was found to be 40 nm. For films from pure benzene and water droplets containing sodium octylsulfonate the critical thickness was about 35 nm.

Life-Time of Emulsion Films

As pointed out in the Introduction, the life-time, t_{ℓ}, of the film depends both on the critical thickness of rupture, h_{cr}, and the velocity of thinning, V. Expressions for it can be derived by integrating $dt = -dh/V$ from some initial thickness (assumed equal to infinity) to h_{cr}.

With large amounts of surfactant soluble in the film $V \approx V_{Re}$ and the respective life-time, t_ℓ^f, is obtained by using (29). When the surfactant is soluble in the drop, the life-time, t_ℓ^d, is calculated from (65). Neglecting the contribution of Π to ΔP we thus obtain

$$\frac{t_\ell^d}{t_\ell^f} = \left(\frac{a_1^2\ \rho\Delta P}{4\mu^2\ R^2}\right)^{1/3} \frac{(h_{cr}^f)^2}{(h_{cr}^d)^{2/3}} , \qquad (79)$$

where h_{cr}^f and h_{cr}^d are the respective critical thicknesses of rupture. A typical numerical value of the first factor in the right hand side of (79) is 2×10^3. With the values of the critical thicknesses for benzene films, quoted above, $h_{cr}^f = 40$ nm and $h_{cr}^d = 35$ nm, we obtain $t_\ell^d/t_\ell^f \approx 10^{-4}$. The value of this ratio measured in Reference 6 was nearly 10^{-2}. Whatever the reasons for this discrepancy are, it is obvious that both theory and experiment does point out on the very strong dependence of the life-time and hence, the kinetic stability of the emulsions on the solubility of the surfactant: emulsion with surfactant dissolved in the continuous phase will be much more stable than those with surfactant dissolved in the drops. As discussed in References 6,12 this conclusion agrees with the experimental observations and the empirical Bancroft's rule.

All values of the critical thicknesses measured so far[5,16,41] range from 30 nm to 100 nm. If we take h_{cr}^d and h_{cr}^f equal respectively to 30 nm and 100 nm, t_ℓ^d/t_ℓ^f will rise only to 8×10^{-4} and will still be much less than unity. Therefore the above ratio of the life-times depends only slightly on the particular values of the critical thicknesses of rupture. The strong effect of the solubility of the surfactant on the kinetic stability of emulsions can therefore be considered to be due to its influence on the velocity of thinning. This emphasizes again the role of the film thinning as the most important effect determining the kinetic stability of emulsions.

ACKNOWLEDGEMENTS

This work was partially supported by the National Science Foundation, Grant AER 76-81578. We are indebted to Mr. Maldarelli for useful discussions.

6. NOMENCLATURE

a - Adsorption constant; Equation 66.
a_1 - Function of h, defined in[19] (≈ -1.2).
c - Surfactant bulk concentration.
D, D_s - Surfactant bulk and surface diffusivities.
F - Driving force.
h - Thickness of the plane-parallel film.
h_{cr} - Critical thickness of rupture.
k_o - Wave number.
k_B - Boltzmann's constant.
M - Parameter accounting for the effect of Marangoni-Gibbs on the wave motion; Equations 56 and 57.
p - Pressure.
P_c, ΔP - Capillary and driving pressure; Equation 29.
q - Parameter; Equation 45.
r - Radial coordinate.
R, R_c - Film and drop radii.
t - Time.
t_ℓ - Life-time of the film.
T - Absolute temperature.
$U = v_r(z = \pm h/2)$ - Surface velocity.
$\vec{v}, v_r, v_z$ - Fluid velocity and velocity components.
$V = -dh/dt$ - Velocity of thinning.
V_{Re} - Reynolds' velocity; Equation 29.
z - Normal coordinate.

Γ - Adsorption (surface concentration).
Γ_∞ - Maximum surface concentration; Equation 66.
$\Delta_r = \nabla_r \frac{\partial}{\partial r}$ - Operator.
ε^f - Foam parameter; Equation 25.
$\varepsilon^e, \varepsilon_k^e$ - Emulsion parameters; Equations 26 and 60.
ζ - Vertical deviation of the film surface from the undisturbed state; Figure 2.
μ, μ_s - Bulk and surface dynamic viscosities.
$\nu = \mu/\rho$ - Kinematic viscosity.
Π - Disjoining pressure; Equation 13.
ρ - Density.
σ - Interfacial tension between the bulk liquids.
σ^f - Film surface tension; Equation 38.
ω - Wave angular velocity; Equation 34.
$\omega^{(o)}$ - Wave angular velocity for tangentially immobile film surface; Equation 55.

∇ - Hamilton's operator.
$\nabla_r = \frac{1}{r}\frac{\partial}{\partial r} r$ - Operator.

Superscript * denotes quantities referring to the film.
Subscript "o" at c, p, Γ and σ denotes equilibrium value.

REFERENCES

1. J.T. Davies and E.K. Rideal, "Interfacial Phenomena," Academic Press, New York and London, 1963.
2. R.H. Ottewill, in "Nonionic Surfactants," M.J. Schick, Editor, p. 627, Marcel Dekker, New York, 1967.
3. H. Sonntag and K. Strenge, "Koagulation und Stabilität Disperser Systeme," VEB Deut. Verlag Wiss., Berlin, 1970.
4. G.D.M. McKay and S.G. Mason, Can. J. Chem. Eng. 41, 203 (1963).
5. A.D. Scheludko, Adv. Colloid Interface Sci. 1, 391 (1967).
6. T.T. Traykov, E.D. Manev and I.B. Ivanov, Int. J. Multiphase Flow 3, 485 (1977).
7. V.N. Beshkov, B.P. Radoev and I.B. Ivanov, Int. J. Multiphase Flow 4, 563 (1978).
8. A. Scheludko, Proc. Koninkl. Nederl. Akad. Wet. B65, 87 (1962).
9. V.G. Levich, "Physico-Chemical Hydrodynamics," Englewood Cliffs, 1962.
10. C. Sternling and L. Scriven, A.I.Ch.E. J., 5, 514 (1959).
11. J.C. Berg in "Recent Developments in Separation Science," N. Li, Editor, Vol. 2., p. 1, CRS Press, Cleveland, 1972.
12. J. Lucassen, M. van den Tempel, A. Vrij and F. Hesselink, Proc. Koninkl. Ned. Akad. Wet. B73, 108 (1970).
13. A. Vrij, F. Hesselink, J. Lucassen and M. van den Tempel, Proc. Koninkl. Ned. Akad. Wet. B73, 124 (1970).
14. J.F. Patzer and G.M. Homsy, J. Colloid Interface Sci. 51, 499 (1975).
15. R.K. Jain, and E. Ruckenstein, J. Colloid Interface Sci. 54, 108 (1976).
16. I.B. Ivanov, B.P. Radoev, E.D. Manev and A.D. Scheludko, Trans. Faraday Soc. 66, 1262 (1970).
17. I.B. Ivanov and D.S. Dimitrov, Colloid Polym. Sci. 252, 982 (1974).
18. T.T. Traykov and I.B. Ivanov, Int. J. Multiphase Flow. 3, 471 (1977).
19. I.B. Ivanov and T.T. Traykov, Int. J. Multiphase Flow. 2, 397 (1976).
20. D.S. Dimitrov and I.B. Ivanov, J. Colloid Interface Sci. 64, 97 (1978).
21. I.B. Ivanov, Doctor of Science Dissertation, University of Sofia, Sofia, 1977.
22. I.B. Ivanov, R.K. Jain and P. Somasundaran (1978), to appear.
23. B.P. Radoev, D.S. Dimitrov and I.B. Ivanov, Colloid Polym. Sci. 252, 50 (1974).
24. H. Lamb, "Hydrodynamics," University Press, Cambridge, 1963.
25. I.B. Ivanov, D.S. Dimitrov and B.P. Radoev, Kolloid.Zh. (1977), in press.
26. L.E. Scriven, Chem. Eng. Sci. 12, 98 (1960).
27. M. Hennenberg, T.S. Sørensen and A. Sanfeld, J. Chem. Soc., Faraday Trans. II 73, 48 (1977).

28. M.G. Velarde, J.L. Ibanez, T.S. Sorensen, A. Sanfeld, M. Hennenberg, "Proc. Levich's Conference (1977)" to appear.
29. H.C. Maru, V. Mohan and D.T. Wasan, Chem. Eng. Sci. (1979), to appear.
30. H. Brenner and L.G. Leal, J. Colloid Interface Sci. (1979), to appear.
31. E. Lucassen-Reynders, and J. Lucassen, Adv. Colloid Interface Sci. 2, 347 (1969).
32. B.V. Toshev and I.B. Ivanov, Colloid Polym. Sci. 253, 558 (1975).
33. O. Reynolds, Phil. Trans. Roy. Soc. London 177, 157 (1886).
34. I.B. Ivanov and B.V. Toshev, Colloid Polym. Sci. 253, 593 (1975).
35. R.J. Gumerman and G.M. Homsy, Chem. Engng. Commun. 2, 27 (1975).
36. E.D. Manev, C.S. Vassilieff, and I.B. Ivanov, Colloid Polym. Sci. 254, 99 (1976).
37. J. Teissie, J.F. Tocanne and A. Baudras, Eur. J. Biochem. 83, 77 (1978).
38. A. Poskanzer, F.C. Goodrich, J. Colloid Interface Sci. 52, 213 (1975).
39. A. de Vries, in "Proc. IIIrd Congress of Detergency," Vol. 2, p. 566, Cologne, 1960.
40. A. Vrij, Disc. Faraday Soc. 42, 23 (1966).
41. E.D. Manev, A.D. Scheludko and D.R. Exerowa, Colloid Polym. Sci. 252, 586 (1974).

PREDICTING THE INTERFACIAL ACTIVITY OF ALKYLARYLSULFONATES

John J. Meister

Center for Macromolecular Science
University of Florida
420 Bryant Space Sciences Building
Gainesville, Florida 32611

Studies on the boundary (surface and interfacial) tension of aqueous solutions of hydrocarbon sulfonates show that the structure of the sulfonate molecule has a pronounced effect on the capacity of the sulfonate to reduce boundary tension. By considering a large body of boundary tension data in the literature, one can predict that certain molecular structures are more effective than others for reducing oil-water interfacial tension, the variable controlling the capacity of a sulfonate solution to recover oil. Within specific molecular weight limits, aqueous solutions of di(branched alkyl)arylsulfonates and di(n-alkyl) arylsulfonates, both structures with the hydrophilic group in the middle of the molecule, will produce minimum interfacial tensions against oil.

The structural characteristics which make these molecules exhibit maximum interfacial activity are: (1) that the sulfonate group be attached to the aromatic ring next to a long alkyl chain, (2) that the alkyl portion of the molecule consist of at least two parts of equal length which are placed at equally-spaced locations around the aromatic ring, and (3) that the alkyl chain be branched.

INTRODUCTION

Previous research work[1] has shown that in order to mobilize significant amounts of waterflood residual oil, it is necessary to reduce the interfacial tension between the oil and an aqueous solution to less than 0.01 dyne/cm. Wade and co-workers[2] have demonstrated that an aqueous solution of a petroleum sulfonate having a given equivalent weight will produce a minimum interfacial tension when the oil contacted by that aqueous solution has a particular alkane carbon number. Wade and co-workers have also conducted a study on the effect of hydrocarbon sulfonate structure on interfacial tension.[3,4,5,6,7] Wade's investigation (see reference 2, Figure 6) reaches a conclusion identical to one of a series of predictions on preferred structures in hydrocarbon sulfonates made in an unpublished report.[8]

The report proposed that a certain type of structure should appear in the product of a commercial synthesis of a petroleum sulfonate. A petroleum sulfonate which contained a large fraction of materials generally representative of the desired structure was predicted to be more effective in reducing interfacial tension than a sulfonate prepared from an arbitrarily chosen refinery hydrocarbon.* The predictions of this work were made by correlating a large body of literature data on the structures of sulfonate molecules with the boundary tension data produced by dilute aqueous solutions of the molecules. The term boundary tension is used here to cover both the surface tension and the interfacial tensions of a surfactant solution.

Since a large body of data on sulfonate behavior at various interfaces has been correlated, specific statements about the maximally effective sulfonate for the reduction of interfacial tension at a particular oil-water interface cannot be made. However, the correlated data does indicate that certain structural characteristics are common to materials which produce minimum boundary tensions.

VARIABLES CONTROLLING INTERFACIAL TENSION

The three physical variables which control the interfacial tension (γ) at a planar boundary between a pure hydrocarbon and an aqueous solution of a pure hydrocarbon sulfonate held at constant temperature, are the surface excess (Γ), the critical micelle concentration (c.m.c.), and the concentration of surfactant (χ).[9] The surface excess expresses the extra amount of one component that has collected as an interfacial film at the boundary between two phases. The critical micelle concentration is the surfactant concentration at which micelles begin to form and concentration can

---

*Reactants for synthesis were an alkyl and an aromatic refinery stream. The alkylaromatic product would then be sulfonated. This investigation sought to answer the question, "What refinery products should be reacted in what manner to yield a petroleum sulfonate with the greatest potential for reducing interfacial tension?"

be expressed as the mole fraction of surfactant in aqueous solution.

While the Gibbs equation for a two-component, two-phase system does not apply to the three-component system of oil, water and sulfonate, it does show the basic relationship between the three variables controlling interfacial tension:

$$\Gamma = \frac{d\gamma/d\ln(a)}{RT} \qquad (1)$$

The variable "a" in Equation (1) is the activity of solute in the system and is related to mole fraction by

$$a = f\chi \qquad (2)$$

where f is the activity coefficient and χ is the mole fraction of the solute.

Equation (1) shows that to obtain a low boundary tension, a surfactant must:

1. form an interfacial film (have a surface excess, $\Gamma \neq 0$, since if $\Gamma = 0$, $d\gamma/d\ln(a) = 0$),
2. have a non-zero and preferably large activity coefficient, $f \neq 0$,* and
3. have, for materials of approximately equal surface excess, as high a c.m.c. as possible.*

Four structural features affect the three variables controlling boundary tension. These features are: chain length, chain branching, hydrophilic and/or aromatic group location and the unity of the alkyl chain.

Data will be presented to show the effect of changing each one of the above four sulfonate structural features on the variables controlling interfacial tension. These data are all boundary tension values for aqueous solutions of alkylarylsulfonates against air, mineral oil, kerosene or paraffins. After the cause and effect relationship between structure changes and boundary behavior has been established, the relationships will be used to predict which hydrocarbon sulfonate structures should be used as models for the synthesis of petroleum sulfonates.

---

*Equation (2) shows that f should be large so that a maximum change in activity occurs for each change in concentration. The critical micelle concentration should be large because above the c.m.c., surfactant activity becomes a constant causing $d\ln(a)$ and $d\gamma$ to approach 0.

These data have been drawn from the literature. The data of Figure 1 came from reference 10, and the data of Figure 2 came from reference 11, that of Figure 3 from reference 12, that of Figure 4 from reference 13, and the data of Table I came from reference 14.

DATA

Chain Length

As the length of the alkyl chain on an alkylarylsulfonate increases, the c.m.c. decreases and the surface excess* increases, causing the boundary tension of a sulfonate solution at fixed concentration to drop. But, when the length of the alkyl chain exceeds 14 carbon atoms, these trends reverse.† The addition of methylene groups to the straight chain of an alkylarylsulfonate which already contains 14 or more carbon atoms causes the surface excess to decrease, the c.m.c. to remain approximately constant or increase and the boundary tension of sulfonate solutions to increase. These changes are shown in Figure 1. The boundary tension behavior of solutions of n-alkylbenzenesulfonates implies that alkylarylsulfonates containing straight alkyl chains of 16 or more carbon atoms should be avoided. The converse of this rule, that alkylarylsulfonates containing less than 14 carbon atoms in their straight alkyl chain should be avoided, is not true, however. As the aromatic group increases in size (benzene to naphthalene) or the number of alkyl groups attached to an aromatic ring increases, the minimum length of an alkyl chain which, when attached to an aromatic group, will produce an effective agent for reducing boundary tension, decreases.[20] Therefore, alkylarylsulfonates can contain straight alkyl chains of less than 14 carbon atoms and still produce minimum interfacial tensions. Optimum behavior at the boundary is achieved in these shorter chain sulfonates by changing other structural features of the sulfonate molecule.

---

*Surface excesses were calculated using the Gibbs equation of references 15 and 16 and compensating for acid neutralization of the dissociated sodium alkylarylsulfonate. This method was shown to be accurate by determinations of the surface excess of radioactive surfactants.[15]

†Other anionic, cationic, and nonionic surfactants show a continued, though sometimes smaller, decrease in the c.m.c. until 18 methylene groups have been added to the alkyl chain.[17,18] Increases in the surface excess of these materials as the alkyl chain is extended from 14 to 18 methylene groups are insignificant, however.[19]

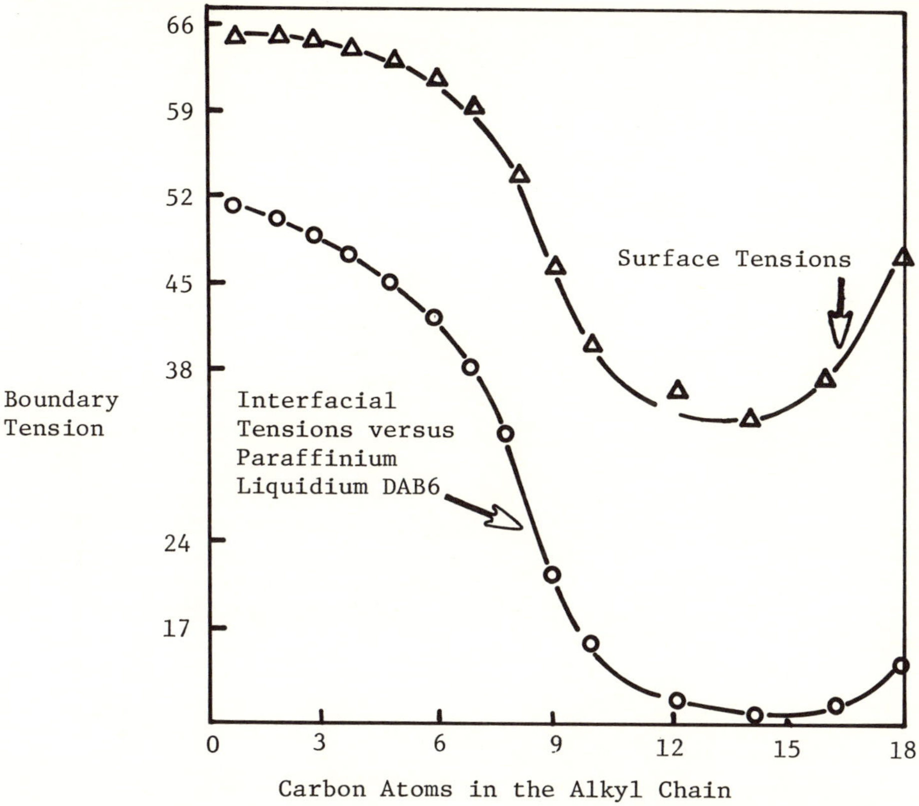

Figure 1. Plot of Surface and Interfacial Tensions of 0.005 Mole/Liter Aqueous Solutions of Sodium N-alkylbenzenesulfonates Versus Chain Length (Temperature = 60°C, Data from Reference 10).

Chain Branching

When an alkyl side group is added to the straight alkyl chain of a hydrocarbon sulfonate, the c.m.c. of the compound increases, the surface excess of the surfactant decreases and, as a result, the branched alkylarylsulfonate produces a lower boundary tension, possibly at a higher concentration,[12] than does an equal molecular weight n-alkylarylsulfonate. Figure 2 shows this effect. Minimum boundary tensions for the branched alkyl group of a mono-alkylbenzenesulfonate will be obtained only if the alkyl group contains eight or more carbon atoms.

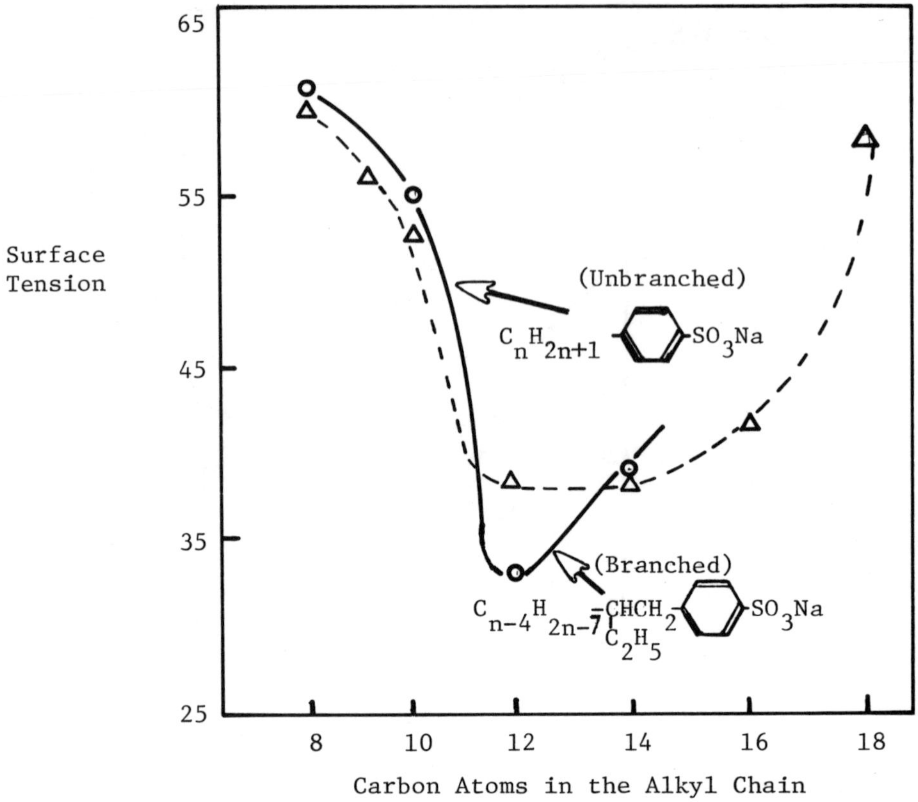

Figure 2. Surface Tension of Aqueous Solutions of Unbranched and Beta Branched Sodium Paraalkylbenzenesulfonates. (Temperature = 75°C, Concentration = 2 X 10^{-3} Moles/Liter, Data from Reference 11).

Hydrophilic and/or Aromatic Group Position

As the sulfonate and aromatic groups move from the end of the alkyl chain toward its middle, the c.m.c. of the sulfonate increases, the surface excess of the material goes down and, as a result, the sulfonate produces a lower interfacial tension, often at a higher concentration, than does an equal molecular weight sulfonate with its sulfonate and aromatic groups located terminally on the alkyl chain. Figure 3 and references 2 and 21 verify this rule. Positioning the sulfonate group adjacent to a long alkyl chain increases the c.m.c. and decreases the boundary tension at the c.m.c., as the data in Table I show.

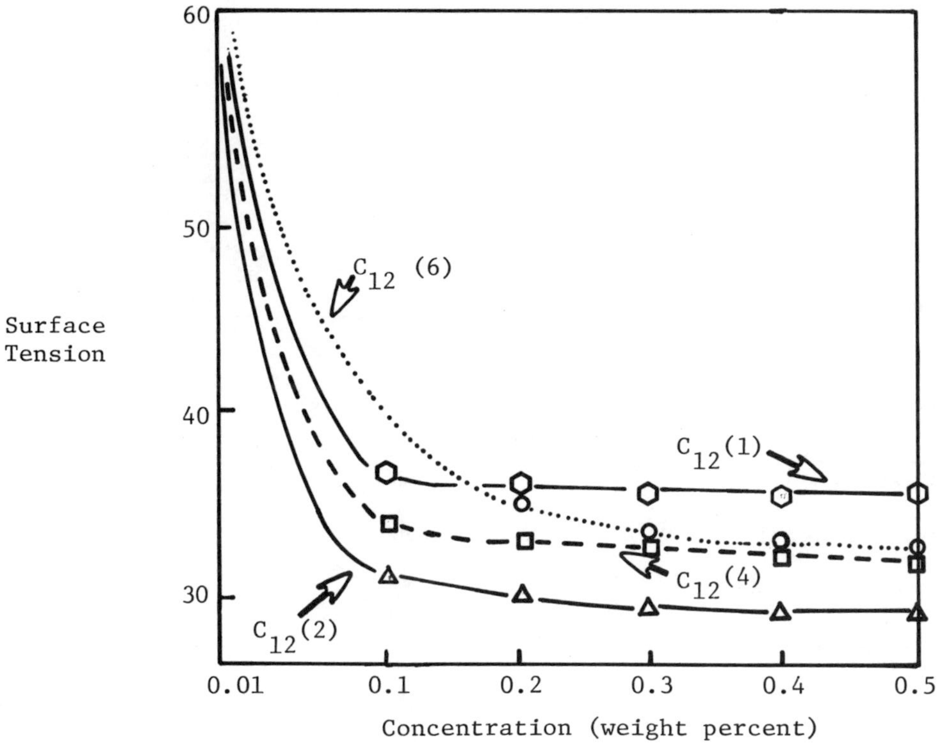

Figure 3. Surface Tension of Isomers of Sodium Dodecylbenzene-sulfonate (Data from Reference 12).

Unity of the Alkyl Chain

Breaking the alkyl chain into two equal parts and attaching these parts to the aromatic group of an alkylarylsulfonate causes the surface excess to decrease and the c.m.c. to increase.[14,22] Thus, the dialkyl form of the sulfonate will give a lower boundary tension, at a higher concentration, than will its monoalkyl analog. Also, alkylbenzenesulfonates with 16 carbon atoms in two chains reduce boundary tension further than do alkylbenzenesulfonates with 14 carbon atoms in any mono or dialkyl arrangement. By splitting the alkyl chain, the limit on the number of alkyl carbon atoms found in straight, single-chain sulfonates can be bypassed.[14] Figure 4 demonstrates these phenomena. Maximum reduction of boundary tension appears to occur when the alkyl group is broken into equal fractions and is situated at equally spaced points around the aromatic group (Table I).

TABLE I. Chain Fractionation Effects in Sodium Tetradecylbenzenesulfonates

(Temperature - 75°C, Data from Reference 14).

Compound	Critical Micelle Concentration (millimoles/l)	Surface Tension at 5 millimoles/l (dynes/cm)
Sodium para tetradecylbenzenesulfonate	0.67	36.3
2,5 ________, _______ benzenesulfonate		
methyl, tridecyl	0.86	36.2
ethyl, dodecyl	1.27	36.0
propyl, undecyl	1.68	35.6
heptyl, heptyl	4.75	29.1

CONCLUSIONS

The data shows that minimum boundary tensions are obtained with sulfonates which have the sulfonate group located near the center of the hydrocarbon chain. Sulfonates with this structure are called wetting agents and are exemplified by molecules such as sodium 1,4-di(n-octyl)benzene-2-sulfonate.

Trends in the previously presented data suggest certain sulfonate structures will be more effective than others in lowering boundary tension. The capacity of the recommended structures to reduce boundary tension will be influenced by the presence of salt and cosurfactant as well as by the sulfonate concentration. Wade[2,3,4,5,6,7,21] has shown that the nature of the organic phase contacted by the aqueous sulfonate solution also influences interfacial tension. The effects of these other variables are not considered in the following ordered list of recommended sulfonates.

Molecular structures which may be used as models for the synthesis of sulfonates for the reduction of interfacial tension in oil recovery are, in decreasing order of effectiveness, as follows: (1) sodium 1,4-di(2'-ethylhexyl)benzene-2-sulfonate,

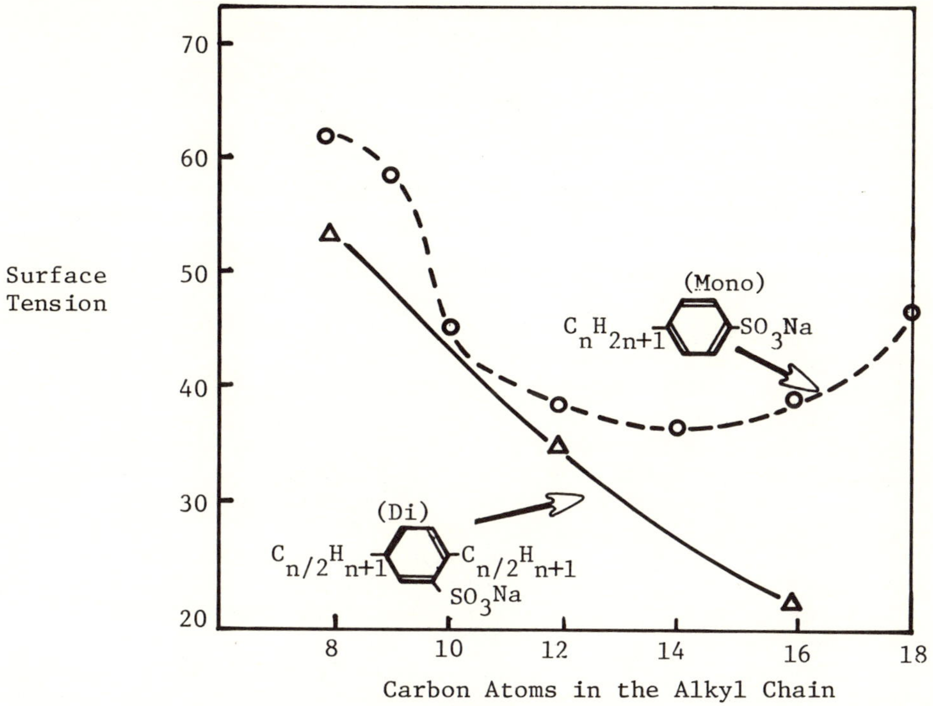

Figure 4. Surface Tension of Aqueous Solutions of Sodium Para-n-alkylbenzenesulfonates and Sodium Para-di-(n-alkyl)benzenesulfonates as a Function of Chain Length. (Temperature = 60°C, Concentration = 2.5×10^{-3} Moles/Liter, Data from Reference 13).

(2) sodium 1,4-di(n-octyl)benzene-2-sulfonate,
(3) sodium 1-hexyloctylbenzene-2'-sulfonate, and
(4) sodium 1-(2'-propylundecyl)benzene-2-sulfonate.

The preferred sulfonate structures listed above can be obtained on a commercial scale either by sulfonating feedstreams which contain the molecules with the appropriate structure or by synthesizing such molecules from feedstreams of lower molecular weight hydrocarbons.

NOMENCLATURE

a = relative activity
R = Gas Constant, 8.314×10^7 erg/(°K-mole)
T = absolute temperature, °K
γ = interfacial tension, dynes/cm
Γ = surface excess, moles/cm^2
χ = mole fraction of solute

REFERENCES

1. R. N. Healy and R. L. Reed, paper SPE 5817, "Proceedings of the Fourth Symposium on Improved Oil Recovery," p. 266, Society of Petroleum Engineers, Dallas, 1976.
2. W. H. Wade, R. L. Cash, T. L. Cayias, and R. G. Fournier, paper SPE 5813, "Proceedings of the Fourth Symposium on Improved Oil Recovery," p. 217, Society of Petroleum Engineers, Dallas, 1976.
3. P. H. Doe, M. El-Emary, W. H. Wade and R. S. Schechter, J. Amer. Oil Chem. Soc. 54, (12), 570, (1977).
4. P. H. Doe, M. El-Emary, W. H. Wade and R. S. Schechter, J. Amer. Oil Chem. Soc. 55, (5), 505, (1978).
5. P. H. Doe, M. El-Emary, W. H. Wade and R. S. Schechter, J. Amer. Oil Chem. Soc. 55, (5), 513, (1978).
6. J. C. Morgan, R. S. Schechter, and W. H. Wade, "Improved Oil Recovery by Surfactant and Polymer Flooding," D. O. Shah and R. S. Schechter, Editors, pp. 101-118, Academic Press, New York, 1977.
7. P. H. Doe, M. El-Emary, W. H. Wade, and R. S. Schechter, Paper presented at the Symposium on Chemistry in Oil Recovery, Division of Petroleum Chemistry, American Chemical Society Meeting, Anaheim, March, 1978.
8. J. J. Meister, R. and D Report #7202-75, Phillips Petroleum Company, Bartlesville, Oklahoma, 1975.
9. M. J. Rosen, J. Colloid Interface Sci. 56, 320, (1976).
10. L. G. Vol'foon, N. N. Mel'nikov, Zhur. Obshchei Khim., 20, 2089, (1950).
11. H. Köelbel and P. Kuehn, Angew. Chem., 71, 211, (1959).
12. W. Griess, Fette Seifen enschl Anstrichmittel, 57, 24-32, 168-172, 236-240, (1955).
13. H. Amatsu and M. Shimoyamada, J. Chem. Soc. Japan, Ind. Chem. Sect. 57, 379, (1954). (Translation on file at John Crerar Library, Chicago, Ill.)
14. H. Köelbel, D. Klamann, and E. Wagner, in "Proceedings of the Third International Congress on Surface Activity," Vol. 1, pp. 27-30, Verlag der Universitatstruckerei, Mainz, Germany, 1961. (Translation on file at the John Crerar Library, Chicago, Ill.)
15. D. J. Salley, A. J. Weith, Jr., A. A. Argyle, and J. K. Dixon, Proc. Roy. Soc. (London), A203, 42, (1950).
16. J. K. Dixon, C. M. Judson, and D. J. Salley, in "Monomolecular Layers," H. Sobotka, Editor, pp. 63-106, American Association for the Advancement of Science, Washington, D.C. 1954.
17. E. C. Evers and C. A. Kraus, J. Amer. Chem. Soc. 70, 3049, (1948).
18. H. C. Evans, J. Chem. Soc. (London), p. 579, (1956).
19. F. van Voorst Vader, Trans. Faraday Soc. 56, 1067 (1960).

20. M. G. Zimina and N. P. Apukhthina, Colloid Journal of the U.S.S.R. (Translation, New York), 21, (1), 41-47, (1959).
21. M. El-Emary, J. C. Morgan, P. H. Doe, and W. H. Wade, paper B-6, Proceedings of the 2nd ERDA Symposium on Enhanced Oil and Gas Recovery, Tulsa, Sept. 9-10, 1976.
22. F. Asinger, Jo. Prakt. Chem. 23, (4), 89, (1964).

DESORPTION OF SODIUM LAURYL SULFATE FROM POLYSTYRENE LATEX PARTICLE SURFACES

S. M. Ahmed, M. S. El-Aasser, F. J. Micale, G. W. Poehlein* and J. W. Vanderhoff
Emulsion Polymers Institute
Lehigh University
Bethlehem, Pennsylvania 18015

*Georgia Institute of Technology
Atlanta, Georgia 30332

The adsorption of emulsifier on latex particle surfaces often determines the stability of the latex. However, relatively few adsorption isotherms have been published because these experiments are difficult and time-consuming. This paper describes the determination of adsorption isotherms using a new serum replacement technique, which was developed to characterize latex particle surfaces by removing adsorbed emulsifier from the latex particle surfaces and solute electrolyte from the aqueous phase. The latex is confined in a cell with a Nuclepore filter membrane, and double-distilled deionized water is pumped through the latex to replace the serum. This method allows complete recovery of the serum as well as determination of the concentration profile of the desorbing species in the effluent stream. To determine adsorption isotherms, a known amount of emulsifier is added to a cleaned latex and the concentration profile of the emulsifier in the effluent stream is measured. A material balance between added emulsifier and desorbed emulsifier (from the concentration profile) gives the adsorption isotherm. This adsorption isotherm is correlated with the predictions of a mathematical model of the process. The adsorption of technical grade sodium lauryl sulfate on a Dow monodisperse polystyrene latex of 190nm diameter determined at 23 $\pm$ 2° follows a Langmuir adsorption isotherm. The molecular area at saturation is 42 $Å^2$ and the equilibrium constant is 2.35 x 10^3 liters/mole.

INTRODUCTION

The adsorption-desorption behavior of emulsifiers and water-soluble polymers on latex particle surfaces is important in latex technology. For example, the adsorption of emulsifier molecules on the latex particle surfaces often determines the stability of the latex, and the viscosity is controlled by addition of water-soluble polymers. In all hypotheses of the loci of particle initiation --- emulsifier micelles, adsorbed emulsifier layers, aqueous phase, or monomer droplets --- the number of polymer particles that form and persist throughout the polymerization is determined by the adsorption of emulsifier on the polymer-water or monomer-water interfaces, the equilibrium between adsorbed and solute emulsifier, the rate of attainment of equilibrium as the polymer-water interfacial area increases and the monomer-water interfacial area decreases, and the molecular area of the emulsifier.

Despite the importance of the adsorption-desorption behavior of emulsifiers in latexes, there is little information in the literature on the adsorption of emulsifiers and water-soluble polymers on latex particle surfaces, mainly because the experiments are difficult and time-consuming, e. g., the determination of an adsorption isotherm of sodium lauryl sulfate on a Dow monodisperse polystyrene latex of 88nm diameter using the modified Wilhelmy plate method took several weeks[1].

Recently, a new "serum replacement" technique has been developed to clean latexes for characterization[2]. This technique removes the solute electrolyte, emulsifier, and water-soluble polymer from the aqueous phase of the latex and the adsorbed emulsifier and water-soluble polymer from the latex particle surfaces. It can also be used to exchange protons for the counter-ions of the bound anionic surface groups, to allow subsequent determination of these groups by titration with base. It also allows complete recovery of the aqueous serum of the latex, which can be analyzed to determine the concentration profile of the desorbing species.

This paper describes the application of this serum replacement technique to the determination of the adsorption-desorption behavior of emulsifiers on the latex particle surfaces in a reasonable time using a simple experimental procedure.

SERUM REPLACEMENT TECHNIQUE

The details of the serum replacement technique have been reported elsewhere[2] and therefore will be described only briefly here. The latex is confined with a Nuclepore filtration membrane in a stirred flow-through cell, and double-distilled deionized water is pumped through the latex, replacing the serum at a constant flow rate. Continued pumping completely removes the solute electrolyte and adsorbed emulsifier from the latex. For characterization of latexes stabilized by bound surface sulfate groups introduced by persulfate initiator, dilute hydrochloric acid is pumped through the latex to replace the sodium and potassium counter-ions with protons; the excess hydrochloric acid is removed by again pumping double-distilled deionized water through the latex. The latex is then characterized by conductometric or potentiometric titration with base to determine the number of these bound surface sulfate groups.

The application of this serum replacement technique to determine the adsorption-desorption behavior of emulsifier on latex particle surfaces requires only the measurement of the concentration profile of the desorbing emulsifier. This concentration profile is described by the earlier mathematical model based on mass balance[2], which describes the concentration profiles of solute electrolyte, solute and adsorbed emulsifier, and solute and adsorbed water-soluble polymer in the effluent stream for both equilibrium and non-equilibrium processes. This model is described in detail elsewhere[2] and therefore will only be summarized here.

The equations for the concentration profiles are given below for both solute species and adsorbable species, assuming that the volumetric flow rates of the feed and exit streams are the same, the feed stream is mixed instantly with the latex in the cell so that the concentration of solute species in the exit stream is the same as in the cell, and the filtration membrane has no effect on the concentration of solute species in the exit stream.

Concentration Profile of Solute Species

The concentration profile of the solute species is given by

$$C_N = C_{No} \exp(-t/\tau) \qquad \tau = (V/F) \tag{1}$$

Where $\underline{C_N}$ is the concentration of the solute species at time $\underline{t}$, $\underline{C_{No}}$ the initial concentration of solute species, τ the mean residence time of the water in the cell, $\underline{V}$ the volume of the aqueous phase in the cell, and $\underline{F}$ the volumetric flow rate through the cell.

Concentration Profile of Adsorbable Species

The concentration profiles of adsorbable species can be divided into three cases: (i) the concentration of adsorbable species C_A is high enough for the surface of the particles to be saturated, leaving an excess of adsorbable species in the serum as solute species, i. e., $C_A > C_{Asat}$, where C_{Asat} is the saturation concentration; (ii) the concentration of the adsorbable species is equal to, or less than, the saturation concentration (i. e., $C_A \leq C_{Asat}$) and the concentration in the serum is in equilibrium with that adsorbed on the particle surface and the adsorption-desorption equilibrium is described by a Langmuir adsorption isotherm; (iii) the concentration of adsorbable species is equal to, or less than, the saturation concentration (i. e., $C_A \leq C_{Asat}$) and the concentration in the serum is not in equilibrium with that adsorbed on the latex particle surfaces.

For $C_A \leq C_{Asat}$, the concentration of emulsifier is more than sufficient to saturate the surface of the latex particles, and the excess emulsifier in the aqueous serum will be removed as if it were solute species, so Equation 2 is analogous to Equation 1.

$$C_A = C_{A_o} \exp(-t/\tau) \tag{2}$$

For $C_A \leq C_{Asat}$ where the concentration of adsorbable species in the serum is in equilibrium with that adsorbed on the particle surfaces according to the Langmuir adsorption isotherm

$$k_a C_A (S_o - S) = k_d S \tag{3}$$

where S_o is the total surface area of the latex particles, S the surface area covered with emulsifier, and k_a and k_d the rate constants for adsorption and desorption, respectively.

The concentration profile is given by:

$$dC_A/dt = C_A/(V/F)[1 + (S_o b/a_s N_A)\{1/(1 + bC_A)^2\}] \tag{4}$$

where a_s is the molecular area of the adsorbable species at saturation, N_A Avogadro's number, and $b = k_a/k_d$ the equilibrium constant. Integration of Equation 4 at constant F and V gives

$$-\ln(C_A/C_{A_o}) - (S_o b/a_s N_A)\ [\ln\{C_A(1 + bC_{A_o})/C_{A_o}(1 + bC_A)\} + b(C_{A_o} - C_A)/(1 + bC_{A_o})(1 + bC_A)] = t/\tau \tag{5}$$

For $C \leq C_{A_{sat}}$ where the concentration of adsorbable species in the serum is not in equilibrium with that adsorbed on the particle surfaces

$$dC_A/dt = -(1/\tau)[C_A - k_d\{(S/S_o) - (bC_A(S_o - S)/S_o)\}] \quad (6)$$

$$dS/dt = a_s N_A k_d [bC_A\{(S_o - S)/S_o\} - (S/S_o)] \quad (7)$$

Equations 6 and 7 can be integrated numerically to determine the value of $\underline{C}_A$.

The foregoing mathematical models were correlated with experimental results for solute electrolyte and adsorbed emulsifier with and without latex particles[2].

The adsorption isotherm can be constructed by fitting the experimental results with theoretical curves for selected values of $\underline{a}_s$ and $\underline{b}$. Alternately, the concentration profile can be integrated to calculate the amount of adsorbable species removed over a period of time, and the adsorption isotherm can be calculated from the mass balance with the added adsorbable species.

EXPERIMENTAL DETAILS

Materials

The emulsifeir used in these experiments was technical grade sodium lauryl sulfate (99% pure; Maprofix 563; Onyx Chemical Co.), which was used without further purification. The monodisperse polystyrene latex used (LS-1102-A; The Dow Chemical Co.) had a number-average diameter of 190nm (determined by electron microscopy). The water used was double-distilled and deionized; its conductivity was ca. 4×10^{-7} $ohm^{-1}cm^{-1}$.

Experimental Procedure

Latex samples (300 cc) were prepared with known amounts of sodium lauryl sulfate emulsifier such that the solids contents were 3.0% by volume in the final sample. The samples were mixed thoroughly and allowed to stand overnight to equilibrate (with one exception). The equilibrated sample was placed in the cell, and double-distilled deionized water was pumped through the latex. The effluent stream was separated into 60 cc samples, and the conductivity of each sample was measured. The temperature of the samples was 23 ± 2°. The serum replacement was continued until the conductivity of the effluent samples was very close to that of the feed water. The concentration of the desorbing species in the effluent samples was determined using the previously-measured conductivity-concentration calibration curve at the appropriate temperature.

RESULTS AND DISCUSSION

Figure 1 shows the conductivity-concentration curve used to determine the concentration of sodium lauryl sulfate in the effluent stream. The variation is linear on a log-log plot, with the inflection point at 2.5 x 10^{-3}M representing the critical micelle concentration of this technical grade sodium lauryl sulfate. Figure 2 shows the concentration profiles of sodium lauryl sulfate in the effluent stream for six different concentrations added to the cleaned polystyrene latex. The concentration profiles are expressed as the variation of C_A with q/V, where q is the total cumulative volume of the effluent stream. Thus the term q/V represents the total effluent volume in multiples of the sample volume V. This method of expression was used because the flow rates of the feed and exit streams were not constant, so that q/V is a better measure of the progress of the serum replacement than t/τ. The break in the concentration profile for the experiment using 1 x 10^{-2}M sodium lauryl sulfate is due to the excess emulsifier in the aqueous phase, which can be washed out without changing the equilibrium until its aqueous concentration reaches the critical micelle concentration.

Integration of the concentration profiles of Figure 2 (i. e., the area under the curves multiplied by the sample volume) over a given range gives the total amount of emulsifier removed in that time period. A mass balance of the amount of sodium lauryl sulfate added to the latex minus the amount in the aqueous phase and the total amount removed up to that time gives the amount adsorbed on the latex particles. Table I gives the mass balance for the sample containing 6 x 10^{-3}M sodium lauryl sulfate, and Figure 3 shows the adsorption isotherm obtained from these data and from the other experiments shown in Figure 2.

These results were also used to generate the linear Langmuir plots according to

$$1/n = (1/N) + (1/C_A N\, b) \tag{8}$$

where n is the number of sodium lauryl sulfate molecules adsorbed per unit area and $N = 1/a_s$ the value of n at saturation.

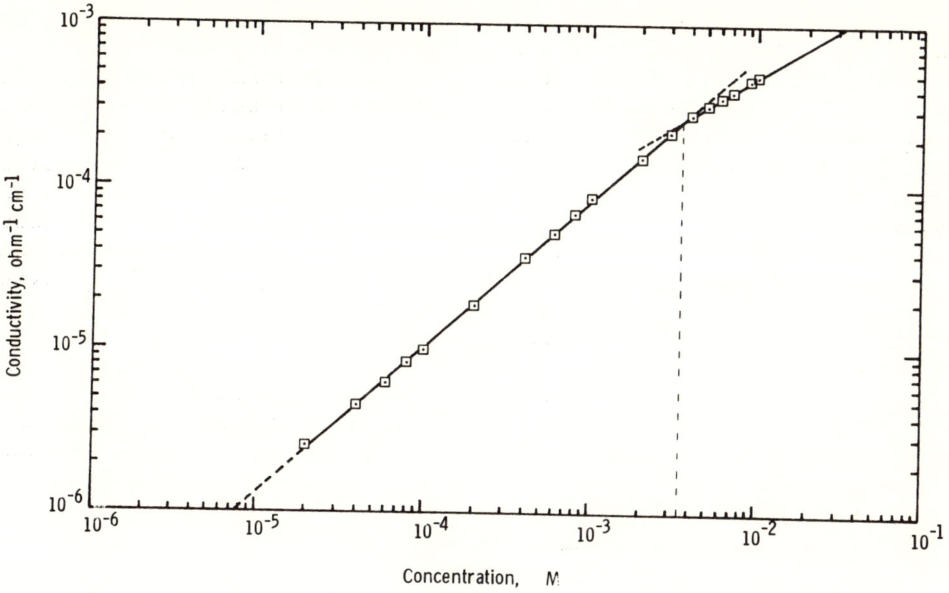

Figure 1. Variation of log conductivity with log sodium lauryl sulfate concentration (23$\pm$ 2°).

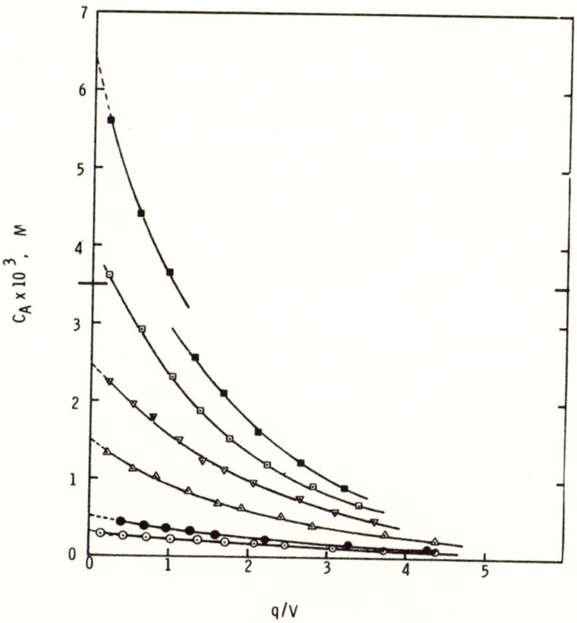

Figure 2. Variation of sodium lauryl sulfate concentration in the affluent stream with effluent volume as a function of sodium lauryl sulfate concentration in the latex: ⊙ 1 x 10^{-3}M ● 2 x 10^{-3}M; △ 4 x 10^{-3}M; ▽ 6 x 10^{-3}M; ⊡ 8 x 10^{-3}M ■ 1 x 10^{-2}M.

Table I. Mass Balance of Sodium Lauryl Sulfate during Desorption by Serum Replacement (300 cc latex; 3.0% solids; 6×10^{-3}M sodium lauryl sulfate)

Time, Hr.	Aqueous Phase Concentration		Flow Rate, cc/hr	Sodium Lauryl Sulfate Collected, moles $\times 10^4$	Sodium Lauryl Sulfate on Particle Surface	
	M $\times 10^3$	moles $\times 10^4$			moles $\times 10^4$	moles/cm^2 $\times 10^{10}$
0	2.80	8.15	0	0	9.31	3.45
2	2.18	6.34	51	2.29	8.83	3.27
3	1.95	5.56	48	0.94	8.67	3.21
4.5	1.60	4.65	51	1.38	8.20	3.03
6	1.31	3.81	55	1.25	7.79	2.88
7	1.17	3.40	58	0.71	7.49	2.77
8	1.02	2.97	61	0.69	7.23	2.68
10	0.80	2.33	66	1.29	6.58	2.44
12.1	0.62	1.81	71	1.13	5.97	2.21
13	0.55	1.61	74	0.40	5.77	2.14
15	0.43	1.25	78	0.75	5.38	1.99
initial total	6.00	17.46	--	--	--	--

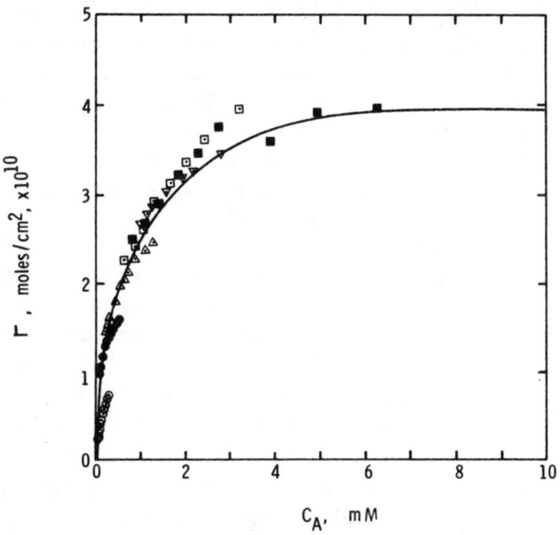

Figure 3. Adsorption isotherm of sodium lauryl sulfate on polystyrene latex particles: variation of concentration adsorbed with concentration in the aqueous phase: initial concentration: ⊙ 1×10^{-3}M; ● 2×10^{-3}M; ◬ 4×10^{-3}M; ▽ 6×10^{-3}M; ⊡ 8×10^{-3}M; ■ 1×10^{-2}M.

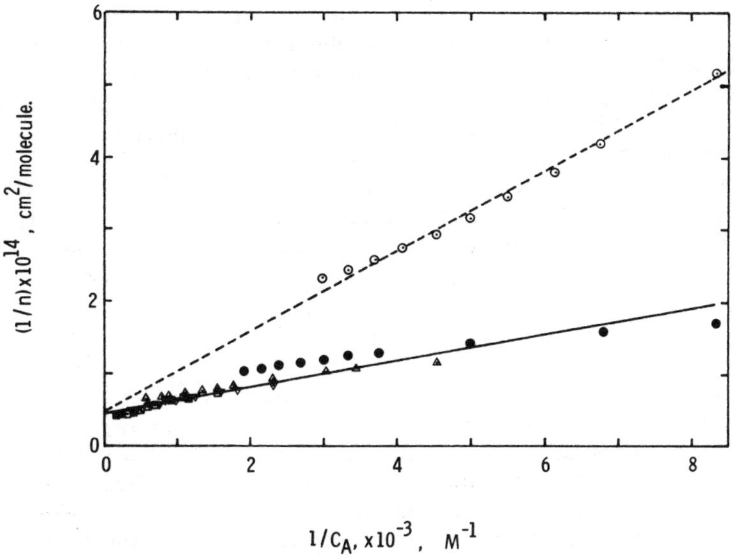

Figure 4. Variation of 1/n with $1/C_A$ for the adsorption of sodium lauryl sulfate on polystyrene latex particles; initial concentration: ⊙ 1×10^{-3}M; ● 2×10^{-3}M; ◬ 4×10^{-3}M; ▽ 6×10^{-3}M; ⊡ 8×10^{-3}M; ■ 1×10^{-2}M.

Figure 4 shows the $(1/\underline{n})-(1/\underline{C_A})$ plots for the experimental results shown in Figure 3. For Langmuir adsorption behavior, these plots should form a straight line of slope $(1/\underline{Nb})$ and intercept $(1/\underline{N})$. The points for the five samples containing $2\text{-}10 \times 10^{-3}$M sodium lauryl sulfate coincide in a straight line, which by least-squares analysis gives values of $\underline{b} = 2.35 \times 10\text{-}3$ liters/mole and $\underline{a_s} = 42$ Å^2; the solid line of the adsorption isotherm of Figure 3 represents these values. The points for the sample containing 1×10^{-3}M sodium lauryl sulfate deviate from linearity and show a higher value of the slope, indicating a lower value of $\underline{k_a}$ or a higher value of $\underline{k_d}$. This sample was not equilibrated overnight, but was subjected to serum replacement immediately after addition of the emulsifier. The non-linearity of the points is attributed to the failure of the sample to reach equilibrium, and the lower value of $\underline{b}$ to a lesser extent of adsorption.

Table II compares the values of $\underline{a_s}$ and $\underline{b}$ from this work with earlier values determined using different methods. The 42 Å^2 value of $\underline{a_s}$ found in this work is at the lower range of the values reported in the literature; however, it is close to the 46 Å^2 value obtained by surface tension measurements, which were carried out under extreme conditions to achieve equilibrium between the solute and adsorbed emulsifier[1].

Figure 5 compares the experimental and theoretical concentrations of sodium lauryl sulfate in the effluent stream. The solid line shows the theoretical variation of the left-hand side of Equation 5 (which is equivalent to t/τ) with $\underline{q}/\underline{V}$. The experimental values are from the experiments in which the latex contained 4×10^{-3}M, 6×10^{-3}M and 1×10^{-2}M sodium lauryl sulfate, calculated using the foregoing values $\underline{a_s} = 42$ Å^2 and $\underline{b} = 2.35 \times 10^3$ liters/mole. The least-squares analysis of these data[5] show a linear correlation which is statistically significant at the 95% confidence level.

SUMMARY

The serum replacement technique, which was developed to clean latexes for characterization, provides an easy, rapid method for determining adsorption isotherms of latex particles by measuring the rate of emulsifier desorption. Using this technique, the adsorption of sodium lauryl sulfate on 190nm-diameter Dow monodisperse polystyrene latex particles was shown to follow Langmuir adsorption behavior. Moreover, the adsorption behavior can be described by a mathematical model for this type of adsorption. Other mathematical models have been developed for the cases in which the emulsifier concentration exceeds the saturation concentration and the adsorbed emulsifier is not in equilibrium

Table II. Molecular Area of Sodium Lauryl Sulfate at Polystyrene-Water Interface at the Critical Micelle Concentration.

Reference	Method	Molecular Area, $Å^2$	b, liters/mole
Sawyer & Rehfeld[3]	conductometric titration	65	----
Brodnyan & Kelley[4]	dialysis & titration with cationic emulsifier	53	8.0×10^3
van den Hul & Vanderhoff[1]	surface tension	46	6.34×10^2
this work	serum replacement	42	2.35×10^3

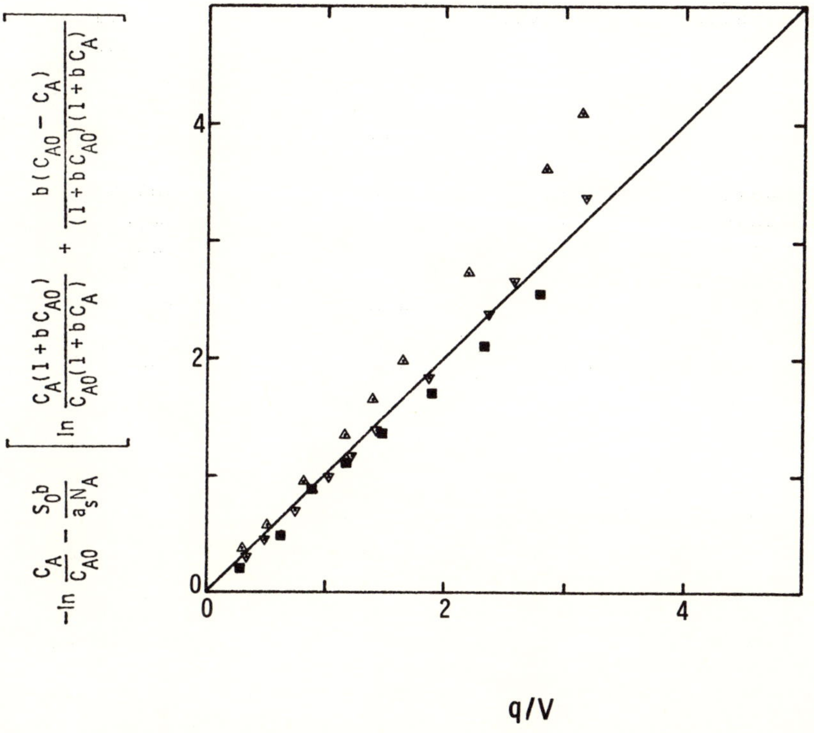

Figure 5. Comparison of experimental and theoretical concentration profiles of sodium lauryl sulfate in the effluent stream; initial concentration: △ 4×10^{-3}M; ▽ 6×10^{-3}M; ■ 1×10^{-2}M.

with the solute emulsifier. The results show that the molecular areas of this technical grade sodium lauryl sulfate is 42 $\AA^2$ and the equilibrium constant is 2.35×10^3 liters/mole.

REFERENCES

1. H. J. van den Hul and J. W. Vanderhoff, in "Polymer Colloids," R. M. Fitch, Editor, Plenum Press, New York, 1971.
2. S. M. Ahmed, M. S. El-Aasser, G. H. Pauli, G. W. Poehlein, and J. W. Vanderhoff, accepted for publication in J. Colloid Interface Sci.
3. W. M. Sawyer and S. J. Rehfeld, J. Phys. Chem. 67, 1973 (1963).
4. J. G. Brodnyan and E. L. Kelley, Polymer Preprints 7, 827 (1966).
5. G. Snedecor, "Statistical Methods," 5th edition, Iowa State University Press, 1956.

Part VII
General Papers

EFFECT OF LARGE ION COMPLEXATION ON THE AQUEOUS STABILITY OF ACYLCHOLINESTERS

E. Tomlinson, S.S. Davis and J.E. Brown

School of Pharmacy and Pharmacology,
Bath University, Bath, AVON, U.K. and
Department of Pharmacy, Nottingham University,
Nottinghamshire, U.K.

Micellar solubilization of solutes is generally regarded as the mechanism by which protection is afforded by surfactants to compounds which are likely to undergo degradation. In this contribution both theoretical and experimental treatments are presented which suggest that for systems in which the degrading solute is ionised and the surfactant is of opposite electrical charge, then complexation between the two ions may be the prime stabilization mechanism. These treatments do not preclude subsequent solubilization of any formed complex. The interaction between the cholinesters acetylcholine chloride, and propionyl, butyryl, myristyl and succinylcholine iodide with a series of alkyl sulfates has been studied, the interaction being characterised by the stoichiometric solubility product. A relationship between ester hydrolysis half-life and solubility product has been demonstrated.

INTRODUCTION

Attempts at the stabilization of drug molecules from degradation in aqueous solution have been performed in numerous ways. Nogami[1] has stated that whereas the oxidation route to degradation may easily be stopped by elimination of oxygen in the system and/or by the addition of a stabilizer, the reduction process on the other hand is far less easy to inhibit. Methods which have been proposed[1] include (1) adjustment of pH, (2) complex formation by the addition of a third substance, (3) reactivity change through adjustment of dielectric constant, and (4) the addition of organic solvents or cosolutes. With regard to this final method the use of surfactants as stabilizers has received attention over the past decade. Since surfactants form micelles it is generally argued[2] that the use of surfactant results in solubilization of a major portion of the drug which hence becomes initially unavailable for reduction.

Using acylcholinesters as model solutes Nogami and his co-workers in a series of papers [1,3,4] have attempted to show that the stability of such compounds is affected in the presence of anionic surfactants by their micellar solubilization. Their arguments have been based largely on the evidence that there exists a good correlation between the apparent distribution of the acylcholinester into the micellar phase and the magnitude of the observed stabilization effect. Similarly Riegelman[2] has reported that the hydrolysis rate of benzocaine (ρ-aminoethylbenzoate) is reduced in the presence of cetylpolyoxyethylene ethers, sodium dodecylsulfate and hexadecyltrimethylammonium bromide. Comparable effects have been reported by Mitchell[5], Sheth and Parrott[6] and Hamid and Parrott[7] . Other compounds of pharmaceutical interest which have been protected from degradation by the addition of surfactants include methantheline bromide, homatropine and chlorbutol.

In systems where the degrading solute is ionised, and where the surfactant is ionic and of opposite electrical charge, apart from micellar solubilization a number of other competing physicochemical equilibria can take place. These include ion-pair formation and complex coacervation. Since it is possible that these additional equilibria can also be at least partly responsible for the protection against degradation, we have re-examined the results of Nogami[1,3,4] for the protection of acylcholinester degradation in the presence of alkylsulfates by considering those ionic interactions possible between the two ions. In this contribution we present both theoretical and experimental treatments which suggest that complexation may be primarily responsible for the protection of acylcholinesters from hydrolytic degradation by anionic surfactants.

EXPERIMENTAL

Materials

Acetylcholine chloride, propionylcholine iodide, butyrylcholine iodide, myristylcholine iodide and succinylcholine iodide were of Analar grade and obtained from Koch-light Laboratories. The alkylsulfates used were sodium octylsulfate, sodium decylsulfate (ex Eastman organic Chemicals); sodium dodecylsulfate was obtained from British Drug Houses and was purified as reported previously[8], sodium tetradecylsulfate was from Mann Research Laboratories.

Water doubly distilled from an all glass still was used, its specific conductance being about 1 x 10^{-6} $ohm^{-1}.cm^{-1}$.

Conductimetric Titration

A conductivity bridge (Wayne Kerr type B642), which was continously and automatically balanced, was connected to a Mullard dip-type conductivity cell (constant 1.42 cm^{-1}) placed within a thermostatted (25°C) water-jacketted 100 cm^3 beaker. Delivery of titrant was maintained constant using a motorised automatic syringe (Braun). The operation and calibration of this automated conductimetric titrimeter has been described in detail elsewhere.

The titrimeter was used to measure both possible self-association of either ion, as well as the complexation points between the oppositely charged ions (as characterised by the stoichiometric solubility product).

Interactions examined were between the four alkylsulfates and succinylcholine iodide and between all the choline salts and sodium dodecylsulfate.

THEORETICAL

Consider the interaction between a monovalent alkylsulfate ion, A^-, and a monovalent cation B^+. This will be governed by the solubility product (K_s) between the two ions, thus:

$$A^- + B^+ \rightleftharpoons A.B \quad (1)$$

such that at the solubility product value we may write in concentration terms:

$$K_s = [A^-] . [B^+] \quad (2)$$

If it is assumed that X is the amount of complexing ion (A^- and B^+) removed from solution upon complexation, then above the solubility product we may write:

$$K_s = [A^-_o - X] . [B^+_o - X] \quad (3)$$

where the subscript o refers to the original concentration of each ion. This treatment assumes that the K_s value is constant and that the concentration of the electrolytes does not vary considerably from their activities in these solutions. For a 1:1 interaction the quadratic form of Equation (2) may be used[8] to obtain the value of X, whereas for a 2:1 interaction a cubic expression is required[9].

If A^- is in excess of B^+ then the formed complex (which is hydrophobic) may be solubilized by the micelles of the alkylsulphate. As B^+ remaining in solution hydrolyses, then some of this (solubilized) complex will be mobilized. This serves to maintain the B^+ monomer concentration in solution.

Above the solubility product if B_s is the amount of B^+ monomer remaining in solution, and if this is degrading by a first-order process then the change of total base with time may be written as:

$$\frac{dB}{dt} = B_o - B_sK_1t \tag{4}$$

where K_1 is the first order rate constant.

With no precipitate (i.e. below the solubility product) the total base will degrade in a first order manner, such that its half-life ($t\frac{1}{2}$) may be given by:

$$t\tfrac{1}{2} = \frac{0.693}{K_1} \tag{5}$$

with surfactant,

$$\frac{B_o}{2} = B_o - \frac{K_sK_1t\frac{1}{2}}{A_s} \tag{6}$$

where A_s is the amount of alkylsulfate monomer remaining in solution. Thus:

$$\frac{B_oA_s}{2} = B_oA_s - K_sK_1t\tfrac{1}{2} \tag{7}$$

$$t\tfrac{1}{2} = B_oA_s/2K_sK_1 \tag{8}$$

Assuming that the first order rate constant for hydrolysis in the absence of surfactant is independent of alkyl chain-length of base, then in the presence of the surfactant we may write:

$$t\tfrac{1}{2} = \frac{k}{K_S}, \quad \text{where } k = \frac{B_oA_s}{2K_1} \tag{9}$$

For interacting systems of large organic ions of opposite electrical charge it has been shown [10,11,12,13] that the stoichiometric solubility product changes with alkyl chain-length of either ion, such that:

$$\log K_s = a - bn \qquad (10)$$

where n is the carbon number of the alkyl chain and a and b are constants. By substituting this expression into Equation (9) and taking logarithms we may write:

$$\log t\tfrac{1}{2} = \log k - a + bn \qquad (11)$$

or

$$\log t\tfrac{1}{2} = k' + bn \qquad (12)$$

A number of consequences arise from this treatment.

1. The stability of the base should increase linearly with increased alkyl chain length of either ion (Equations 11 and 12)

2. The stability should increase with increased concentration of surfactant (Equations 3 and 9).

3. An alteration in K_s caused by for example a change in environment (such as ionic strength or temperature) should be reflected in a change in base stability. Thus if K_s increases the protection afforded by the surfactant should fall, i.e. a more unstable system results.

RESULTS AND DISCUSSION

The chemical stability of acylcholinesters in water in the absence and presence of various concentrations of sodium dodecylsulfate has been well documented by Nogami and co-workers[1,3,4]. Figure (1) is a representation of those results, and shows that there is little effect of ester alkyl chain-length on stability, but that in the presence of 0.5% w/v sodium dodecylsulfate (at 70^oC) there is a linear increase in base half-life with increase in chain-length of the cholinester.

This observation is in agreement with the first consequence of the theoretical treatment as developed in the preceding section that an increase in chain-length of the base ion should produce an increase in the stability in the presence of the oppositely charged ion. The half-life of the C2 analogue for example is 80 minutes in the presence of 0.5% w/v sodium dodecylsulfate, and that of the C8 homologue is increased to 5,040 minutes. The half-life of methantheline bromide at 70^oC has similarly been shown[3] to be increased by an increase in the alkyl chain-length of the protecting surfactant (at constant concentration). For example the $t\tfrac{1}{2}$ of methantheline bromide is increased from 0.6 hours to greater than 32 hours when the protecting alkylsulphate is changed from the C8 homologue to the C16 homologue.

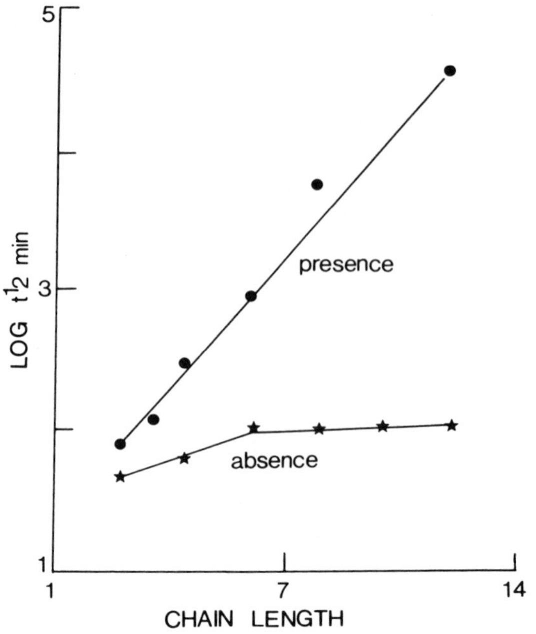

Figure 1. Chemical stability of acylcholinesters in the absence and presence of 0.5% w/v sodium dodecylsulfate at 70°C. Plot constructed from data taken from Reference 1.

The theoretical treatment given predicts that acylcholinester stability should increase with increased concentration of surfactant. Indeed this has been demonstrated experimentally, for example, the half-life of acetylcholine sulfate in 0.5% w/v sodium dodecylsulfate is 80 minutes whereas in 1.15% w/v surfactant, it rises to 127 minutes. Similarly for methantheline bromide in the presence of sodium dodecylsulfate at pH 7.7 and 70°C the $t_{½}$ values are 140 minutes (0.1%) and 740 minutes (0.2%).

To examine the hypothesis that complexation could be controlling rates of hydrolysis, the solubility products between sodium dodecylsulfate and the acylcholinesters, and between succinylcholine iodide and the alkylsulfates have been measured in water at 25°C. Additionally the effect of added salt (sodium chloride) on these interactions has been determined. Figure (2) shows the found relation between the alkylsulfates' chain lengths and their aqueous critical micelle concentrations (CMC) at 25°C. As often found there is a constant decrease in log CMC with increase in chain length. The computed Δ log CMC being -0.37, which gives a $\Delta\Delta G^{o}$ for the transfer of a methylene unit from an aqueous environment to a micellar core phase as -2.15 $kJ.mol^{-1}$. This compares to

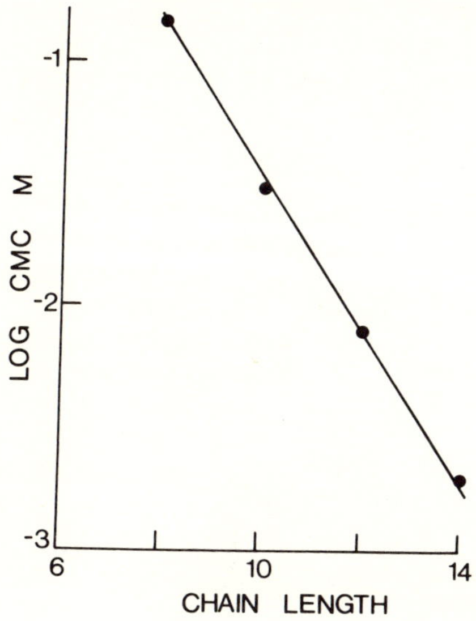

Figure 2. Critical micelle concentrations versus alkyl chain length for a series of alkylsulfates determined at 25°C.

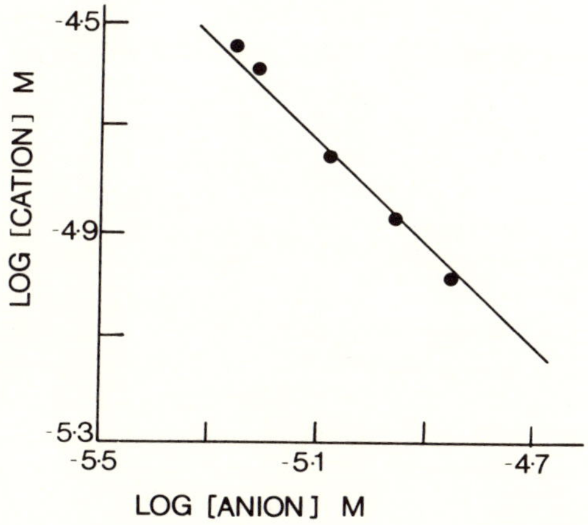

Figure 3. Double logarithm plot for the sodium dodecylsulfate/tetradecylcholine iodide system at the complexation point between these ions, at 25°C.

literature values[14] of Δ log CMC, -0.3, and $\Delta\Delta G^o(CH_2)$, -1.71 $kJ.mol^{-1}$. Subsequent complexation studies were performed at surfactant concentrations well below these measured critical micelle concentration values.

The interaction between sodium dodecylsulfate and acetylcholine chloride, and propionyl, butyryl and myristylcholine iodide was found to be 1:1, as determined by measuring the complexation end-points using different initial concentrations of surfactant in the titration cell. Figure (3) shows that for the interaction of sodium dodecylsulfate with tetradecylcholine iodide a double logarithm plot of concentrations of each ion at the complexation point has a slope value of 1.0.

Table (I) gives all the stoichiometric solubility products for these interactions. It can be seen from Figure (4) that for the interactions between the acylcholinesters and sodium dodecylsulfate there exists a linear relationship between the logarithm of the solubility product and the carbon number of the choline alkyl chain. Equation (13) describes this relationship, i.e.

$$\log K_s^{1:1} = -4.76 - 0.36\,n \qquad (13)$$

Interaction of the alkylsulfates with succinylcholine iodide (Table I) gives rise to a similar relationship although a 2:1 stoichiometry was found due to the divalency of succinylcholine iodide.

Thus the basic assumptions made in developing the theoretical model, (i.e. that solubility product varies linearly with alteration of alkyl chain length of either ion), have been shown by ex-

Table I. Solubility Product Values for the Interactions Between Alkylsulfates and Acylcholinesters at 25°C.

sodium dodecylsulfate/ acylcholinesters systems		succinylcholine iodide/alkyl sulfates systems	
ester chain length	$K_s^{1:1}$ ($mol.dm^{-3}$)	surfactant chain length	$K_s^{2:1}$ ($mol.dm^{-3}$)
2	7.53×10^{-6}		
3	1.05×10^{-6}	10	7.94×10^{-10}
4	3.07×10^{-7}	12	3.55×10^{-10}
14	1.67×10^{-10}	14	4.22×10^{-13}

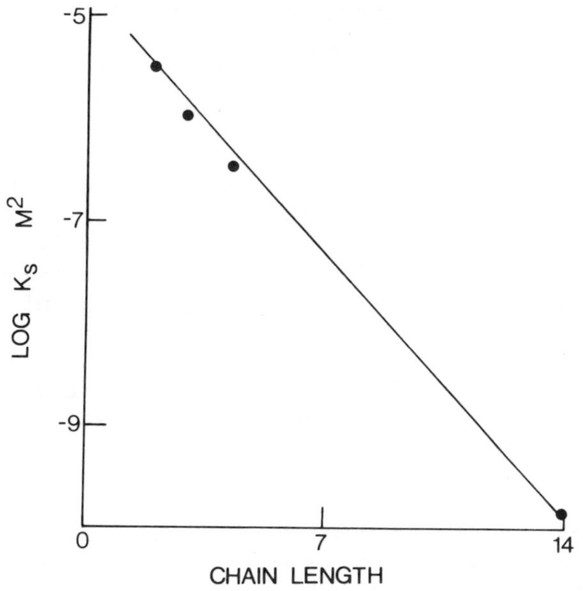

Figure 4. Relationship between solubility product and ester alkyl chain length for the interactions between sodium dodecylsulfate and acylcholinesters at 25°C.

periment to be valid. The final inference from the treatment is that apart from constitutional changes such as structural modifications, alteration in solubility product caused by environmental changes would be reflected by equivalent changes in stability. Nogami[3] has reported that an increase in ionic strength, (effected by an alteration in the buffer strength of the system from 1X to 4X), caused the aqueous stability of methantheline bromide at 70°C in the presence of 0.5% w/v sodium dodecylsulfate to decrease. That is the half-life of the salt decreased from >720 minutes in 1X buffer, to 600 minutes in 2X buffer, to 435 minutes in 4X buffer. We have found[10,13] with other systems that an increase in salt concentration depresses the ionic surfactant critical micelle concentration though it increases the stoichiometric solubility product. It has therefore been of importance to examine the effect of salt on (a) the CMC of sodium dodecylsulfate and (b) the stoichiometric solubility products between sodium dodecylsulfate and the acylcholinesters. As previously reported[12] the surfactant CMC is decreased by the addition of salt, and Figure (5) shows that the solubility product is increased.

If micelle solubilization was the mechanism of protection against degradation, then a decrease in CMC (as caused by the addition of salt) should result in a greater concentration of micellar phase and thus a greater protection. The findings of Nogami however show the reverse. This observation (Figure 5) that K_s increases with salt addition agrees with the complexation theory of protection, that is, if complexation is hindered then the protection afforded by the mechanism will be reduced.

Additionally it should be noted that for the acylcholinesters Nogami and others[3] have shown that the decomposition of methantheline bromide while retarded in the presence of 0.1% sodium dodecylsulfate, is actually slightly increased in the presence of a cationic surfactant (hexadecyltrimethylammonium bromide).

Recalling Equations (10, 11 and 12) then from Nogami's study (Figure 1) the following relationship for the protection of hydrolysis by addition of 0.5% w/v sodium dodecylsulfate may be written:

$$\log t_{1/2} = k' + 0.27\, n \qquad (14)$$

From this present study (Equation 13) assuming that complexation is the protecting mechanism, then we may write the following by combining Equations (9, 12 and 13) i.e.

$$\log t_{1/2} = k' + 0.36\, n \qquad (15)$$

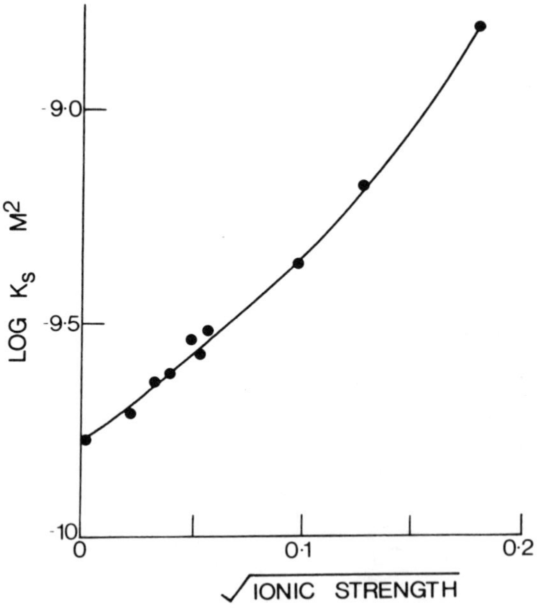

Figure 5. Effect of added salt (sodium chloride) on the solubility product between sodium dodecylsulfate and tetradecylcholine iodide, at 25°C.

Comparison of Equations (14) and (15) shows that the methylene group contributions found experimentally by Nogami (0.27) differ from those computed from the solubility product values as measured experimentally by us (0.36). Equation (14) was derived from data at 70°C whereas the solubility products were measured at 25°C. It has been considered[15] that as temperature increases the methylene group contributions will decrease due to a loss in water structure. Thus temperature effects could well be causing the variance observed for CH_2 group values.

CONCLUSIONS

It is now possible to write the following Scheme to describe a mechanism of base stability in the presence of an oppositely charged surfactant.

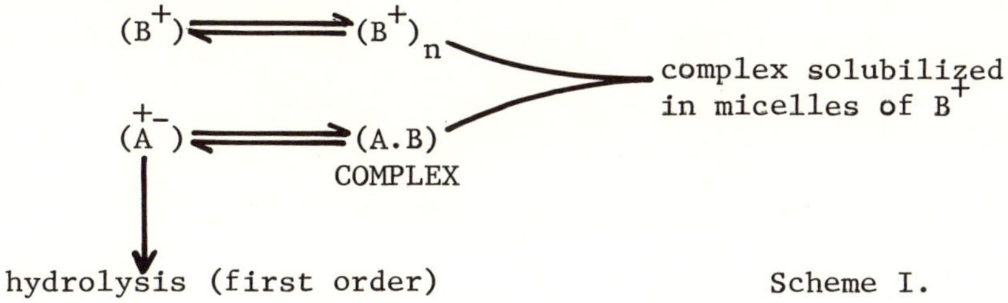

Scheme I.

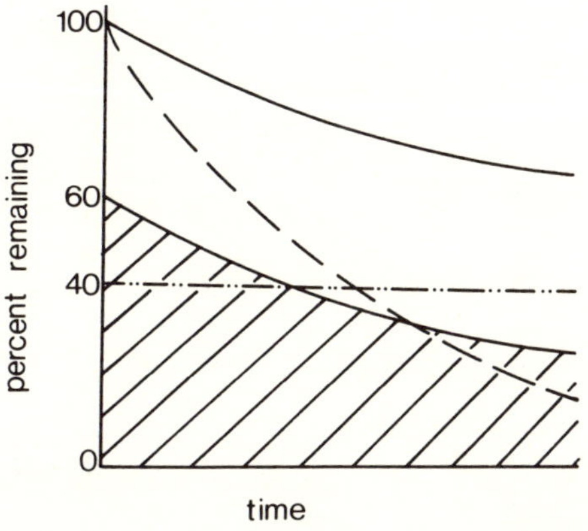

Figure 6. Graphical representation of possible mechanism of hydrolysis of acylcholinesters in the presence of a complexing surfactant.

——— -observed loss rate in the presence of surfactant
— — -loss rate with no surfactant
—··— -constant amount of free base available for hydrolysis (mobilized from complex)

-crossed area is amount of complex remaining.

The complexation mechanism of protection does not preclude that there can be subsequent solubilization of the complex. Hydrolysis of free base results in a mobilization of the solubilised complex to maintain the equilibria shown in the Scheme.

Figure (6) is a graphical representation of this Scheme and illustrates how the formation of a complex between the surfactant molecules and the cholinester can cause a reduction in the rate of degradation of the base by removing from solution a significant proportion of free base so reducing the amount available for hydrolysis.

The hydrophobic cationic ester molecules can also be solubilized into the anionic micelles and retained within the Stern layer and stabilized by complexation. Such a process is a variation on that outlined by Scheme I but also focuses on the importance of ionic interactions for the stability of drug molecules in a micellar system.

REFERENCES

1. H. Nogami, J. Hasegawa and M. Iwatsuru, Chem. Pharm. Bull., 18, 2297-2302 (1970).
2. S. Riegelman, J. Pharm. Sci., 49, 339-343 (1960).
3. H. Nogami, S. Awazu, K. Watanabe and K. Sato, Chem. Pharm. Bull., 8, 1136-1141 (1960).
4. H. Nogami, S. Awazu and M. Iwatsuru, Chem. Pharm. Bull., 11, 1251-1255 (1963).
5. A.G. Mitchell, J. Pharm. Pharmac., 14, 172-176 (1962).
6. P.B. Sheth and E.L. Parrott, J. Pharm. Sci., 56, 983-986 (1967).
7. I.A. Hamid and E.L. Parrott, J. Pharm. Sci., 60, 901-906 (1971).
8. G.I. Mukhayer, S.S. Davis and E. Tomlinson, J. Pharm. Sci., 64, 147-151 (1975).
9. E. Tomlinson and S.S. Davis, J. Colloid Interface Sci., 66 335-344 (1978).
10. G.I. Mukhayer, Ph.D. Thesis, Aston University (1974).
11. G.I. Mukhayer and S.S. Davis, J. Colloid Interface Sci., 53, 224-234 (1975).
12. G.I. Mukhayer and S.S. Davis, J. Colloid Interface Sci., 56, 350 (1976).
13. E. Tomlinson and S.S. Davis, Unpublished results. (1975)
14. E.D. Goddard and G.C. Benson, Canad. J. Chem., 35, 986 (1957).
15. S.S. Davis, T. Higuchi and J.A. Rytting, Adv. Pharm. Sci., 4, 73-261 (1974).

ON THE INFLUENCE OF AMPHIPHILIC SUBSTANCES ON THE MUTUAL SOLUBILITIES IN BINARY LIQUID SYSTEMS, II

C.-U. Herrmann+), U. Würz, and M. Kahlweit
Max-Planck-Institut für biophysikalische Chemie
(Karl-Friedrich-Bonhoeffer-Institut),
D-3400 Göttingen, FRG

This paper continues the investigations on the influence of amphiphilic substances on the mutual solubilities in binary liquid mixtures. For experimental reasons, C_6H_6, used as oil in the preceding investigations, was replaced by p-Xylene. In this paper, the question studied is: Whether a single non-ionic amphiphilic substance can be as effective as the combination of alcohol and ionic surfactants in obtaining macroscopically homogeneous solutions with high mole fractions of oil and water? The experiments show that with appropriate substances like polyglycolethers, similar effectivities can be reached. X-ray scattering measurements indicate that the microscopic structure in these ternary systems is similar to that in the quarternary systems. The addition of inorganic electrolytes to the systems leads to the conclusion that the water structure in the solution may have a considerable effect on the effectivity of the amphiphilic substances.

+) Part of Ph.D.Thesis, Göttingen 1978

INTRODUCTION

In a preceding paper[1] we have studied the influence of alcohols (as cosurfactants) and of NaDS (as surfactant) on the mutual solubilities between C_6H_6 (as oil) and H_2O. The influence was discussed in view of the predictions by Wagner[2], that amphiphilic substances with equal strong interactions between their oleophilic and hydrophilic groups and the oil and water molecules, respectively, should lead to the highest effectivity in obtaining high mutual solubilities.

We found that although the lower alcohols (e.g. C_2H_5OH) are more effective than the higher ones (e.g. $C_5H_{11}OH$) if used as additive alone, however, the effectivity of the higher alcohols is more strongly enhanced by addition of an ionic surfactant (e.g. NaDS) as fourth component.

We further suggested to present the result with the triangular phase diagram of the three liquids as basis (see Figure 1b) and the concentration of the surfactant as ordinate. The advantage of

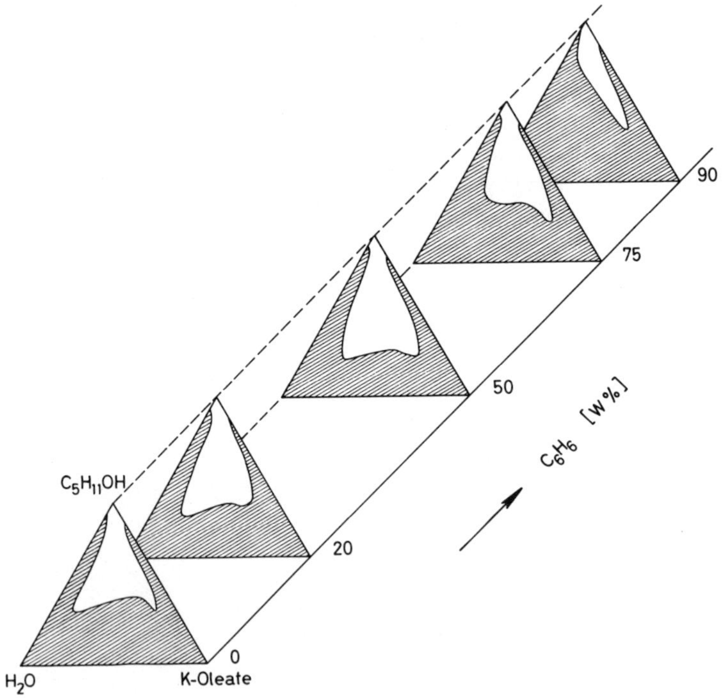

Figure 1a. Phase diagram of the system C_6H_6-H_2O-$C_5H_{11}OH$-K-Oleate, as published in Reference 3.

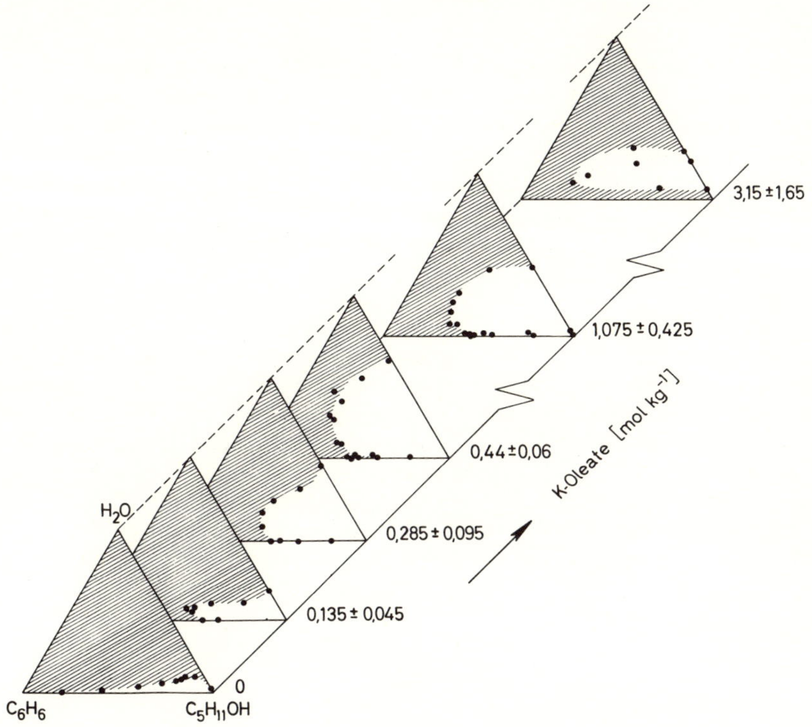

Figure 1b. Data of Figure 1a plotted according to our mode of presentation.

this presentation is demonstrated in Figure 1, where in (a) we have reproduced the data of the system H_2O-$C_5H_{11}OH$-K-Oleate with C_6H_6 as oil (in wt.%), as published by Friberg and Burasczeska[3]. Figure 1b shows the same data according to our mode of presentation: the basis is the well known phase diagram of the ternary system C_6H_6-H_2O-$C_5H_{11}OH$ (in wt.%), the ordinate the concentration of K-Oleate (in mol per kg solvent). This diagram shows two macroscopically homogeneous regions: a smaller one (omitted in the Figure) in the H_2O corner, and a larger one (shown white in the Figure) in the alcohol corner. With increasing surfactant concentration, these homogeneous regions first increase, then pass through a maximum and decrease again. The initial increase is due to the increasing solubilization of the oil and water molecules by the combination of alcohol and surfactant molecules, whereas the decrease of the homogeneous regions is due to the fact that the solubility limits of the surfactant advance into the phase diagram as its total concentration increases.

As far as the microscopic structure of the homogeneous solutions is concerned, the experiments - in particular small angle X-ray scattering measurements - indicate the existence of so called o/w micelles in the H_2O corner, solubilized by mixed layers of surfactant and alcohol molecules (Figure 10 in Reference 1). Close to the alcohol corner, one may assume alcohol aggregates (Figure 11 in Reference 1), whereas close to the boundary of the miscibility gap, the existence of w/o aggregates is indicated, again solubilized by mixed (inverse) layers of surfactant and alcohol molecules.

In systems with a single homogeneous region, like in C_6H_6-H_2O-C_3H_7OH, extending from the H_2O corner around the miscibility gap to the C_6H_6 corner, the addition of a surfactant leads to an apse-like shape of the inhomogeneous region, with a critical line on its surface, which starts at the critical point of the ternary basis. In such systems one then has to distinguish between three principal microscopic structures: the o/w aggregates in the H_2O rich region, the critical fluctuations close to the critical line, and the w/o aggregates in the oil rich region.

TERNARY SYSTEMS

In this paper we shall study the question: How far can a nonionic amphiphilic substance combine the effects of alcohol and ionic surfactants in increasing the mutual solubilities of oil and water? (See also Reference 4). This question was raised by the consideration that the hydrophilic group of NaDS seems to be much stronger than its oleophilic group, which expresses itself in a much higher solubility of the surfactant in H_2O than in C_6H_6. One may then think of increasing its oleophilicity by increasing the chain length. Indeed, if Na-Oleate is used instead of NaDS, the effectivity increases. It seems, however, more appropriate to change to nonionic surfactants with weaker hydrophilic groups, in particular to such substances where the strength of the hydrophilic as well as that of the oleophilic group can be changed stepwise and independently.

For this purpose we have chosen the polyglycolethers, which may be written as

$$P_{ij} \equiv \underbrace{H - [CH_2]_i}_{\text{oleophilic}} \; | \; \underbrace{[O - (CH_2)_2]_j - OH}_{\text{hydrophilic}}$$

where the oleophilicity may be increased by increasing i, while the hydrophilicity may be increased by increasing j. Further, we have changed from C_6H_6 to p-Xylene as oil, since the latter has the lower vapor pressure, which makes it more convenient for the experiments. In the following experiments we have varied i between 1 and 5, and j between 0 and 3.

Figure 2a shows the phase diagrams for j = 0 and i = 2,3,4,5, i.e. with alcohols as additives. Again, A denotes the oil; B: H_2O; and C the additive. As one can see, here propanol is the most effective alcohol, whereas with benzene as oil we found propanol and ethanol to be almost equally effective (see Figure 1 in Reference 1). Figure 2b shows the diagrams for j = 1. The mutual solubilities have increased, but the order of effectivity is the same as in Figure 2a. As we increase the hydrophilicity further by adding P_{ij} with j = 2 (Figure 2c), the mutual solubilities increase further, but now the substance with the higher oleophilicity (i = 4)

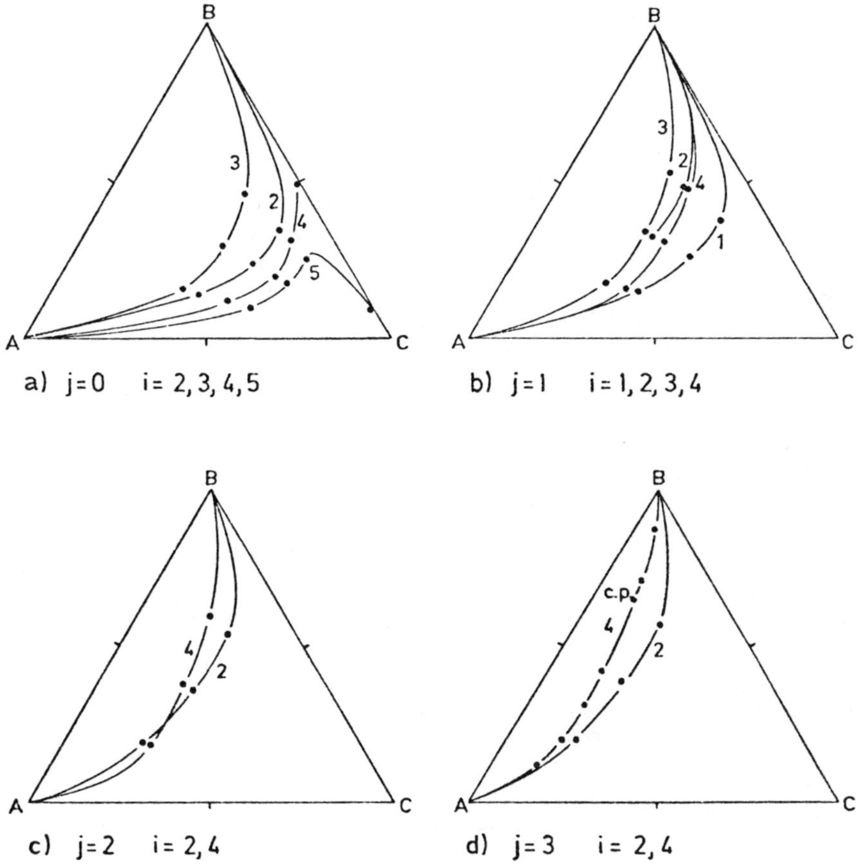

Figure 2. Phase diagrams of the ternary systems p-Xylene-H_2O-P_{ij} at 25 °C (in mole fractions).

has overtaken the one with the lower oleophilicity (i = 2) in the H_2O rich region, in accord with the considerations presented in the paragraph following Figure 1 in Reference 1. This effect increases as we add P_{ij} with j = 3 (Figure 2d), where we have reached almost the same effectivity as with the combination of $C_5H_{11}OH$ and NaDS in the C_6H_6-H_2O system (see Figure 9 in Reference 1).

These experiments thus show that appropriate nonionic amphiphilic substances with amphiphilic groups of balanced strength can reach a similar effectivity as the combination of an alcohol and an ionic surfactant.

If one increases the amphiphilicity drastically by using Triton X-100 (j ≈ 10), where the oleophilic group consists of a benzene ring with an octyl group, one can reach even higher effectivities (Figure 3). Here, close to the center of the A-B side, about four Triton molecules keep 48 xylene molecules and 48 water molecules in homogeneous solution.

X-RAY SCATTERING CURVES

We have then again studied the X-ray scattering along the straight line extending from the C corner to the center of the A-B side, with P_{43} as additive C. Close to the C corner we found scattering curves similar to those in the alcohol corner (curve 1 in Figure 12 of Reference 1), indicating again quasi-lamellar aggregates of the triethylglycolmonobutylether. About halfways between the C corner and the miscibility gap, the shallow maximum has moved towards lower angles. At the miscibility gap, the scattering curve

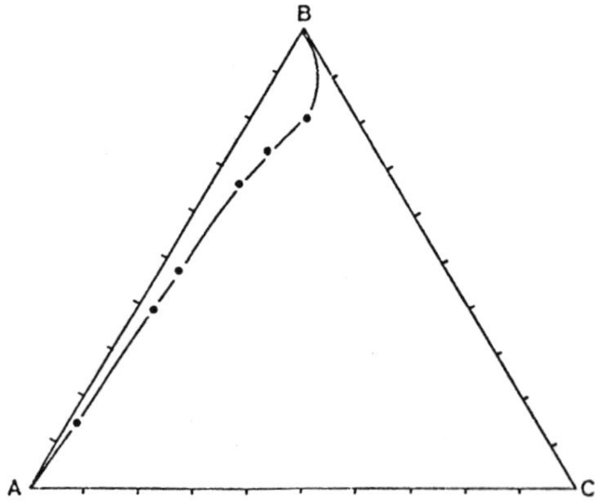

Figure 3. Phase diagram of the ternary system p-Xylene-H_2O-Triton-X-100 at 25 °C (in mole fractions).

has become similar to curves 3 and 4 in Figure 12 of Reference 1, with a single maximum at zero angle. As one now moves along the miscibility gap, starting in the oil rich region, moving towards the critical point the scattering curves maintain their shape, the peak at zero angle, however, becoming increasingly narrower as one approaches the critical point, indicating increasing sizes of the aggregates, which seem to gradually change into critical fluctuations. After having passed the critical point, i.e., in the H_2O rich region, the maximum remains at zero angle but broadens again. A second maximum at higher angles, as found in the case of ionic micelles in H_2O did not appear, possibly because of the low electron density in the hydrophilic groups of the polyglycolethers.

INFLUENCE OF TEMPERATURE AND IONIC ADDITIVES

Contrary to the quarternary systems investigated in Reference 1, increasing temperature leads to an increase of the miscibility gap in the A-B-P_{ij} systems. Table I gives the mole fractions x_C of P_{43} at the miscibility gap with equal mole fractions of xylene and H_2O.

With respect to the influence of added electrolytes, experience shows that in the case of micellar solutions of ionic surfactants (like NaDS) the addition of inorganic salts decreases the cmc, irrespective of the nature of the ions. In the case of nonionic surfactants (like Triton), however, it was found that the turbidity point either increases or decreases with added inorganic salts, depending mainly on the nature of the anion[5]: while NO_3^- and, in particular, ClO_4^- ions increase the turbidity point, SO_4^{--} ions decrease it. Cl^- ions have only little influence. The order

$$ClO_4^- < NO_3^- < Cl^- < SO_4^{--}$$

reminds one of the so called Hofmeister rule[6], found with the influence of inorganic salts on the stability of protein sols.

Table I. Mole Fraction x_C at the Miscibility Gap with Equal Mole Fractions of A and B as Function of Temperature.

ϑ [°C]	x_C
15	0.12
20	0.126
25	0.147
30	0.153
35	0.168
40	0.183

Table II. Mole Fraction x_C at the Miscibility Gap with Equal Mole Fractions of A and B in the Presence of Electrolytes at 25 °C.

Additive	x_C
NaDS	0.087
$NaClO_4$	0.135
-	0.147
NaCl	0.162
Na_2SO_4*	0.181

Table II gives the mole fractions x_C of P_{43} at the miscibility gap with equal mole fractions of xylene and H_2O. The concentrations of the additives were 10^{-5} mol per cm^3 of the initial xylene-H_2O mixtures, which were then titrated with P_{43} until the solutions became homogeneous. The only exception was Na_2SO_4, for which the increase of the miscibility gap was so drastic that the experiments had to be carried out with 10^{-6} mol per cm^3 initial binary mixture*.

As one can see, the addition of an ionic surfactant (NaDS) again increases the mutual solubilities, although not to the extent as in the combination with an alcohol as cosurfactant. For the inorganic salts, however, we find the same order as above: ClO_4^- ions, known as water structure breakers, increase the mutual solubilities, while structure builders, like SO_4^{--} ions, decrease them.

The effect differs with respect to the region of the phase diagram. Figure 4 shows that the increase of the miscibility gap due to the presence of SO_4^{--} ions is much less pronounced in the water-rich region than in the oil-rich region, i.e., in that region where water tends to precipitate.

The effect of the water structure breakers and builders may be qualitatively interpreted as follows: In view of the low ratio of amphiphilic molecules to oil and water molecules, the model of spherical "inverse micelles" in the oil rich region with bulk water, surrounded by a layer of amphiphilic molecules, seems at least to be questionable. Instead, one may think of star like arrangements of the amphiphilic molecules, with the hydrophilic groups turned inwards, each hydrophilic site binding one or more H_2O molecules. The relation between these bound water molecules and the water molecules in the surrounding solution is then governed by a law of mass action. If structure breakers are added to the solution, the equilibrium is shifted towards the "micelles", whereas, if water structure builders are added, the equilibrium is shifted towards water clusters in the solution, which may then act as nuclei for the precipitation of water droplets.

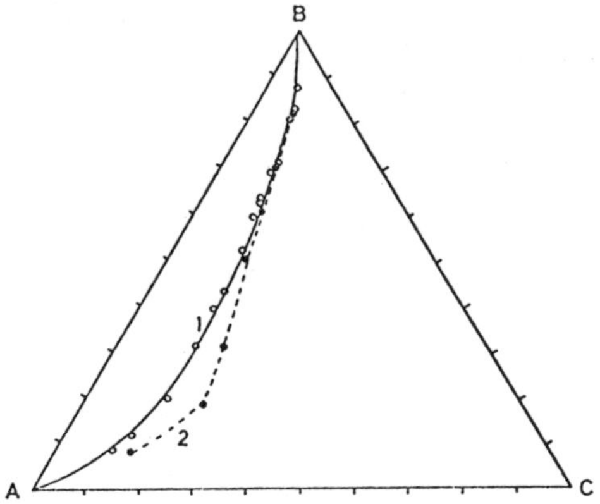

Figure 4. Increase of the miscibility gap in the system p-Xylene-H_2O-P_{43} (1) due to the presence of SO_4^{--} ions (10^{-5} mol per cm^3 initial p-Xylene-H_2O mixture) at 25 °C (2).

Admittedly, this model is only qualitative, but the experiments seem to indicate that the effect of the water structure in the oil-rich region of the phase diagram may play a considerable role in these processes.

REFERENCES

1. C.U. Herrmann, U. Würz, and M. Kahlweit, Ber.Bunsenges.Phys. Chem. 82, 560 (1978).
2. C. Wagner, Z.Phys.Chem. (Leipzig) 132, 273 (1928).
3. S. Friberg and I. Burasczeska, Prog.Colloid Polym.Sci. 63, 1 (1978).
4. S. Friberg and I. Lapcsynska, Prog.Colloid Polym.Sci. 56, 16 (1975).
5. W.A.P. Luck, Top.Curr.Chem. 64, 113 (1976).
6. W. Hofmeister, Arch.Exp.Pathol.Pharmakol. 24, 247 (1888).

THE INTERACTION OF PHENOTHIAZINES WITH ALKYL SULFATES

E. Tomlinson[1], S. S. Davis[2] and G. I. Mukhayer[3]

[1]School of Pharmacy and Pharmacology
University of Bath, United Kingdom
[2]Department of Pharmacy, University of Nottingham, United Kingdom
[3]Faculty of Pharmacy, University of Khartoum, Sudan

A study on the thermodynamics of complex formation between some phenothiazines and alkyl sulfates reveals expected enthalpy/entropy compensation effects. However, examination of the entropy change/temperature relationships of some of the phenothiazines shows quite marked deviations from linearity at higher temperatures.

The results are discussed in terms of group substitution effects. The possible relationships that these observations could have to the biological activity of phenothiazines is examined.

INTRODUCTION

Large organic ions of opposite charge can interact in aqueous solution to give complexes. Such interactions can have importance in the pharmaceutical sciences. For example, in the formulation of medicines it is important to remember that many drug species are large ionizable molecules that may form complexes with other drug species, dyes, surface active agents or preservatives[1,2]. In addition large cationic drug species may interact with natural ionizable materials, e.g. the bile salts[3].

Detailed studies on the stoichiometry and thermodynamics of the interaction of large anions and cations have been reported by us in previous papers[1,4,5,6]. The utility of these complexation systems as models for the drug-receptor interaction have also been discussed[7]. The presence of ionizable groups in drug molecules affects both their lipid solubility and their transport through biological membranes. Ion-pair formation increases lipid solubility[8] and the magnitude of the effect will depend on the size and hydrophobic character of the ion-pairing species. The partitioning of drug molecules (usually between 1-octanol and water) is often used as a measure of drug lipophilicity and partition data are used frequently in structure-activity correlations[9]. We have noted previously[10] that the way in which substituent groups change the partition coefficients of molecules are mirrored by the changes that occur in the solubility product for the interaction of the ionized drug molecule with a suitable large ion of opposite charge. This type of interaction occurs through a combination of electrostatic (coulombic) and hydrophobic interactions.

In order to investigate these effects in more detail four different phenothiazine derivatives have been selected as cationic species and sodium dodecyl sulfate as the complexing anion. Solubility product values have been measured at a range of temperatures. The results are discussed in terms of the mechanism of interaction of large organic ions and enthalpy/entropy compensation effects. The possible use of complexation data in biological activity-molecular structure relationships is also considered.

MATERIALS AND METHODS

Sodium dodecyl sulfate (SDDS) was a sample of high purity obtained from British Drug Houses, Poole, United Kingdom. This was recrystallized several times and the purity of the resultant was checked using gas-liquid chromatography and surface tension measurements[4]. The four phenothiazines, promazine, chlorpromazine, trimeprazine and triflupromazine were gifts from May and Baker, Dagenham, United Kingdom and Smith Kline and French, Welwyn Garden City, United Kingdom. They were used without further purification. The structures are shown in Scheme I.

Water, doubly distilled from an all-glass still was used. The specific conductance was about 1×10^{-6} ohm^{-1} cm^{-1}.

Conductimetric titrations were performed using a conductivity bridge (Wayne-Kerr B642) which was continuously and automatically balanced and was connected to a dip-type conductivity cell (Mullard) contained in a beaker thermostated to $\pm 0.1^{\circ}$C. Delivery of titrant was by a motorized automatic syringe (Braun). Full details of the use of this apparatus in complexation studies have been published elsewhere[1,11]. The complexation end-point was easily distinguished by an abrupt change in the specific conductance versus volume of titrant plot. The pH of the titration

Structure of Phenothiazines

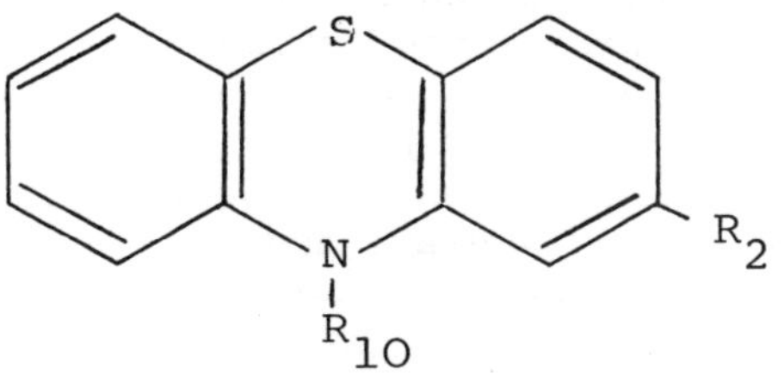

Phenothiazine	R_{10}	R_2
Promazine	$-(CH_2)_3\ N(CH_3)_2$	H
Chlorpromazine	$-(CH_2)_3\ N(CH_3)_2$	Cl
Triflupromazine	$-(CH_2)_3\ N(CH_3)_2$	CF_3
Trimeprazine	$-CH_2-CH(CH_3)-CH_2-N(CH_3)_2$	H
Promethazine	$-CH_2-CH(CH_3)-N(CH_3)_2$	H

Scheme I

solution was close to neutrality such that in all cases it could be assumed that the phenothiazines (pKa values > 9.0) were in a fully ionized state.

Complexation was described by the solubility product, K_s, calculated from the equation:

$$K_s = [\text{phenothiazine}]\cdot[\text{SDDS}] \qquad (1)$$

and is taken to represent the point at which an insoluble phase begins to form.

All experiments were conducted at low concentrations (10^{-5}-10^{-4} mol.dm^{-3}) of the interacting species and the concentrations of the two species can be taken as being the same as their activities.

RESULTS

Solubility product values for the interaction of SDDS with the 4 phenothiazines are listed in Table I.

From Table I it can be seen that in all cases a 1:1 interaction was observed. The change in solubility product with temperature is shown in Figure 1 and has been expressed by means of a polynomial expression:

$$\text{Log } K_s = A - BT + CT^2 - DT^3 \qquad (2)$$

The values for the various constants are given in Table I. Enthalpy (ΔH_f) and entropy (ΔS_f) values for complex formation were derived by substituting the values of T in Equation (2) by increments of 0.2° upto ± 0.4° from the temperature where the actual value of ΔH_f was calculated by least squares analysis of the slope of the resulting log K_s vs T^{-1} plot, and are given in Table II. Their mean standard deviations, as calculated by the Please method for propagation of errors, were ±0.8 and ±2.3 for ΔH and ΔS respectively.

Group contributions to the thermodynamics of the complexation process have been calculated at two representative temperatures (Table III).

In processes involving phase separation phenomena in aqueous environment it is often instructive to plot ΔS versus ΔH and to

Table I. Interaction of SDDS with Phenothiazines.

Compound	K_s at 25°C ($\times 10^{-9}$)	Stoichiometry (1:n)	log K_s=A-BT+CT²-DT³ A	B	C	D
Promazine	8.4	1:0.93	65.3	0.74	2.4×10^{-3}	2.5×10^{-6}
Chlorpromazine	2.6	1:0.90	165.8	1.67	5.5×10^{-3}	5.7×10^{-6}
Triflupromazine	2.4	1:0.93	158.2	1.61	5.1×10^{-3}	5.3×10^{-6}
Trimeprazine	3.9	1:0.99	206.4	2.12	6.9×10^{-3}	7.4×10^{-6}
Promethazine[a]	13.4	---	---	---	---	---

[a]Data from G. I. Mukhayer, Ph.D. Thesis, University of Aston, 1974

Table II. Selected Thermodynamic Parameters for the Interaction of SDDS with Phenothiazines.

Phenothiazine	T(^{o}K)	log K_s	ΔG_f	ΔH_f	ΔS_f
			(kJ mol^{-1})		(J mol^{-1} K^{-1})
Promazine	283.15	-8.38	-45.4	-24.5	74.0
	293.15	-8.21	-46.1	-33.0	44.6
	303.15	-8.03	-46.6	-34.0	22.5
	313.15	-7.76	-46.5	-44.3	7.2
	323.15	-7.52	-46.6	-46.1	1.5
Chlorpromazine	283.15	-8.78	-47.6	-8.9	136.5
	293.15	-8.61	-48.7	-25.4	78.1
	303.15	-8.45	-49.1	-38.1	36.1
	313.15	-8.24	-49.4	-45.8	11.6
	323.15	-7.94	-49.2	-47.4	5.6
Triflupromazine	283.15	-8.80	-47.7	4.41	183.4
	293.15	-8.72	-48.9	-17.3	108.0
	303.15	-8.56	-49.7	-34.3	50.8
	313.15	-8.35	-50.1	-45.3	15.1
	323.15	-8.09	-50.1	-48.8	4.1
Trimeprazine	283.15	-8.64	-46.8	-10.3	129.0
	293.15	-8.52	-47.8	-27.1	70.5
	303.15	-8.36	-48.5	-38.4	33.4
	313.15	-8.11	-48.7	-42.6	19.4
	323.15	-7.92	-49.0	-38.2	33.5

examine enthalpy/entropy compensation effects[12,13]. This has been done in Figure 2. The slopes of the lines are all similar and correspond to a compensation temperature of about 300°K.

DISCUSSION

The similarities in the log K_s versus temperature relationships (Figure 1) indicates that the various phenothiazine derivatives interact with SDDS in the same general manner. Curves of similar shape have been obtained previously for the interaction of

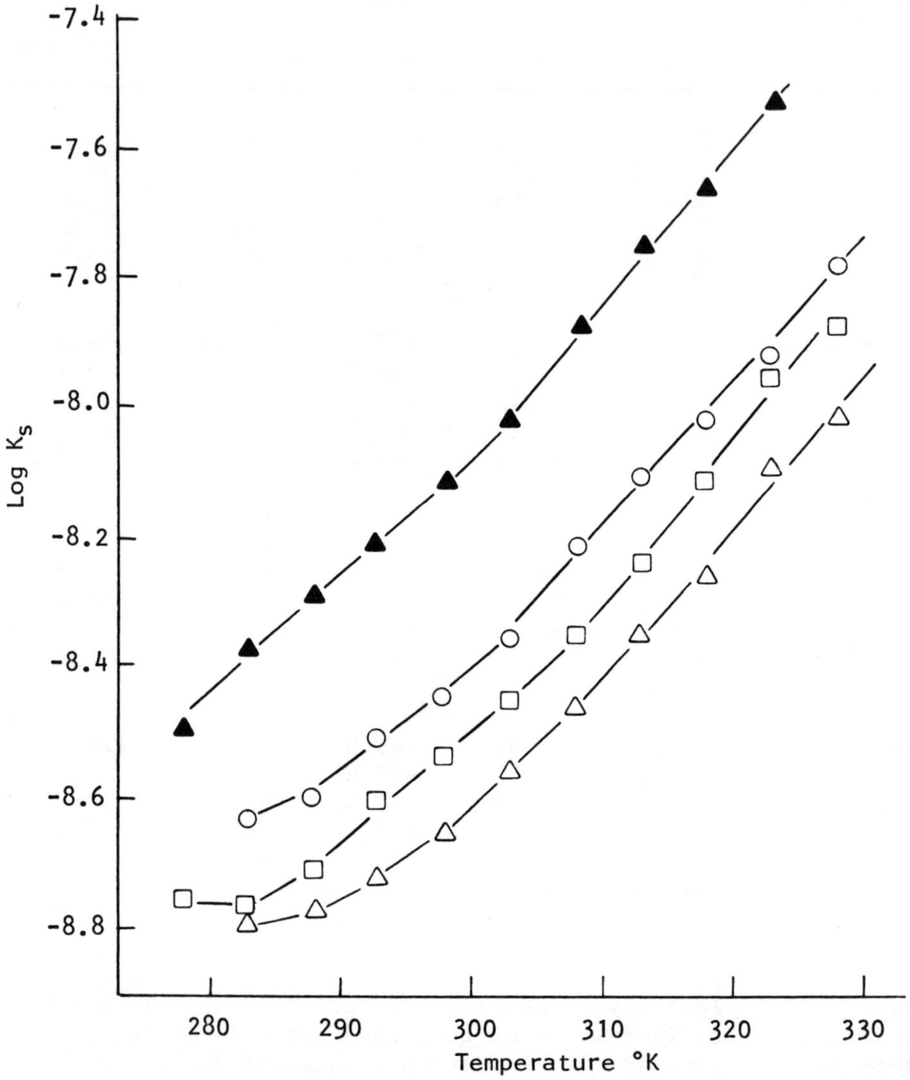

Figure 1. The change of log K_s with temperature, ▲ promazine, □ chlorpromazine, △ triflupromazine, ○ trimeprazine.

Table III. Group Substituent Constants for the Interaction of SDDS with Phenothiazines (Promazine Taken as Parent Molecule).

Group	$\Delta\Delta G_f$ (kJ mol^{-1}) 25°C	40°C	$\Delta\Delta H_f$ (kJ mol^{-1}) 25°C	40°C	$\Delta\Delta S_f$ (J mol^{-1} K^{-1}) 25°C	40°C
H (Promazine)	0	0	0	0	0	0
2-Cl (Chlorpromazine)	-2.5	-2.9	+4.3	-1.5	22.5	4.4
2-CF_3 (Triflupromazine)	-3.1	-3.5	+10.1	-1.0	44.4	7.9
Branching (Trimeprazine)	-2.0	-2.2	+3.0	+1.7	16.8	12.2

SDDS with benzyltriphenylphosphonium chloride and its derivatives[4,5]. Competitive changes in hydrophobic interactions and the altered dielectric constant of water were discussed as a means of explaining the data. It can be seen from Table II that at low temperatures the entropies of complex formation are large and positive, while the enthalpy of complex formation is in most cases negative but small. Such data are characteristic of hydrophobic bond formation; the main drawing force for the interaction beween two large organic ions of opposite charge[14]. The two centers of opposite charge provide an enhancing effect[15].

Lobos[16] has reported on the formation of complexes between various phenothiazines and anionic xanthene dyes such as rhodamine B, Eosin Y and erythrosin B and has discussed spectral changes in terms of a charge transfer complexation mechanism. We believe that an alternative explanation could be an anion-cation interaction where greater credit is given to the importance of hydrophobic interactions.

As the temperature is raised the entropy of complex formation between SDDS and the phenothiazines falls and the enthalpy of complex formation becomes more greatly negative. Thus, at higher temperatures the electrostatic interaction is the main driving force for complexation and the hydrophobic effect is of much lesser importance.

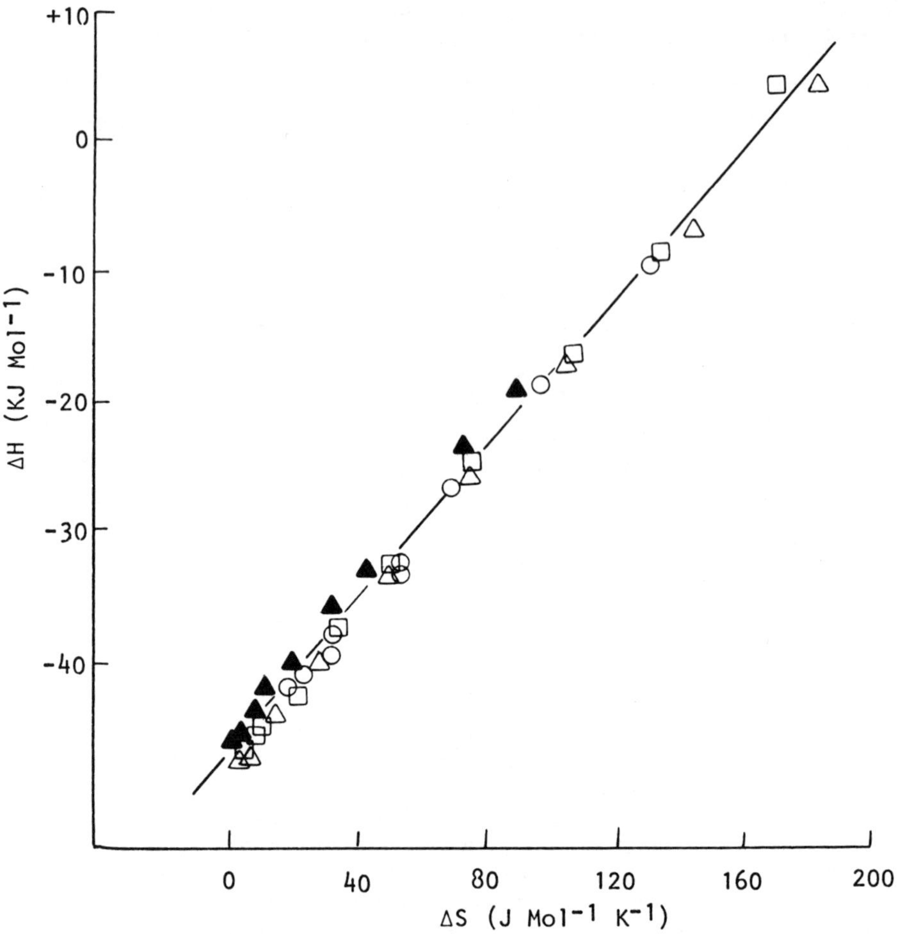

Figure 2. Enthalpy/Entropy plot for the interaction of phenothiazines with SDDS. Legend as for Figure 1.

In spite of the large changes in ΔH_f and ΔS_f the free energies of complex formation change little with temperature. As has been noted previously, compensation between ΔS and ΔH can lead to small changes in ΔG[17]. The group substituent constants for the interaction of SDDS with the phenothiazines listed in Table III provide a number of interesting points. The substitution of hydrogen in the R_2 position by chlorine or CF_3 causes a significant reduction in the solubility of the complex (a 3.3 fold change in K_s which is equivalent to a 1.8 fold ($(3.3)^{1/2}$) change in solubility at 25°C. Branching, that is, the presence of a 2-CH_3 group in the R_{10} moiety (trimeprazine) gives rise to about a two-fold decrease in K_s at 25°C. In contrast the substitution of a 2-methyl ethyl

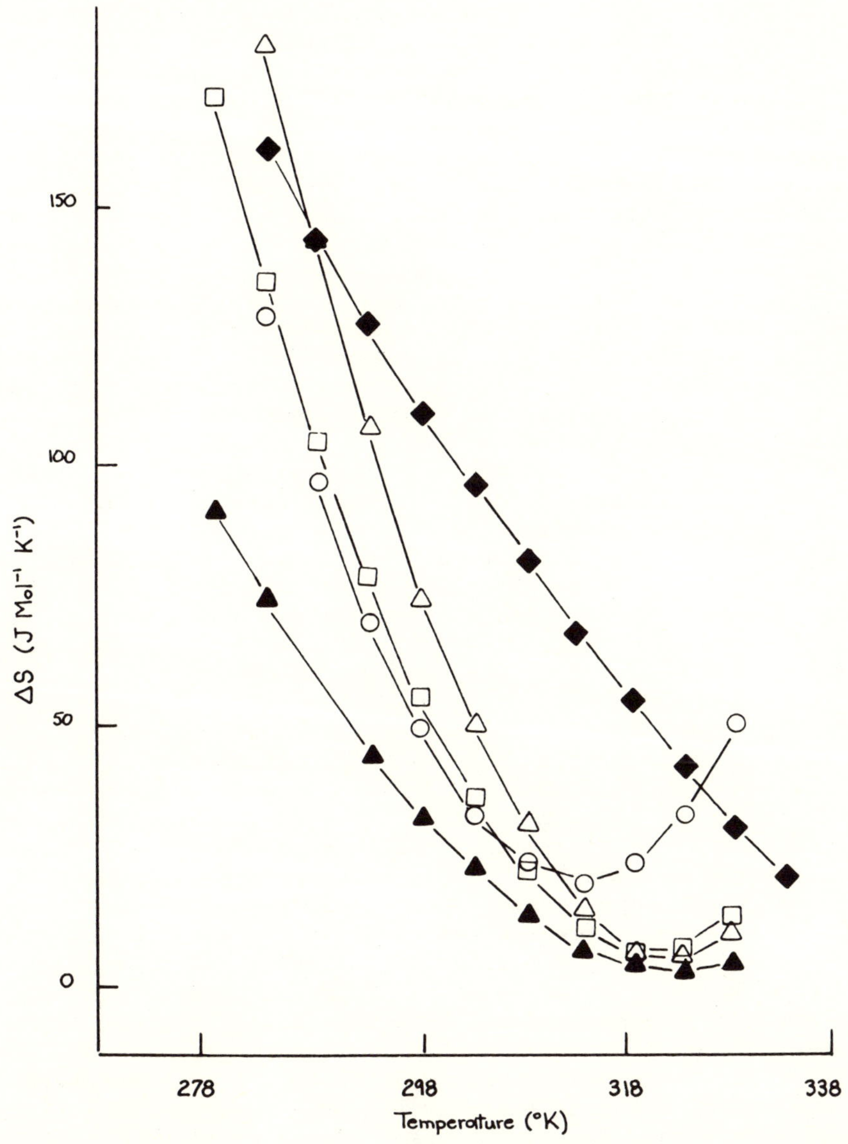

Figure 3. The change in ΔS_f with temperature. Legend as for Figure 1. ◆ benzyltriphenylphosphonium chloride - SDDS interaction.

function for n-propyl (compare promethazine to promazine) gives rise to a 1.6 fold increase in K_s and an increased solubility of the complex. The addition of a CH_2 group to the alkyl chain at R_{10} (compare promethazine to trimeprazine) produces a 3.4 fold decrease in K_s. These changes in K_s, expressed as $\Delta \log K_s$ correlate well with similar group values derived from partition coefficient measurements (1-octanol/water)[9].

In all cases we see that a 25°C $\Delta\Delta H_f$ is positive (and large for the case of CF_3) and it is the positive change in $\Delta\Delta S_f$, due to hydrophobic effects that give rise to the reduction of the solubility of the complex. At 40°C the $\Delta\Delta G_f$ values are little different to those at 25°C, however, the $\Delta\Delta H_f$ and $\Delta\Delta S_f$ values show a different picture. $\Delta\Delta H_f$ values for chloro- and CF_3 substitution are now negative and the $\Delta\Delta S_f$ values have fallen to a fifth of their values at 25°C. Hence it can be seen that at 40°C the effect of chloro- and CF_3 groups on solubility is through both electrostatic and hydrophobic effects. Interestingly for the CH_3 group in trimeprazine $\Delta\Delta H_f$ is still positive and $\Delta\Delta S_f$ is little changed from the value at 25°C. These results are a further clear illustration of the limited value of free energy data. The $\Delta\Delta G_f$ values listed in Table III are all within the range -2.0 to -3.5 kJ mol^{-1} and change little with temperature. In contrast the $\Delta\Delta H_f$ and $\Delta\Delta S_f$ values range from +10.1 to -1.5 kJ mol^{-1} and 44.4 to 4.4 J mol^{-1} K^{-1} respectively. The differences between R_{10} and R_2 substitution are clearly evident from the $\Delta\Delta H_f$ and $\Delta\Delta S_f$ values, whereas they are not from the $\Delta\Delta G_f$ values alone.

The change in ΔS_f with temperature is shown in Figure 3. It can be noted that ΔS_f falls progressively with rise in temperature to a minimum value and then rises again. In previous studies on the interaction of SDDS with various phosphonium cations ΔS_f has been found to fall monotonically with temperature and no evidence of a minimum was observed[2,3]. The nature of this minimum, that is reversal in the entropy values, is to be investigated further in future studies. We believe it reflects the tendency of the phenothiazines to undergo self-association, together with the possible formation of ion-pair or mixed micellar species. Florence and others have evaluated the micellar aggregation of phenothiazines using a variety of techniques[18,19,20]. They considered that in aqueous environment 10 monomers could become stacked vertically with the alkyl side chains and nitrogen groups alternating to form an approximately spherical unit in solution. Critical micelle values for the phenothiazines are listed in Table IV. In future studies we propose to investigate the possibility of mixed aggregates forming between SDDS and the phenothiazines. It should be noted, however, that the so called micelle formation by phenothiazine derivatives is probably rather different to micelle formation in a typical surfactant solution. Mittal and Mukerjee[21] have commented that there is an absence of strong cooperativity of self-association with the phenothiazines.

Table IV. Properties of the Phenothiazines.

Physical Properties

Phenothiazine	pKa	Log Partition Coefficient Chloroform pH 1	Log Partition Coefficient Dodecane pH 7	Log Partition Coefficient Octanol Free Base	Solubility Free Base Mol dm^{-3} $x10^{-3}$	Relative Surface Activity	CMC Mol dm^{-3} $x10^{-2}$		K_s $x10^{-9}$
Promazine	9.4	0.59	2.39	4.55	50	2.5	1.3	1.1	8.4
Chlorpromazine	9.3	1.09	2.56	5.16	8	1.0	0.3	0.4	2.6
Triflupromazine	9.2	1.30	2.92	5.19	5	0.24	0.25	--	2.4
Trimeprazine	---	1.06	---	---	--	1.8	--	0.95	3.9
Promethazine	9.1	-1.20	---	---	55	2.7	50	1.8	13.4
Reference	22	23	24	25	22	26	20	27	

Biological Activity

	Hemolytic Potency	Log K (Binding to BSA)
Promazine	0.36	3.45
Chlorpromazine	1.00	3.85
Triflupromazine	1.37	3.95
Trimeprazine	0.46	3.41
Promethazine	0.01	3.27
Reference	23	28

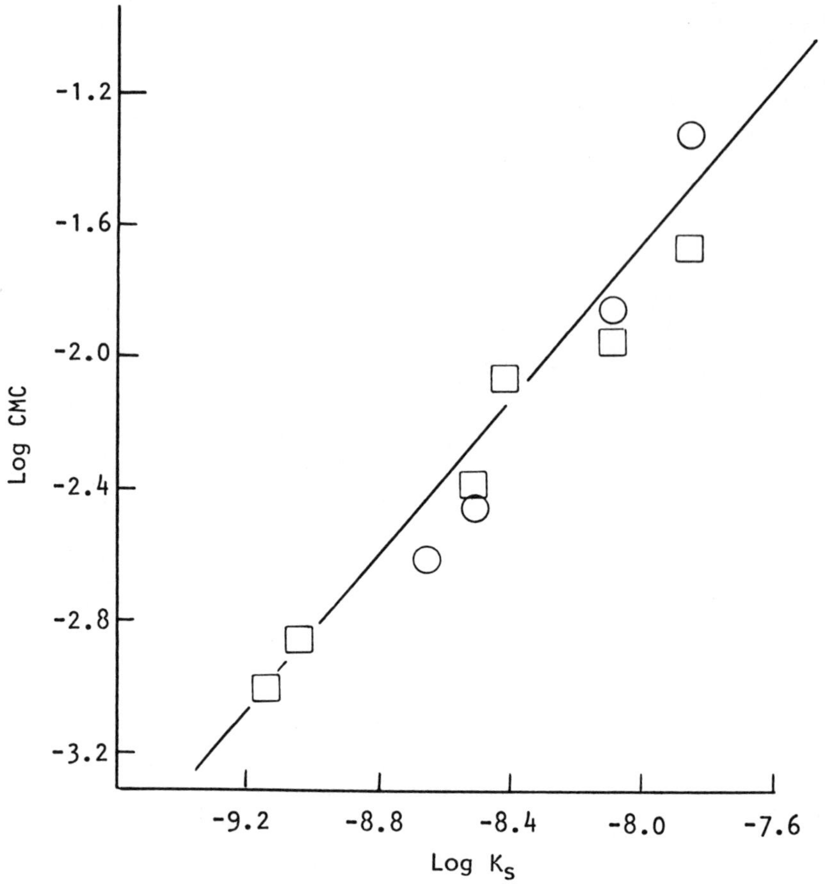

Figure 4. Correlation between log K_s and log CMC values. Data from References 20, 27. Additional K_s values taken from G. I. Mukhayer, Ph.D. Thesis, University of Aston, 1974.

The change of K_s with phenothiazine structure can be compared with similar changes that occur in other physical properties such as partition coefficients, solubility, surface activity and micelle formation (Table IV). It can be noted that in general the properties follow the order promethazine, promazine, trimeprazine, chlorpromazine, triflupromazine. The listed physical properties all reflect in different ways the interaction of the phenothiazine species with water and the change in hydrophobicity with change in chemical structure. A good correlation between log K_s and log CMC is shown in Figure 4.

The partition study of Murthy and Zografi[24] is of note.

Experiments were performed using two different organic solvents, dodecane and 1-octanol. For the latter solvent the authors investigated the ion-pair extraction of chlorpromazine as the methane, ethane and propane sulfonates. The extraction constant increased with increase in chain length sulfonate. Thoma and Arning[29] have found a linear relationship between the partition coefficients of phenothiazines (1-octanol and arachis oil/buffer) and surface tension values. Similarly Keipert et al.[27] have studied the effects of molecular modification on CMC values and have reported a correlation between these and the binding of phenothiazines to macromolecules (polyvinylpyrrolidone and dextran).

Relationships between the physical properties of phenothiazines and biological activity have been explored by Domino et al.[30] and Florence[31]. The increased hydrophobicity due to groups such as chloro- and CF_3 in the R_2 position are in good agreement with biochemical and biological response parameters. For example, Table IV lists relative hemolytic potency values and Baur[23] has demonstrated an excellent correlation between these parameters and therapeutic potency.

The Japanese group of Nambu and Nagai[28,32,33] have considered the adsorption and binding properties of phenothiazines. Binding data for the interaction of various species with bovine serum albumin (BSA) were well correlated with surface activity and partition coefficient data[28]. Some of their binding values are given in Table IV. Moreover, Nambu and Nagai[28] demonstrated an interesting relationship between binding constants and biological activity in the form of 5-hydroxytyptamine releasing activity of blood platelets and antiamphetamine, antiapomophine and antityptamine responses. Similar correlations could be obtained using the log K_s values for the 1:1 interaction between the phenothiazines and SDDS. Thus, the derived K_s values and the ΔH_f and ΔS_f terms might find value in structure-activity relationships of drugs and the prediction of active compounds.

REFERENCES

1. G. I. Mukhayer and S. S. Davis, J. Colloid Interface Sci., 53, 224, (1975).
2. P. H. Elworthy, A. T. Florence and C. B. MacFarlane, "Solubilization by Surface Active Agents," pp. 11, 217. Chapman and Hall Ltd., London 1968
3. B. W. Barry and G. M. T. Gray, J. Colloid Interface Sci., 52, 327, (1975).
4. G. I. Mukhayer and S. S. Davis, J. Colloid Interface Sci., 56, 350, (1976).
5. G. I. Mukhayer and S. S. Davis, J. Colloid Interface Sci., 59, 350, (1977).

6. E. Tomlinson and S. S. Davis, J. Colloid Interface Sci., 66, 335-344 (1978).
7. E. Tomlinson and S. S. Davis, in "Biological Activity and Chemical Structure," J. A. Keverling Buisman, Editor, Elsevier, Amsterdam, 1978.
8. E. Tomlinson and S. S. Davis, J. Pharm. Pharmacol., (Suppl.) 28, 75P, (1976).
9. C. Hansch in "Drug Design," E. J. Ariens, Editor, Vol. 1, p. 271, Academic Press, New York, 1971.
10. G. I. Mukhayerand S. S. Davis, J. Pharm. Pharmacol., (Suppl.) 24, 129P, (1973).
11. G. I. Mukhayer, S. S. Davis and E. Tomlinson, J. Pharm. Sci., 64, 147 (1975).
12. O. Exner, Coll. Czech. Chem. Commun., 40, 2762 (1975).
13. G. C. Kresheck in "Water, A Comprehensive Treatise," F. Franks, Editor, Vol. 4, p. 1, Plenum Press, New York, 1975.
14. G. Nemethy, Angew. Chem. Int., 6, 195, (1967).
15. R. M. Diamond, J. Phys. Chem., 67, 2513, (1963).
16. E. Lobos, Nature, 209, 201, (1966).
17. F. Franks, in "Water, A Comprehensive Treatise," F. Franks, Editor, Vol. 4, p. 1, Plenum Press, New York, 1975.
18. A. T. Florence and R. T. Parfitt, J. Phys. Chem., 75, 3554, (1971).
19. A. T. Florence and R. T. Parfitt, J. Pharm. Pharmacol. (Suppl.), 22, 121S, (1970).
20. D. Attwood, A. T. Florence and M. N. Gillan, J. Pharm. Sci., 63, 988, (1974).
21. K. L. Mittal and P. Mukerjee, in "Micellization, Solubilization and Microemulsions," K. L. Mittal, Editor, Vol. 1, p. 1, Plenum Press, New York, 1977.
22. A. L. Green, J.Pharm. Pharmacol., 19, 10, (1966).
23. E. W. Baur, J. Pharmacol. Exp. Ther., 177, 219 (1971).
24. K. S. Murthy and G. Zografi, J. Pharm. Sci., 59, 1281 (1970).
25. C. Hansch, "Partition Coefficient Data File," Claremont College, Pomona, California, 1975.
26. G. Zografi and M. V. Munshi, J. Pharm. Sci., 59, 819 (1970).
27. S. Keipert, J. Becker and R. Voight, Pharmazie, 31, 296 (1976).
28. N. Nambu and T. Nagai, Chem. Pharm. Bull., 20, 2463 (1972).
29. K. Thoma and M. Arning, Arch. Pharm., 309, 873 (1976).
30. E. F. Domino, R. A. Hudson and G. Zografi in "Drugs Acting on the Central Nervous System," A. Burger, Editor, Vol. 2, p. 327, Dekker, New York, 1968.
31. A. T. Florence, Adv. Colloid Interface Sci., 2, 115 (1968).
32. N. Nambu, S. Sakurai and T. Nagai, Chem. Pharm. Bull., 23, 1404 (1975).
33. N. Nambu, T. Nagai and H. Nogami, Chem. Pharm. Bull., 19, 1058 (1971).

ORDER-OF-MIXING EFFECTS IN SULFONATE SURFACTANT SOLUTIONS

P. B. Lorenz, M. B. Kayser, M. A. Hsieh, and M. K. Tham

U.S. Department of Energy
Bartlesville Energy Technology Center
Bartlesville, Oklahoma

Petroleum sulfonates in aqueous-alcohol solutions have properties that depend on the order of mixing of the components sulfonate/alcohol, water, and salt. A study of two such sulfonates is reported here. Amoco Floodaid 141, a proprietary sulfonate/alcohol blend, was investigated in 5.4% (active sulfonate) dispersions at final salinities between 0.10 and 0.30 mol $NaCl/dm^3$. Witco TRS 16 was investigated in 4.5% dispersions, comparing the effect of isobutyl alcohol, ethylene glycol monobutyl ether, and an ethoxylated pentanol at two concentrations and at salinities from 0.10 to 0.22 mol $NaCl/dm^3$. Observations were made of microscopic structure, along with viscosity, electrical conductance and reactance, stability, and phase behavior and interfacial tension with oil. With different mixing procedures, differences were observed that persisted in some cases well beyond a week. The two sulfonates behaved differently in some respects, but both showed order-of-mixing effects at the higher salinities. The order-of-mixing effects were associated with characteristic microscopic structures. For both sulfonates, the least-favorable mixing procedure was dispersing in water first and then adding salt.

INTRODUCTION

The Department of Energy is conducting a small field test of the surfactant technique for tertiary oil recovery. The surfactant was supplied in concentrated form by Amoco Chemical Co. under the trade name Floodaid 141. It was convenient to dilute the material in two steps, first commercially to 28% with equipment capable of handling the high-viscosity concentrate, and then in the field to 12% for injection. In lab-testing the product, we observed striking differences in the properties, depending on when salt was added in the overall mixing routine.[1,2] Viscosity and conductance showed the strongest effects. Also affected were the stability of the dispersions, and the phase volumes and interfacial tension on contact with oil. The differences often persisted for weeks.

Order-of-mixing effects for sulfonates have been noticed in many laboratories. The phenomenon was the subject of a patent by Mobil Oil.[3] Interpretation is made more difficult because the results are affected by mechanical treatment, by the details of the mixing procedure (for example, which liquid is stirred and which is poured), and by temperature.[4]

During the later stages of the present work, two papers from the University of Minnesota[5,6] were presented that supported the conclusions we were reaching: that a petroleum sulfonate disperses in a colloidal form that depends on the salt concentration first encountered. Memory effects when salt concentration is changed are caused by the slowness with which the colloidal form adjusts to a new salinity. Using spectroturbidimetry and studies with the polarizing microscope, the Minnesota group showed that the dispersed phase was birefringent and contained most of the surfactant. Our work uses microscopic observations in conjunction with viscosity and electrical measurements to investigate some additional properties and the influence of compositional parameters.

EXPERIMENTAL

A standard two-step procedure for preparation of sulfonate solutions was used in most cases. (The term "solution" is used loosely for a suspension or emulsion.) The first dispersion of the sulfonate/alcohol concentrate was made by dropwise addition to the stirred aqueous medium, so the sulfonate would immediately experience the salinity environment specified for this step. The second dilution was made by slow addition of brine or water to the mixture, so the change to final salinity would be monotonic. Preparation and storage were at ambient temperatures of 22 - 25° C. In most experiments the final mixtures were allowed to sit undisturbed between samplings. In the experiments on TRS 16 all mixtures were stirred gently or rotated (6 RPM), constantly, throughout the series of measurements.

For microscopic observation the sample was imbibed into a glass cell of internal dimensions 0.0002 x 0.0015 x 0.05 m, and the ends sealed with Apiezon grease. The cells were viewed about 2 hr after preparation, to allow liquid crystalline structures to re-form after flow into the cell. A Nomarski optical system was used at 160 X magnification. The strong illumination necessary caused thermal distrubances, so observations were kept brief.

Viscosity measurements were made at 25.0° C in a Wells-Brookfield cone and plate instrument, at several rotation rates depending on the viscosity level. Most of the fluids were thixotropic. The sample was "conditioned" by running at a standard shear rate until fairly stable, then briefly switching to another shear rate for measurement and restabilizing at the standard rate. Viscosities effective at 10 sec^{-1} are reported. When the data were linear on a log-log plot, the power law parameters were evaluated by least squares. Otherwise a graphical interpolation was made to get the value and slope at 10 sec^{-1}.

Electrical conductance was measured (at 25.0° C) in a Jones-type cell with lightly platinized electrodes. The measurements were made on a Foy-Martell bridge[7] with grounding and shielding appropriate for audio-frequencies. Readings were taken at several frequencies between 250 and 1000 hertz. The resistance changed with time rapidly at first, usually increasing several percent above the value taken when the cell was first filled. The reading at 20 minutes was arbitrarily adopted as a standard. Attempts to measure resistance while circulating fluid through the cell, or to get resistance as a function of shear rate in a capillary viscometer, failed to give stable results. Conductance must be regarded as a somewhat imprecise property.

Resistance data were drift-corrected and fitted to the impedance function of the equivalent circuit shown in Figure 1. The standard deviation of the data from the calculated curve was usually less than 2% of the difference between R_o and the measured resistances. The equivalent parallel capacitance did not appear to change with time.

Phase volumes were measured with dodecane as oil. Oil and surfactant were weighed into precision-bore tubes (0.00186m i.d.), which were stoppered and shaken vigorously for 30 sec on a modified particle-grinding machine. After 2 hr they were centrifuged at 20,000 G for 30 min, and again after 15 hr for 60 min. Boundary positions were measured with a cathetometer. This procedure did not achieve complete phase equilibrium, but was adequate for comparing order-of-mixing effects.

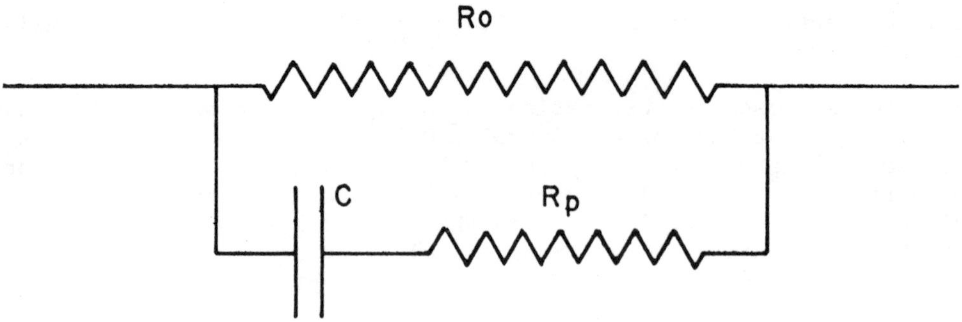

Figure 1. Equivalent circuit used to interpret conductance results. R_o is the resistance at infinite frequency. C, R_p are equivalent parallel capacitance and resistance.

Interfacial tensions were measured by the spinning drop method. To get prompt readings on transient systems, the fluids were not pre-equilibrated, but enough time was allowed in the measuring cell for the drop to reach constant dimensions.

RESULTS AND DISCUSSION

Further Studies on Floodaid 141

Floodaid 141 contains 45 wt% active sulfonate, as a blend of petroleum sulfonates with an average molecular weight of 450. It contains 15 wt% of Cosurfactant 121 (an ethoxylated pentanol), along with 20% unreacted oil, water, and a small amount of inorganic salts.

Figure 2 shows photomicrographs of the 28% Floodaid 141 solutions. The higher salt concentration (0.42 mol NaCl/dm^3) gave coarse structures. In water the material had a finer structure, but occurred in clumps. The structure in a solution of 0.15 mol NaCl/dm^3 was perhaps even finer. This is the optimum salt concentration[8] for this surfactant; that is, it gives the lowest interfacial tension and the most favorable phase relations for recovery of our crude oil.

When these 28% solutions were diluted to 12% in such a way that they all had the same salinity (Figure 3), the very coarse structures in the strong salt solution were converted to coarse grains ("brine first"). The clumps that formed in water persisted ("water first"). The material mixed with a solution of 0.15 mol NaCl/dm^3 and diluted with the "same brine" was very finely dispersed. Samples taken after several days indicated a slow trend toward same-

A B C

Figure 2. Photomicrographs of 28% dispersions of Floodaid 141, dispersed in: A NaCl solution at 0.42 mol/dm^3; B water; C NaCl solution at 0.15 mol/dm^3. Each field is 300 μm across.

A B C

Figure 3. The mixtures of Figure 2 after dilution. All three samples contain 12 wt-% Floodaid 141 at 0.132 mol $NaCl/dm^3$. A Brine first, "Br-1"; B Water first, "W-1"; C Dispersed and diluted in the same (0.15 mol/dm^3) brine, "SB".

ness; i.e., the "brine-first" structures grew a little finer and the "same-brine" structures grew a little coarser.

In work at Carnegie Mellon University[9] it was found that at low surfactant and salt concentration, there were discrete droplets of liquid crystal in a continuous brine phase. At high concentrations of surfactant and salt there was a single liquid crystalline phase. There was an intermediate region in which the dispersed phase was slowly transformed to a continuous phase. This was the region of optimum performance. The coarse structures seen in the stronger brine in Figure 2 were probably the single liquid crystalline phase, but otherwise our patterns under the microscope did not follow the same succession.

Figure 4 shows a salt scan of solutions made in one step at salinities up to half-normal. The region with the finest structure is the region where the viscosity starts increasing rapidly.

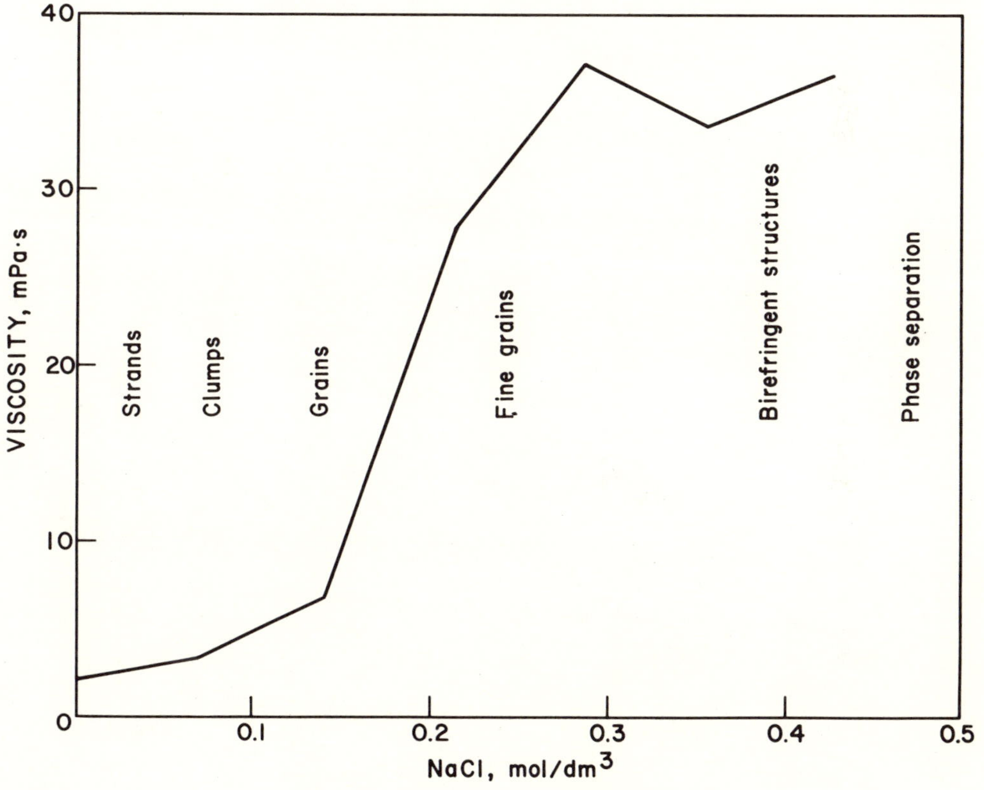

Figure 4. Viscosity and microscopic appearance of 12% Floodaid solution dispersed in one step.

Figure 5 shows the viscosities when solutions were made in two steps designed for several salinities. At low salinity there was little order-of-mixing effect. At high salinity the brine-first dilution gave low viscosity. The middle range is the interesting part of the salt scan. Around 0.15 mol NaCl/dm^3 the viscosity is still low although one might expect it to increase with smaller particles. Evidently interaction between particles is weak. When solutions are diluted into this region from higher or lower salinity, the viscosity is higher and particle size is larger.

One sample was stirred constantly. Its viscosity was higher than the corresponding stagnant sample, and increased faster with time. This represents a more rapid approach to final equilibrium.

Portions of the material from each preparation were set aside in tubes and watched for stability characteristics. After five days some tubes showed a tendency to clear in the top, indicating there were no particles fine enough to remain in suspension. Some

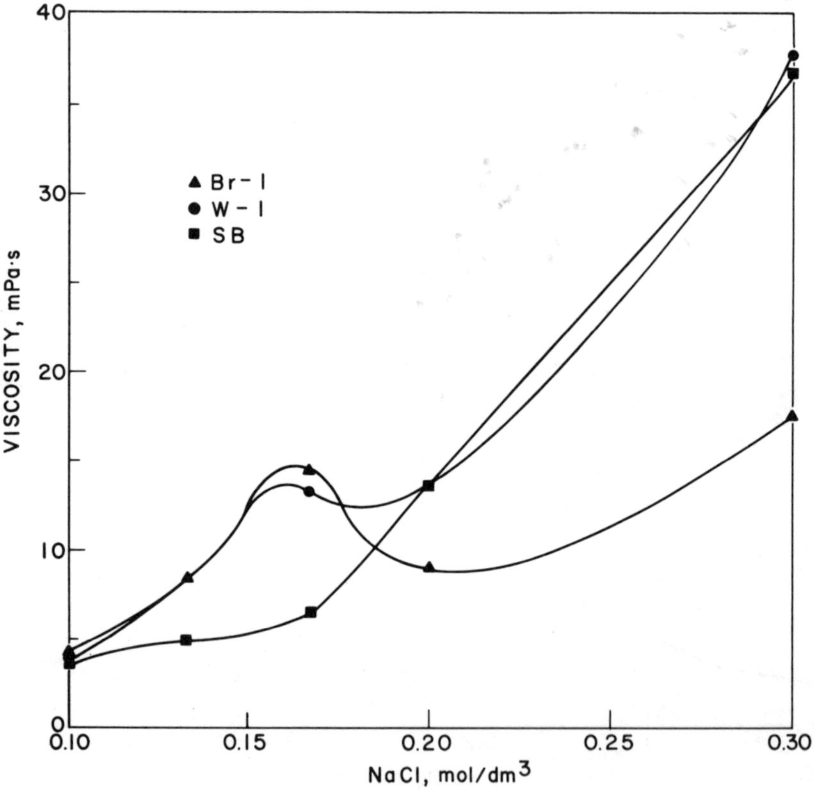

Figure 5. Viscosity of 12% Floodaid 141 solutions dispersed in two steps. Measured after 24 hr.

tubes had a sediment in the bottom, i.e., there were some particles settling faster due to size or density. The pattern was as shown:

	BRINE FIRST (Br-1)	WATER FIRST (W-1)	SAME BRINE (SB)
Clearing in top	None	⩾.20 mol/dm^3	⩾.13 mol/dm^3
Sedimentation in bottom	None	⩽.13	.10 (only)

When water-first preparations were made up at 0.13 mol NaCl/dm^3 or below, fines remained suspended in the top and sediment formed at the bottom. That is, there was a wide distribution of particle sizes. At higher final salinity, the reverse was true, so the distribution must have been narrowed. But in the brine-first preparation, microscopic observations showed large structures, so the lack of sediment suggests that liquid crystals were formed with density close to the isotropic liquid.

Other Sulfonates

Exploratory measurements were made on several systems, as shown in Table 1. All the surfactants are petroleum sulfonates, except the sodium dodecylbenzene sulfonate (SDBS), and Amoco 151 which is a sulfonated polybutene. All but SDBS contain unreacted oil.

Table 1. Sulfonate/Alcohol Systems at 0.15 mol NaCl/dm^3

	Sulfonate ave. molecular weight	Order of mixing effect
TRS 10-410/IBA[a]	420 (350 to 450)	small
TRS 18/Amoco 121[b]	525	too viscous to compare
TRS 18/EGBE[c]	525	no
TRS 40/Amoco 121	340	no
1840[d]/Amoco 121	451	yes
TRS 16/Amoco 121	473 (420 to 520)	yes
TRS 16/IBA, 2:1[e]	473	no
TRS 16/IBA, 10:1	473	yes
TRS X-101/IBA	418	no
Petrosteps/IBA	420, 450, & 465	no
Amoco 151/Amoco 121	452	no
SDBS[f]/IBA	348	no

a Isobutyl alcohol
b Ethoxylated pentanol
c Ethylene glycol monobutyl ether
d Mixture of TRS 18 and TRS 40
e Weight ratio
f Sodium dodecylbenzene sulfonate

A few generalizations can be drawn from the results. The alcohol had a strong influence on the order-of-mixing effect. The effect was frequently associated with a rapid increase in viscosity as salinity increased, and with a region of fine structure between regions of coarser surfactant structure. It was also frequently associated with high surfactant molecular weight.

A Study of TRS-16

TRS 16 was chosen for an investigation of salt, alcohol, and structural effects. This Witco product is 62% active, contains 33% unreacted oil, and only 0.5% inorganic salt.

Figure 6 shows the result of comparison of different alcohols. The ratio of alcohol to sulfonate on a molecular basis was about 1:0.9 in each case. Cosurfactant 121 gave the most favorable results, because there was a distinct mixing effect, and the viscosities were low. High viscosities are always more non-Newtonian and hard to reproduce.

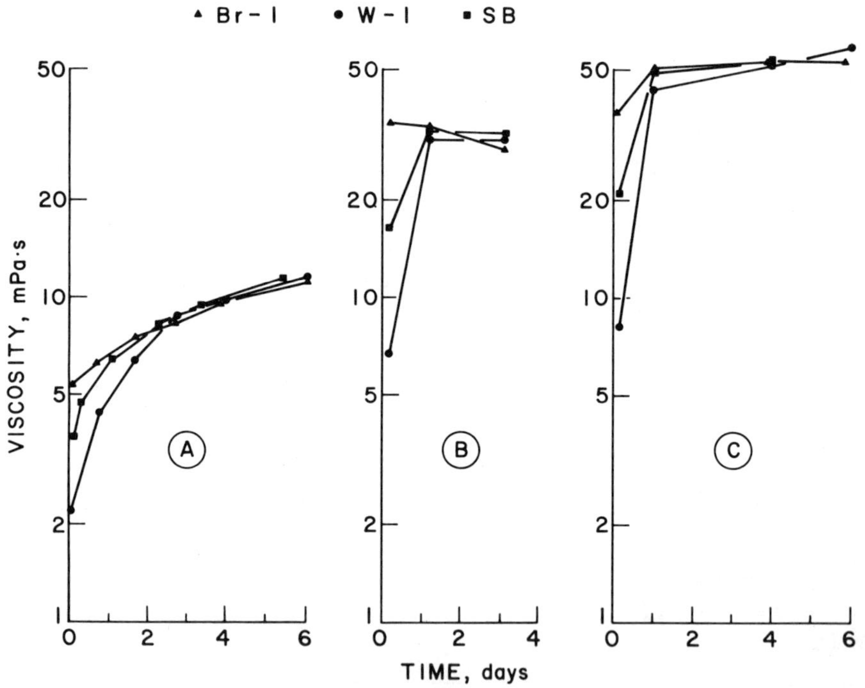

Figure 6. Viscosity of TRS 16 (4.1 wt-% active, 0.14 mol $NaCl/dm^3$) with various alcohols. Weight ratios: A TRS 16/Cosurfactant 121 = 5 (17% alcohol); B TRS 16/IBA = 9.7; C TRS 16/EGBE = 6.1.

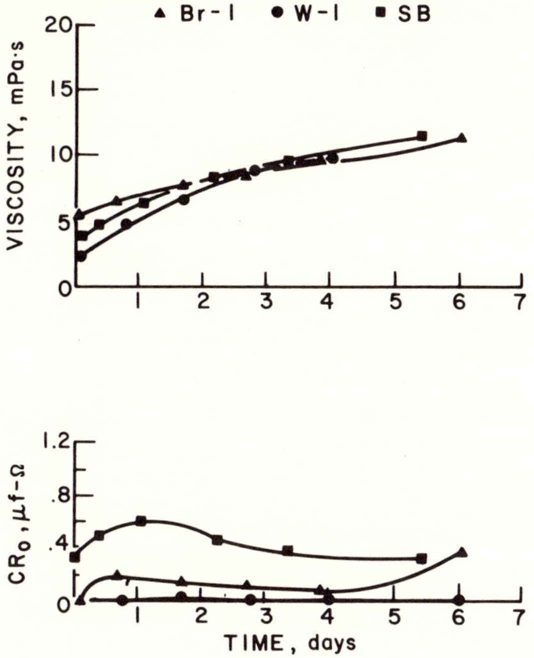

Figure 7. Viscosity and equivalent parallel capacitance (x R_o) of TRS 16 (4.1 wt-% active, 0.14 mol NaCl/dm^3) with Cosurfactant 121 (17% of concentrate).

Subsequent experiments were all done on the TRS 16/Cosurfactant 121 system. Figure 7 shows the results at 0.14 mol NaCl/dm^3 and 17% alcohol. (Values for alcohol content refer to the composition of the sulfonate/alcohol concentrate.) A small difference in viscosity disappeared after a few days, but the capacitance had differences that persisted: same-brine values positive, and water-first values staying at zero. The electrical conductance by itself was not very interesting. It seemed to be determined largely by viscosity changes. This effect overwhelmed any independent contributions of degree of ionization.

Figure 8 illustrates results at lower alcohol content and Figure 9 gives a synoptic view of the effects of salt and alcohol. Shown are the viscosities both when the solutions were first made up, and after the values had leveled off. Mixing effects are promoted by high salt and suppressed by high alcohol. This would be expected for the formation of liquid crystals. The low initial viscosity for water-first dilution is a general phenomenon for all sulfonate systems displaying order-of-mixing effects. Figure 10 shows the same-brine dilution had a high capacitance for all compositions of the TRS 16/Cosurfactant 121 system.

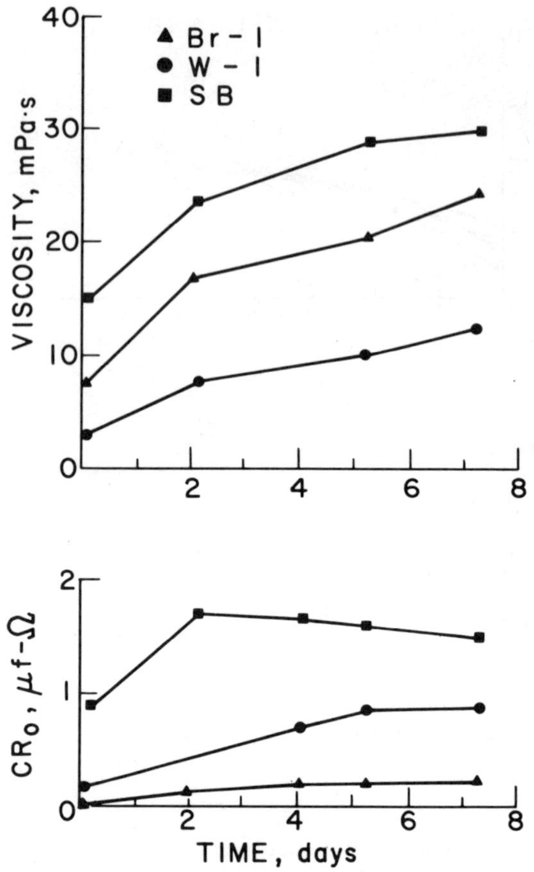

Figure 8. The system of Figure 7 with alcohol reduced to 10% of concentrate.

Some interpretation of these results is provided by the microscopic structure. Figure 11 shows samples after the first step of dispersion. The sample in half-normal brine separated into a surfactant phase and a clear, colorless phase. The surfactant phase was highly viscous and the dispersed colorless phase coalesced very slowly. It is drops of the colorless phase that are seen in Figure 11. The surfactant phase itself had no visible structure. The dispersion in water again consisted of clumps. As a matter of fact, it formed a macroscopic sediment in the container. The dispersion in 0.14 mol NaCl/dm^3 formed a uniform suspension, stable even on centrifugation.

Figure 12 shows that these characteristics persist on dilution.

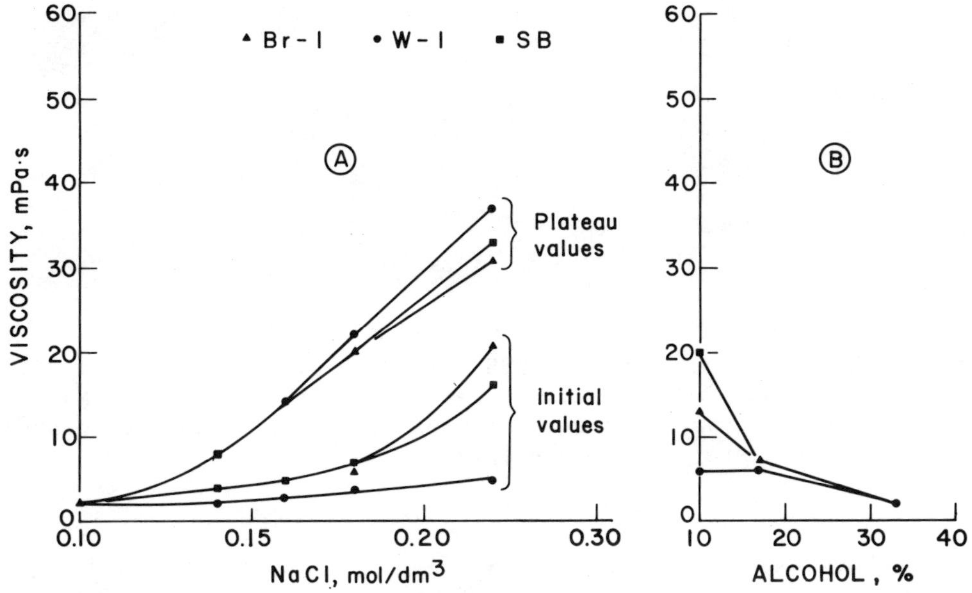

Figure 9. The effect of salt and alcohol concentration on viscosity of TRS 16 (4.1 wt-% active). A 17% Cosurfactant 121; B 0.14 mol $NaCl/dm^3$, 30-hr values.

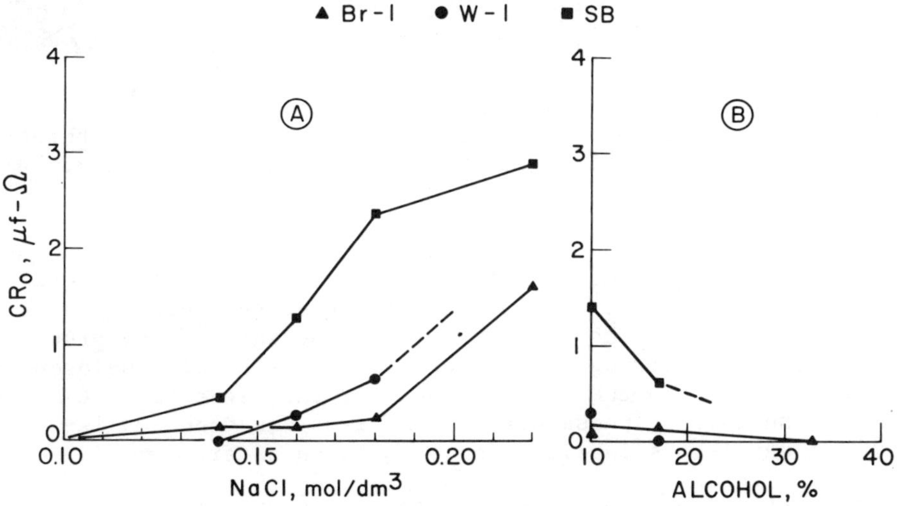

Figure 10. The effect of salt and alcohol concentration on equivalent parallel capacitance (x R_o) of TRS 16 (4.1 wt-% active). A 17% Cosurfactant 121; B 0.14 mol $NaCl/dm^3$, 30-hr values.

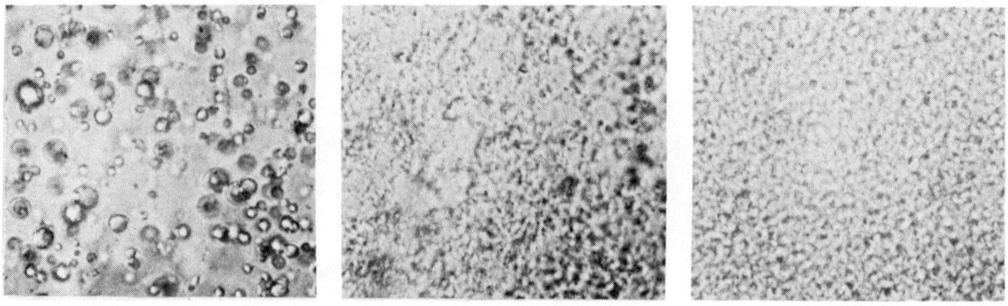

A B C

Figure 11. Photomicrographs of TRS 16/10% Cosurfactant 121. A 27%, at 0.504 mol NaCl/dm^3; B 9.25% in water; C 6.66% at 0.14 mol NaCl/dm^3. (Percentage values are the amount of weight of the sulfonate/alcohol concentrate in the samples.)

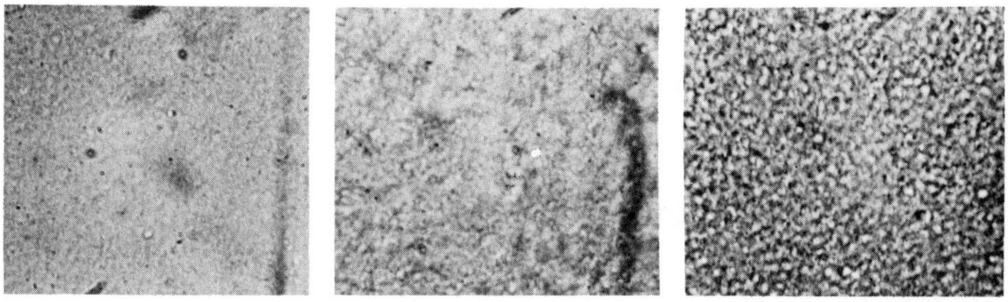

A B C

Figure 12. The mixtures of Figure 11 after dilution. All three samples contain 4.1 wt-% active TRS 16 at 0.14 mol NaCl/dm^3.

Figure 13 shows the results of phase volume tests. There were five major layers; an oleic layer, three surfactant layers, and a bottom phase. The bottom phase in the water-first preparation was cloudy and birefringent. Nevertheless, it seemed analogous to the aqueous layer in the other tubes. If this is a correct assumption, the surfactant phase with water-first was much smaller, that is, there was less solubilization of oil and water.

The water-first system had a slightly higher interfacial tension than the other two: 40 x 10^{-6}N/m vs 30 x 10^{-6}. The same trend was observed at Minnesota,[5,6] but is opposite to that reported by Mobil.[3]

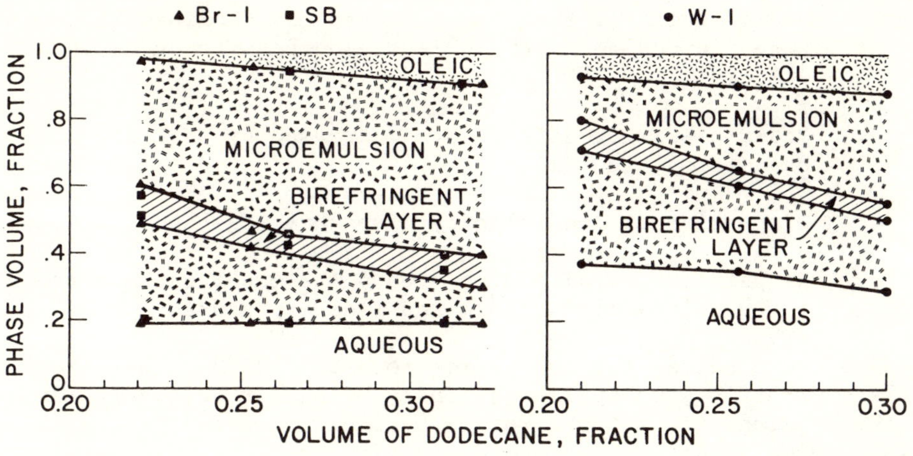

Figure 13. Phase volumes of TRS 16 (4.1 wt-% active, with 10 wt-% of Cosurfactant 121 in concentrate, at 0.14 mol $NaCl/dm^3$) with dodecane. The entire microemulsion phase was somewhat birefringent, but the central layer was more so.

CONCLUSIONS

We have looked in detail at only two sulfonates. TRS-16 behaves differently from Floodaid 141, but they do have some features in common. Neither showed an order-of-mixing effect at final salinity of 0.1 mol $NaCl/dm^3$. Both had a fine-grained structure around 0.14 mol $NaCl/dm^3$ and a rapid increase in viscosity above this concentration. They both formed heterogeneous structures in water that gave an unstable suspension with low viscosity. These properties of water-first preparations, along with the phase behavior and the interfacial tension, are all unfavorable.

The high capacitance of the same-brine dilution with TRS 16 suggests that the stability was due to electrical charges on the particles. The low viscosity would then be characteristic of a lyophobic colloid. The initial low viscosity of water-first samples would be like a coagulated lyophobic colloid. If these speculations are correct, the dispersions in the mid-range of salinity and the lyophilic liquid crystalline dispersions at high salinity differ in more than degree.

We have shown:

1. Order-of-mixing effects seen with petroleum sulfonate solutions include differences in viscosity, electrical properties, stability, phase behavior with oil, and interfacial tension.

2. Microscopic observations indicate that colloidal structures formed on initial dispersion persist on further dilution.

3. Order-of-mixing effects are increased by salt and decreased by alcohol.

4. Dispersion at low salinity gives heterogeneous structures.

5. Dispersion at salinities around the usual optimum range gives relatively uniform and fine structures.

One can conclude for the sulfonates studied that they should be mixed directly with optimum-salinity brine for best performance, and that mixing with water first is harmful. Order-of-mixing effects must be taken into account in designing the optimum surfactant formulation, and in considering the influence on surfactant of salinity changes encountered in the reservoir.

REFERENCES

1. C. J. Walker, F. W. Burtch, R. D. Thomas, and P. B. Lorenz, Oil and Gas J. 74 (39), 60 (1976).
2. R. D. Thomas, C. J. Walker, and F. W. Burtch, in "Proc. Third ERDA Symposium on Enhanced Oil and Gas Recovery," Vol 1, p. A-7, Petroleum Publishing Co., Tulsa, Okla., 1977.
3. P. M. Dunlap and H. L. Townsend, Canadian Patent 887,470 (1971).
4. M. B. Kayser, P. B. Lorenz, R. D. Thomas, and M. K. Tham, paper presented at Pentasectional Meeting of the American Chemical Society, Norman, Okla., March, 1977.
5. E. I. Franses, H. T. David, W. G. Miller, and L. E. Scriven, Preprints, Div. of Petroleum Chem. American Chemical Society, 23 (2), 644 (1978).
6. J. E. Puig, H. T. Franses, H. T. Davis, W. G. Miller, and L. E. Scriven, Preprint 7055, Symposium on Improved Oil Recovery, p. 189, Society of Petroleum Engineers of A.I.M.E., Dallas, Tex., 1978.
7. W. L. Foy and A. E. Martell, Rev. Sci Instrum. 19, 628 (1948).
8. R. L. Reed and R. N. Healy in "Improved Oil Recovery by Surfactant and Polymer Flooding," D. O. Shah and R. S. Schechter, Editors, p. 383, Academic Press, New York, 1977.
9. C. A. Miller and T. Fort, Jr., U.S. Dept. of Energy Report SAN/0018-3, available from National Technical Information Service, Springfield, Va., 1977.

PHASE DIAGRAMS OF SURFACTANT SYSTEMS - THE SYSTEM WATER-HYDROCARBON - OXYETHYLATED - n-DECANOL

K. J. Lissant and G. M. Bradley

Petrolite Corporation

St. Louis, Missouri 63119

Ternary systems of water, hydrocarbon and non-ionic surfactant were studied for a series of oxyethylated n-decanols made by commercial techniques. A commercial aliphatic hydrocarbon solvent, Shellflex 131, was used as the oil phase. The series consisted of seven samples with two to seven moles of ethylene oxide/mole of decanol plus one sample from which unreacted decanol was removed by vacuum distillation. Chain length distributions were determined by gas chromatography. Phase diagrams were obtained at 25°C and five regions were found: two liquid crystal, two micellar and one O/W dispersion. The data show that phase diagram techniques can be extended to commercial grade materials and that the results parallel those obtained for pure surfactants.

INTRODUCTION

Although phase diagrams are recognized as an important tool in studying oil/water/surfactant systems, few studies have been reported using non-ionic surfactants. n-Dodecanol ethers have been studied most extensively. Harusawa, Nakamura and Mitsui[1] studied monodisperse pentaoxyethylene dodecylether at 10°, 30°, 40°, and 60° C. Mitsui and Machida[2] measured solubilization with a number of surfactants, including dodecyl ethers with 3, 5, 10, and 20 moles of ethylene oxide/mole of alcohol. Smirnova, Koretskii and Sokolvskaya[3] studied micelle formation and water solubilization of dodecyl ethers with 1.9, 3.1, 4.0, and 5.2 moles of ethylene oxide/mole of alcohol.

Most studies have been conducted with carefully purified surfactants, using pure hydrocarbons. We wished to see whether phase diagram techniques could give meaningful results when applied to commercial grade materials. We therefore used surfactants made by commercial techniques and selected as a hydrocarbon a well known commercial solvent.

EXPERIMENTAL

Alfol-10, a Conoco product which is greater than 98% n-decanol, was reacted with ethylene oxide catalyzed by sodium hydroxide in a pilot scale reactor. The oxide was added in stages to produce seven samples ranging from .55 to 2.0 weights of ethylene oxide per weight of Alfol-10. The average compositions are shown in Table 1 as ratios of ethylene oxide to decanol. The mole ratios were computed directly from the weight ratios. Part of sample S-52 was distilled under vacuum to remove unreacted decanol. The distillate was 18% v/v of the original sample and contained 88% n-decanol. The distilled sample is designated S-52P.

Chain length distributions were determined by gas chromatography with a flame ionization detector at 340°C. The column was 4' x 1/8"SS, 3% OV-1 on 80/100 Chromosorb G (HP). The temperature was programmed from 70° to 300° at 4 degrees/minute. Individual oxyethylene n-mer peaks were well separated and were digitally integrated. Results are shown in Figure 1, in which the area percents have been normalized and the length of each segment is proportional to the reduced percentage of the species with the given degree of polymerization. Unreacted decanol is shown cross-hatched. The various molecular weight averages could not be calculated since individual response factors were not available and the gas chromatographic data were biased in favor of lower molecular weights. The calculated weight average molecular weight of the distilled sample, S-52P, was the same as that of S-54, the next higher member of the series.

Table 1. Compositions of Oxyethylated n-Decanol Samples, Expressed as Ethylene Oxide (EO) Added per Unit of Decanol.

Sample Number	Moles EO	Weight EO
S-50	2.0	0.55
S-52	2.7	0.75
S-54	3.6	1.0
S-55	4.5	1.25
S-57	5.4	1.5
S-59	6.3	1.75
S-61	7.2	2.0

The oil used for the phase diagrams was Shellflex 131, a commercial aliphatic solvent from Shell Oil Company, which is low in aromaticity with over 78% aliphatic hydrocarbons and an estimated average molecular weight of 270. Detailed characterization data is available from Shell Oil Co.

The phase diagram data were obtained by placing measured volumes of the surfactant, Shellflex 131, and water into glass tubes. The tubes were stoppered and the contents thoroughly mixed. The tubes were thermally equilibrated in a water bath at 25°C, inspected, remixed, and again allowed to equilibrate. The process was repeated as necessary until no further changes were observed.

Once a constant state was achieved, the number of observable phases were recorded. The tubes were inspected between crossed polarizing filters for anisotropy. Clear, one phase, compositions were tested with a two-wire probe for electrical conduction. Opaque compositions were also tested for conduction to determine whether the external phase was "oil" or "water". Other observations such as color, opalescence and viscosity were also recorded.

The states observed in the tubes may be classified into five general types:

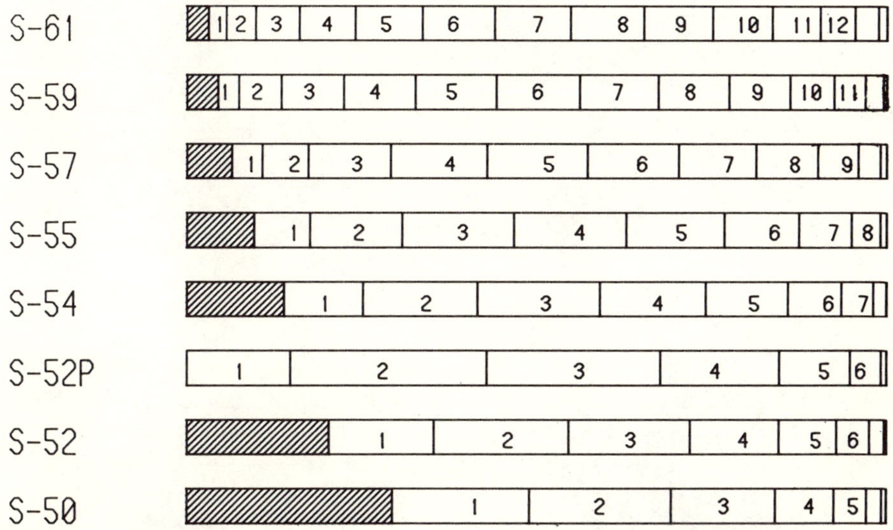

Figure 1. Chain-length distributions of oxyethylated n-decanol samples as determined by gas chromatography. Bars are denoted by the degree of polymerization of the given oligomers and their lengths are proportional to the normalized area percents. Decanol is shown cross-hatched.

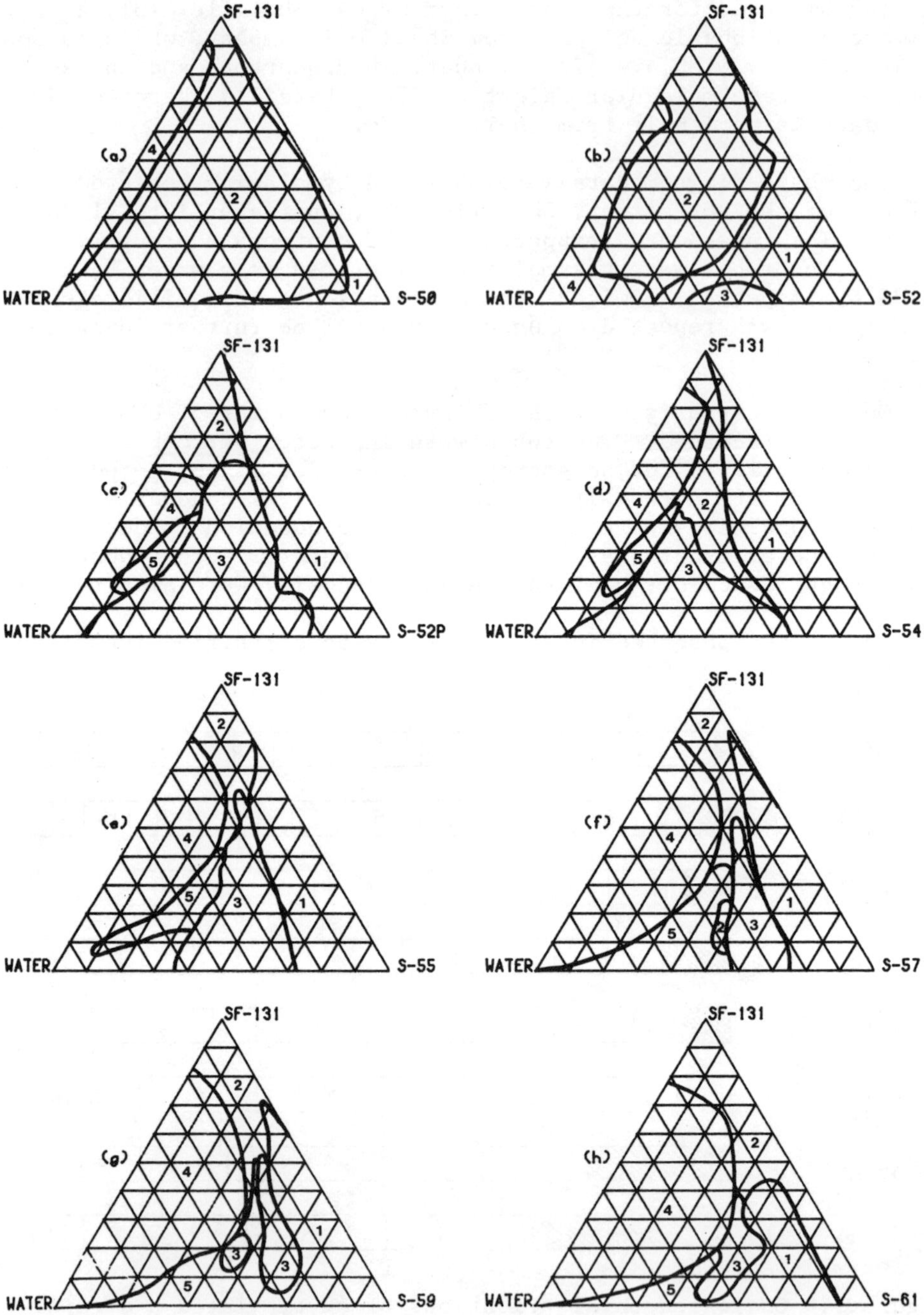

Figure 2. Phase diagrams of the system water-Shellflex 131-oxyethylated decanols. The numbers within the ternary diagrams are the phase designations as defined in the text.

Type One is single phase, clear, isotropic and nonconductive or slightly conductive and is considered to be an inverse micellar phase or a phase in which oil and water are solubilized in an excess of surfactant.

Type Two separates into two clear phases.

Type Three is anisotropic, clear or hazy and conductive and is probably a liquid crystal phase.

Type Four is stable dispersion which is opaque, white and conductive. At the lower phase ratios creaming occurs, but the cream layer, which rises to the top, is stable. Clearly the dispersion is oil-in-water.

Type Five is single phase, clear, isotropic, and conductive and is considered to be a normal micellar phase, in which oil may be solubilized.

The data points, characterized by type and composition, were plotted by computer on a triangular diagram. Lines encompassing regions of common type were drawn by hand. Questionable borders were checked. Each final phase diagram (Figures 2a-2h) is a composite of 300-400 data points. The raw data is available in tabular form from the authors.

DISCUSSION

The first member of the series (Figure 2a) is a rather poor surfactant. Region 2 occupies the majority of the phase diagram. The next compound (Figure 2b) has a greatly expanded region 1 and s small region 3 near the water-surfactant side. Figure 2c is quite different from Figure 2b; region 3 occupies approximately half the phase diagram and a small region 5 is present. Figure 2d, however, is similar to Figure 2c, in that the same five regions are present in roughly the same places on the phase diagrams. Region 3 is larger in Figure 2c than in Figure 2d.

In the next phase diagram (Figure·2e), region 3 has narrowed and now points toward the oil corner. The regular micellar region 5 is larger and extends practically to the water corner. In Figure 2f the anisotropic region 3 is narrower and does not extend as far toward the oil corner. Region 5 is now larger and extends to the water/surfactant side of the phase diagram. Region 1 is not much changed but has pulled away from the oil/surfactant side; that is, the surfactant is not soluble in oil but a small amount of water allows micelles to form resulting in clear solutions. A separate region 2 has appeared but our experiments were not sufficiently detailed to find a connection, if any, to the other region 2.

In the next phase diagram (Figure 2g) is a smaller region 3 which no longer extends to the water/surfactant side. A separate anisotropic region has appeared adjacent to region 4. The other three regions are not much changed except that 5 and 1 are now connected, throwing doubt on our simple nomenclature for region 5 and 1 as normal and inverse micelles. A smooth transition as in Figure 2g requires a more complex structure. At levels of oil greater than 4%, a liquid crystal region exists between regions 1 and 5, as would be expected.

The last member of the series, S-61, solubilizes less (Figure 2h) than its immediate predecessors. Both 5 and 1 regions are smaller and connected as before. In the 1 region, 5-10% water is required for a clear solution. Only one anisotropic region 3 is present which we believe to be the anisotropic region appearing for the first time in Figure 2g since this region 3 is connected to the dispersion region 4 and the trend of the other anisotropic region was to decline. The 4 region has gradually increased with increasing ethylene oxide content to occupy, in this case, half the phase diagram.

The phase diagrams in Figure 2 are well-defined, in the sense that distinct phase boundaries exist, and display regular trends. We must, however, compare our results with those from pure systems to decide whether the behaviors are the same. In our series, the water solubilization region (type one) was largest for S-52, the 2.7 mole adduct, while the oil solubilization region (type five) was largest for S-57, the 5.4 mole adduct. In the case of dodecyl ethers[2] the 5 mole adduct solubilized more than the 3 mole or 10 mole adducts, although the phase diagrams do not distinguish between our regions 1, 3, and 5. Another group reported[3] that solubilization of water was much greater for a 3.1 mole adduct than for a 1.9 mole adduct, with a 4.0 mole adduct being slightly poorer. If the first workers were observing oil solubilization, then the reported results for dodecyl ethers are consistent with our results for decyl ethers.

Our phase diagrams may be compared with those of Marusawa, Nakamura and Mitsui[1]. Figure 2f resembles closely the phase diagram of monodisperse pentaoxyethylene dodecyl ether ($C_{12}E_5$) at 30°C[1]. Further comparisons are consistent with the well-known inverse relationship between temperature and oxyethylene chain length. Our two 3 regions correspond to the phases designated by Harusawa, Nakamura, and Mitsui as LC_1 with hexagonal structure and LC_2 with lamellar structure. The liquid crystal region present in Figure 2a-2f corresponds to LC_2. In Figure 2g the small region 3 adjoining region 4 must be LC_1, since the other region 3 is separated from region 4 as in Figure 2b-2f. By the same logic, the region 3 in Figure 2h is LC_1 and the lamellar phase is not present.

In comparing commercial materials with pure mono-disperse surfactants two differences must be considered, polydispersity and unreacted alcohol. In our series the polydispersity and average molecular weight increase as the amount of n-decanol decreases. Comparison of Figure 2b with Figure 2c indicates the presence of unreacted n-decanol supresses the formation of certain phase regions. Comparison of Figure 2c with Figure 2d, which are of similiar average molecular weight, indicates that average molecular weight is of more importance than degree of polydispersity. Comparison of Figure 2c with the published data on pure n-dodecanol derivatives further strengthens this postulate.

In this paper we have shown that phase diagrams of commercial surfactants with water and commercial solvents can be obtained and that the results parallel those obtained with pure materials. Hence, phase diagrams techniques are useful for investigating commercial products.

ACKNOWLEDGEMENTS

We wish to express our appreciation to Bill Cheng and his pilot plant staff for preparing samples, to Jack Ludwig for gas chromatographic analyses and to Bill Paley for vacuum distillation.

REFERENCES

1. F. Harusawa, S. Nakamura, and T. Mitsui, Colloid. Polym. Sci. 252, 613 (1974).
2. T. Mitsui and Y. Machida, J. Soc. Cosmet. Chem. 20, 199 (1969).
3. A. V. Smirnova, A. F. Koretskii and N. A. Sokolovskaya, Kolloidn. Zh. 38, 726 (1976).

TOLERANCE OF PETROLEUM SULFONATES TO THE PRESENCE OF CALCIUM IONS

M.J. Meister*, C.A. Wilson, and A.G. Collins

Department of Energy, Bartlesville Energy Research Center

P. O. Box 1398, Bartlesville, OK 74003

The calcium tolerance of 22 commercially available petroleum sulfonates ranged from 250 to 3000 ppm calcium. We defined calcium tolerance to be the point at which 5 wt.% of the total sulfonate in an aqueous solution was precipitated by calcium ions. Specifically, the level of calcium tolerated increased logarithmically as the average equivalent weight (AEW) of the sulfonates decreased,

$$\log Ca = 0.67 - 0.0057\ AEW.$$

Certain blends of the petroleum sulfonates tolerated higher concentrations of calcium ions than were expected. Sodium also precipitated, perhaps as a coprecipitate or an occlusion. The sulfonates were mixed with varying amounts of calcium and allowed to react at 30°C. Each sample contained 3 wt.% active sulfonate. After removal of the precipitate by centrifuging and filtering, the amount of unreacted sulfonate was determined indirectly, by measuring the calcium and sodium concentrations remaining in solution by atomic absorption spectrophotometry. Precipitation of petroleum sulfonates by multivalent cations (e.g., calcium ions) removes the valuable surfactant from surfactant floods used for enhanced oil recovery. Scarcely any previous work has been done on surfactant depletion by multivalent cations.

*Present Address: Department of Chemical Engineering, University of Florida, Gainesville, Florida 32611 U.S.A.

INTRODUCTION

One major problem with anionic surfactant floods, for enhanced oil recovery (EOR) is the loss of surfactant to precipitation by multivalent cations[1]. Multivalent cations may be present in the water used in preparing the surfactant flood. They may be introduced by water already present in the reservoir, which comes in contact with the surfactant flood, or they may be dissolved or introduced by ion exchange from the reservoir rock itself. Brine preflushes to remove multivalent cations are not always effective[2].

High concentrations of multivalent cations can deplete enough surfactant from the flood to make this method of oil recovery uneconomical. Hence surfactants for EOR should be able to tolerate significant concentrations of multivalent cations. Such surfactants could greatly increase the number of reservoirs in which a surfactant flood can be used successfully.

Surfactant loss by precipitation from the oil recovery flood is not the only factor considered when designing the flood; other factors also affect oil recovery. The ability of the flood to 1) recovery oil (lowering interfacial tension between oil and the surfactant flood) 2) move through the reservoir (dispersion characteristics), and 3) resist loss through adsorption onto the reservoir rock must also be considered.

Petroleum sulfonates, selected for this study, are widely used by industry in tertiary (enhanced) oil recovery systems; hence, they are more likely candidates for EOR.

The research described in this paper compared 22 commercially available surfactants by their tolerances to precipitation by calcium ions, the most abundant multivalent cation in a reservoir. Sixteen of the surfactants studied were sodium petroleum sulfonates. And three of these petroleum sulfonates were blends of the other 13 petroleum sulfonates. The rest of the surfactants were sodium salts of four synthetic sulfonates and their blends. The literature[3] reports that one of the four, sodium isobutene sulfonate (Amoco Sulfonate 151), is exceptionally tolerant to multivalent cations.

Table I lists all the surfactants and specifies the included amounts of oil and salt reported by the producers. No additional oil, salt, or cosurfactant was employed in any of the following tests.

Table I Commercial Sodium Petroleum Surfactants

Key to Figures 1, 4, 5, and 6	Petroleum Sulfonate	Average Equivalent Weight+	Composition of Supplied Sulfonate Mixtures+			Control Number or Sample Number	Comment
			wt% Sulfonate	wt% Salt	wt% Oil		
A-390	Conoco A-390 Na Sulfonate	540	20.5	0.5	2.0	8656 I	
MH	Morco H-62	520	62.0	0.4	34.0		
W 18	Witco Petronate TRS-18	495	62	0.5	33	45989	
DNNS	King Nasul SS	483	50				Sodium Dinonyl Naphthalene Sulfonate
SR	Shell Sodium Sulfonates-Regular 85100	465	62.5	0.7		S-76-310	
P465	Stepan Petrostep Sulfonate 465	465	57.8	2.7	24.0	413	
MM	Morco M-62	465	62.0	0.4	34.0		
P450	Stepan Petrostep Sulfonate 450	450	59.6	2.0	13.5	381	
CB 450	Conoco 450 EW Na Sulfonate Blend	450	24.4	0.9	2.5	86581	Blend of A-390 and N5B
10-410	Witco Petronate TRS 10-410	(422)	(62)	(0.4)	(32.2)	45992	
AM-151	Amoco Sulfonate 151	420	47-52	15 max	8-18	T-77-119	Sodium isobutene sulfonate
P420	Stepan Petrostep Sulfonate 420	420	60.0	4.7	15.6	484	
12B	Witco Petronate TRS 12B	410	62	3.5	15	45991	
CB 408	Conoco 408 EW Na Sulfonate Blend	408	32.5	1.2	2.8	8657 I	Blend of A-390 and N5B
10-80	Witco Petronate TRS 10-80	405	80	0.7	11.3	37096	
PDBS	Stepan Pentadecyl Benzene Sulfonate	(390.6)	75	1.5-3.5			Sodium pentadecyl benzene sulfonate
N5B	Conoco N5B Na Sulfonate	360	52.9	2.2	4.2	8655 I	
DDBS	Cities Service Sul-Fon-Ate AA-10	(348.5)	96.0	2.0	0		Sodium dodecyl benzene sulfonates
W40	Witco Petronate TRS 40	335	40-43	12 max	18 max	45993	

\+ Data provided by the Suppliers of the sulfonates.
( ) Data not provided by the Suppliers.

EXPERIMENTAL

Sample Preparation

We prepared a 10 wt.% active sulfonate solution from each of the supplied commercial petroleum sulfonate mixtures, and stirred it for three days for complete dispersal. Suppliers values for wt.% active sulfonate in the original mixture were used. See Table I. The samples for our tests were mixed in the following order:

weighed amounts of the 10 wt.% sulfonate solution, then of a calcium solution, plus boiled (carbon dioxide free) distilled water. Each test sample was 3 wt.% active sulfonate (L_{total}).

Calcium concentration, present in successive samples, varied from zero up to 0.075M (3000 ppm) calcium (Ca_{total}). The upper limit depended on the sulfonate being studied. We placed each sample under a nitrogen atmosphere, then in a water bath at 30.0 $\pm$ 0.3°C, for three days. A prepared sulfonate blank, no calcium added, allowed measurement of the amount of calcium (and sodium) originally in the sulfonate mixture.

Sample Separation

After equilibration the samples were centrifuged, then again placed in the bath to return to equilibrium. To separate the precipitate from the supernatant solution, most samples were filtered through a millipore membrane, 0.45 or 0.65 μm MF. Some of the high average equivalent weight sulfonate samples, however, required 1.2μm or even 5.0μm membranes. In each case we used the finest membrane which allowed the supernatent liquid to filter easily.

Approximately half of the samples were not centrifuged. These early samples produced a greater scatter in the data than the later centrifuged samples, (however, each of the curves in Figure 1 contain several centrifuged points).

The sample blanks were not centrifuged or filtered.

Sample Analysis

The amount of unprecipitated sulfonate was determined indirectly by measuring the amount of calcium and sodium left in the filtrate. We tested for calcium and sodium on a Perkin-Elmer atomic absorption spectrophotometer, model 403*, using the standard addition method and the instrument settings suggested by Perkin-Elmer[4]. Sodium was measured at 330.2 nm. Lanthanum, suggested by Perkin-Elmer to control ionization and ion interferences while measuring calcium, precipitates the sulfonate. We followed Ward and Biechler's[5] suggestion of substituting sodium for lanthanum in the calcium analysis.

*Reference to specific brands of equipment is made for identification only and does not imply endorsement by the Department of Energy.

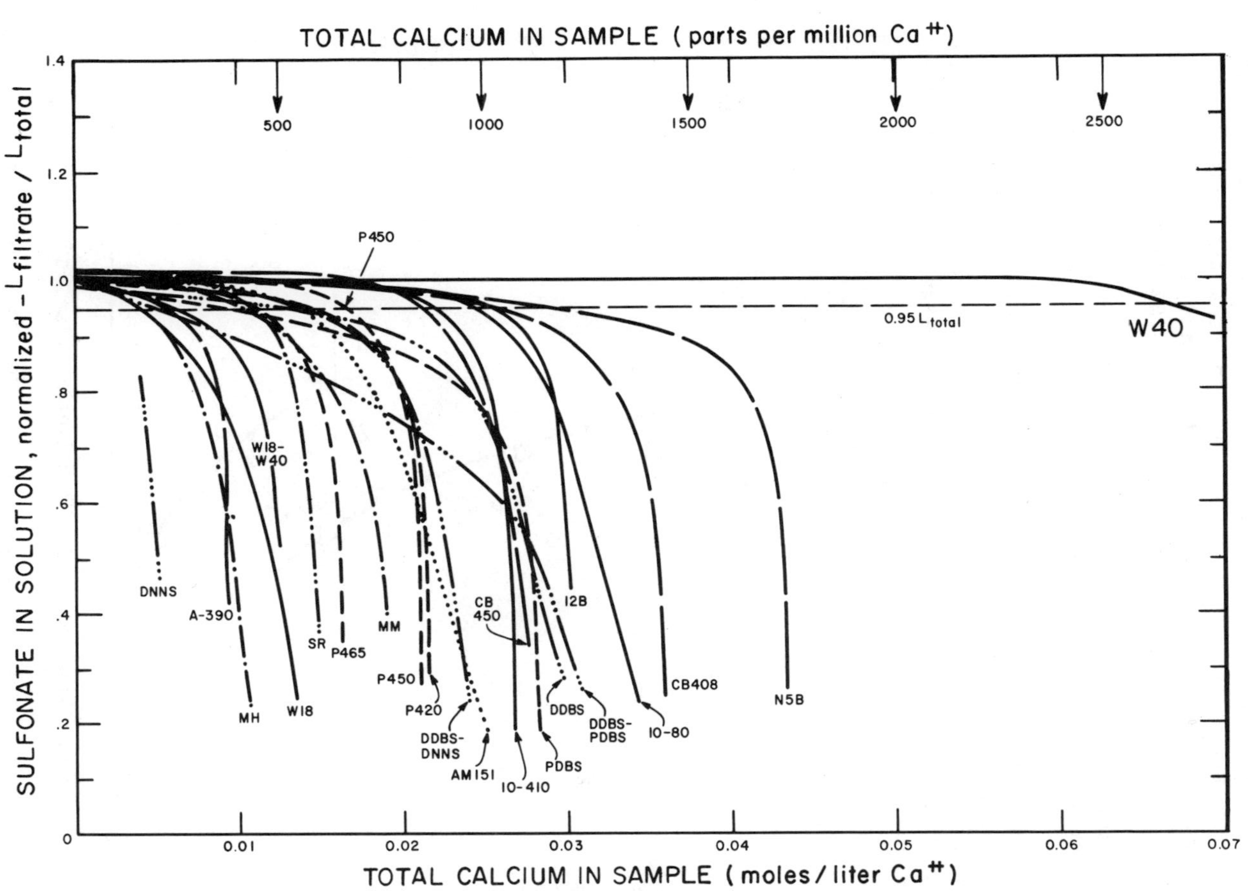

FIGURE 1. Tolerance of Petroleum Sulfonates to the Presence of Calcium Ions at 30°C and 3 wt.% Active Sulfonate (moles/liter).

RESULTS

The tests show that sodium precipitated along with the calcium precipitate. See Figure 2. Large amounts of sodium were in the samples, from the sulfonates themselves and from the inorganic salt (probably Na_2SO_4). Therefore sodium precipitation had a significant effect on the calculation of the unprecipitated sulfonate.

The discovery of sodium precipitation suggests that other cations could also be reacting with the sulfonate. Tests for potassium and magnesium show less than 1% of the total sulfonate, L_{total}, could be a potassium or magnesium salt. In most oil reservoir brines[6] any other cations are present in much smaller quantities than the above cations. So the sulfonates (sulfonated petroleum fractions) probably do not contain significant amounts of other cations.

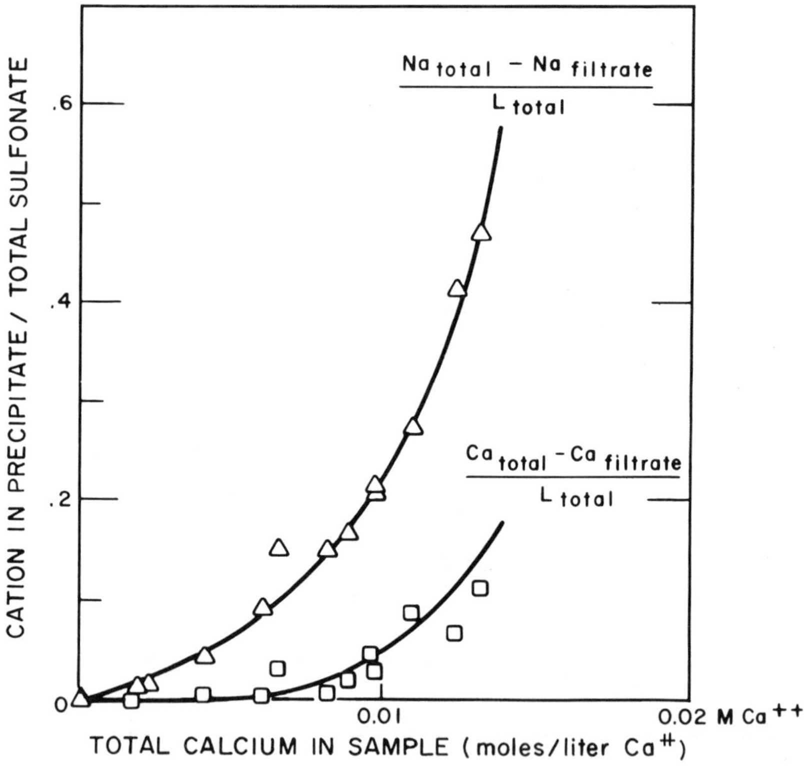

FIGURE 2. Calcium and Sodium Sulfonate Precipitation for Witco TRS 18 at 30°C, 3 wt.% Sulfonate (moles/liter).

Data Analysis

We assumed that the form of the calcium petroleum sulfonate precipitate is $Ca(RSO_3)_2$, where R is some alkylaryl group, and the sodium sulfonate precipitate is $NaRSO_3$. Letting L represent the concentration of petroleum sulfonates, the molar sulfonate concentration in the filtrate is

$$L_{filtrate} = L_{total} - 2(Ca_{total} - Ca_{filtrate}) - (Na_{total} - Na_{filtrate}). \quad (1)$$

All concentrations are expressed in units of molarity.

The normalized sulfonate concentration ($L_{filtrate}/L_{total}$) was plotted against the total calcium (Ca_{total}) present in the sample. See Figure 1. Each resultant curve indicates the resistance of the petroleum sulfonate to precipitation by calcium ions. The number of points in each sulfonate curve is between 11 and 32.

Experimental scatter for most of the curves is within $\pm$ 3% to $\pm$ 5% sulfonate for $L_{filtrate}/L_{total} \geq 0.90$. As the dilution factors increased, to analyze the filtrates for calcium, scatter in the curves also increased. In the DNNS sulfonate curve, the scatter of the points, for Ca_{total} less than about 0.004 M Ca, is very large. So its calcium tolerance, defined in the next section, is between 0 and 0.004 (Figure 4).

To compare this atomic absorption method of determining the sulfonate curves (Figure 1) with a direct sulfonate analysis, a methylene blue titration was performed. Sodium dodecyl benzene sulfonate (Research Inorganic/Organic Chemical Corp., No. NA-219) was the standard. The results of the methylene blue titration on Witco TRS 18 filtrates are within the experimental error of the sulfonate curve. See Figure 3.

DISCUSSION AND CONCLUSIONS

Calcium and Sodium Precipitation

Very little petroleum sulfonate is precipitated at low levels of calcium. The calcium sulfonate mixture is very water soluble up to some Ca_{total}, which is characteristic of the petroleum sulfonate mixture being tested. As more calcium is added, precipitation begins and the samples go through an opaque region, where the amount of precipitated sulfonate is rapidly increasing. At higher calcium concentrations, samples have a clear supernatant liquid and a voluminous amount of precipitate.

The sodium salt of the petroleum sulfonate is precipitating as a co-precipitate or as an occlusion with the calcium sulfonate precipitate. See Figure 2. At least part of the sodium precipitate probably is salting out, as the total concentration of ions (ionic strength) increases. The ionic strength in the samples ranges from about 0.05 to 0.75 in units of molarity times ionic charge squared divided by two.

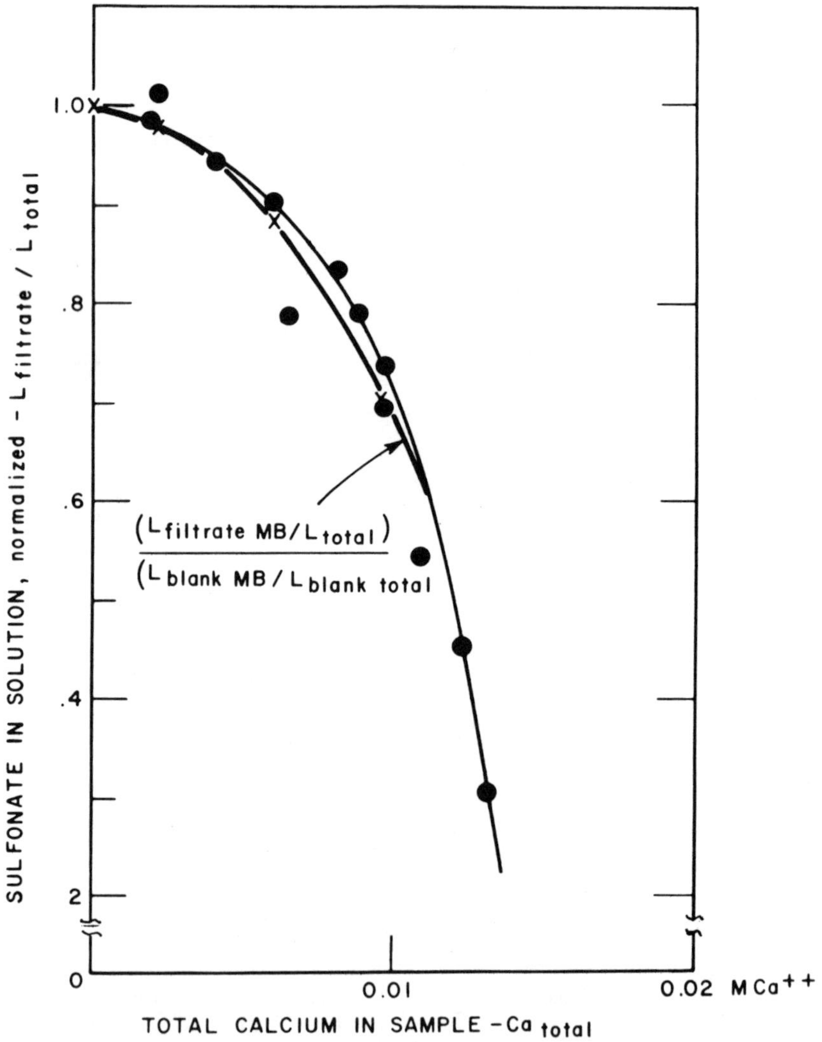

FIGURE 3. Comparison of Our Indirect Sulfonate Determination with Methylene Blue Titration for Witco TRS 18 at 30°C, 3 wt. % Sulfonate (moles/liter).

Comparison by AEW

The sulfonate curves (Figure 1) for the tested commercial sulfonates can be compared using the amount of added calcium, Ca_{total}, required to cause each sulfonate to precipitate. We defined calcium ion tolerance as the amount of Ca_{total} which causes a precipitation loss of 5% of the sulfonate placed in the sample (Ca_{total} at 95% L_{total}). See Figure 1 for the 0.95 L_{total} values. In general, the tolerance of each sulfonate mixture to precipitation by calcium is inversely proportional to the average equivalent weight (AEW) of the mixture. See Figures 1 and 4. So for example the

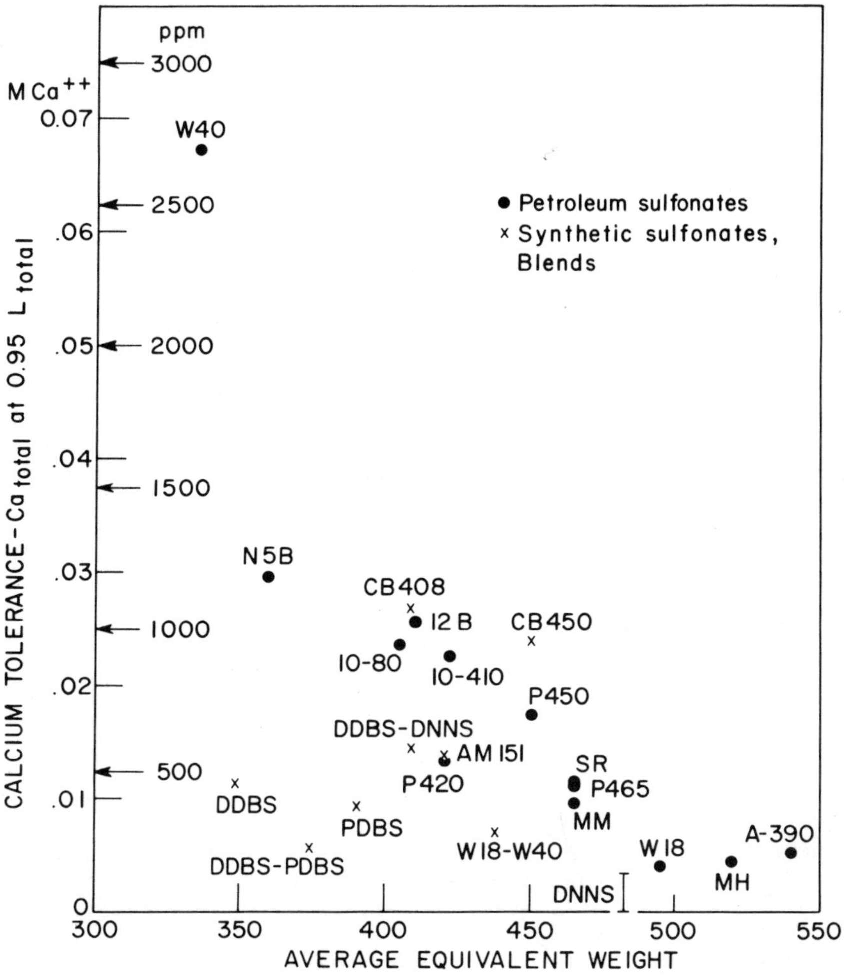

FIGURE 4. Calcium Tolerance as a Function of Average Equivalent Weight at 95% Total Sulfonate (30°C, 3 wt% Sulfonate).

sulfonate mixture which tolerated the greatest amount of calcium was Witco Petronate TRS 40. It has the lowest AEW, 335. However, it is not necessarily the best petroleum sulfonate surfactant for any EOR flood. Sulfonates with an AEW in the range of 375 to 475 are believed to be the best for oil recovery[8].

Calcium Tolerance

It was assumed for Figure 4, that a loss of 5% of the surfactant in a flood would be acceptable for the definition of calcium tolerance. Since the data scatter of the sulfonate curves is ± 3% to ± 5% sulfonate in this region, a smaller precipitate loss could not be reliably read from Figure 1. In an actual surfactant flood the concentration of the sulfonate probably could be increased above 3 wt.% active sulfonate to compensate for this loss.

The calcium tolerance points in Figure 4 of the petroleum sulfonates appear to form a curve. The synthetic sulfonates, however, are below this line.

Curve Fitting the Data

Since the pattern of the petroleum sulfonate points in Figure 4 suggested logarithmic behavior, a semi-log plot of the data was made. See Figure 5. The log of the calcium ion tolerance was plotted against the AEW of each sulfonate.

Least-squares polynomial curve fits[9] were made of the petroleum sulfonate points in Figure 5. Blends and synthetic sulfonates were not included in the fits. The data were weighed uniformly and gave the best fit for a straight line

$$\text{Log}\,(\text{Ca}_{\text{total}} \text{ at } 95\%\ \text{L}_{\text{total}}) = a + b\ \text{AEW}. \tag{2}$$

where

$$a = 0.67 \pm 0.27$$

and

$$b = -0.0057 \pm 0.0006.$$

The standard error in the coefficients indicates that the intercept of the line could be varied by a significant fraction without changing the fit of the line; however, the slope is relatively fixed. The standard error in log (Ca_{total} at 95% L_{total}) was calculated for the 95% confidence level and plotted on Figure 5. It is the band surrounding the least squares fit of the data.

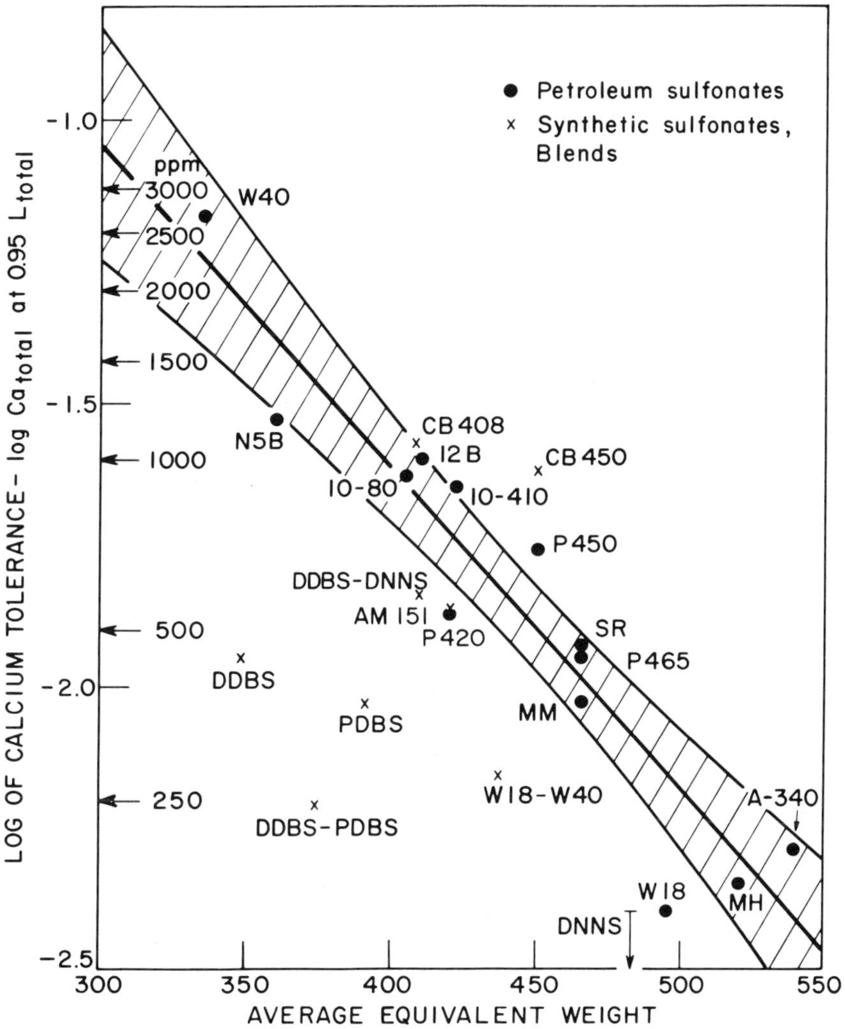

FIGURE 5. Semilog Plot of Calcium Tolerance as a Function of Average Equivalent Weight at 95% Total Sulfonate (30°C, wt.% Sulfonate).

Comparison of Calcium Tolerances

The line or band in Figure 5 suggests that there is an expected or average calcium tolerance for any mixture of petroleum sulfonates, and that this expected tolerance depends on the AEW of the mixture, Equation (2). Hence, the calcium tolerance of each sulfonate in this study can be described as relatively less or more tolerant than the least-squares fit of all the petroleum sulfonate tolerance data.

Conoco 450 EW Blend was relatively more tolerant than any of the other sulfonates tested. It tolerated 450 ppm (0.0112M) more calcium than would be expected from the above data fit, Equation (2). Stepan Petrostep Sulfonate 450 (P450) could tolerate about 185 ppm (0.0047 M) more calcium than expected. At the other extreme was Cities Service Sul-Fon-Ate AA-10 (DDBS) which could only tolerate about one-fourth as much calcium as a petroleum sulfonate of the same AEW.

Mixtures

A second interesting feature of Figures 4 and 5 is suggested by the relative calcium ion tolerances of the four Conoco petroleum sulfonates. Conoco 408 EW (CB408) and Conoco 450 EW (CB450) Na Sulfonate Blends are mixtures of Conoco N5B Na Sulfonate and Conoco A-390 Na Sulfonate. Both blends are further above the line (relatively more tolerant) than either of their components. See Figure 6. This synergistic behavior may indicate that appropriately increasing the complexity of a petroleum sulfonate mixture will increase its tolerance to precipitation by calcium ions.

We made a blend of Witco TRS 40 (W40) and Witco TRS 18 (W18), which has an AEW of 437. Its calcium tolerance is further below the line in Figure 6 (relatively less tolerant) than either of its components.

We also made blends of DDBS/PDBS and DDBS/DNNS. These blends are relatively less and more tolerant, respectively than their components. See Figure 6.

Both of the Conoco blends and the DDBS/DNNS blends are relatively more tolerant than their components. However, the other two blends, W18-W40 and DDBS/PDBS, actually bring on precipitation at relatively lower levels of calcium than their components. Hence, the choice of the components for a highly calcium tolerant petroleum sulfonate mixture is very important.

The idea that complexity is related to calcium tolerance is further supported by the very low tolerances of the relatively pure sulfonates: DDBS, PDBS, DNNS, AM151. Isobutene sulfonate (AM 151) was less tolerant of calcium than the data fit of petroleum sulfonates at 420 AEW, Equation (2). Our results for the isobutene sulfonate are reversed from those of Froning et al.[3] However, their tests included added oil, salt, and several alcohols.

A Proposed Explanation

One possible way to describe the synergistic behavior in Figure 6 is by some mechanism analogous to a lime-soap dispersing agent, LSDA.[10] The bulk of a LSDA molecule causes a water-external soap

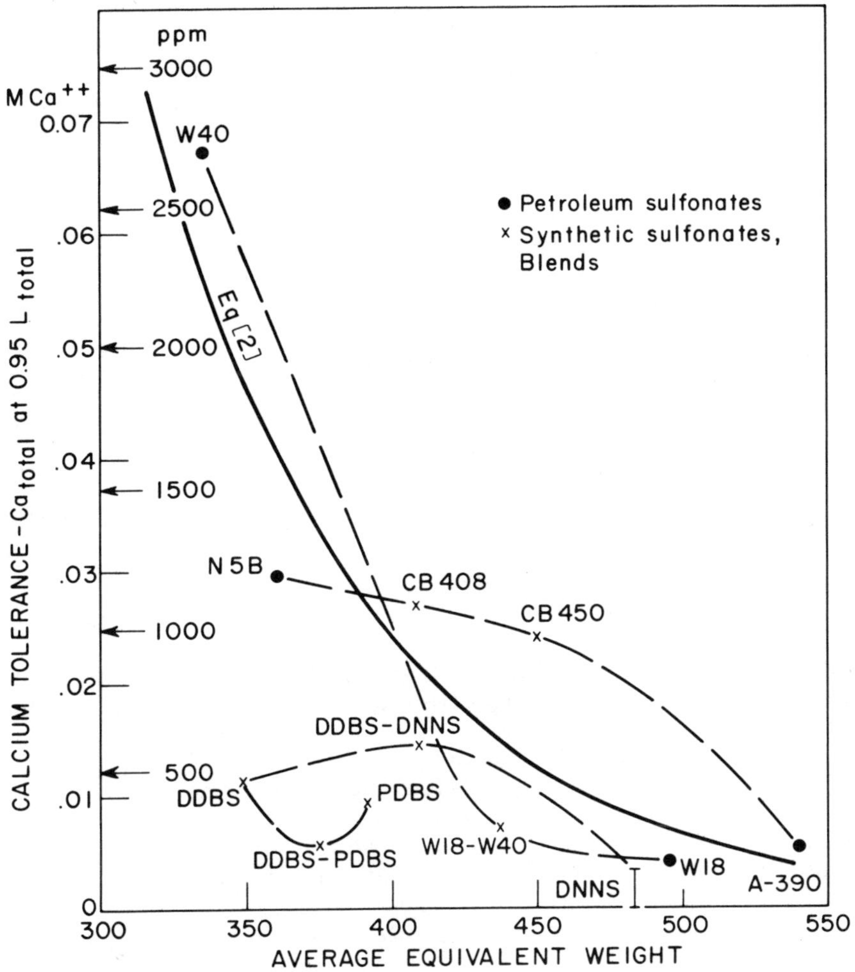

FIGURE 6. Calcium Tolerance of Blends as a Function of Average Equivalent Weight at 95% Total Sulfonate (30°C, 3 wt.% Sulfonate).

micelle to retain its correct curvature. Thus, the soap-LSDA micelle can resist inversion and subsequent precipitation by calcium ions.

Sulfonate molecules of certain types of physical sizes and shapes may also act like LSDA's in complex mixtures. For example, DNNS may be a lime soap dispersing agent for DDBS.

While the types of molecular size and shape for improved calcium tolerance have not been determined, the DDBS/DDNS blend in Figure 6 is suggestive.

SUMMARY

Calcium tolerance of petroleum sulfonates depends on AEW and the composition of the sulfonate mixture. The dependence on AEW is given in Equation (2). Synergistic compositions may be a result of the sulfonate molecules acting as LSDA's.

Within the AEW range of 375 to 475, certain petroleum sulfonates are relatively more tolerant to calcium than the other sulfonates studied. They are CB450, P450, CB408, and 10-410. Amoco Sulfonate 151 is not exceptionally calcium tolerant.

Petroleum sulfonates, in the form of the sodium salt, precipitates along with the calcium precipitate. It may be a coprecipitate with the calcium or an occlusion.

REFERENCES

1. M.J. Meister, G.K. Kettenbrink, and A.G. Collins, ERDA-BERC/IC-76/3, BETC, Box 1398, Bartlesville, Okla., 74003 (1976)
2. F.W. Smith, SPE Preprint 6598, SPE-AIME International Symposium on Oilfield and Geothermal Chemistry, LaJolla, Calif. June 27-28, 1977.
3. H.R. Froning, and L.E. Treiber, SPE Preprint 5816, Improved Oil Recovery Symposium, Soc. Pet. Eng., AIME, Tulsa, Okla., Mar.22-24, 1976.
4. Perkin-Elmer Instrument Manual, "Analytical Methods for Atomic Absorption Spectrophotometry," Perkin-Elmer, Norwalk, Conn., Sept. 1976 Edition.
5. D.A. Ward, and D.G. Biechler, At. Absorpt. Newsl. 14, 29 (1975).
6. A.G. Collins,"Geochemistry of Oilfield Waters," pp. 212-219, American Elsevier Scientific Publishing Co., New York, 1975
7. L. Smith, E.W. Malmberg, H.W. Kelley, and S. Fowler, SPE Preprint 5369, California Regional Meeting, Soc. Pet. Eng., AIME, Ventura, Calif., April 2-4, 1975.
8. W.W. Gale and E.I. Sandvik, Soc. Pet. Eng. J., 13, 191 (1973).
9. E.M. Puch and G.H. Winslow,"The Analysis of Physical Measurements," Addison - Wesley, Reading, Mass., 1966.
10. W.M. Linfield, in "Anionic Surfactants, Part 1" W. M. Linfield, Editor, Ch. 1, Marcel-Dekker, Inc., New York, 1976.

ABOUT THE CONTRIBUTORS

Here are included brief biographical sketches of only those authors who have contributed to this volume. Biosketches of contributors to Volume I are included in that volume.

Syed Mahmood Ahmed is a doctoral candidate in the Department of Chemical Engineering at Lehigh University. He is a graduate of Osmania University, Hyderabad, and got his M.S. in Chemical Engineering from Lehigh University in 1976. He has been associated with Emulsion Polymers Institute - Center for Surface and Coatings Research for about four years.

Mats Almgren is presently Visiting Assistant Professor at the Radiation Laboratory, University of Notre Dame. He is a Lecturer in Physical Chemistry at Chalmers University of Technology in Gothenburg, Sweden.

K. P. Ananthapadmanabhan is a graduate student working towards his D.E.Sc. degree in the Henry Krumb School of Mines, Columbia University. He received his B.E. degree from the Indian Institute of Technology, Bombay, and M.S. in 1977 from Columbia University. At present, he is studying the associative interactions in aqueous surfactant solutions and their role in flotation and other related phenomena.

Ronald E. Barden is Associate Professor of Chemistry and Biochemistry at the University of Wyoming. He received his Ph.D. in Biochemistry from the University of Wisconsin, Madison in 1969. He is the recipient of a Research Career Development Award from NIH. His research activities are focused on enzymology (affinity labels, kinetics), micelles and microemulsions.

Guy M. Bradley joined Petrolite Corporation in 1976. He received a B.S. in Chemistry from the Carnegie Institute of Technology in 1966 and Ph.D. in Physical Chemistry from the University of California, Berkeley, in 1971. His research interests have been emulsion stabilization and destabilization, particularly those involving crude oil.

J. E. Brown is with the Bath University, Bath, U.K., and holds a B.Sc. degree.

C. A. Bunton is Professor of Chemistry at the University of California, Santa Barbara. His B.Sc. and Ph.D. degrees are from the University College, London. He has had visiting appointments at universities in Europe and North and South America. His research interests include miceller catalysis and inhibition.

A. G. Collins is Project Leader (oilfield brine research) at the Bartlesville Energy Research Center. He received his M.S. in Chemistry from Kansas State College in 1955 and his M.S. in Geology from the University of Tulsa in 1972. Mr. Collins is listed in American Men of Science and Who's Who in America (South and Southwest).

Ingvar Danielsson is Professor of Physical Chemistry, Åbo Akademi, Abo (Turku), Finland. He obtained his Phil. Dr. degree in 1956 from the University Åbo Akademi. He has published about 50 papers in the area of association colloids.

Stanley S. Davis is Lord Trent Professor of Pharmacy, University of Nottingham, U.K. His research interests include solution thermodynamics, drug formulation and biopharmaceutics. He obtained his B. Pharm. and Ph.D. degrees from London University, and has held various appointments in the U.K. and the U.S. He has published over 100 papers in the field of colloid and pharmaceutical science.

Andres Denss is presently a postdoctoral fellow in the Department of Chemistry, University of Missouri - Rolla. He received his Ph.D. degree in 1977 from the University of Basel.

Jose G. Dominguez is presently at ECOPETROL, Bogota, Columbia. He received his Ph.D. in Chemical Engineering in 1977 and M.S. in Petroleum Engineering in 1974 from the University of Kansas. He graduated from the Universidad Imperial de Santander in Columbia. His interests involve the use of microemulsions and polymer solutions in enhanced oil recovery processes.

K. D. Dreher is a Senior Research Chemist at Marathon Oil Company's Denver Research Center. Since being employed by Marathon in 1967, he has been engaged in research associated with tertiary oil recovery processes. He joined Marathon after two years postdoctoral appointment at the Krumb School of Mines, Columbia University. He served as Chairman of the 1979 SPE-AIME International Symposium on Oilfield and Geothermal Chemistry.

Hans-Friedrich Eicke is Professor of Physical Chemistry at the University of Basel, Switzerland. He received his Ph.D. from the University of Gottingen (Max-Planck - Institute for Physical Chemistry) in 1961. He has published more than 50 papers dealing with surface active electrolytes in hydrocarbon solutions, inverted micelles, and microemulsions. He is co-author (with B. Lindman and H. Wennerstrom) of a monograph on micelles in aqueous and non-polar surfactant solutions soon to be published by Springer Verlag, Berlin.

Mohamed S. El-Aasser is Associate Professor of Chemical Engineering and Co-Director of the Emulsion Polymers Institute at Lehigh University. He received his B.S. and M.S. from Alexandria University in Egypt, and Ph.D. in Chemistry from McGill University in 1972. He is the advisor of the AIChE student Chapter at Lehigh University. Among his research interests are polymer synthesis and characterization, emulsion polymers and latex technology.

Mahmoud M. El-Emary is currently Associate Research Professor (on leave) at the Egyptian Petroleum Research Institute, Nasr City, Cairo. He received his B.S. degree from Cairo University in 1959 and Ph.D. in Physical Organic Chemistry in 1966 from the University of Texas at Austin. He has about 25 publications in the area of synthesis of petroleum additives and surfactants.

Eleanor J. Fendler is Associate Professor of Chemistry at Texas A & M University. She obtained her Ph.D. degree in 1966 from the University of California, Santa Barbara. She was an NIH Research Development Awardee from 1971 - 1976. She has published more than 70 papers in the areas of miceller catalysis; NMR spectroscopy; and physical, organic, bioorganic and radiation chemistry. Also, she is co-author (with J.H. Fendler) of the book Catalysis in Micellar and Macromolecular Systems published in 1975. Her research interests include biomedical functions of surfactants.

F. C. Goodrich is Professor of Chemistry at Clarkson College of Technology. He received his Ph.D. in Chemistry in 1952 from Columbia University. He has been visiting professor at U.C. Berkeley - 1969; U.S.C., Los Angeles - 1972; and Universite Libre de Bruxelles, Belgium - 1977. He is a member of the editorial boards of J. Colloid Interface Science, and Surface and Colloid Science Series. He has authored the book A Primer of Quantum Chemistry published in 1972 by Interscience. His research interests are capillary thermodynamics and fluid mechanics, and statistical mechanics of interfaces.

D. W. Green is Professor of Chemical and Petroleum Engineering and Co-Director of the Tertiary Oil Recovery Project at the University of Kansas. He holds a B.S. degree in petroleum engineering from the University of Tulsa, and M.S. and Ph.D. in Chemical Engineering from the University of Oklahoma. His research interests involve enhanced oil recovery processes and computer modeling of hydrocarbon and ground water reservoir systems.

Marja-Riita Hakala is a Research Assistant at the Finnish Research Council for Natural Sciences. She obtained her B.Sc. degree in 1977 from the University Åbo Akademi, Åbo (Turku),Finland. She has published five papers in the field of association colloids.

Shigeo Hayano is Professor at the Institute of Industrial Science, University of Tokyo. He received his Dr. Eng. degree in 1964 from the University of Tokyo. His present research interests are electrochemical approach to surfactant solutions and colloid chemical aspects of marine pollution by spilled oils.

Clarence Hermansky is currently enrolled in the graduate program as a research assistant at Drexel University. He received his B.S. in Chemistry from Drexel University in 1977. With the degree, he received the Alexander B. Kornilew Award for distinguished undergraduate research.

C.-U. Herrmann is presently working for his Ph.D. at the Max-Planck-Institute für biophysikadische Chemie. He graduated from the University of Gottingen.

Smith L. Holt became Professor and Head, Department of Chemistry, University of Georgia, September 1, 1978. He received his Ph.D. from Brown University in 1965. He is a member of the Corporation of Inorganic Syntheses and has served as Professor Associe at the University of Brodeaux. His research interests include bio-inorganic and solid state chemistry as well as microemulsions as reaction media.

M. S. Hsieh spent two summers as a Physical Science Aid at the Bartlesville center while studying at Princeton University for a B.S. in Chemistry.

I. B. Ivanov is Associate Professor of Physical Chemistry at the University of Sofia, Sofia, Bulgaria. He is currently a Visiting Professor in the Department of Chemical Engineering, Columbia University. He received his Ph.D. degree from the University of Moscow in 1969 and his D.Sc. from the Bulgarian Academy of Sciences and the University of Sofia in 1977. His research interests are in the realm of thin liquid films as well as adsorption, intermoleculer interactions and aggregation in solutions of surfactants.

Rakesh K. Jain is currently on the faculty of Chemical Engineering Department, Carnegie-Mellon University. He obtained his Ph.D. in Chemical Engineering from the University of Delaware in 1975. He has published in the areas of mass and heat transfer and growth in tumors, and stability of thin liquid films with applications in industrial and biological systems.

Stanley C. Jones is a Research Associate in Production with Marathon. He joined Marathon Oil Company's Denver Research Center in 1962 after receiving M.S. and Ph.D. degrees from the University of Michigan. He has several publications and numerous patents relative to enhanced oil recovery by microemulsion flooding. He was Program Chairman of the SPE-AIME 1977 Annual Technical Conference and Exhibition. He is currently involved with enhanced oil recovery and the measurement of fundamental rock properties.

Margareta Jorpes-Friman is a Research Assistant in the Department of Physical Chemistry, Åbo Akademi, Åbo (Turku), Finland. She obtained her M.Sc. degree in 1974 from the University Åbo Akademi. Her research interests are in the area of emulsion stability.

M. Kahlweit is Director at the Max-Planck-Institute für biophysikalische Chemie.

Marshall Kayser is employed as a Petroleum Engineer with the U.S. Department of Energy. He received his degree in Chemical Engineering from Oklahoma State University. He has experience in refining and in laboratory studies of permeability, wettability and micellar-polymer systems, and has co-authored publications in these areas.

David J. Koranek is currently working at Dow Chemical Corp., Freeport, Texas. He received his M.S. degree in 1977 from Texas A & M University.

Christos Koukounis is presently a graduate student at the University of Texas at Austin and will be receiving his M.S. in chemical engineering in December 1978.

K. J. Lissant is presently employed at Petrolite Corporation where he joined in 1944 as a Research Physical Chemist. He received his M.S. in 1943 from Washington University in St. Louis and Ph.D. in 1947 from Stanford University. Dr. Lissant has pioneered in the technology of high-internal-phase-ratio emulsions and has been active in recent years in the application of this technology to many areas including applications for rocket, jet and automotive fuels. He has published numerous papers and has been awarded over 30 patents. He is listed in American Men of Science.

P. B. Lorenz has been a Research Chemist at the Bartlesville Energy Technology Center since 1949, when he joined the staff directly after receiving his Ph.D. from Harvard University. He has worked on various problems associated with petroleum production. He also developed a radiotracer method of estimating "rubble-ization" of oil shale after underground detonation. His work has appeared in various journals and government reports.

Raymond Mackay is Associate Professor of Chemistry at Drexel University, Philadelphia. He received his B.S. in 1961 from Rensselaer Polytechnic Institute and Ph.D. in Chemistry from the State University of New York at Stony Brook in 1966.

Jean Meister is presently associated with the Department of Chemical Engineering, University of Florida, Gainesville. She received her B.S. degree from Penn State and M.S. from the University of California, Riverside. Before joining the University of Florida, Ms. Meister was employed as a Research Chemist at the Bartlesville Energy Research Center.

John J. Meister joined the Center for Macromolecular Sciences at the University of Florida, Gainesville, in August 1978 as a postdoctoral fellow. He received his B.S. degree in Chemistry and Mathematics in 1968 from Penn State, and Ph.D. from California Institute of Technology in 1973. From 1973 - 1978 he worked on enhanced oil recovery methods for the Phillips Petroleum Company. He has authored two papers and holds four patents.

Fortunato J. Micale is Associate Professor of Chemistry at Lehigh University. He received his Ph.D. in Physical Chemistry from Lehigh University. A specialist in surface and colloid chemistry, he has investigated the solid/gas and solid/liquid interfacial properties of fine particles. He has served as a consultant for several corporations and is the author of a number of scientific publications. His name appears in Who's Who, and American Men of Science.

*Kashmiri Lal Mittal** is presently employed at the IBM Corporation in Hopewell Junction, N.Y. He received his B.Sc. in 1964 from Panjab University, M.Sc. (first class first) in Chemistry in 1966 from Indian Institute of Technology, New Delhi, and Ph.D. in Colloid Chemistry in 1970 from the University of Southern California. In the last few years, he has organized and chaired a number of very successful international symposia and in addition to this two-volume set, he has edited seven more volumes as follows: Adsorption at Interfaces, and Colloidal Dispersions and Micellar Behavior (1975); Micellization, Solubilization, and Microemulsions, Volumes 1 & 2 (1977); Adhesion Measurement of

*As the editor of this two-volume set.

Thin Films, Thick Films, and Bulk Coatings (1978); and Surface Contamination: Its Genesis, Detection, and Control, Volumes 1 & 2 (August, 1979). In addition to these volumes, he has published about 40 papers in the areas of surface and colloid chemistry, adhesion, polymers, etc. He has given or is scheduled to give many invited talks on the multifarious facets of surface science, particularly adhesion, on the invitation of various societies and organizations in many countries and is always a sought-after speaker. He is a member of many professional and honorary societies, is a Fellow of the American Institute of Chemists, is listed in American Men and Women of Science and Who's Who in the East. Recently he has been appointed a member of the editorial boards of a number of scientific and technical journals. He started the highly-acclaimed short course on adhesion in the United States in 1976.

J. C. Morgan is presently employed at the Research Centre of British Petroleum Company in Sunbury-on-Thames, Middlesex, England. He obtained his Ph.D. in Chemistry from the University of Bristol. His research interests are in the various areas of tertiary oil recovery.

G. I. Mukhayer is Senior Lecturer, Faculty of Pharmacy, Khartoum, Sudan. His research interest is colloid chemistry. He obtained his Ph.D. degree from the University of Aston, Birmingham, U.K., in 1974.

Gary W. Poehlein is Director, School of Chemical Engineering, Georgia Institute of Technology. He received his Ph.D. in Chemical Engineering in 1966 from Purdue University. He worked with Proctor and Gamble from 1958 - 1961, and was at Lehigh University (1965 - 1978) before joining Georgia Institute of Technology.

Steven N. Rosenthal attended Texas A & M University as a graduate student. His graduate research concerns the self-association behavior of naturally occurring surfactant systmes. He has co-authored a review chapter.

Jean-Louis Salager is currently teaching at the Universidad de los Andes, Merida, Venezuela. He received his Ph.D. in Chemical Engineering in 1977 from the University of Texas at Austin. He has about ten publications.

R. S. Schechter is the E.J. Cockrell Professor of Chemical and Petroleum Engineering at the University of Texas at Austin and also is currently Chairman of the Petroleum Engineering Department. He has a B.S. from Texas A & M and a Ph.D. from the University of Minnesota all in Chemical Engineering. He has authored and co-authored more than 100 papers and three books and is a member of the National Academy of Engineers.

Noriko Shinozuka is Research Associate at the Institute of Industrial Science, University of Tokyo. He received his Dr. Eng. degree in 1966 from the University of Tokyo. His present research interests are electrochemical application of surfactant solutions and environmental chemistry.

P. Somasundaran is Professor of Mineral Engineering in the Henry Krumb School of Mines, Columbia University. He received his Ph.D. from the University of California, Berkeley, in 1964. He has authored more than 100 scientific publications and is the author/editor of two books. His research interests include pre-micellar aggregation and other solution chemistry aspects of surfactants, flotation, flocculation, enhanced oil recovery, and chemomechanical effects on grinding and biosurfaces.

M. K. Tham is a Chemical Engineer at the Bartlesville Energy Technology Center. He earned his B.Sc. Eng. degree from Rangoon University and Ph.D. from the University of Florida. His research areas include gaseous diffusion in electrolytes, transport properties and surface and interfacial properties of surfactants. He is the author of a number of publications in these areas.

J. Kerry Thomas is Professor of Chemistry, University of Notre Dame. He obtained his Ph.D. degree in 1957 from the University of Manchester. While working at Argonne National Laboratory (1960 - 1970) he developed the short-pulsed nanosecond laser and pulse radiolysistechnique. In 1974, he was given the research award of the Radiation Research Society. In 1975, he was a Gäst Professor at the Hahn Meitner Institute in Berlin. He is the author of over one hundred research publications.

Umberto Tonellato is Lecturer of Organic Chemistry at the Institute of Organic Chemistry, University of Padova, Padova, Italy. He received his degree in Chemistry at the University of Padova in 1960. His current research concerns with the chemistry of vinyl cations and functional micellar catalysis. He is the author of 50 publications.

T.T. Traykov graduated in 1974 and received his Ph.D. degree in 1977 from the Faculty of Chemistry, University of Sofia, Sofia, Bulgaria. His research interest is in the field of physico-chemical hydrodynamics of thin liquid films.

John W. Vanderhoff is Associate Director - Coatings, Center for Surface and Coatings Research, and Professor of Chemistry, Lehigh University. He received his Ph.D. degree from the State University of New York at Buffalo. Before joining Lehigh University, he was associate scientist in the physical research laboratory, Dow Chemical Company, Midland. In 1965, Dr. Vanderhoff was co-winner of the Union Carbide Chemistry Award of the American Chemical Society. He holds six U.S. patents and 22 corresponding foreign patents, and has written more than 80 technical papers for scientific journals. His fields of specialization are polymer, colloid, and surface chemistry, in particular emmulsion polymerization, uniform particle size latexes, characterization and applications of latexes.

Eugenia Vasquez is presently residing in Caracas, Venezuela. Ms. Vasquez received M.S. in Chemical Engineering in June 1978 from the University of Texas at Austin.

William H. Wade is Professor of Chemistry at the University of Texas at Austin. He received his B.S. from St. Mary's University, San Antonio in 1951 and Ph.D. in 1955 from the University of Texas at Austin. He has written about 70 publications in the area of surface chemistry.

G. Paul Willhite is Professor of Chemical and Petroleum Engineering and Co-Director of the Tertiary Oil Project at the University of Kansas. He received his B.S. degree from Iowa State and Ph.D. from Northwestern University, both in Chemical Engineering. His research interests have focused on transport phenomena in porous media, including use of polymers and microemulsions to recover oil from depleted reservoirs.

Carol Wilson is employed as a Research Chemist at the Bartlesville Energy Research Center. She has a B.S. degree in Chemistry from Wichita State University.

U. Würz is presently working as Assistant at the Max-Planck-Institute für biophysilkalische Chemie. He received his Ph.D. from the University of Frankfurt/Main.

SUBJECT INDEX

Pages 1-516 appear in Volume 1
Pages 517-940 appear in Volume 2